HIGH RESOLUTION NUCLEAR MAGNETIC RESONANCE SPECTROSCOPY

VOLUME 2

High Resolution Nuclear Magnetic Resonance Spectroscopy

IN TWO VOLUMES

J. W. EMSLEY, J. FEENEY

AND

L. H. SUTCLIFFE

VOLUME 2

PERGAMON PRESS

OXFORD · LONDON · EDINBURGH · NEW YORK
PARIS · FRANKFURT

PHYSICS

Pergamon Press Ltd., Headington Hill Hall, Oxford
4 & 5 Fitzroy Square, London W.1

Pergamon Press (Scotland) Ltd., 2 & 3 Teviot Place, Edinburgh 1

Pergamon Press Inc., 44–01 21st Street, Long Island City, New York 11101

Pergamon Press S.A.R.L., 24 rue des Écoles, Paris 5e

Pergamon Press GmbH, Kaiserstrasse 75, Frankfurt-am-Main

First edition 1966

Library of Congress Catalog Card No. 64–19591

1756/66

ACKNOWLEDGEMENTS

We are indebted to the publishers of scientific journals and books for allowing us to reproduce the figures listed below.

J. Chem. Phys. 10.2; 10.4; 10.6; 10.7; 10.9; 10.22; 10.23; 10.24; 10.28; 10.31; 10.32; 10.39; 10.41; 10.54; 10.56; 10.57; 10.58; 10.59; 10.60; 10.61; 11.3; 11.9; 11.10; 11.22; 12.7; 12.8; 12.9; 12.12; 12.15; 12.16; 12.17; 12.24; 12.25; 12.27; 12.28; 12.29; 12.46.
Inorg. Chem. 11.23; 12.37.
J. Amer. Chem. Soc. 10.1; 10.5; 10.8; 10.10; 10.11; 10.12; 10.18; 10.19; 10.21; 10.34; 10.36; 10.37; 10.44; 10.48; 11.4; 11.5; 11.6; 11.14; 11.20; 11.21; 12.10; 12.19; 12.20; 12.21; 12.35; 12.36; 12.43; 12.44; 12.48.
J. Phys. Chem. 11.15; 11.16; 12.5.
Can. J. Chem. 10.13; 10.14; 10.15; 10.16; 10.20; 10.27; 10.35; 10.47; 11.19; 12.26.
Mol. Phys. 10.17; 10.33.
Helv. Chim. Acta, 10.25.
Trans. Faraday Soc. 10.29.
Discuss. Faraday Soc. 10.40; 10.46; 10.49; 10.50; 11.13; 12.2; 12.3; 12.4; 12.47.
Arkiv. Kemi, 10.30; 10.42; 10.43.
J. Poly. Sci. 10.51; 10.53.
Anal. Chem. 10.52; 11.25.
Proc. Chem. Soc. 11.12; 12.30; 12.32.
Proc. Roy. Soc. 12.31; 12.42.
J. Chem. Soc. 11.18.
J. Inorg. Nuc. Chem. 12.1.
Annals N.Y. Acad. Sci. 12.13; 12.18; 12.23.
Academic Press, N.Y. 12.33; 12.45.
Zeit. anorg. Chem. 12.41.

CONTENTS

VOLUME 2

FOREWORD xix

PREFACE xxi

10. CORRELATIONS OF ^{1}H RESONANCE SPECTRAL PARAMETERS WITH MOLECULAR STRUCTURE 665

Alkanes 666

10.1 Chemical shifts of alkane derivatives 666

10.1.1 Correlation of electronegativity of substituents with ^{1}H chemical shifts of methyl derivatives, CH_3X 666
Methyl halides 667
Other methyl derivatives 668
10.1.2 Correlation of chemical shift parameters with the electronegativity of substituents in ethyl derivatives 670
Metal ethyl derivatives 675
10.1.3 Propyl and isopropyl derivatives 676
10.1.4 Contributions to the shielding of hydrogen nuclei from C—H and C—C bond anisotropic effects 676

10.2 Spin–Spin coupling constants in alkane derivatives 677

10.2.1 Coupling constants between *geminal* hydrogen nuclei on saturated carbon atoms 677
10.2.2 Coupling constants between hydrogen nuclei on adjacent carbon atoms 678
10.2.3 Signs of H—H coupling constants 681
10.2.4 Long range coupling constants between hydrogen nuclei in saturated systems 683

10.3 Miscellaneous alkyl compounds 685

10.3.1 Group IVB methyl derivatives 685
10.3.2 Alkyl derivatives of elements having nuclear magnetic moments 686
10.3.3 Miscellaneous metal alkyl derivatives 689
10.3.4 2,3-Disubstituted butanes 690
10.3.5 Cyclopropane and its derivatives 690
Effect of ring size on shielding of ring hydrogen nuclei in cyclic molecules 692
Substituted cyclopropanes 692
Epoxides 695
10.3.6 Cyclohexane derivatives 696
(a) ^{1}H chemical shifts in cyclohexane derivatives 696
(b) Coupling constants in cyclohexane derivatives 700
(c) Configurational effects in acetylated carbohydrates 701
(d) *Cis*- and *trans*-4-t-butylcyclohexyl alcohols and acetates 703

(e) Determination of the configuration of cyclohexane derivatives using NMR 703
$1\alpha,3\alpha$-Dimethoxy-2β-acetoxycyclohexane 703
$1\alpha,3\beta$-Dimethoxy-2α-acetoxycyclohexane 703
(f) Acetylated aldopentapyranose derivatives 704
(g) 1,2,3,4,5,6-Hexachlorocyclohexanes 705
(h) Tetra-O-acetyl-1,4-dideoxy-1,4-dinitro-neo-inositols 705
(i) Derivatives of acetoxycholestanone 706
(j) Monosubstituted cyclohexane derivatives 706
(k) Disubstituted cyclohexanes 708
(l) Decalins 709
(m) 10-Methyl decalols 709

Alkenes 710

10.4 Vinyl derivatives, $CH_2{=}CHX$ 710

10.4.1 Correlation between *geminal* coupling constants, J^{gem}_{HH}, and the H—C—H bond angles 711
10.4.2 *Vicinal* coupling constants in alkenes 712
Signs of H—H coupling constants in unsaturated systems 712
10.4.3 Correlation between coupling constants and the electronegativities of the substituents in vinyl derivatives 714
10.4.4 Changes in chemical shifts in vinyl groups with changes in the electronegativity of the substituents 717
10.4.5 Correlation of chemical shifts in vinyl systems with Hammett σ-constants 717
10.4.6 Correlation of chemical shifts in vinyl systems with group dipole moments 718
10.4.7 Anomalous ^1H chemical shifts in vinyl systems 719
Vinyl cyanide, $CH_2{=}CHCN$ 719
Styrene, $CH_2{=}CHC_6H_5$ 719
Vinyl ethers, $CH_2{=}CHOR$ 721
10.4.8 Vinyl chloride and chloroethylenes 722
10.4.9 Propene-1, butene-1 and hexene-1 723
10.4.10 Spin coupling constants in alkene-1 derivatives 726

10.5 Disubstituted olefines 727

10.5.1 *Cis*- and *trans*-disubstituted olefines 729
10.5.2 2-Substituted propenes 730
10.5.3 2,3-Disubstituted propenes 732
10.5.4 The effects of methyl group substitution on the ^1H resonance spectra of ethylenic molecules 733
Vinyl cyanide and cyanopropenes 734

10.6 Trisubstituted olefines 735

10.6.1 1-Substituted isobutenes 735
10.6.2 $\alpha\beta$-Unsaturated esters 737

10.7 Long range spin coupling via olefinic systems 740

10.8 Miscellaneous olefines 741

10.8.1 Conjugated dienes 741
10.8.2 Metal alkene derivatives 742
Metal vinyls 742
Cyclopentadienyl derivatives 743
10.8.3 Methyl groups in conjugated polyenes 744
10.8.4 Induced ring currents in annulenes 745

Acetylenes 745

10.9 Acetylene and related molecules 745
10.9.1 Propargyl halides, $XCH_2C{\equiv}CH$ 747

10.10 Spin–Spin coupling constants in acetylenic systems 748

10.11 Solvent effects on the chemical shifts of hydrogen nuclei in acetylenic molecules 749

Aromatic molecules 749

10.12 Benzene derivatives 749
10.12.1 The effects of solvents on the resonance spectra of aromatic compounds 749
10.12.2 Monosubstituted benzenes 750
Shielding of *ortho*-hydrogen nuclei 752
Shielding of *para*-hydrogen nuclei 752
Shielding of *meta*-hydrogen nuclei 752
10.12.3 Correlation of ^1H chemical shifts in monosubstituted benzenes with Hammett σ-constants 752
10.12.4 Disubstituted benzene derivatives 754
10.12.5 Halogenated benzene derivatives 760
10.12.6 Substituted xylenes 761
10.12.7 Hydroxy benzenes 763
10.12.8 Aromatic alkoxy compounds 764
10.12.9 Aromatic aldehydes 765
10.12.10 Trisubstituted benzenes 767
10.12.11 Biphenyls 767
10.12.12 Indene 769
10.12.13 Aromatic ring currents 770

10.13 Polynuclear aromatic molecules 770

10.14 Spin–Spin coupling in aromatic molecules 770

10.15 Aromatic ions 774
10.15.1 Triaryl carbonium ions 774
10.15.2 9,10-Dimethyl-1,2-benzanthracene carbonium ion and other aromatic carbonium ions 775
10.15.3 Azulinium ion and related species 778
10.15.4 Cyclopentadienyl anion ($C_5H_5^-$) and tropylinium cation ($C_7H_7^+$) 779

Heterocyclic compounds 782

10.16 Furan and substituted furans 782

10.17 Pyrrole and substituted pyrroles 787
10.17.1 Chemical shifts in pyrroles 789
10.17.2 Porphyrins 792
10.17.3 Indoles 794

10.18 Pyridine and related molecules 794

10.19 The effects of solvents on the ^1H resonance spectra of unsaturated heterocyclic ring compounds 798

10.20 Quinolines 798

10.21 Thiophene and substituted thiophenes 802

10.22 Thiazoles and methyl substituted thiazoles 805

Large complex organic molecules 806

10.23 Alkaloids 806

Lunacrine 806
Lunine 808

10.24 Steroids 808

10.25 Fatty acids 812

10.26 Amino acids and peptides 812

10.27 Miscellaneous studies 812

10.28 Detection of C-methyl groups by NMR 814

Hydrogen atoms attached to atoms other than carbon 816

10.29 Hydrogen attached to oxygen atoms 816

10.30 Hydrogen attached to nitrogen atoms 818

10.31 Hydrogen attached to boron atoms 820

10.32 Hydrogen attached to sulphur atoms 820

10.33 Hydrogen attached to silicon atoms 821

10.34 Hydrogen attached to germanium, tin and lead atoms 823

10.35 Hydrogen attached to transition metal atoms 825

Miscellaneous studies 826

10.36 Contact chemical shifts in paramagnetic species 826

10.37 NMR studies of high polymer solutions 829

10.37.1 Segmental motion in polymers 829
10.37.2 The use of NMR in determining the molecular structures of polymers 831
Butadiene–isoprene copolymers 831
Poly(*n*-1)-methyl-1-alkenes 833
10.37.3 Determination of the stereochemical configurations of polymers by NMR 833
10.37.4 The use of spin decoupling in the determination of polymer structures 835
10.37.5 The use of deuteration in the determination of polymer tacticities by NMR 836
Polypropylene 836
Polystyrene 838

10.38 Empirical estimation of chemical shifts 838

10.39 Medium effects in liquids 841

10.39.1 The effects of solvents on the resonance spectra of acetylenic molecules 848

10.39.2 The effects of solvents on the resonance spectra of aromatic molecules 851
10.39.3 The effects of solvents on the resonance spectra of unsaturated heterocyclic ring molecules 855

10.40 Medium effects in gases 857

11. ^{19}F NUCLEAR MAGNETIC RESONANCE STUDIES 871

11.1 Introduction 871

11.2 Fluorine chemical shifts 874

11.3 ^{19}F spin–spin coupling constants 875
Effect of temperature on coupling constants 878
Long range ^{19}F coupling constants 879

11.4 Binary fluorides 880

11.5 Halofluorohydrocarbons 883

11.6 Substituted fluoroalkanes 885

11.6.1 Relative signs of ^{19}F spin coupling constants in fluoroalkanes 888
11.6.2 NMR parameters obtained from conformational studies of substituted ethanes 889

11.7 Fluorocarbon compounds containing nitrogen 889

11.8 Other fluorocarbon derivatives 890

11.9 Perfluoroalkyl and perfluoroacyl metal compounds 895

11.10 Fluorinated aromatic compounds 897

11.10.1 ^{19}F chemical shifts of benzene derivatives 897
11.10.2 Spin–Spin interaction in fluorinated aromatic compounds 901
Relative signs of ^{19}F spin coupling constants in aromatic compounds 902
11.10.3 Substituted benzotrifluorides 903
11.10.4 Polysubstituted fluorobenzene derivatives 905
11.10.5 Fluoronaphthalenes 905

11.11 Fluoroalkenes 906

11.11.1 Perfluorovinyl derivatives 906
11.11.2 Other fluoroalkenes 908
11.11.3 Coupling constants in fluoroalkenes 909
11.11.4 Relative signs of ^{19}F coupling constants in fluoroalkenes 914
11.11.5 Information obtained from examination of the ^{13}CF satellites in the ^{19}F spectra of fluoroalkenes 914

11.12 Fluoroacetylenes 916

11.13 Fluorinated cyclic compounds 916

11.13.1 Cyclopropane derivatives 916
11.13.2 Mono- and disubstituted derivatives of tetrafluorocyclobutane 917
11.13.3 Fluorinated cyclohexanes 920
Perfluorocyclohexane C_6F_{12} 920
Monosubstituted perfluorocyclohexanes 921
Dihydroperfluorocyclohexanes $C_6F_{10}H_2$ 922
Cis- and *trans*-perfluorodecalin 922
Fluorinated cyclohexenes 925

11.13.4 Fluorinated heterocyclic compounds 925
Perfluoropiperidine C_5NF_{11} 925
$(CF_2)_4Fe(CO)_4$ 926
Fluorinated heterocyclic derivatives of sulphur, selenium and phosphorus 926
Miscellaneous cyclic compounds 927

11.14 Methyl and ethyl fluorosilanes R_xSiF_{4-x} 927

11.15 Antimony pentafluoride 928

11.16 Compounds containing fluorine–sulphur bonds 930
11.16.1 Sulphur hexafluoride and its monosubstituted derivatives 930
11.16.2 Disubstituted derivatives of sulphur hexafluoride 935
11.16.3 Sulphur tetrafluoride, SF_4 936
11.16.4 Perfluoroalkyl derivatives of SF_4 937

11.17 Other fluorine–sulphur containing compounds 939
(a) Fluorine fluorosulphonate 939
(b) Thionyl tetrafluoride 939
(c) Pentafluoro sulphur hypofluorite 939
(d) $S_3O_8F_2$ 939
(e) Thiocarboxylic acids 939
(f) Thioalcohols 940

11.18 Interhalogen compounds 940
11.18.1 Chlorine trifluoride 940
11.18.2 Bromine trifluoride 942
11.18.3 Iodine and bromine pentafluorides 943
11.18.4 Perchloryl fluoride, $FClO_3$, and related compounds 943

11.19 Compounds containing boron–fluorine bonds 944
11.19.1 Boron trifluoride and related compounds 944
11.19.2 The BF_4^- ion 946

11.20 Compounds containing nitrogen–fluorine bonds 946

11.21 Compounds containing oxygen–fluorine bonds 948

11.22 Compounds containing phosphorus–fluorine bonds 949

11.23 Complex compounds 952
11.23.1 Complexes of boron trifluoride 952
11.23.2 Complexes of metal tetrafluorides 952
11.23.3 Other metal fluoride complexes 953

11.24 Fluorine-containing polymers 954

11.25 Miscellaneous studies 956

12. NMR Spectra of Nuclei other than Hydrogen and Fluorine 969

12.1 Boron 970
12.1.1 ^{11}B chemical shifts 971
12.1.2 $^{11}B—^{1}H$ spin–spin interaction 976
12.1.3 Boron hydrides 977
Diborane, B_2H_6 978
Substituted diboranes 979
Other boranes 980
Tetraborane, B_4H_{10} 981

Pentaborane-9, B_5H_9 983
Pentaborane-11, B_5H_{11} 983
Hexaborane, B_6H_{10} 984
Decaborane, $B_{10}H_{14}$ 984
The $B_3H_8^-$ ion 984
The $B_{11}H_{14}^-$ ion 984
B_9H_{15} and $B_{10}H_{15}$ 985
Substituted boranes 985
Diammoniate of diborane, $B_2H_6(NH_3)_2$ 986
12.1.4 Borohydrides 987
Sodium borohydride, $NaBH_4$ 987
Aluminium borohydride, AlB_3H_{12} 987
12.1.5 Other boron resonance studies 987
The BF_4^- ion 987
$(CH_3)_2PHBH_3$ 987

12.2 Carbon 988
12.2.1 Experimental procedures for ^{13}C resonance measurements 988
12.2.2 ^{13}C chemical shifts 992
12.2.3 Correlation of ^{13}C chemical shifts with electronegativities of groups attached to carbon atoms 995
12.2.4 Methyl and ethyl derivatives of group IV elements 999
12.2.5 Alkenes 999
12.2.6 Acetylenes 1001
12.2.7 Aromatic compounds 1001
Monosubstituted benzenes 1002
Other aromatic compounds 1005
12.2.8 Pyridine and substituted pyridines 1008
12.2.9 ^{13}C chemical shifts of carbonyl groups 1009
12.2.10 Miscellaneous studies 1010
12.2.11 Spin–Spin interaction between ^1H and ^{13}C nuclei 1011
Coupling between directly bonded atoms 1011
12.2.12 Additivity effects in $^1H—^{13}C$ and in $^{19}F—^{13}C$ coupling constants 1017
12.2.13 J_{CH} additivity relationship for sp^2 hybridised carbon atoms 1019
12.2.14 Relationship of J_{CH} with J_{HH}^{vic} and J_{HH}^{gem} values in ethylenes 1020
12.2.15 Correlation between $^1H—^{13}C$ coupling constants and ^1H chemical shifts 1020
12.2.16 $^{13}C—^{19}F$ coupling constants 1022
12.2.17 ^{13}CH satellite spectra of symmetrically substituted benzenes 1022
12.2.18 Long range $^{13}C—^1H$ coupling constants 1027
Measurement of long range $^{13}C—^1H$ coupling constants 1028
12.2.19 $^{13}C—^{13}C$ spin coupling constants 1029
12.2.20 Miscellaneous $^{13}C—^1H$ coupling constants 1031

12.3 Nitrogen 1031
12.3.1 ^{14}N chemical shifts 1034
12.3.2 NMR effects associated with the quadrupole moment of the nitrogen nucleus 1037
12.3.3 Long range $^1H—^{14}N$ spin coupling constants 1040
12.3.4 Structure determinations using ^{14}N resonance 1041
Cyanamides and carbodi-imides 1041

12.4 Oxygen 1041
12.4.1 ^{17}O chemical shifts 1042
12.4.2 Effects of paramagnetic ions on ^{17}O chemical shifts 1047
12.4.3 $^1H—^{17}O$ spin coupling in water 1048

12.5 Silicon 1048
12.5.1 ^{29}Si chemical shifts 1051
12.5.2 Spin coupling constants involving ^{29}Si nuclei 1051

12.6 Phosphorus 1052
12.6.1 ^{31}P chemical shifts 1054
12.6.2 Spin–Spin interactions involving ^{31}P nuclei 1061
12.6.3 Applications of ^{31}P resonance to structure determinations 1068
Organic phosphites 1068
Oxyacids containing two phosphorus atoms 1069
Tetrapolyphosphate ion, $P_4O_{13}^{6-}$ 1071
Alkali metal salts of dialkyl phosphonates 1072
Condensed phosphates 1072
Pentavalent phosphorus thioacids 1074
Phosphorus pentachloride 1074
Diphosphine, P_2H_4 1074
Stereoisomers of substituted diphosphines 1074
Miscellaneous studies 1074
12.6.4 Quantitative analysis 1075
Non-cyclic phosponitrilic compounds 1077

12.7 Cobalt 1078
12.7.1 ^{59}Co chemical shifts 1078
Solvent effects on ^{59}Co chemical shifts 1081
Temperature dependence of ^{59}Co chemical shifts 1081
12.7.2 Rate processes involving cobalt 1082

12.8 Tin 1082
12.8.1 ^{119}Sn chemical shifts 1083
Solvent effects on ^{119}Sn chemical shifts 1084
12.8.2 Mixed tin(IV) halides 1084
12.8.3 ^{119}Sn spin–spin coupling constants 1086

12.9 Thallium 1088
12.9.1 ^{205}Tl chemical shifts 1088
12.9.2 Spin–Spin coupling involving thallium 1090
12.9.3 Structure of thallous ethoxide, $TlOC_2H_5$ 1091

12.10 Miscellaneous nuclei 1092
12.10.1 Deuterium 1092
12.10.2 Alkali metals 1092
Sodium, ^{23}Na 1092
Rubidium, ^{87}Rb and caesium, ^{133}Cs 1093
12.10.3 Aluminium, ^{27}Al 1093
12.10.4 Halogens 1095
Chlorine, ^{35}Cl and ^{37}Cl 1095
Iodine, ^{127}I 1096
12.10.5 Copper, ^{63}Cu 1096
12.10.6 Arsenic, ^{75}As 1097
12.10.7 Selenium, ^{77}Se 1097
12.10.8 Antimony, ^{121}Sb 1097
12.10.9 Platinum, ^{195}Pt 1097
12.10.10 Mercury, ^{199}Hg and ^{201}Hg 1097
12.10.11 Lead, ^{207}Pb 1100
12.10.12 Niobium, ^{93}Nb 1101
12.10.13 Nuclear magnetic moments 1102

APPENDIX A TABLE OF NUCLEAR PROPERTIES 1109

APPENDIX B TABLE OF τ-VALUES FOR A VARIETY OF ORGANIC COMPOUNDS 1115

APPENDIX C CHARTS OF ^{1}H CHEMICAL SHIFTS AND COUPLING CONSTANTS 1131

APPENDIX D TABLE OF ^{1}H CHEMICAL SHIFTS IN SOME DIAZO-COMPOUNDS 1139

APPENDIX E TABLE OF SUBSTITUENT SHIELDING EFFECTS, S_o AND S_m, IN BENZENES 1140

APPENDIX F TABLE OF ^{31}P CHEMICAL SHIFTS 1143

NAME INDEX—VOLUME 2 xxiii

SUBJECT INDEX xxxiii

VOLUME 1

FOREWORD xvii

PREFACE xix

1. INTRODUCTION 1
   - Historical 1
   - High resolution NMR spectroscopy 4

2. GENERAL THEORY OF NUCLEAR MAGNETIC RESONANCE 10
   - 2.1 The classical mechanical description of the resonance condition 10
   - 2.2 The quantum mechanical description of nuclear magnetic resonance 15
   - 2.3 The population of spin states 16
   - 2.4 Spin–Lattice relaxation 18
   - 2.5 Mechanisms of spin–lattice relaxation 20
   - 2.6 Spin–Spin relaxation 28
   - 2.7 Line widths for liquids 30
   - 2.8 Saturation 33
   - 2.9 Radiofrequency magnetic susceptibility and the Bloch equations 34
   - 2.10 Transient effects 40
   - 2.11 Nuclear induction 44
   - 2.12 The measurement of relaxation times 46

3. THE ORIGIN OF CHEMICAL SHIFTS AND SPIN–SPIN COUPLING 59
   - Introduction 59
   - 3.1 The chemical shift 59
   - 3.2 Spin–Spin coupling 61
   - *Chemical shifts* 65
   - 3.3 Bulk diamagnetic shielding 65
   - 3.4 Chemical shielding in atoms 66
   - 3.5 Magnetic shielding in molecules. Perturbation theory 68
   - 3.6 Variation theory applied to the calculation of molecular shielding constants 77
   - 3.7 The induced current model for magnetic shielding in molecules 79

3.8 Interatomic currents 81
3.9 The influence of an applied electric field on shielding constants 85
3.10 The effect of molecular interactions on shielding constants 90
3.11 The effect of isotopic substitution on shielding constants 99
3.12 Temperature dependence of shielding constants 101
Spin–Spin coupling 103
3.13 Theory of spin–spin coupling 103
3.14 Calculation of spin–spin coupling constants 105
3.15 The coupling constant and the anisotropy of the shielding coefficient 113
Effects in paramagnetic materials 115
3.16 Contact shifts 115
3.17 The Overhauser effect 116

4. THE CALCULATION OF SHIELDING CONSTANTS OF NUCLEI IN MOLECULES 120
4.1 The hydrogen molecule 120
4.2 Simple hydrides 124
4.3 The calculation of shielding constants by the induced current model 130
4.4 Shielding constants and the magnetic anisotropy of chemical bonds 133
4.5 Chemical shifts of hydrogen nuclei in aromatic molecules 140
4.6 Calculations of chemical shifts of fluorine nuclei in molecules 151
4.7 Chemical shift calculations for miscellaneous nuclei 157

5. THEORETICAL CALCULATIONS OF SPIN–SPIN COUPLING CONSTANTS OF SIMPLE MOLECULES 160
5.1 Hydrogen deuteride, HD 160
5.2 Methane 163
5.3 Ethanes and ethylenes 166
5.4 Coupling constants between hydrogen nuclei separated by four σ-bonds 174
5.5 Long range H—H coupling constants in unsaturated compounds 176
5.6 Aromatic hydrocarbons 180
5.7 Ammonia 183
5.8 Aliphatic and aromatic fluorocarbons 183
5.9 ^{13}C—H coupling constants 191

6. NMR SPECTROMETERS AND THEIR ACCESSORIES 200
6.1 Basic requirements 200
6.2 The magnet 201
6.3 The sample holder 207
6.4 Magnetic field sweep 223
6.5 The radiofrequency oscillator and receiver 227
6.6 Intensity measurements and quantitative analysis 234
6.7 Calibration of spectra by the sideband method 236

6.8 Double irradiation 240
6.9 Commercial NMR spectrometers 248

7. Experimental Procedures 256
7.1 Preparation of the sample 256
7.2 Reference compounds 260
7.3 Sample containers 268
7.4 Recording the spectrum 272

8. The Analysis of High Resolution Spectra 280
8.1 Introduction 280
8.2 Notation 283
8.3 Quantum mechanical formalism 287
8.4 Factorising the secular equation 290
8.5 The Hamiltonian 290
8.6 Spin angular momentum 291
8.7 Basic product functions 297
8.8 Basic symmetry functions 298
8.9 Construction of basic symmetry functions 299
8.10 Calculation of the matrix elements of the Hamiltonian 304
8.11 Transition intensities 306
8.12 Equivalent nuclei 307
8.13 The analysis of spectra characterised by one coupling constant 310
8.14 Spectra characterised by two coupling constants 356
8.15 Spectra characterised by three coupling constants 357
8.16 Spectra characterised by four coupling constants 392
8.17 Spectra characterised by six coupling constants 416
8.18 Other methods of analysing spectra 428
8.19 Analytical aids 442

9. The Effects of Chemical Equilibria and Molecular Conformational Motion on NMR Spectra 481
9.1 Theoretical considerations 481
9.2 Electron exchange reactions 502
9.3 Ion and group exchange reactions 507
9.4 Hydrogen bonding 534
9.5 Hindered internal rotation 551
9.6 Inversion of nitrogen compounds 574
9.7 Conformation of saturated ring compounds 575

Appendix A Table of Nuclear Properties 589

Appendix B Table of Predicted Values of Shielding Contributions from Ring Currents in Aromatic Hydrocarbons 595

Appendix C Compilation of Volume Diamagnetic Susceptibilities of Organic Compounds 605

Appendix D Line Frequencies and Relative Intensities of AB_2 Spectra 625

Appendix E Line Frequencies and Relative Intensities of AB_3 Spectra 629

Appendix F Line Frequencies and Relative Intensities of AB_4 Spectra 635

Appendix G Line Frequencies and Relative Intensities of Half of A_2B_2 Spectra 645

Appendix H Line Frequencies and Relative Intensities of A_3B_2 Spectra 649

Appendix I Miscellaneous Spin Systems—Notes and Literature References 661

Name Index—Volume 1 xxi

Subject Index xxxi

FOREWORD

IT IS less than 20 years ago that nuclear magnetic resonance was first observed in bulk matter. This new form of spectroscopy quickly proved to have useful applications in physics and chemistry, and with the discovery of the "chemical shift" in 1949 it became clear that this was to be a most important field of study for the chemist. As the design of magnets reached quite remarkable performances, more and more subtle effects became apparent, and today nuclear magnetic resonance is applied to a quite astonishing range of chemical and physical problems. The most extensive applications to chemistry come from the so-called "high resolution spectroscopy", and this important part of the subject is reviewed most thoroughly in this book.

Although much useful information can be derived from purely empirical applications of NMR, a great wealth of data can often be derived only from a proper analysis and understanding of the spectra. A detailed account of the theory and analysis of high resolution spectra is given at length in this book, which will be of great value to all magnetic resonance spectroscopists. There is also a full discussion of other factors which can affect the spectra, profusely illustrated with examples from the literature.

In addition to the theoretical part, this book contains a remarkable collection of data for reference purposes. A considerable proportion of the work done so far has been summarised in compact form, which is most useful for reference. Nuclear resonance work is now being published at an ever-increasing rate, which has now reached about 2000 papers a year, and the authors are to be congratulated for having encompassed the work so far in a single book.

R. E. RICHARDS

PREFACE

IN WRITING this monograph we have been bold enough to attempt to provide a detailed account of the basic theory underlying high resolution nuclear magnetic resonance (NMR) spectroscopy and also to present a survey of the major applications to problems in physics and chemistry. We have aimed at being as comprehensive as possible with the intention that almost all the text will interest everyone actively engaged in NMR spectroscopy. Because the subject is so vast, the authors are not competent to be critical throughout. Indeed, the phenomenal increase in the published work on NMR will soon make impracticable the task of containing full coverage of the topic within a single text. Already, several aspects of the subject are so well developed that they merit individual presentation in monographs written by the appropriate specialists.

It has been necessary to divide our monograph into two volumes, the first one of which is concerned primarily with basic theory and spectral analysis (Chapters 1 to 9) while the other contains most of the published work on structural applications of high resolution NMR spectroscopy (Chapters 10 to 12). From the extensive cross-referencing, the reader will be aware that the book has been written as a single entity.

A prerequisite for the successful application of NMR is the ability to analyse a spectrum in order to obtain the chemical shift and spin coupling constant parameters. Therefore, we have made the chapter on the analysis of spectra, Chapter 8, the mainspring of the book and we have covered the subject as fully as possible. This section has been written keeping in mind the reader who does not have a strong background in quantum mechanics, hence a rather detailed account has been given of the theory behind spectral analysis. Nearly all the spectral systems which have been analysed are described and the analyses of some of the spectral types are discussed in great detail to illustrate the general method. This chapter provides an introduction to the analysis of NMR spectra and also serves as a reference source for the practising spectroscopist.

The basic theory of NMR is dealt with in Chapters 2, 3 and 9, and the aim has been to cover the background of all major applications of NMR rather than to attempt a unified and mathematically rigorous treatment. Chapters 4 and 5 review the progress made in relating chemical shifts and coupling constants to the electronic structure of molecules, while Chapter 9 covers the applications of NMR to kinetic processes. Chapters 10, 11 and 12 contain a survey of the applications of NMR to the determination of molecular structure: Chapter 10 deals with hydrogen resonance, Chapter 11 with fluorine resonance and Chapter 12 covers all the remaining suitable magnetic nuclei. All three chapters hold many reproductions of spectra and many compilations of chemical shifts and coupling constants. This particular volume should be invaluable to those who have some knowledge of the fundamentals of NMR and wish to use the technique as an analytical tool.

The practical aspects of NMR spectroscopy are dealt with in Chapters 6 and 7. Chapter 6 covers the theory of the instrumentation required for the measurement of high resolution NMR spectra and also describes the types of spectrometer available commercially. In Chapter 7 is given a discussion of all the practical factors which need to be considered in obtaining NMR spectra. This chapter is intended primarily for those new to the subject and includes preparation of the sample, tuning the spectrometer and measurement of spectra. The material for this chapter has been drawn not only from the authors' own experience but also from many discussions with other workers in the field. In particular, much valuable information has been obtained from the contributions to the monthly letters on NMR (MELLONMR) edited by Drs. A. A. Bothner-By and B. A. Shapiro of the Mellon Institute, Pittsburg, U.S.A.

We would like to acknowledge the many helpful discussions we have had with Drs. R. J. Abraham and J. Lee. We are also indebted to Drs. R. J. Abraham, T. B. Grimley and G. Skirrow, who have given up much of their time to read the manuscript, for their suggestions and constructive criticisms of the text.

In the course of preparing this monograph we have been particularly fortunate in the help given by those who have supplied us with unpublished data and with manuscripts prior to publication. Their help has enabled us to cover the scientific literature up to the end of 1963. We would like to thank especially Dr. G. V. D. Tiers for allowing us to reproduce his compilation of τ-values and also Professors H. S. Gutowsky, G. G. Hall and J. D. Roberts and Drs. R. J. Abraham, J. D. Baldeschwieler, C. N. Banwell, A. A. Bothner-By, F. A. Bovey, P. L. Corio, R. Freeman, P. C. Lauterbur, A. Malera, W. G. Schneider, G. W. Smith, F. C. Stehling, G. V. D. Tiers and the Office of Naval Research of the U.S.A.

We wish to thank Professors C. E. H. Bawn, C.B.E., F.R.S. and W. K. R. Musgrave for their encouragement at all times.

We also thank all the authors and editors who have given us permission to reproduce figures and diagrams from their publications.

We would be grateful if readers would draw our attention to any errors which they may encounter in the text.

CHAPTER 10

CORRELATIONS OF ^{1}H RESONANCE SPECTRAL PARAMETERS WITH MOLECULAR STRUCTURE

NUCLEI with magnetic moments have often been described as probes capable of transmitting information of the detailed electronic environment in which they reside via their resonance absorption spectra. Although a great deal of effort has been applied to the theoretical interpretation of observed nuclear shielding and spin–spin coupling constants, in most cases, one must be satisfied with a qualitative explanation of their meaning. Consequently, much of the valuable information potentially available from NMR measurements is, at the moment, unattainable. Until such time that accurate estimates of the spectral parameters of molecules containing more than a few atoms can be predicted from quantum mechanical considerations, we must content ourselves with making correlations between spectral and molecular parameters. An abundance of correlations of this type has been pointed out in the literature and the purpose of this chapter is to present such data together with the characteristic values of ^{1}H chemical shifts and H—H spin coupling constants for the various classes of molecule. Correlations between spectral and structural parameters play an important role in assisting attempts to reach a theoretical understanding of the spectral constants. Furthermore, from empirical correlations one can often make predictions of chemical shifts and coupling constants which are useful in the NMR analysis of molecules of unknown molecular structure. In work of this nature, familiarity with the many correlations and trends encountered is necessary if the maximum amount of information is to be extracted from the NMR data. Many of the τ values quoted here have been taken from the unpublished list of NMR data measured and compiled by Dr. G. V. D. Tiers (see Appendix B). Wherever possible, chemical shifts have been transferred to the τ scale (referred to as "τ" values) and given together with the original raw data. Chemical shifts obtained by extrapolating from one reference to another are often unreliable due to uncorrected solvent and bulk diamagnetic susceptibility effects. In cases where such discrepancies would be appreciable, a conversion has not been attempted but an approximate conversion factor is supplied.

Several factors can influence the shielding of a hydrogen nucleus in a molecule: these have been considered in detail elsewhere (see Chapters 3 and 4). In the absence of effects from bulk diamagnetic susceptibility and intermolecular interactions, the main shielding factors are:

(1) *Diamagnetic shielding of the nucleus by the electron cloud in which it resides.* Neighbouring electronegative groups will influence the electron cloud via inductive effects through the bonds and thus cause variations in this term (see Section 3.4).

(2) *Neighbour anisotropic shielding effects.* These effects are important if the hydrogen nucleus is near to a magnetically anisotropic centre in the molecule. Such a centre can be provided by a neighbouring atom, group or bond having different values for the transverse (χ_T) and longitudinal (χ_L) components of its magnetic susceptibility (e.g. aromatic rings, C=O, —C≡C— and C—X (halogen) bonds). Whether the hydrogen nucleus is shielded or deshielded depends on the relative values of the susceptibility components of the adjacent system and on the molecular geometry (see Section 4.4).

C—C single bonds are thought to affect the shielding of neighbouring hydrogen nuclei by this mechanism.

(3) *Intramolecular electric field effects.* If the molecule has a permanent dipole moment then the associated electric field can influence the shielding of hydrogen nuclei by interacting with their electron clouds (see Section 3.9).

(4) "*C—C bond shifts*". For hydrogen nuclei in alkanes, Dailey[(7)] has suggested that an additional deshielding factor, referred to as a "C—C bond shift", must be taken into account. The origin of the effect is somewhat obscure but it is not considered to be a C—C bond anisotropic effect. It has been suggested that when a C—C bond replaces a C—H bond there could be an appreciable change in the electronic excitation energy, *E*, which increases the paramagnetic contribution to the shielding.

ALKANES

10.1 Chemical Shifts of Alkane Derivatives

10.1.1 Correlation of Electronegativity of Substituents with ^{1}H *Chemical Shifts of Methyl Derivatives,* CH_3X

Many workers have attempted to relate hydrogen chemical shifts in alkyl groups with the electronegativity of substituent groups. A correlation of this type would be expected if the diamagnetic contribution to the shielding of hydrogen nuclei in substituted alkanes is the dominant shielding factor, since the electron density in the immediate vicinity of a hydrogen nucleus will depend on the proximity and nature of an electron withdrawing substituent. Increasing the electronegativity of the substituents will decrease the electron density around a neighbouring hydrogen nucleus and thus cause deshielding. Shoolery[(1)] was the first to observe that a simple relationship exists between electronegativity of substituents and the ^{1}H chemical shifts in alkyl derivatives. Meyer, Saika and Gutowsky[(2)] also found evidence to support this generalisation. Later, Gutowsky and Meyer[(3)] examined a series of methyl derivatives and observed a reverse trend in chemical shift behaviour with increase of electronegativity of the substituents and it became obvious that other shielding factors would need to be considered. Additional factors which are now known to have an appreciable influence on the ^{1}H chemical shifts are the bulk diamagnetic susceptibility effect of the substance and the neighbour diamagnetic anisotropy effects due to induced electronic circulations within neighbouring atoms, bonds or groups (see Section 4.4). The effect of intramolecular electric fields on the shielding of hydrogen nuclei in alkanes has not been considered in any detail(24).

Methyl Halides. Allred and Rochow(4) have made a detailed study of the hydrogen resonance spectra of a series of methyl halides. In order to overcome bulk diamagnetic susceptibility effects they examined the molecules at very low concentrations in carbon tetrachloride (a much-used solvent in NMR work on account of its chemical inertness and magnetic isotropy). If the same solvent is used for all the methyl halides, each will experience the same bulk diamagnetic susceptibility shielding effect in highly dilute solutions. A further consequence of diluting the samples is to eliminate shielding effects due to weak intermolecular interactions (such as hydrogen bonding). In practice it is necessary to extrapolate the ^{1}H chemical shifts measured for a series of dilute solu-

TABLE 10.1 ^{1}H CHEMICAL SHIFTS OF SOME METHYL DERIVATIVES(4)

Methyl resonances, ppm from H_2O reference			0% CCl_4 "τ"†
Compound	Pure liquid δ	0% in CCl_4 δ	
CH_3NO_2	1·19	0·48	5·69
CH_3F	2·10	0·53	5·74
$(CH_3)_2SO_4$	1·03	0·85	6·06
$(CH_3)_2CO_3$	1·36	1·02	6·23
$CH_3OC_6H_5$	1·83	1·10	6·31
CH_3COOCH_3	1·65	1·14	6·35
$(CH_3)_2SO_3$	1·48	1·21	6·42
$(CH_3O)_4Si$	1·50	1·23	6·44
$(CH_3O)_3B$	1·64	1·26	6·47
CH_3OH	1·85	1·39	6·60
CH_3OCH_3	2·63	1·55	6·76
CH_3Cl	2·10	1·74	6·95
CH_3COBr	2·15	1·98	7·19
CH_3Br	2·02	2·10	7·31
$CH_3COC_6H_5$	3·00	2·25	7·46
$CH_3C_6H_5$	3·25	2·47	7·68
CH_3I	2·00	2·60	7·81
$(CH_3CO)_2O$	3·04	2·60	7·81
CH_3COOH	3·19	2·69	7·90
$(CH_3)_2CO$	3·34	2·70	7·91
CH_3COOCH_3	3·28	2·78	7·99
CH_3CN	3·15	2·89	8·10
$CH_3C(NOH)CH_3$		2·98	8·19
$(CH_3)_3N$	3·18		
$C(CH_3)_4$	4·35	3·85	9·06

† The approximate conversion equation is "τ" = $5{\cdot}21 + \delta_{H_2O}$

tions to infinite dilution ...

tions to obtain the chemical shifts at infinite dilution. The chemical shift data for the methyl halides is included in Table 10.1. The ^1H chemical shifts of the pure methyl halides are seen to be very similar but on diluting the samples with carbon tetrachloride the chemical shifts become very different. When the extrapolated chemical shifts of the methyl halides are plotted against the Huggins electronegativities[5] of the halides a very good linear relationship is observed (see Fig. 10.1). This indicates that no major changes in the hybridisation of the alkyl carbon atoms accompanies a change in the halide substituent. Allred and Rochow also reported parallel linear relationships between chemical shifts and electronegativity for methyl halides in several different solvents. The

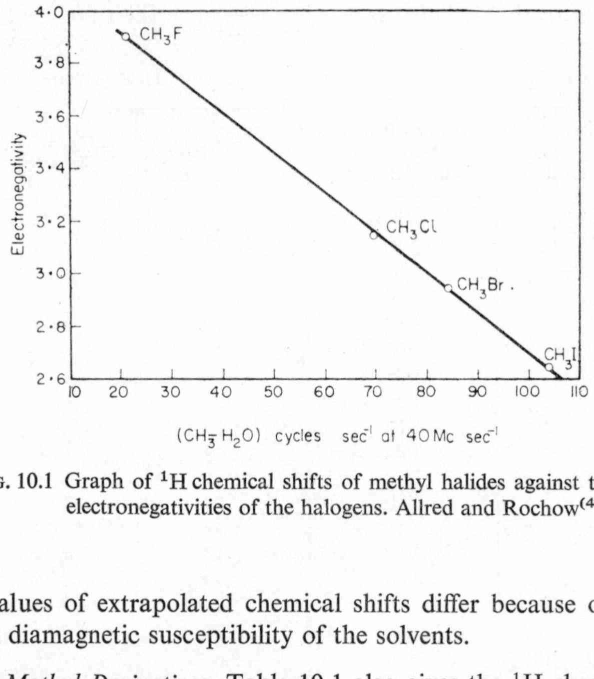

FIG. 10.1 Graph of ^1H chemical shifts of methyl halides against the Huggins electronegativities of the halogens. Allred and Rochow[4].

actual values of extrapolated chemical shifts differ because of differences in the bulk diamagnetic susceptibility of the solvents.

Other Methyl Derivatives. Table 10.1 also gives the ^1H chemical shifts of a series of methyl derivatives measured from a water external reference signal. Both the chemical shift of the pure substance and that of a dilute solution of the alkyl in carbon tetrachloride are given here. Allred and Rochow[4] have explained the shifts qualitatively in terms of changes in bond hybridisation accompanying changes in the electronegativity of the substituent. For a series of methyl derivatives where the hybridisation is fairly constant, the observed trends in chemical shifts can be correlated with electronegativity. It should be stated, however, that Fig. 10.1 does not give a general linear plot for correlating all methyl chemical shifts with the electronegativity of the substituent. Allred and Rochow[4] made no allowance for neighbour diamagnetic anisotropic effects and the more recent work of Spiesecke and Schneider[6] on alkyl derivatives has indicated where such effects cannot be neglected. These workers measured the chemical shifts of gaseous samples of several methyl derivatives using methane gas as an internal reference. By examining gaseous samples they eliminated any specific solvent effects while the use of an internal reference overcomes bulk diamagnetic susceptibility corrections. Table 10.2 gives the ^{1}H chemical shift values and the temperatures at which they were measured for the methyl derivatives. In Fig. 10.2 the chemical shifts of the methyl derivatives are plotted against the electronegativity of the substituents. For molecules where one would expect to find a large neighbour diamagnetic anisotropic effect (CH_3I, CH_3Br,

TABLE 10.2 THE ^{1}H CHEMICAL SHIFTS FOR A SERIES OF GASEOUS METHYL DERIVATIVES[6]

CH_3X Compound	Temp °C	Chemical shift ppm †
CH_4	22	0
CH_3F	22	−4·00
CH_3Cl	22	−2·71
CH_3Br	92	−2·32
CH_3I	109	−1·85
$(CH_3)_2O$	22	−3·10
$(CH_3)_3N$	120	−2·03
$(CH_3)_4C$	110	−0·83
CH_3CH_3	22	−0·75
$(CH_3)_2S$	108	−1·90
CH_3CN	150	−1·53
$(CH_3)_2CO$	140	−1·82
CH_3CHO	122	−1·79
CH_3NO_2	166	−3·91
$(CH_3)_4Si$	100	+0·13
$(CH_3)_4Ge$	120	0·00
$(CH_3)_4Sn$	100	+0·10
$(CH_3)_4Pb$	170	−0·57

† Chemical shifts measured in ppm from a methane gas internal reference "τ" $= 9{\cdot}7 + \delta_{CH_4}$ (approximate conversion).

CH_3Cl and $(CH_3)_2S$) the points on the graph are well removed from the simple linear correlation line. The deviation of these points from the general linear correlation line indicates the extent to which diamagnetic anisotropic effects are influencing the shielding. Figure 12.15 shows a similar graph for the ^{13}C chemical shifts in methyl groups: the halides again exhibit a large deviation from the normal correlation line. Spiesecke and Schneider have interpreted the deviations in the ^{1}H resonance spectra of methyl and ethyl derivatives in terms of neighbour anisotropic effects based on the model shown in Fig. 4.2. Cavanaugh and Dailey[7] are of the opinion that magnetic anisotropic effects associated with the C—X bond in methyl halides will not be important in the shielding of ^{1}H nuclei but in view of the work of Spiesecke and Schneider[6] this assertion does not appear to be well founded.

Bothner-By and Naar-Colin[8] have studied the NMR spectra of a comprehensive series of haloalkanes. In the case of methyl halides, they find that the electronegativity of the substituent and the magnetic anisotropic effects of the C—X bond operate together to produce the least shielding in methyl chloride and most in methyl iodide. Thus, only in the absence of neighbour diamagnetic anisotropic effects are the inductive electron-withdrawing effects of the substituents the dominant feature controlling shielding in methyl derivatives. Allred and McCoy[436] have considered the ^{1}H chemical shifts of methyl derivatives of Zn, C, N, O and F and discuss their results mainly in terms of bond polarities. Several other studies of alkanes have been reported[467, 472].

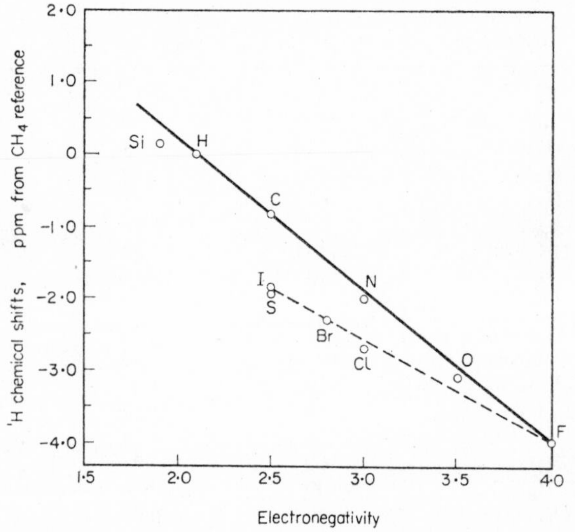

FIG. 10.2 Graph of the ^{1}H chemical shifts for methyl derivatives CH_3X against the electronegativity of the substituents. Spiesecke and Schneider[6].

10.1.2 Correlation of Chemical Shift Parameters with the Electronegativity of Substituents in Ethyl Derivatives

Dailey and Shoolery[9] have examined the NMR spectra of a large group of ethyl derivatives with a view to correlating the Huggins electronegativities of the substituents with the shielding of the α-methylene hydrogen nuclei. In order to overcome bulk diamagnetic susceptibility effects they measured the chemical shifts of the α-CH_2 group with respect to the β-CH_3 group as indicated in Fig. 10.3. Other workers have since repeated this work under more rigorous conditions and Table 10.3 contains the chemical shifts for fourteen ethyl derivatives measured at infinite dilution in carbon tetrachloride solution[7]. The results for the carbon tetrachloride solutions can be fitted into a revised Dailey–Shoolery[9] equation which represents the observed linear relationship

$$\text{Electronegativity} = 0{\cdot}684\Delta + 1{\cdot}78 \qquad (10.1)$$

where $\Delta = \delta_{CH_3} - \delta_{CH_2}$ in ppm. This equation can be used to predict the electronegativity of a substituent if the internal chemical shift of its ethyl derivative is known. Included in Table 10.3 are the calculated electronegativities for a series of substituents. Groups which might show neighbour anisotropic shielding effects must be regarded with caution in using correlations of this kind. If this internal chemical shift difference, (Δ), is to be meaningful in terms of inductive effects then it must be assumed that only the α-CH_2 group is influenced by the substituent and that contributions to the shielding from diamagnetic anisotropic effects of neighbouring groups are unimportant. Neither assumption is valid: Allred and Rochow have examined dilute solutions of ethyl halides in carbon tetrachloride and they find that the CH_3 groups do not have the same

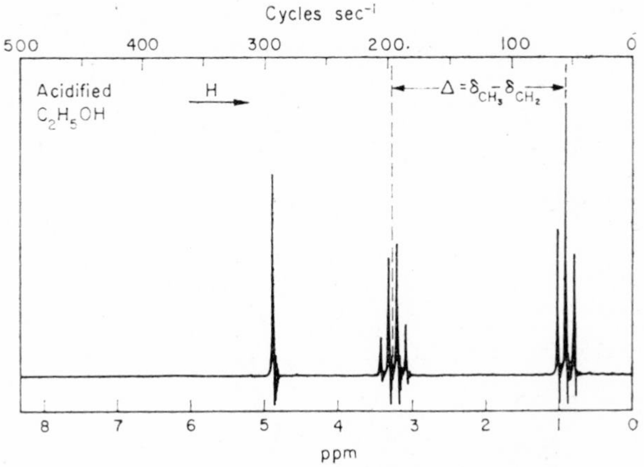

FIG. 10.3 Typical first order ¹H resonance spectrum of an ethyl group.

chemical shift at infinite dilution. In fact the chemical shifts of the CH_3 groups in ethyl halides indicate that the shielding of the hydrogen nuclei at the β-position increases as the electronegativity of the substituent increases. Examination of Tables 10.3 and 10.4 shows that the chemical shifts of the methyl groups in several ethyl derivatives vary over a range of about 1 ppm. Spiesecke and Schneider attribute the success of the linear correlation of Δ with electronegativity to the fact that neighbour diamagnetic anisotropic contributions to the ^1H shielding of the CH_2 and CH_3 groups in ethyl derivatives are about equal in magnitude and opposite in direction, and lead to a fortuitous cancellation.

When the individual chemical shifts of the methylene and methyl group in gaseous derivatives are plotted against the electronegativity of the substituent, one obtains the expected linear relationships (see Fig. 10.4 and Table 10.4). The α-CH_2 chemical shift-electronegativity correlation line has a similar gradient to that observed in methyl derivatives but the actual chemical shifts are less than those in the corresponding CH_3X compounds. This is as expected in view of the greater electronegativity of the methyl group compared with a hydrogen atom. Once again the halides show anomalous chemical shifts due

TABLE 10.3 THE ^{1}H CHEMICAL SHIFTS OF SEVERAL ALKYL COMPOUNDS[7] (MEASURED IN ppm FROM A METHANE REFERENCE)

Substituent	Methyl	Ethyl		Calculated electro-negativity	Isopropyl		Propyl		
	α ppm	α ppm	β ppm		α ppm	β ppm	α ppm	β ppm	γ ppm
Cl	−2·83*	−3·25*	−1·10*	3·25	−3·92*	−1·32*	−3·25	−1·58	−0·83
Br	−2·47*	−3·15*	−1·43*	2·96	−3·98*	−1·50*	−3·12	−1·67	−0·83
I	−1·93*	−2·93*	−1·65*	2·66	−4·02*	−1·67*	−2·93	−1·65	−0·80
OH	−3·17*	−3·37*	−0·95*	3·43	−3·72	−0·93	−3·27	−1·30	−0·70
CN	−1·75*	−2·12	−1·08	2·49	−2·45	−1·12	−2·07	−1·48	−0·88
COOH	−1·85*	−2·13	−0·93	2·60	−2·33	−0·98	−2·08	−1·45	−0·77
C_6H_5	−2·12*	−2·40*	−0·98*	2·75	−2·67*	−1·02*	−2·37	−1·42	−0·73
—O—	−3·02*	−3·15*	−0·92*	3·31	−3·33	−0·85	−3·05	−1·32	−0·70
—S—	−1·87*	−2·27	−1·02	2·64	−2·70	−1·02	−2·20	−1·37	−0·75
CHO	−1·95*	−2·23	−0·90	2·69	−2·17*	−0·90*	−2·12	−1·42	−0·75
NH_2	−2·23	−2·52	−0·87	2·91	−2·85*	−0·80*	−2·38	−1·20	−0·70
—S_2—		−2·45	−1·12	2·69			−2·40	−1·48	−0·80
NO_3^-		−4·27	−1·17	3·90	−4·93	−1·15	−4·15	−1·55	−0·82
NO_2	−4·07*	−4·15	−1·35		−2·50*	−1·30*	−4·05	−1·78	−0·80
F	−4·05*								
H	−0·00	−0·63						−1·12	−0·68

The chemical shifts were measured in ppm from a benzene reference (extrapolating to infinitely dilute solutions in CCl_4) and then transferred to the CH_4 reference scale.

No corrections for bulk diamagnetic susceptibility differences were made.

* Taken from Appendix B.

"τ" $= 9{\cdot}78 + \delta_{CH_4}$ (Approximate conversion)

to neighbour diamagnetic anisotropic effects. Examination of Fig. 10.4 indicates a linear correlation of methyl group chemical shifts with the electronegativity of substituents in ethyl derivatives. The trend, though much less pronounced

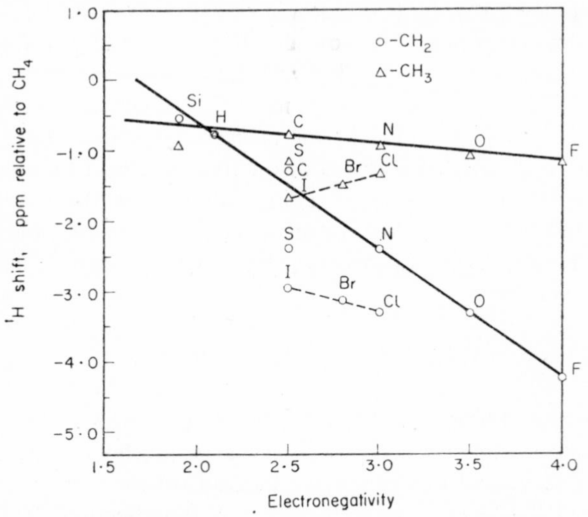

FIG. 10.4 The ^{1}H chemical shifts of CH_3CH_2X compounds plotted against the electronegativity of X. Spiesecke and Schneider(6).

TABLE 10.4 ^{1}H CHEMICAL SHIFTS OF GASEOUS CH_3CH_2X COMPOUNDS REFERRED TO A CH_4 REFERENCE(6)

CH_3CH_2X compound	Temp. °C	Chemical shifts ppm	
		CH_2	CH_3
CH_3CH_2F	40	−4·23	−1·14
CH_3CH_2Cl	113	−3·22	−1·29
CH_3CH_2Br	130	−3·12	−1·47
CH_3CH_2I	168	−2·97	−1·66
$(CH_3CH_2)_2O$	95	−3·30	−1·02
$(CH_3CH_2)_3N$	150	−2·39	−0·90
$(CH_3CH_2)_4C$	220	−1·27	−0·72
$(CH_3CH_2)H$	22	−0·75	−0·75
$CH_3CH_2CH_2CH_3$	95	−1·21	−0·81
$(CH_3CH_2)_2S$	170	−2·38	−1·10
CH_3CH_2CN	155	−1·96	−1·08
$(CH_3CH_2)_4Si$	220	−0·57	−0·90
$(CH_3CH_2)_4Pb$	145	−0·74	−0·74

"τ" $= 9{\cdot}78 + \delta_{CH_4\ int.}$ (Approximate conversion) than that for the $\alpha-CH_2$ groups, is in the same direction for all the ethyl derivatives except those containing diamagnetic anisotropic centres (S, I, Br, Cl, etc.). There is a remarkable parallel between the chemical shifts observed in the ^{13}C and ^{1}H resonance spectra (compare Fig. 10.4 with Fig. 12.16). The absolute chemical shifts of the α-CH_2 and β-CH_3 hydrogen nuclei in ethyl compounds, extrapolated to infinite dilution in carbon tetrachloride, cannot be explained in terms of electronegativity considerations and magnetic anisotropic effects alone and Cavanaugh and Dailey[7, 83] have suggested that a further shielding factor arising from the C—C bond must also be considered. Some evidence for this suggestion is provided by the measured chemical shifts of alkyl halides included in Table 10.3. There is a distinctive negative increment in the shielding of the α-hydrogen nucleus on going from the methyl to the ethyl to the isopropyl derivatives and this increment is directly proportional to the number of C—C bonds. Thus the chemical shifts of the isopropyl derivatives are shown to be given by

$$\delta\alpha\,(\text{isopropyl X}) = \delta\,(\text{methyl X}) - 2\delta(\text{C—C})_{\text{X}} \qquad (10.2)$$

where $\delta(\text{C—C})_{\text{X}}$ is the difference $\{\delta(\text{methyl X}) - \delta\alpha(\text{ethyl X})\}$. Magnetic anisotropic effects cannot explain this large observed "C—C bond shift". Similar "C—C bond shifts" have been observed in the shielding of the α-hydrogen nuclei in monosubstituted cyclohexyl derivatives[83, 380] (see Section 10.3.6). The "C—C bond shift" is not considered to be the magnetic anisotropic effect associated with a C—C single bond: it is suggested that when a C—C bond replaces a C—H bond there might be an accompanying change in the electronic excitation energy, E, which features in the paramagnetic component of the Ramsey[10] shielding expression (see Section 3.5) and would thus give rise to an appreciable change in overall shielding. Because of the linear correlation between internal chemical shifts and electronegativity of substituents in ethyl compounds, such an effect must influence nuclei in the α- and β-positions equally: estimates of the contribution to the shielding of hydrogen nuclei from this "C—C bond shift" have been made by Cavanaugh and Dailey[7, 11]. Spiesecke and Schneider[6] cite strong evidence to suggest that any deviation from the simple correlation between chemical shifts and electronegativities of the neighbouring substituents arises from neighbour anisotropic effects. It is obvious from the divergence of opinion on this matter that more definite conclusions will not be forthcoming until we overcome the limitations of the assumed model which considers the chemical shifts to be composed of several local independent contributions.

It should be mentioned that the shielding effects of intramolecular electric fields in alkanes have been considered only in a few cases. Musher[24] has shown that the low field shielding of the α-CH_2 hydrogen nuclei in ethanol can be explained solely on this basis. The contribution to the ^{1}H shielding from the van der Waals' interactions within the molecule is thought to be appreciable in halogenated compounds: an increase in such dispersion effects would cause a decrease in shielding[449].

Metal Ethyl Derivatives. The ^{1}H resonance spectra of several metal ethyl derivatives have been measured and it is observed that the internal chemical shift values when substituted into equation (10.1) do not predict reasonable values for the electronegativities of the metals concerned. Table 10.5 gives the

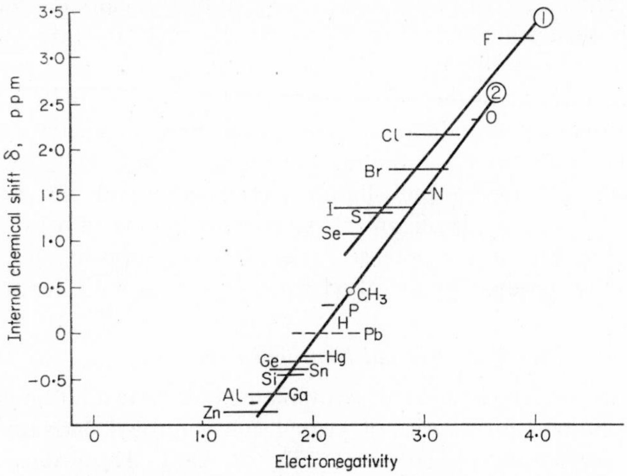

FIG. 10.5 Graph of the internal chemical shifts ($\Delta = \delta_{CH_3} - \delta_{CH_2}$) against the electronegativity of a substituent E_X in ethyl derivatives of general formula $(C_2H_5)_nX$. The horizontal bar shows the range of electronegativity values obtained from different approaches. Narasimhan and Rogers[12].

TABLE 10.5 THE ^{1}H INTERNAL CHEMICAL SHIFTS OF SOME METAL ETHYL DERIVATIVES

Compound	$\delta_{CH_3} - \delta_{CH_2}$ ppm	Reference
$Zn(C_2H_5)_2$	−0·848	12
$Ge(C_2H_5)_4$	−0·307	12
$Li(C_2H_5)$	−2·19	349
$SiCl_3(C_2H_5)$	+0·195	12
$SiCl_2(C_2H_5)_2$	+0·015	12
$Ga(C_2H_5)_3$	−0·560	12, 14
$Si(C_2H_5)_4$	−0·420	15

internal chemical shifts for several pure liquid ethyl derivatives. The separations of the CH_3 and CH_2 resonance signals in metal ethyl derivatives are usually quite small with the CH_3 group nuclei being less shielded than those of the CH_2 group. This is expected from simple inductive considerations, the highly electron-repelling metal atoms being more electropositive than hydrogen atoms. Figure 10.5 shows a plot of the internal chemical shifts ($\Delta = \delta_{CH_3} - \delta_{CH_2}$) against the electronegativity of the substituent X in a series of metal ethyl derivatives of general formula $(C_2H_5)_nX$. A fairly linear plot (line 2) is obtained and this is compared with a similar linear plot (line 1) for other ethyl derivatives. The two plots differ quite markedly and it is necessary to modify the Dailey–Shoolery equation correlating the internal chemical shifts with electronegativity of substituent in the following manner[12, 13]:

$$E_X = 0{\cdot}62\Delta + 2{\cdot}07. \qquad (10.3)$$

The order of electronegativity values (E_x) predicted by this equation for Group IVB elements in their ethyl derivatives is the same as that found by Allred and Rochow[65] from considering the methyl derivatives.

No doubt the shielding of the α-CH_2 group in metal alkyls will be influenced by factors other than simple inductive effects such as the diamagnetic anisotropic effects associated with the C—X bond. In the series $Si(C_2H_5)_4$–$SiCl_3C_2H_5$ the δ values measured on the pure liquids vary linearly with the number of chlorine atoms attached to the silicon[12]. An increase in the number of chlorine atoms causes the silicon to increase its electron withdrawing power with respect to the ethyl group. Several alkyl tin compounds have recently been studied[482].

10.1.3 Propyl and Isopropyl Derivatives

Table 10.3 lists the chemical shifts, extrapolated to infinite dilution in carbon tetrachloride solutions, for a series of propyl and isopropyl derivatives[7, 11]. In the propyl derivatives, the chemical shifts of the α-CH_2 groups are very similar to those of the analogous groups in the corresponding ethyl derivative while the terminal CH_3 groups are fairly insensitive to changes in electronegativity of the substituents. The trends in the observed chemical shifts could not be related in a simple manner to the electronegativity of the substituent indicating that there are appreciable contributions to the shielding from sources other than the inductive effect (either magnetic anisotropic effects or a "C—C bond shift" must be present). The presence of rotational isomerism is a further complicating factor in molecules of this type.

10.1.4 Contributions to the Shielding of Hydrogen Nuclei from C—H *and* C—C *Bond Anisotropic Effects*

Several workers have considered the possibility of long range contributions to the shielding of hydrogen nuclei from diamagnetic anisotropic effects of C—C and C—H bonds[16–19] (see Section 4.4.2). Guy and Tillieu[19] have calculated the magnitudes of the transverse and longitudinal susceptibilities of C—C and C—H bonds and using these values estimates of the anisotropic diamagnetic shielding contributions have been made. The variational calculation of Tillieu led to a value for $\Delta\chi^{C-C}$ of $+1{\cdot}21 \times 10^{-30}$ cm^3 molecule^{-1} while the values obtained experimentally[16, 21, 22, 159] range from $+2$ to $+10$ ($\times 10^{-30}$) cm^3 molecule^{-1}. Experimental attempts to calculate this parameter are complicated by the difficulty of resolving the shielding effects due to this source from those arising from other factors (such as the anisotropic shielding effects of the C—H bonds). In all cases the value of $\Delta\chi^{C-C}$ is indicated to be positive, although Pople[26] has pointed out that this appears to be inconsistent with the fact that long chain paraffinic compounds have their axis of greatest diamagnetism in the chain direction. Zürcher[25] has recently made some calculations of $\Delta\chi^{C-C}$ using a least squares treatment and he has obtained a value in reasonable agreement with Tillieu. He also calculated that $\Delta\chi^{C-H}$ is appreciable. Tillieu predicted $\Delta\chi^{C-H}$ values ranging from $+0{\cdot}24$ to $+1{\cdot}50$ ($\times 10^{-30}$) cm^3 molecule^{-1} depending upon the chosen wavefunction. Pople's theory of anisotropic contributions to nuclear shielding does not predict a contribution for C—C single bonds due to the *a priori* nature of the calculation[(26)]. Insufficient is known at the present time to enable a more definite evaluation of the anisotropic shielding effect of a single C—C bond. Single C—C bonds have much smaller diamagnetic anisotropic effects than double and triple bonds due to the strong delocalisation of charge associated with the σ bond resulting from overlap of sp^3 hybridised orbitals.

10.2 Spin–Spin Coupling Constants in Alkane Derivatives

Coupling constants often reflect the stereochemistry of the interacting nuclei and are thus of vital interest to the structural chemist. Relative and absolute signs of coupling constants can now be measured with near certainty and this information greatly increases both the practical and theoretical significance of correlations between coupling constants and other molecular parameters.

The coupling constants in molecules of the more simple unsubstituted hydrocarbons (ethane, ethylene, acetylene) are of greater theoretical significance than those of the substituted molecules. These values can be obtained only by examining the molecules after a suitable isotopic replacement which causes magnetic non-equivalence of the nuclei without appreciably changing the electronic configuration of the molecule[(28, 42, 431)] (e.g. CH_3D or $H_2^{13}C{=}^{12}CH_2$).

Banwell and Sheppard[(34)] have written a review on H—H coupling constants observed in the spectra of hydrocarbon groupings.

10.2.1 Coupling Constants Between Geminal Hydrogen Nuclei on Saturated Carbon Atoms

Using a valence bond approach, Karplus and co-workers deduced a relationship between the coupling constants for *geminal* hydrogen nuclei and the H—C—H bond angles[(28–30)]. This relationship was later modified by Gutowsky and Somers[(31)] who introduced a correction for the vibrational effects within the —CH_2 group. However, the theory predicts that the *geminal* H—H coupling constants in alkane derivatives are positive and of the same sign as the *vicinal* H—H coupling constants. This is in contradiction to observed experimental results which clearly indicate J_{HH}^{gem} values to be negative in alkanes[(32)]. Hence the theoretical predictions must be regarded as incorrect. The calculation of *geminal* H—H coupling constants involves the cancellation of fairly large terms and does not lend itself to an exact evaluation. The disagreement between observed and calculated J_{HH}^{gem} values may be due to either the use of inaccurate molecular wavefunctions or from invalid approximations made in the calculation (see Section 5.3.2).

McConnell[33] has used a molecular orbital approach to the problem and this has also led to positive J_{HH}^{gem} values. However, by using a Dirac vector model, the same author has predicted that *geminal* H—H coupling constants can be negative[35].

Tables 5.5 and 5.6 list some *geminal* H—H coupling constants for several substituted methanes and ethanes[34]. For symmetrical molecules, deuteration techniques must be used to obtain the *geminal* coupling constants[28, 36, 37]. In four of the molecules examined, it was possible to show that the *geminal* coupling constant is negative with respect to the *vicinal* coupling constant (which is thought to have an absolute positive sign)[32]. It is therefore reasonable to assume that the *geminal* coupling constants in Table 5.5 are negative in sign[34], contradicting the theoretically predicted values (see Section 5.3.3).

10.2.2 Coupling Constants Between Hydrogen Nuclei on Adjacent Carbon Atoms

The spin–spin coupling constants observed in the spectra of alkanes must be considered to be averaged values of the coupling constants in the various rotational isomers. Karplus[39] has used valence bond theory to calculate the contact contribution to the spin–spin coupling of two hydrogen nuclei on adjacent carbon atoms (*vicinal* hydrogen nuclei) in terms of the dihedral angle φ (see Section 5.3.1) and has obtained the relationships

$$J_{HH}\,(\text{contact}) = 8{\cdot}5\cos^2\varphi - 0{\cdot}28 \text{ cycles sec}^{-1} \qquad (10.4)$$

$$(0^\circ \leqq \varphi \leqq 90^\circ)$$

$$J_{HH}\,(\text{contact}) = 9{\cdot}5\cos^2\varphi - 0{\cdot}28 \qquad (10.5)$$

$$(90^\circ \leqq \varphi \leqq 180^\circ).$$

Because the contact term is by far the largest contribution to the spin coupling between hydrogen nuclei, then equations (10.4) and (10.5) predict values of coupling constants in reasonable agreement with experimental values. Table 5.1 provides typical values of predicted *vicinal* coupling constants for various dihedral angles.

To obtain an approximate theoretical value for $J_{CH_3-CH_3}$ in ethane, the coupling constant expression can be averaged in a simple manner to account for the internal rotation to give

$$\langle J_{HH'}\rangle_{av} = [2\,J_{HH'}(\varphi = 60^\circ) + J_{HH'}(\varphi = 180^\circ)]/3 = 4{\cdot}2 \text{ cycles sec}^{-1}.$$

Sheppard and Lynden-Bell[42] have measured the $J_{CH_3-CH_3}$ coupling constant in ethane in the ^{13}CH satellite spectra of the molecule and their observed value ($J = 8{\cdot}0$ cycles sec^{-1}) is much higher than the theoretical value. Bothner-By and Glick[40] have likewise measured high values for $J_{CH_3-CH_2}$ spin coupling in ethyl derivatives ($J_{CH_3-CH_2} = 6{\cdot}0$ to $7{\cdot}4$ cycles sec^{-1}).

Equations (10.4) and (10.5) can be applied more rigorously to estimate spin–spin coupling constants in molecules where the conformation (and thus the dihedral angle) is known as for certain cyclohexane derivatives. By examining a series of acetylated sugars, Lemieux and co-workers[41] have succeeded in

TABLE 10.6 FIRST ORDER J_{HH}^{vic} COUPLING CONSTANTS † OF SEVERAL ETHYL COMPOUNDS[40, 53]

$(CH_3CH_2)_nX$

Substituent X	Coupling constant J_{av} (cycles sec^{-1})
H	8·0 ± 0·1
CH_3	7·26 ± 0·1
OH	6·97 ± 0·1
O_2CH	6·93 ± 0·1
F	6·9 ± 0·1
Cl	7·07 ± 0·1
Br	7·25 ± 0·1
I	7·16 ± 0·1
SH	7·27 ± 0·1
CN	7·24 ± 0·1
CO_2H	7·41 ± 0·1
N	6·96 ± 0·1
O	6·96 ± 0·1
Li	8·4
S	7·42 ± 0·05
Co	7·5 ± 0·1
Hg	7·0
N	6·9
P(III)	7·6
Sn(IV)	8·2
Pb(IV)	8·2
Si(IV)	7·9 ± 0·02
CH_2CN	7·7
CH_2Cl	7·4
CH_2Br	7·3
CH_2I	7·2
$(O)_2C{=}O$	6·96 ± 0·1

† Compilation of coupling constants made from a survey of the literature by Abraham and Pachler[53].

measuring the coupling constants between two *axial* hydrogen nuclei on adjacent carbon atoms (J_{aa} = 5 to 8 cycles sec^{-1}, φ = 180°), two *equatorial* hydrogen nuclei on a pair of adjacent carbon atoms (J_{ee} = 3–4 cycles sec^{-1}, φ = 60°) and an *axial* and *equatorial* hydrogen nucleus on adjacent carbon atoms (J_{ae} = 2–3 cycles sec^{-1}, φ = 60°). A comparison of these values with the expected theoretical values, shown in Table 5.1, shows them to be in fairly good agreement with each other. However, Musher[378] has found J_{ae}^{vic} and J_{aa}^{vic} values in 1,1,4,4-tetramethylcyclohexyl-2,6-diacetate which are in poor agreement with the Karplus theoretical values (see Section 10.3.6b). It is seen that the Karplus equations (10.4) and (10.5) for predicting J_{HH} values in the H—C—C—H′ system generally produce lower values than those observed experimentally. Schug, McMahon and Gutowsky[43] have used the Karplus equations to estimate the effects of torsional vibrations and reorientations about the C—C bond on the averaged coupling constants in substituted ethanes. They found that the torsional vibrations cause the *trans* and *gauche* coupling constants to be temperature dependent, the dependencies being of opposite sign for the two coupling constants. However, the average coupling is temperature independent in molecules which have barriers with threefold symmetry: this is because vibrational effects are cancelled as a result of the internal rotation (typical molecules with threefold symmetry are ethane and 1-substituted ethanes). Hence, ethyl nitrate shows a constant $J_{CH_3-CH_2}$ value of 6·92 cycles sec^{-1} over a 100°C temperature range[43]. Several other workers have used the Karplus equation to study the conformations of both five[44-46] and six membered rings[47-49].

Bothner-By and Glick[40] have reported several first-order coupling constants for a series of alkanes and these are included in Tables 10.6 and 10.7. For ethyl and isopropyl compounds, the J_{CH_3-CH} coupling constants show a linear correlation with the electronegativity of the substituent. It should be noted that the H—H coupling constants for these molecules were obtained by assuming the ^{1}H spectra to be first-order. Conroy[51] has shown that $J_{H-C-C-H'}$ values will depend on the electron density at the hydrogen nuclei, which is consistent with the observations of Bothner-By and Glick.

More accurate *vicinal* coupling constants have since been obtained from a wider range of molecules[15, 52, 487], and for ethanes a revised $J_{CH_3-CH_2}$ coupling constant/electronegativity relationship

$$J_{CH_3-CH_2} = 7{\cdot}9 - 0{\cdot}7\Delta E \tag{10.6}$$

has been suggested[34, 42]. ΔE is the difference in electronegativity between the substituent X and the hydrogen atom (E_X—E_H) and 7·9 cycles sec^{-1} is close to the observed *vicinal* coupling in ethane. Equation (10.6) can predict $J_{CH_3-CH_2}$ values to within $\pm 0{\cdot}3$ cycles sec^{-1}.

Abraham and Pachler[53] have made a more general correlation of J_{HH}^{vic} values in CH—CH fragments with the sum of the electronegativities, $\sum E$, of atoms bonded directly to the carbon atoms. They find that the relationship

$$J = 8{\cdot}0 - 1{\cdot}0 \sum E, \tag{10.7}$$

describes adequately the *vicinal* H—H coupling constants in ethyl derivatives and ethanes of general formula XCH_2CH_2Y and CH_3CHXY (see Tables 10.6 and 10.7) although it is not the best linear correlation for any one class of molecules. For molecules of general formula XCH_2CH_2X it is necessary to examine their ^{13}CH satellite spectra to obtain J_{HH}^{vic} values[50].

Conroy[51] has used a M.O. approximation to obtain a relationship between $J_{H-H'}$ coupling constants and the dihedral angle in H—C—C—H′ systems. From his results a calculated curve can be plotted to enable one to

TABLE 10.7 VICINAL H—H COUPLING CONSTANTS† IN SOME SUBSTITUTED ETHANES[40,53]

XCH$_2$ · CH$_2$Y			CH$_3$ · CHXY		
Substituents X	Y	Coupling constants J_{av} (cycles sec^{-1})	Substituents X	Y	Coupling constants J_{av} (cycles sec^{-1})
Cl	Cl	6·83 ± 0·1	Me	Me	6·8 ± 0·2
Br	Cl	6·87 ± 0·1	Me	Co	6·49 ± 0·1
Br	Br	7·37 ± 0·1	Me	I	6·42 ± 0·1
Br	OH	6·00 ± 0·1	Me	Br	6·40 ± 0·1
Cl	OH	5·83 ± 0·1	Me	Cl	6·31 ± 0·1
MeO	OH	5·33 ± 0·1	Me	NH$_2$	6·11 ± 0·1
MeCO	CO$_2$H	6·80 ± 0·1	Me	OH	6·05 ± 0·1
MeCO	CO$_2$Me	6·80 ± 0·1	CO$_2$H	CO$_2$H	7·22 ± 0·2
MeO	O$_2$CMe	5·33 ± 0·1	Br	Br	6·24 ± 0·4
Cl	O$_2$CMe	5·97 ± 0·1	Cl	Cl	6·1 ± 0·15
			OH	OH	5·26 ± 0·07
OH	OH	5·27	Cl	CO$_2$H	6·94 ± 0·03
MeO	MeO	5·3	Br	CO$_2$H	6·92 ± 0·01
			OH	CO$_2$H	6·97 ± 0·02
			Cl	OEt	5·28 ± 0·1
			Me	CO$_2$H	7·2 ± 0·1
			Me	O	5·98 ± 0·1
			Br	CHBrCO$_2$H	6·70 ± 0·1

† Compilation of coupling constants made from a survey of the literature and from original measurements by Abraham and Pachler[53].

predict the order of magnitude of the coupling constant for a particular dihedral angle. Good agreement between observed and calculated $J_{H-C-C-H'}$ values is found in most cases.

10.2.3 Signs of H—H *Coupling Constants*

It should be mentioned that caution must be exercised in applying the bond angle/coupling constant relationships to any particular class of molecules since several instances have been discovered where they appear to break down (dioxolanes[54], epichlorohydrin[55], (2,2)metacyclophane[56], diethyl sulphite[57]). In all cases the *geminal* and *vicinal* H—H coupling constants are observed to have opposite signs when the Karplus theory predicts them both to have the same sign. This suggests that one or both of the theoretical calculations are incorrect. Although absolute signs of coupling constants are predicted from the theory, it is usually possible to measure only relative signs of the coupling constants directly from the spectra. Karplus[58] has suggested an indirect method for the experimental determination of absolute signs of coupling constants which has been successfully applied to a wide range of molecules by Lauterbur and Kurland[32]. Theory predicts that coupling constants between directly bonded carbon and hydrogen atoms (J_{C-H}) are almost certainly positive and since it is often possible to determine relative signs of J_{HH} and J_{CH} values within the same molecule, the absolute signs of the former can be inferred. Having established the absolute sign of a coupling constant involving hydrogen nuclei in a particular group it is then possible to use this to deduce the absolute signs of coupling constants in molecules containing this group and where the relative signs of coupling constants are already known. Table 10.8 is a collection of absolute signs of H—H coupling constants obtained in this manner for

TABLE 10.8 ABSOLUTE SIGNS OF H—H COUPLING CONSTANTS

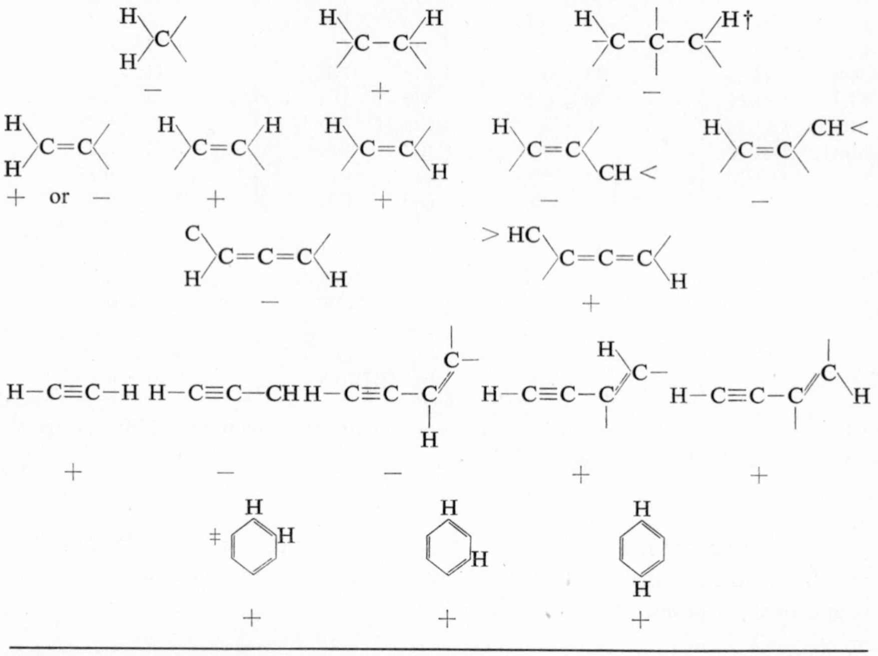

† In the molecule where this coupling constant was measured, a very small negative value was observed (0·3 cycles sec^{-1}): hence it is possible that the sign will not always be the same for coupling constants of this type.

‡ Reference 38.

J(H—C—O—H) is positive[464].

several systems. A more direct method of measuring the absolute sign of a coupling constant can be achieved by observing the effect on spin–spin multiplets of applying a large electric field to the sample. As yet, this method has not been used successfully to measure the absolute signs of J_{HH}^{gem} and J_{HH}^{vic} in alkanes.

In view of the fact that J_{HH}^{gem} values in alkanes have the opposite sign to that predicted by Karplus and co-workers[28–30] further theoretical calculations will be necessary. The evidence available at the moment suggests that the theoretical calculations for J^{vic}_{HH} values are reasonably sound. Now that an understanding of the absolute signs of the various coupling constants has been achieved more confidence can be placed in empirical correlations of H—H coupling constants with molecular parameters.

10.2.4 Long Range Coupling Constants Between Hydrogen Nuclei in Saturated Systems

It is unusual for hydrogen nuclei separated by more than three saturated bonds to be appreciably coupled by spin–spin interaction. There are, however, several molecules which do show coupling behaviour of this type. For example the ^{1}H resonance spectrum of the aldehyde hydrogen nucleus in methacrolein dimer (I) is a doublet with a field independent splitting of 1·3 cycles sec^{-1}[59]. The splitting is probably due to long range coupling with one of the ring hydrogens in the β-position to the aldehyde group.

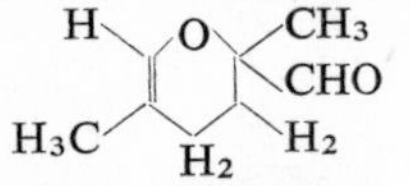

(I)

By examining deuterated molecules one can exclude the possibility of coupling between the olefinic and aldehydic hydrogen nuclei.

Another example of long range H—H spin coupling is provided by 1,2-dibromo-2-phenylpropane[59] which would be expected to exist mainly in the configuration with the bulky bromine atoms *trans* to each other as shown in structure (II)

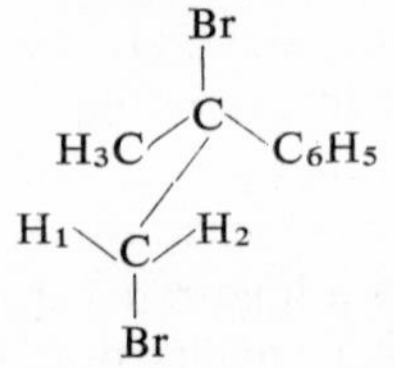

(II)

From the ^{1}H resonance spectrum of this molecule it is obvious that one of the two non-equivalent hydrogen atoms (H_1 or H_2) is coupling with the *C*-methyl group (J_{CH_3-H} = 0·65 cycles sec^{-1}). By examining specifically deuterated 1,2-dibromo-2-phenylpropane molecules (III) and (IV) the long range J_{H-CH_3} coupling is shown to involve the hydrogen nucleus *trans* to the methyl group.

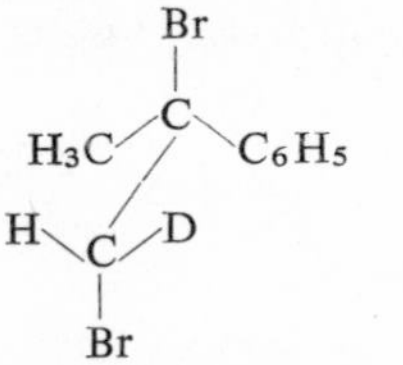

(III)

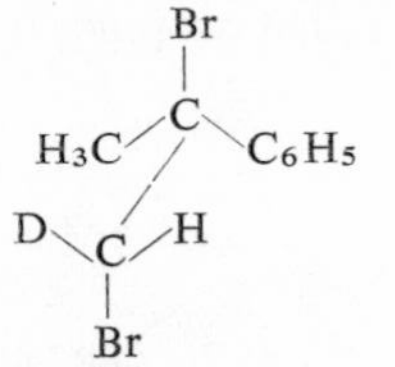

(IV)

Both examples quoted (I and II) are characterised by being present in a fixed conformational state.

An interesting long range coupling constant has been observed in the ^{13}CH satellite spectrum of acetone ($J_{CH_3-CH_3}$ = 0·54 cycles sec^{-1})[60]. Previously, the only molecules showing appreciable long range H—H spin coupling through σ-bonded systems have existed in a preferred conformation whereas acetone shows free rotation about its C—C bonds at room temperature. Karplus[61, 62] has indicated that large long range H—H coupling constants between nuclei separated by π-bonds might be explained in terms of contributions from low-lying $^3\pi$ states and σ—π interactions[63] in the C—H bonds. It has been suggested that low-lying states can also make significant contributions to the H—H coupling of nuclei in σ-bonded systems which are *geminal* to an unsaturated bond as in acetone.

The appearance of long range H—H coupling constants in the methacrolein dimer[59] (structure I in this section) and in methyl formate[64] may be due to the effects of the adjacent carbonyl group.

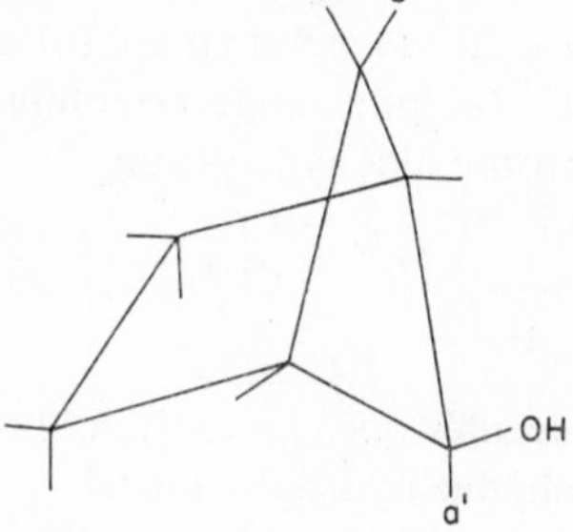

(V)

A long range coupling constant has been measured across a strained tetracyclobutane ring in derivatives of *exo*-bicyclo [2.1.1] hexane-5-ol (V)[369]. Hydrogen nuclei in the *a* and *a'* positions of derivatives of V are coupled to the extent of 6·8–8·1 cycles sec^{-1}. However, the ring strain is not necessarily a contributory factor in promoting long range coupling except in that it fixes the nuclei in favourable positions for coupling. This conclusion was reached by comparing the stereochemistry of V with that of methyl-α, β-dibromoisobutyrate (VI) where a long range J_{H-CH_3} value of 0·8 cycles sec^{-1} has been reported[59]: this is much smaller than the long range coupling constant observed for compound V since a methyl group hydrogen nucleus will spend only one-third of its time in the favoured position for long range coupling (*trans* to the interacting hydrogen nucleus) and furthermore the two carbon atoms to which are attached the interacting hydrogen nuclei are much further apart in VI than in the cyclobutane ring V. It is noteworthy that there is no measurable long range coupling in the *endo*-dicyclo [2.1.1] hexane -5-ol (VII).

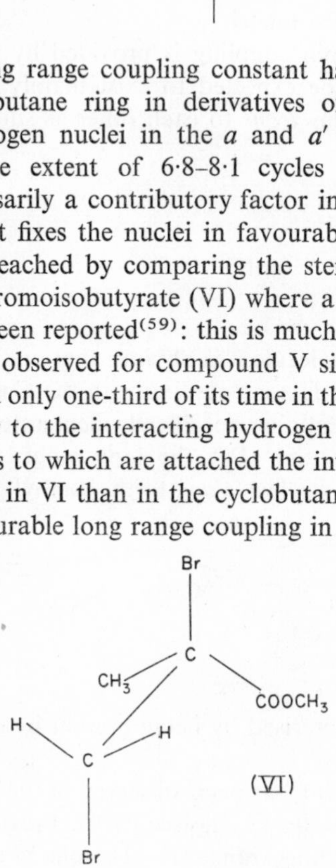

(VI)

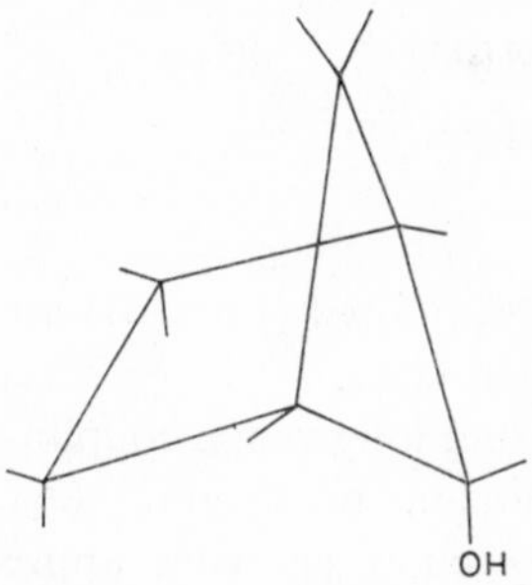

(VII)

Anet[370] has found long range coupling constants between hydrogen nuclei separated by four bonds in 2-*endo*, 3-*endo* camphane -2,3-diols (VIII) (J_{26} = 1·4 and J_{35} = 1·0 cycles sec^{-1})

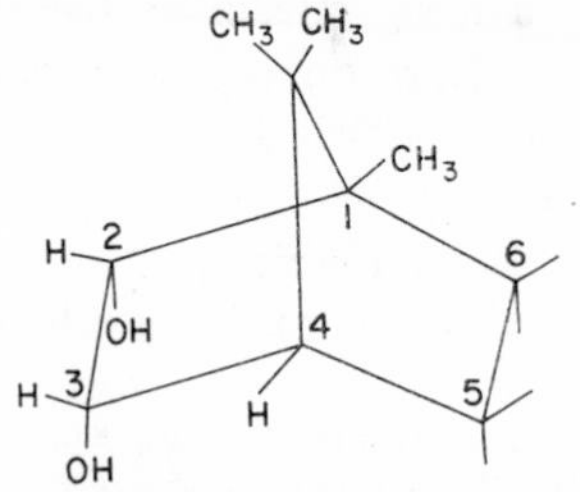

(VIII)

Long range coupling constants have also been measured in conjugated dienes[445], acenaphthenes[433] and several saturated compounds[424].

10.3 Miscellaneous Alkyl Compounds

10.3.1 Group IVB *Methyl Derivatives*

Allred and Rochow[65] have measured the chemical shifts extrapolated to infinite dilution in carbon tetrachloride of the methyl derivatives of carbon, lead, germanium, tin and silicon as part of a more general investigation of the electronegativities of Group IVB elements. By assuming values for the electronegativities of carbon and silicon (2·60 and 1·90 respectively[5]) and also assuming a linear relationship between the methyl chemical shifts and the electronegativity of the substituent they obtained electronegativity values for the remaining Group IVB elements by interpolation. Examination of the chemical shifts for these compounds shown in Table 10.9 indicates that the electronegativities decrease in the order C > Pb > Ge > Sn > Si contrary to the order predicted by other methods[66]. Spiesecke and Schneider[6] have examined the ^{1}H and ^{13}C chemical shifts of gaseous samples of Group IVB methyl derivatives with a view to making a similar correlation with electronegativities. Although the anisotropic effects of the Group IVB element on the shielding of the ^{1}H and ^{13}C nuclei would be expected to be negligible in such compounds, the

Table 10.9 The ^{1}H Chemical Shifts of Methyl Derivatives of Group IVB Elements[66]

Compound †	τ, ppm	Compound	τ, ppm
Me_4C	9·073 ± 0·005	Me_6Ge_2	9·788 ± 0·005
Me_4Si	10·000	Me_6Sn_2	9·790 ± 0·005
Me_4Ge	9·873 [a]	Me_6C_2O	8·752 ± 0·005
Me_4Sn	9·930 ± 0·005	Me_6Si_2O	9·950 ± 0·005
Me_6C_2	9·130 ± 0·007	Me_6Ge_2O	9·700 ± 0·010
Me_6Si_2	9·963 ± 0·002	Me_6Sn_2O	9·730 ± 0·002

† Compounds were examined as 2 to 10 per cent solutions in carbon tetrachloride.
[a] Taken from reference 65.

chemical shifts predict electronegativities similar to those found by Allred and Rochow, in poor agreement with the values obtained by other methods, particularly for the higher members of the series. In an attempt to reach a clearer understanding of the shielding effects in such molecules Brown and Webster[(66)] have examined the ^1H resonance spectra of a series of methyl-chloro-derivatives of carbon, silicon and tin and of hexamethylethane di-t-butyl ether and the corresponding derivatives of silicon, germanium and tin. Their chemical shift results are summarised in Tables 10.9 and 10.10, all measurements being made on dilute solutions in carbon tetrachloride using tetramethylsilane

TABLE 10.10 THE ^1H CHEMICAL SHIFTS OF SOME ALKYL DERIVATIVES OF CARBON, SILICON AND TIN[(66)] OF GENERAL FORMULA $(CH_3)_xMCl_{4-x}$

Compound†	τ, ppm	Compound	τ, ppm
Me_4C	9·073 ± 0·002	Me_2SiCl_2	9·200 ± 0·002
Me_3CCl	8·404 ± 0·005	$MeSiCl_3$	8·858 ± 0·005
Me_2CCl_2	7·828 ± 0·014	Me_4Sn	9·930 ± 0·005
$MeCCl_3$	7·257 ± 0·007	Me_3SnCl	9·368 ± 0·012
Me_4Si	10·000	Me_2SnCl_2	8·835 ± 0·007
Me_3SiCl	9·578 ± 0·002	$MeSnCl_3$	8·353 ± 0·005

† The compounds were examined as 2 to 10 per cent solutions in carbon tetrachloride.

internal reference. It was found that replacement of methyl groups in tetramethyl derivatives of carbon, silicon and tin by more electronegative substituents results in a decreased shielding of the remaining methyl hydrogen nuclei as expected on simple inductive grounds. As the successive replacement of methyl groups by chlorine atoms takes place the shielding of the methyl hydrogen nuclei decreases by roughly equal amounts. Shielding changes are larger in the carbon series than in the silicon series. A similar state of affairs is observed in the shielding of Si—H hydrogen nuclei in methyl chlorosilanes compared with the analogous carbon compounds and this has been explained in terms of double bonding between the silicon and chlorine atoms[(66)]. Such double bonding is not appreciable in the tin compounds and thus similar chemical shift behaviour to the carbon analogues is observed.

In the hexamethyl derivatives of Group IVB elements the methyl hydrogen nuclei are less shielded than in the tetramethyl derivatives in all cases except hexamethylethane. Introduction of an oxygen atom between the two central atoms results in decreased shielding in all four series of molecules.

10.3.2 Alkyl Derivatives of Elements Having Nuclear Magnetic Moments

When alkyl derivatives of elements with magnetic moments are examined by NMR, many interesting and unexpected features are encountered in their spectra. Each component of the ^1H resonance spectrum of an alkyl group attached to a non-magnetic isotope of X is split into a doublet when the alkyl group is bonded to a magnetic isotope of X (spin number $I = \frac{1}{2}$). As early as

1956, Baker[67] had demonstrated that the investigation of NMR satellite spectra of the alkyls of metals with magnetic moments could lead to information concerning the alkyl groups which could not be otherwise obtained. The ^{1}H resonance spectrum of lead tetraethyl at 40·00 Mc sec^{-1} is shown in Fig. 10.6.

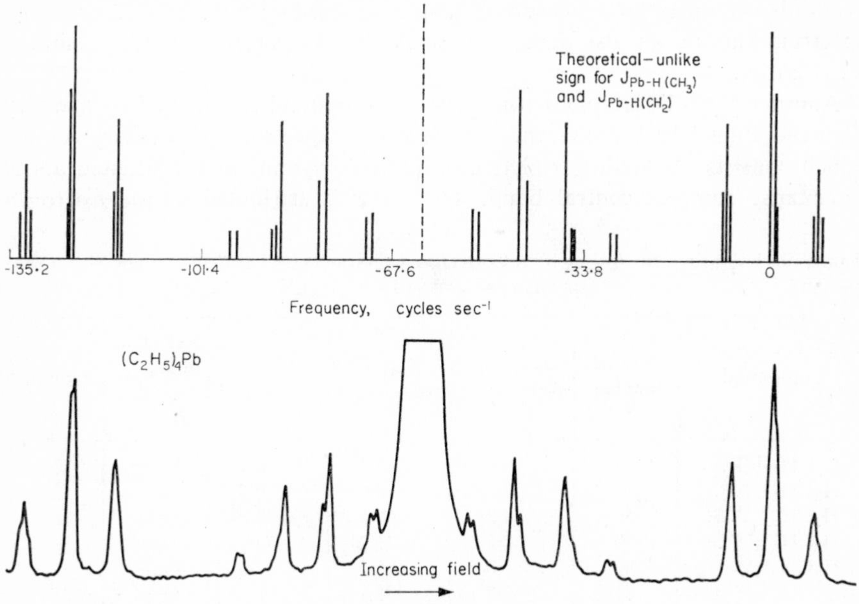

FIG. 10.6 The ^{1}H resonance spectrum of tetraethyl lead at 40·00 Mc sec^{-1}. Narasimhan and Rogers[52].

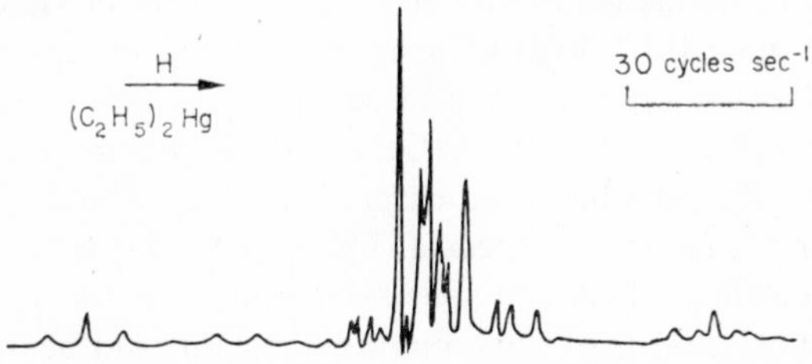

FIG. 10.7 The ^{1}H resonance spectrum of diethyl mercury at 60 Mc sec^{-1}. Narasimhan and Rogers[68].

It can be seen that the spectrum consists of an intense central band situated symmetrically within two pairs of weaker satellite bands. Ethyl groups attached to non-magnetic lead isotopes are responsible for the intense unresolved band in the centre of the spectrum. These ethyl groups do not give the familiar "ethyl" type spectrum since the chemical shift between the CH_2 and CH_3 groups is very small. However, the ethyl groups attached to the magnetic

^{207}Pb isotope (21·11 per cent natural abundance, spin number $I = \frac{1}{2}$) give rise to the satellite spectra which clearly show the familiar ethyl type (A_2B_3) spectrum. Thus the difference in spin coupling between the lead nucleus and the two portions of the ethyl group (J_{Pb-CH_2} and J_{Pb-CH_3}) results in the removal of the degeneracy caused by their chemical shift equivalence (see Section 8.2.1). Not only is it possible to measure the $J_{CH_2-CH_3}$ coupling constant in the satellite spectrum but one can also deduce the small chemical shift difference within the ethyl group.

Another typical example of this class of compound is provided by mercury dialkyls. Figure 10.7 shows the ^{1}H resonance spectrum of mercury diethyl which consists of satellite triplets and quartets, symmetrically situated about an intense complex central band. The latter is attributed to the hydrogen

TABLE 10.11 J_{CH_2-X} AND J_{CH_3-X} SPIN COUPLING CONSTANTS (IN CYCLES SEC^{-1}) IN MOLECULES OF GENERAL FORMULA $(C_2H_5)_nX$

Compound	Atomic number	$J_{CH_3-CH_2}$ cycles sec^{-1}	J_{CH_3-X} cycles sec^{-1}	J_{CH_2-X} cycles sec^{-1}	Rel. signs of J_{CH_3-X} and J_{CH_2-X}	Reference
$(CH_3CH_2)^{19}F$	9	6·9	25·2	46·7	Same	70
$(CH_3CH_2)_3{}^{31}P$	15	7·6	13·7	0·5	Opp.	52
$(CH_3CH_2)_4{}^{117}Sn$	50	~8·2	~68·1	~30·8	Opp.	52
$(CH_3CH_2)_4{}^{119}Sn$	50	8·2	71·2	32·2	Opp.	52
$(CH_3CH_2)_2{}^{199}Hg$	80	7·0	115·2	87·6	Opp.	52
$(CH_3CH_2)_3{}^{205}Tl$	81	~7·7	396	198	Opp.	71
$(CH_3CH_2)_4{}^{207}Pb$	82	8·2	125·0	41·0	Opp.	52
$(CH_3CH_2)_4{}^{14}NBr$	7		1·8	0·0		376, 452

nuclei in ethyl groups attached to mercury isotopes with zero magnetic moment while the former arise from hydrogen nuclei in ethyl groups attached to the magnetic ^{199}Hg isotope (natural abundance 18·86 per cent, $I = \frac{1}{2}$).

For ethyl derivatives of the type $(CH_3CH_2)_nX$ where X has a magnetic moment it is usually possible to measure the J_{CH_3-X} and J_{CH_2-X} coupling constants in their ^{1}H resonance spectra. By carrying out a full analysis of the spectra, accurate values of all the spectral parameters are obtainable and in some cases the relative signs of the coupling constants can be deduced: several such coupling constants are shown in Table 10.11. In other cases, the relative signs of the coupling constants can be measured directly using a spin decoupling technique[(71)]. For all the molecules examined (except ethyl fluoride) J_{CH_3-X} is greater than J_{CH_2-X} and the two coupling constants have opposite signs. This anomalous coupling behaviour has been attributed to occupied *d* orbitals. If *d* electrons are involved in chemical bonding between atom X and the alkyl group they could cause large variations in both the magnitude and sign of the Fermi contact contribution to the spin coupling constants. It is suggested that the 5*d* electrons of Pb, Tl and Hg, the 4*d* electrons of Sn and the lone pair of electrons for P, could all be involved in the C—X bond formation[(70)].

Narasimhan and Rogers[52] have suggested a qualitative explanation of the X—H coupling constants in terms of the "long range" molecular orbital approximation of McConnell[33]. They suggest that various one-electron terms make significant contributions to the Fermi contact interaction between the methyl hydrogen nuclei and the X nucleus. However, because the relative signs of the two X—H coupling constants are the same as those observed for corresponding *geminal* and *vicinal* H—H coupling constants in alkanes, Evans[423] has suggested that the X—H coupling constants are not as anomalous as was first thought. He suggests, for example, that ^{205}Tl—^{1}H coupling constants could operate via a Fermi contact mechanism involving the 6*s* electrons of the thallium atom.

The ^{1}H resonance spectra of dimethyl and diethyl derivatives of Cd and Se have been examined[72]. The metal–hydrogen coupling constants in cadmium diethyl show similar behaviour to those in other metal alkyl compounds, J_{M-CH_3} being larger than J_{M-CH_2}.

Examination of several metal propyl derivatives[73] also reveals that $J_{M-\alpha CH_2}$ is less than $J_{M-\beta CH_2}$ (see Table 10.12), hence this coupling effect is not limited to a methyl group.

TABLE 10.12 COUPLING CONSTANTS (CYCLES SEC^{-1}) OF SOME METAL *n*-PROPYLS[73], $(n\text{-}C_3H_7)_nX$

	Cd	Sn	Hg	Pb
J_{X-C-H}	51·6	49·1	95·0	40·5
$J_{X-C-C-H}$	60·2	67·2	110·3	102·4

10.3.3 Miscellaneous Metal Alkyl Derivatives

A general investigation of the NMR spectra of mercury dialkyls has been conducted and in all the molecules examined, the mercury nucleus couples to a greater extent with the β-CH hydrogen nuclei than with the α-CH hydrogen nuclei[69, 74]. A summary of the measured coupling constants is given in Table 10.13. Hatton and co-workers[425] have measured ^{199}Hg—H coupling constants in an extensive series of CH_3HgX and CH_3CH_2HgX compounds: they observed large increases in the coupling constants when the electronegativity of X is increased.

An investigation of the ^{1}H resonance spectrum of butenyl magnesium bromide in a solution of diethyl ether has established that the structure of this Grignard reagent is almost exclusively $CH_3CH{=}CH{-}CH_2MgBr$[75]. The aliphatic —CH_2 group directly attached to the magnesium gives a high field doublet absorption (τ = 9·3 ppm) indicating the hydrogen nuclei to be in a region of high electron density.

Allyl magnesium bromide has been shown to exist as a rapidly interconverting mixture of the allylic isomers

$$CH_2{=}CH{-}CH_2MgBr \rightleftharpoons BrMgCH_2{-}CH{=}CH_2$$

on the basis of its NMR spectrum (an AX_4 spin system). γ,γ-dimethyl allylmagnesium bromide has also been examined by the NMR technique and shown to be involved in a similar rapid equilibrium. On cooling the sample the single methyl absorption band resolves itself into a symmetrical doublet[77, 78].

In ether solution, butyllithium has been shown to exist as a solvated dimer[441].

TABLE 10.13 ^1H–^{199}Hg SPIN COUPLING CONSTANTS MEASURED IN CYCLES SEC^{-1} FOR A SERIES OF MERCURY ALKYLS[74, 69]

Compound[a]	J_{CH_3-Hg}	$J_{\alpha CH_2-Hg}$	J_{CH_2X-Hg}
$C_2H_5HgCH_3$	129·4	96	93·7
$C_2H_5HgCH_2Cl$	152·2	119·1	46·1
$C_2H_5HgCH_2Br$	134·8	95·8	39·3
$C_2H_5HgCH_2I$	159·2	125·8	40·2
$ClCH_2Hg$n-C_4H_9		115·3	45
$ClCH_2HgCH_3$	115·6		51·9
$ClCH_2HgCH_2Cl$			60
CH_3HgCH_3[b]	102		
$C_2H_5HgC_2H_5$[b]	120	91	
(n–$C_3H_7)_2Hg$[b]		90 (α) 108 (β)	
(i–$C_3H_7)_2Hg$[b]		78 (α) 126 (β)	
CH_3HgCN[c]	178·0		
CH_3HgI[c]	200·0		
CH_3HgClO_4[c]	233·2		

[a] The J values of the mercury dialkyls were obtained in the authors' laboratory unless otherwise stated.
[b] Taken from reference 69.
[c] Taken from reference 425: all the compounds were examined as 5 mole per cent solutions in pyridine.

10.3.4 2,3-Disubstituted Butanes

Anet has pointed out that the two methine hydrogen nuclei in *meso*-and *dl*-2,3-disubstituted n-butanes of general formula $CH_3CHRCHRCH_3$ are magnetically non-equivalent since they are coupled to different extents to the terminal methyl groups[79, 80]. The molecules must therefore be regarded as $X_3AA'X_3'$ systems if their hydrogen resonance spectra are to be fully analysed. Such an analysis[80, 81] has been undertaken for a series of 2,3-disubstituted n-butanes and from the magnitudes of the spin coupling constants between the non-equivalent methine hydrogen nuclei, $J_{AA'}$, qualitative estimates of the populations of the rotameric states have been obtained. Table 10.14 gives a list of the coupling constants measured from the spectra of these molecules. Small 1,3 coupling constants were also measured and in some cases they had opposite signs to the other coupling constants.

Anet has extended his measurements to cyclic 2,3-disubstituted butanes and his results for these molecules are included in Table 10.14.

10.3.5 Cyclopropane and Its Derivatives

The shielding of hydrogen nuclei in three membered rings is somewhat anomalous: a methylene group in cyclopropane (9·78τ) is shielded to a much greater extent than is the methylene group in propane (8·67τ). On simple

TABLE 10.14 ¹H CHEMICAL SHIFTS AND SPIN COUPLING CONSTANTS IN 2,3-DISUBSTITUTED BUTANES[80, 81]

Compound	State[b]	Chemical Shift		Coupling Constants[a] (cycles sec^{-1})			Reference
		τ_{CH_3}	τ_{CH}	$J_{AA'}$	J_{AX}	$J_{AX'}$	
meso-Dibromobutane	Neat	8·16	5·785	7·87	6·57	−0·26	81
meso-Dibromobutane	10·1% in CS_2	8·148	5·930	8·81	6·54	−0·28	81
dl-Dibromobutane	Neat	8·267	5·568	3·03	6·75	+0·02	81
dl-Dibromobutane	10·3% in CS_2	8·265	5·620	3·11	6·74	+0·02	81
meso-Dichlorobutane	Neat	8·427	5·938	6·26	6·48	−0·13	81
meso-Dichlorobutane	10·1% in CS_2	8·400	6·088	7·39	6·45	−0·12	81
dl-Dichlorobutane	Neat	8·465	5·802	3·28	6·57	−0·01	81
dl-Dichlorobutane	10·3% in CS_2	8·473	5·868	3·45	6·47	−0·08	81
meso-Diacetoxybutane	Neat	8·828	5·070	3·53	6·63	+0·03	81
meso-Diacetoxybutane	9·9% in CS_2	8·868	5·173	3·59	6·66	+0·02	81
meso-Diacetoxybutane	9·9% in $(CD_3)_2CO$	8·817	5·060	3·51	6·57	−0·01	81
meso-Diacetoxybutane	10·4% in $HCON(CH_3)_2$	8·813	5·053	3·64	6·59	−0·04	81
dl-Diacetoxybutane	35·2% in CS_2	8·872	5·155	5·12	6·51	−0·08	81
dl-Diacetoxybutane	13·6% in CS_2	8·885	5·194	5·08	6·50	−0·05	81
meso-Diphenylbutane	9·9% in CS_2	9·035	7·192	9·91	6·97	−0·29	81
dl-Diphenylbutane	43·7% in CS_2	8·807	7·168	7·02	7·76	−0·34	81
dl-Diphenylbutane	9·9% in CS_2	8·782	7·158	7·00	7·61	−0·20	81
meso-2,3-Butanediol cyclic carbonate (*cis*)	39% in CCl_4	8·626	4·160	7·35	6·55	−0·15	80
dl-2,3-Butanediol cyclic carbonate (*trans*)	39% in CCl_4	8·587	4·340	7·20	6·10	−0·10	80
cis-2,2,4,5-Tetramethyldioxolane	Neat	8·95 (8·67, 8·78)	5·85	5·85	6·30	−0·25	80
trans-2,2,4,5-Tetramethyldioxolane	Neat	8·85 (8·72)	6·62	8·35	5·90	−0·15	80

[a] $J_{AA'}$ and J_{AX} taken arbitrarily as positive: $J_{AX'}$ then has the sign shown.
[b] Percentages are v/v.

inductive grounds, one would expect a lower electron density around the cyclopropane methylene hydrogen nuclei than around those of the propane molecule thus causing opposite shielding effects to those observed. Although Walsh(82) has suggested that the cyclopropane ring might have a small amount of π-electron character, the large increase in shielding of the cyclopropane CH_2 groups is unlikely to arise from induced ring currents. It can be shown that such an effect would be small and would actually cause deshielding at the positions where the ring hydrogen nuclei reside(83). No satisfactory explanation of these anomalous chemical shifts has been suggested. There is evidence that epoxides show similar anomalous shielding effects(83, 84).

Effect of Ring Size on Shielding of Ring Hydrogen Nuclei in Cyclic Molecules. Wiberg and Nist(348) have measured the ^1H resonance spectra of several cycloalkanes, cycloalkenes and cycloalkanones and their results are summarised in Table 10.15. Dilute solutions of the compounds in carbon tetrachloride were examined to eliminate the possibility of any intermolecular shielding effects. In the cycloalkane series there is a significant decrease in the shielding of the ring hydrogen nuclei as the size of the ring is decreased. An exception to this is found in cyclopropane where the hydrogen shielding is greater than in the larger ring compounds. While the chemical shift differences between cyclopentane, cyclohexane and open chain methylene hydrogen nuclei have been explained in terms of the neighbour diamagnetic anisotropic effect of the C—C bonds in the molecule(159), the shielding of the cyclopropane hydrogen nuclei is much too large to be interpreted in this way. In the cycloalkenes, the olefinic hydrogen nuclei are shielded similarly in the 5 to 8 membered rings while those of cyclobutene experience a lower shielding (due perhaps to increased bond angle deformation) and those of cyclopropene a much lower shielding. The cyclopropene olefinic ^1H shifts can be explained on a ring current model. It is worth mentioning that the ^{13}C nuclei in the 3 membered ring molecule ethylene oxide are shielded by about 30 ppm more than ^{13}C nuclei in six membered rings and straight chain molecules(300).

Substituted Cyclopropanes. Trans-dibromocyclopropane (I) gives rise to a deceptively simple ^1H resonance spectrum which led early investigators to

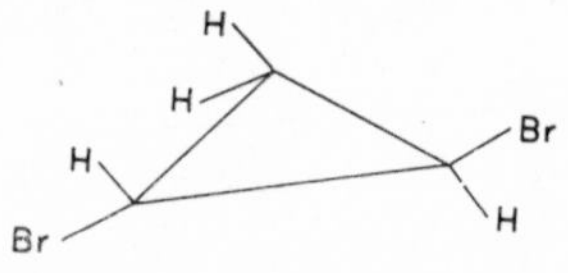

(I)

believe that the *cis* and *trans* H—H coupling constants are equal for this molecule(85). Gutowsky and Grant(86) have shown that a detailed AA′XX′ analysis of the spectrum can be achieved using unequal values of the *cis* and *trans* coupling constants and subsequent investigators of cyclopropane derivatives(87-90) have shown that the *cis* H—H coupling constants are in fact larger than the *trans* coupling constants (see Table 10.16). Such data have been shown to be generally true for cyclopropane derivatives and they will be of

TABLE 10.15 ^{1}H CHEMICAL SHIFTS (τ VALUES) OF SOME CYCLOALKANES, CYCLOALKENES AND CYCLOALKANONES[(348)]

Ring size	Cyclo-alkane[a]	Cycloalkenes[a]				
		=CH	$CH_2C=$	$\Delta\tau$[b]	CCH_2C	$\Delta\tau$[b]
3	9·78(s)	2·99(t)	9·08(t)	0·70		
4	8·04(s)	4·03(s)	7·46(s)	0·56		
5	8·49(s)	4·40(t)	7·72(m)	0·77	8·10(m)	0·39
6	8·56(s)	4·41(t)	8·04(m)	0·53	8·35(m)	0·20
7	8·46(s)	4·29(t)	7·89(b)	0·57	8·38(b)	0·08
					8·51(b)	−0·05
8	8·46(s)	4·44(t)	7·89(b)	0·54	8·50(b)	−0·04

Ring size	Cycloalkanones[a]			
	CH_2—C=O[a]	$\Delta\tau$[b]	C—CH_2—C	$\Delta\tau$[b]
4	6·97(t)	1·07	8·04(q)	0·00
5	7·94(s)	0·55	7·98(s)	0·51
6	7·78(b)	0·78	8·21(b)	0·35
7	7·62(b)	0·84	8·34(b)	0·12
8	7·70(b)	0·76	8·19(b)	0·27
			8·50(b)	−0·04

[a] The letters refer to the number of components of each line: s, singlet; t, triplet; q, quintet; m, incompletely resolved multiplet; b, broad unresolved multiplet. The probable error is ±0·02.
[b] Shift with respect to corresponding cycloalkane.

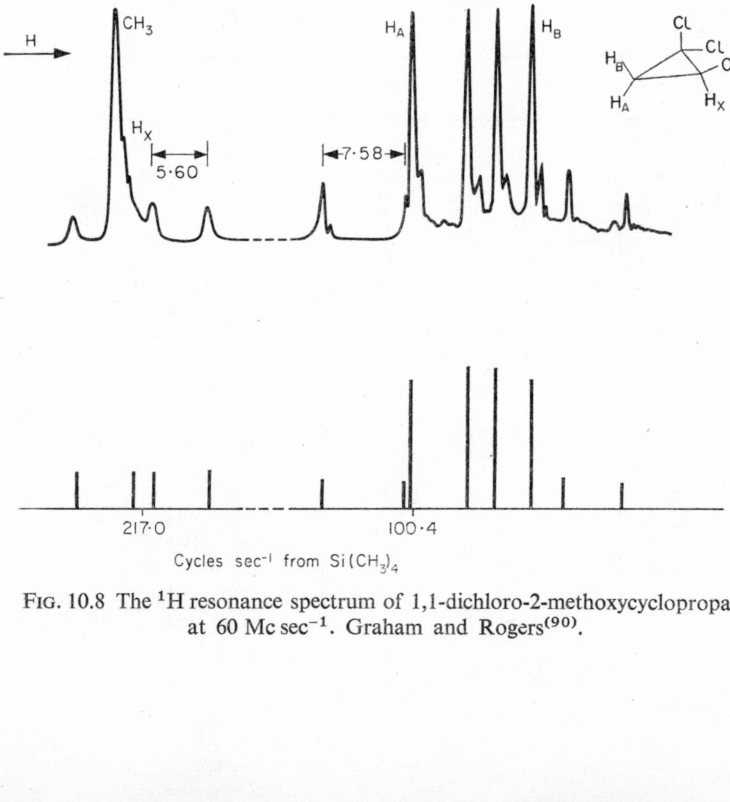

FIG. 10.8 The ^{1}H resonance spectrum of 1,1-dichloro-2-methoxycyclopropane at 60 Mc sec^{-1}. Graham and Rogers[(90)].

TABLE 10.16 ^{1}H CHEMICAL SHIFTS (τ VALUES) AND COUPLING CONSTANTS (CYCLES SEC^{-1}) IN SOME SUBSTITUTED CYCLOPROPANES[(90)]

Compound	Chemical shifts			Coupling constants			Compound	Chemical shifts			Coupling constants		
	τ_A	τ_B	τ_X	J_{cis}	J_{trans}	J_{gem}		τ_A	τ_B	τ_X	J_{cis}	J_{trans}	J_{gem}
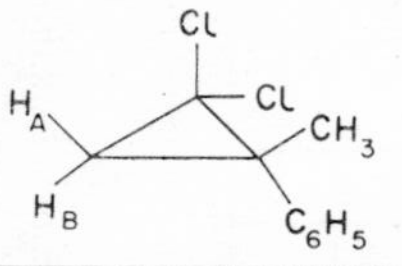	8·29	8·60				7·10	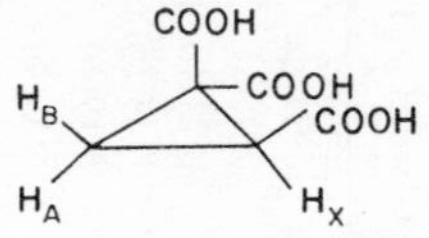	7·70	7·57	6·83	9·33	6·55	4·80
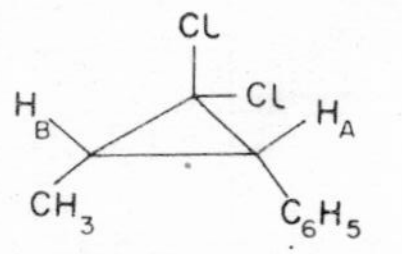	7·79	8·28		8·28			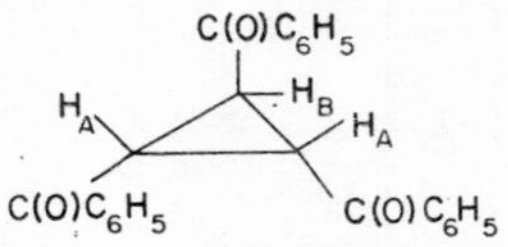	5·87	5·51			5·61	
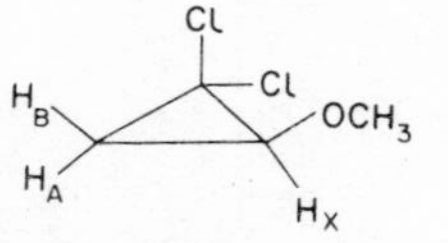	8·34	8·49	6·38	7·90	5·28	8·38	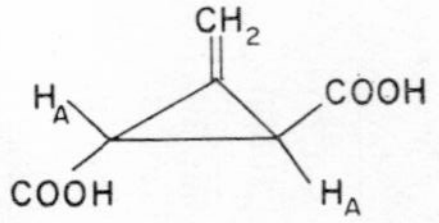	8·17			$J_{H_AH_A'} = 2{\cdot}63$		
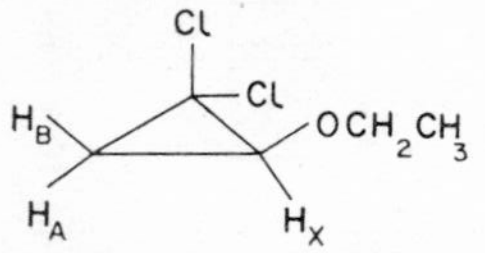	8·49	8·64	6·52	8·25	5·27	8·09							

considerable value in the configurational analysis of the molecules. Graham and Rogers[90] have measured the NMR spectra of a series of substituted cyclopropanes and their results are summarised in Table 10.16. The ^{1}H spectrum of a typical cyclopropane derivative is shown in Fig. 10.8. From an examination of Table 10.16 it is obvious that while the nature of the substituents has little effect on the *cis* and *trans* H—H coupling constants the chemical shifts show a sensitive dependence on the substituents. The chemical shift[63] of the ring hydrogen nuclei is 9·78τ hence the effect of introducing the substituents listed in Table 10.16 is to cause deshielding[85]. Magnetically anisotropic groups, such as phenyl or carbonyl groups have a large deshielding effect on the ring nuclei[90].

Substituted cyclopropanes exist in rigidly fixed conformations and thus lend themselves to studies of the angular dependence of spin-spin coupling constants. The measured values of *cis* and *trans* coupling constants in cyclopropanes are in good agreement with values calculated using valence bond theory[39, 92, 434, 442, 468]. It can be seen from Table 10.16 that the *geminal* H—H coupling constants are the most sensitive to changes in substituents.

The relative signs of the *geminal* and *vicinal* H—H coupling constants in cyclopropane have been shown to be opposite[91] (as is the case for non-cyclic alkanes).

Closs and Closs[88] have used NMR spectroscopy to determine the configuration of several chlorocyclopropanes. This was achieved by assuming the *trans* coupling constant to be greater than the *cis* coupling constant in opposition to the conclusions of Graham and Rogers[90]. Theoretical predictions indicate that the *cis* coupling is the larger and Hutton and Schaefer[350] have recently determined fairly certainly that this is the case.

Epoxides. Table 10.17 contains the ^{1}H chemical shifts of several monosubstituted epoxides. The ring hydrogen nuclei are observed to be more shielded than similar hydrogen nuclei in non-cyclic ethers[83, 84, 93, 485].

TABLE 10.17 THE ^{1}H CHEMICAL SHIFTS OF SOME MONOSUBSTITUTED EPOXIDES[83, 84]

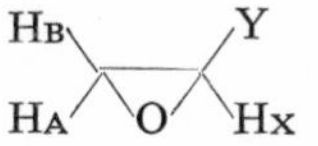

Y	τ_B	τ_A	τ_X
H	7·42	7·42	7·42
OCH_3	7·00	7·06	6·63
C_6H_5	7·19	7·40	6·39
COOH	7·01	7·07	6·53
Cl†	7·17	7·25	5·10
CN	6·98	6·89	6·50

† Taken from reference 83.

The *geminal* and *vicinal* H—H coupling constants in epoxides are opposite in sign.

10.3.6 Cyclohexane Derivatives

Cyclohexane is a non-planar molecule which has been shown to have least ring strain when it adopts a chair conformation as shown in Section 4.4.2. In this form of the molecule there are two positions of substitution on each carbon atom—an *equatorial* and an *axial* position. If the ring molecule is rapidly interconverting between its conformational forms (see Section 9.7.1) at room temperature, then each substituent will spend equivalent periods of time in both the *equatorial* and the *axial* positions. When this state of affairs prevails, NMR measurements can only detect the average environment of a magnetic nucleus involved in the interconversion. When the rate of interconversion becomes sufficiently slow for the NMR technique to "see" a magnetic nucleus in each of its separate conformational environments, information concerning the comparative shielding effects operating at *axial* and *equatorial* positions can be estimated: for our purpose, molecules of this type can be regarded as fixed conformers and separate resonance bands will be observed for nuclei in *axial* and *equatorial* positions. In Section 9.7 an account of the application of NMR to the study of the rate of conformational interconversion in cyclohexane systems has been provided. Examination of cyclohexane derivatives[94, 95, 96, 435, 453] over a range of temperatures can often indicate the conformational state of the molecule (that is, whether fixed or interconverting). It is intended in this section to consider other observations associated with both configurational and conformational effects in cyclohexane derivatives.

(a) ^{1}H *Chemical Shifts in Cyclohexane Derivatives.*

The shielding of the methylene hydrogen nuclei in cyclohexane ($\tau = 8{\cdot}564$) is observed to be appreciably lower than that of a methylene —CH_2 group in a straight chain non-cyclic alkane ($\tau = 8{\cdot}75$ for both n-hexane and n-heptane).

TABLE 10.18 THE SHIELDING DIFFERENCES BETWEEN AXIAL AND EQUATORIAL HYDROGEN NUCLEI (δ_{ae}) IN CYCLOHEXANE DERIVATIVES[85, 96–98]

Compounds	δ_{ae} (ppm)
Cyclohexane[96]	0·46
δ-1.2.3.4.5.6-Hexachlorocyclohexane[97]	0·51
ε-1.2.3.4.5.6-Hexachlorocyclohexane[97]	0·20
myo-Inositol hexaacetate[97]	0·20
cis and *trans* 4-t-Butylcyclohexanol[97]	0·13
cis and *trans* 4-t-Butylcyclohexyl acetate[97]	0·40
Androsterone and *epi*androsterone[98]	0·45
11α- and 11β-Hydroxyprogesterone[98]	0·43

Jackman and Wiley[85] believe this to be due to the contributions to the shielding from neighbour anisotropic effects associated with C—C bonds: moreover, the difference in shielding of hydrogen nuclei in the *equatorial* and *axial* positions can also be explained on this basis. A hydrogen nucleus in an *axial* position is usually shielded more than one in an *equatorial* position by about ~0·1 to 0·6 ppm (see Table 10.18). Jackman[85] calculated the diamagnetic anisotropic contribution to the shielding of hydrogen nuclei using a value of $(\chi_T - \chi_L)$ for single C—C bonds of $+ 5{\cdot}5 \times 10^{-30}$ cm^3 molecule^{-1}. Because the transverse component of the magnetic susceptibility (χ_T) is greater than the longitudinal value (χ_L) the long range shielding effects arising from a single C—C bond will be opposite to those observed for a triple C≡C bond where the transverse component is the smaller of the two. Jackman[85] calculated a value for the difference in shielding between the *axial* and *equatorial* positions of $\delta_{ae} = 0{\cdot}40$ ppm in excellent agreement with the experimental values given in Table 10.18. Musher[17] has also interpreted the chemical shift differences in cyclohexanes in terms of magnetic anisotropic effects.

Moritz and Sheppard[22] have assumed that the internal chemical shifts in propane, isobutane and cyclohexane can all be explained in terms of the magnetic anisotropic effects of the C—C bonds and they have calculated a value for $\Delta\chi^{C-C}$ of $7{\cdot}0 \times 10^{-30}$ cm^3 molecule^{-1} based on this assumption. For cyclohexane they made similar assumptions to those made by Jackman[85] (see Section 4.4.2), namely that only the C_2—C_3 and C_5—C_6 bonds contribute to the differential shielding between *axial* and *equatorial* hydrogen nuclei at the C_1 carbon atom and that the C—H bonds make zero contribution. The internal shielding difference between *axial* and *equatorial* hydrogen nuclei as measured in the low temperature spectrum of cyclohexane is 0·46 ppm and this can be accounted for by the magnetic anisotropic effects of C—C bonds if a value of $\Delta\chi^{C-C}$ of $7{\cdot}0 \times 10^{-30}$ cm^3 molecule^{-1} is assumed. This value is somewhat higher than that predicted by Bothner-By and Naar-Colin[8] ($5{\cdot}5 \times 10^{-30}$ cm^3 molecule^{-1}) based on the chemical shift difference between cyclohexane and cyclopentane and much larger than the theoretically calculated value ($1{\cdot}21 \times 10^{-30}$ cm^3 molecule^{-1}). A value of $\Delta\chi^{C-C}$ of $7{\cdot}1 \times 10^{-30}$ cm^3 molecule^{-1} would completely account for the internal shielding in propane (0·4375 ppm) without invoking the differing inductive effects of CH_2 and CH_3 groups as proposed by Narasimhan and Rogers[16]. Chemical shift differences in other alkanes can also be similarly explained. In the *meso*- and *dl*-forms of 2,3-dihalo butanes there are chemical shift differences between the methine hydrogen nuclei and between the methyl hydrogen nuclei in the two molecules which cannot be due to inductive effects since these are the same in both isomers. Furthermore, magnetic anisotropic shielding effects associated with the carbon–halogen bonds will be the same in both isomers and thus it is reasonable to assume that any chemical shift differences observed are due to anisotropic effects associated with the C—C bonds. A value of $\Delta\chi^{C-C}$ of $7{\cdot}0 \times 10^{-30}$ cm^3 molecule^{-1} is found to be consistent with the observed chemical shift differences in the 2,3-dihalo butane isomers if due regard is paid to the conformational states of the molecules. The agreement between the $\Delta\chi^{C-C}$ values of cyclohexane and of the 2,3-dihalo butanes suggests that ring currents in cyclohexane are unimportant. While the above discussion does not prove that the magnetic anisotropic effect associated with the C—C bond is the only important long range shielding effect, it does suggest that appreciable shielding can originate from this source. Despite the success of this model in predicting the chemical shift differences between the ring hydrogen nuclei in cyclohexane[85] and in methylcyclohexane[95] the model is unable to explain the ring hydrogen chemical shifts in several dimethyl cyclohexanes[95]. Muller and Tosch[95] have studied the ^{1}H resonance spectra of seven dimethylcyclohexanes over a range of temperatures and they have observed that (i) the "normal" chemical shift difference between *axial* and *equatorial* ring hydrogen nuclei ($\sim 0{\cdot}46$ ppm) is very much less in those dimethylcyclohexanes which have one *axial* methyl substituent (ii) for pairs of compounds such as methylcyclohexane and *trans*-1,4-dimethylcyclohexane the chemical shifts of the *axial* hydrogen nuclei in corresponding positions in the molecules are very different (iii) in *cis*-1,3-dimethylcyclohexane, some of the ring hydrogen nuclei resonate at fields of up to 0·6 ppm above that of the methyl resonance bands. None of these observations is consistent with the shielding contributions expected from consideration of inductive and bond anisotropy effects.

Musher[23, 24] has pointed out that intramolecular electrical fields could also be responsible for the observed differences in shielding of *equatorial* and *axial* hydrogen nuclei in cyclohexanes.

Cavanaugh and Dailey[7] have postulated that there is a contribution to the shielding of hydrogen nuclei in alkanes which is due to a "C—C bond shift": the origin of this shift is somewhat obscure but it is not a magnetic anisotropic effect. In order to investigate this effect further, the shielding constants of the α-hydrogen nuclei in a series of monosubstituted cyclohexanes have been determined[83, 380]. It was necessary in most cases to "freeze out" the sample into its fixed conformers to obtain the chemical shifts shown in Table 10.19. In

TABLE 10.19 ^{1}H CHEMICAL SHIFT DATA OF SOME MONOSUBSTITUTED CYCLOHEXANES[83]

Substituent	*Equatorial* α-hydrogen τ	*Axial* α-hydrogen τ	δ_{ae} ppm	*a e* equilibrium shift at 26°C τ	% population in *equatorial* conformer
OH	6·13	6·73	0·60	6·58	7·1
Cl	5·60	6·32	0·72	6·13	21·5
Br	5·40	6·18	0·78	6·02	23·1
I	5·28	6·02	0·73	5·80	24·0
NO_2		5·77		5·78	~0
NH_2		7·53		7·50	~0

Table 10.20 the "C—C bond shifts" for the cyclohexyl derivatives are calculated and compared with the values for the analogous ethyl and isopropyl derivatives: the agreement is quite good. Thus, while Jackman and Wiley[85] interpret such shifts as arising from the anisotropy of the C—C bonds, Dailey *et al.*[83, 380] consider such a contribution to require an implausibly large value for the anisotropy of a C—C bond.

Brownstein[100] has studied several polysubstituted cyclohexanes and has observed a correlation between ^{1}H chemical shifts and the proximity of bulky substituents. Hydrogen nuclei near to substituents are deshielded and the extent to which they are deshielded is proportional to the number and proximity of the substituents. He found that the hydrogen resonance spectra of hexasubstituted cyclohexanes of the same stereochemistry are the same, regardless of

TABLE 10.20 "C—C BOND SHIFT" CONTRIBUTIONS FOR CYCLOHEXYL, ETHYL AND ISOPROPYL DERIVATIVES[83]

Substituent	τ_I Methyl shift	τ_{II} Average shift of *axial/equatorial* α-hydrogen in cyclohexyl	$\frac{1}{2}(\tau_{II} - \tau_I)$ C—C bond-shift	Ethyl C—C bond-shift	Isopropyl C—C bond-shift
OH	6·61	6·43	0·092	0·200	0·267
NH_2	7·55	7·17	0·192	0·283	0·300
Cl	6·95	5·96	0·500	0·417	0·550
Br	7·31	5·78	0·767	0·685	0·767
I	7·85	5·65	1·100	1·000	1·050

TABLE 10.21 THE ^{1}H CHEMICAL SHIFTS OF SOME 1,2,3,4,5,6-HEXASUBSTITUTED CYCLOHEXANES AT 40·00 Mc sec^{-1} [100]

1,2,3,4,5,6-Hexachloro-cyclohexane isomers (Solutions in CH_2Cl_2)	Chemical shift† δ ppm	1,2,3,4,5,6-Hexahydroxy-cyclohexane isomers (OD derivatives)‡	Chemical shift† δ ppm	(δ − 0·85) ppm
α	+0·58	*L*	+1·58	+0·73
	+0·98		+1·98	+1·13
β	+1·30	*scyllo*	+2·05	+1·20
γ	+0·63	*muco*	+1·53	+0·68
δ	+1·18	*myo*	+1·88	+1·03
	+0·65		+1·38	+0·53
ε	+0·80	*treo*	+1·18	+0·33
	+0·63			
		epi	+1·78	+0·93
			+1·73	+0·88
			+1·40	+0·55
		cis	+1·53	+0·68
		allo	+1·38	+0·53

† The ^{1}H chemical shifts measured from CH_2Cl_2 external reference.
‡ The inositols were examined in D_2O solution.
"τ" $= 4{\cdot}7 + \delta_{CH_2Cl_2}$ (very approximate conversion).

whether the substituents are chlorine or hydroxyl groups. In 1,2,3,4,5,6-hexasubstituted cyclohexanes the inductive effects of the substituents on the hydrogen nuclei will be constant and any variation in the chemical shift will be a reflection of long range shielding effects. Although Brownstein chose to discuss his results in terms of "steric effects" he pointed out that the origin of the observed chemical shifts is probably due to neighbour anisotropy effects.

Table 10.21 presents the observed ^{1}H chemical shifts for various analogous stereoisomers of the inositols and hexachlorocyclohexanes (both sets of compounds being 1,2,3,4,5,6-substituted derivatives of cyclohexane). If a constant value of 0·85 ppm is subtracted from all the inositol chemical shifts to allow for differences in the inductive effects of the hydroxyl- and chloro-substituents, the modified chemical shifts are seen to be in fairly good agreement with the values for hexachloro derivatives. In the molecules where δ_{ae} values have been measured, particularly good agreement between the different δ_{ae} values is observed. This suggests that the magnetic anisotropy effects associated with a C—Cl bond and a C—O bond are similar in these molecules.

Muller and Tosch[352] have made a detailed NMR investigation of dimethyl cyclohexanes and related molecules and they have observed anomalous chemical shifts for some of the ring hydrogen nuclei. These chemical shifts could not be explained satisfactorily in terms of inductive or bond anisotropic effects and attempts to rationalise them by considering the possible effects of ring deformations and ring currents were also unsuccessful. They concluded that there is some other factor, at present unrecognised, which is contributing to the shielding in the molecules[352].

(b) *Coupling Constants in Cyclohexane Derivatives.* Musher[378] has examined the ^{1}H resonance spectrum of 1,1,4,4-tetramethyl-cyclohexyl-*cis*-2,6-diacetate

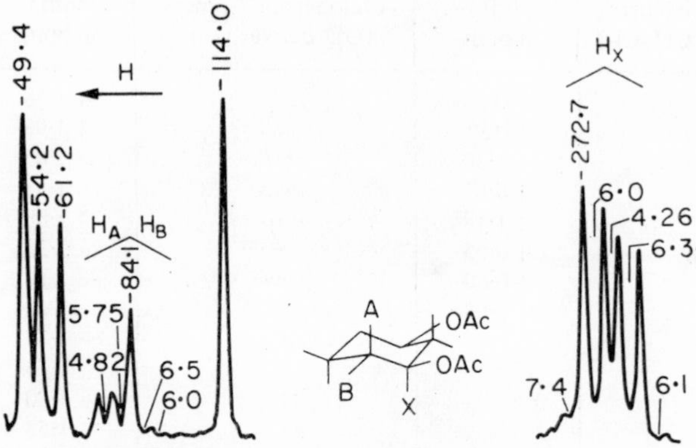

FIG. 10.9 The ^{1}H resonance spectrum at 60 Mc sec^{-1} of 1,1,4,4-tetramethyl-cyclohexyl-*cis*-2,6-diacetate. The peak positions are measured in cycles sec^{-1} from hexamethyldisiloxane internal reference. The X region of the spectrum is not on the same intensity scale as the AB region. Musher[378].

(see Fig. 10.9) which can exist in two conformational states, one with both acetoxy groups in *axial* positions and the other with them both *equatorial*. Because the conformer with both acetoxy groups in *equatorial* positions is of considerably lower energy than the *diaxial* conformer, the molecule will spend most of its lifetime in the energetically favourable *diequatorial* form. Thus the molecule can be considered rigid (in the time-averaged sense). The rigid molecule is symmetrical about an *axial* plane through the 1,4 carbon atoms and the three hydrogen nuclei on each side of this plane can be considered as separate identical ABX spin systems (since there is no coupling between the two ABX systems). A detailed analysis of the ^{1}H resonance spectrum of this compound (shown in Fig. 10.9) gives the following parameters

$$J_{AB} = J_{ea}^{gem} = 12{\cdot}36 \pm 0{\cdot}2 \text{ cycles sec}^{-1}$$

$$J_{AX} = J_{aa}^{vic} = 12{\cdot}35 \pm 0{\cdot}1$$

$$J_{BX} = J_{ea}^{vic} = 4{\cdot}25 \pm 0{\cdot}1$$

$$\left.\begin{aligned} \nu_A &= -1{\cdot}269 \pm 0{\cdot}003 \text{ ppm} \\ \nu_B &= -1{\cdot}400 \pm 0{\cdot}003 \text{ ppm} \\ \nu_C &= -4{\cdot}681 \pm 0{\cdot}003 \text{ ppm} \end{aligned}\right\} \begin{array}{l}\text{Measured from hexamethyldisiloxane} \\ \text{internal reference.}\end{array}$$

Thus the chemical shift difference between the *axial* and *equatorial* hydrogen nuclei is 0·131 ppm, the *axial* nucleus being at the higher field value. The measured values of J_{aa}^{vic} and J_{ae}^{vic} for 1,1,4,4-tetramethylcyclohexyl-*cis*-2,6-diacetate are in fairly poor agreement with theoretical values predicted by the valence bond approach of Karplus ($J_{aa}^{vic} = 9{\cdot}2$ and $J_{ea}^{vic} = 1{\cdot}7$ cycles sec^{-1} are the predicted values). The J^{gem} value is in good agreement with that obtained for deuteromethane(102) (CH_3D, $J_{HH}^{gem} = 12{\cdot}4$ cycles sec^{-1}). It is interesting to observe that the coupling constant between two *axial* hydrogen nuclei on adjacent carbon atoms (J_{aa}^{vic} or J_{AX}) is three times larger than that between *axial* and *equatorial* nuclei on adjacent carbon atoms (J_{ea}^{vic} or J_{BX}). Similar observations(479) have been made in the investigation of dioxane(101) and acetylated sugars(97) where chair conformations similar to those in cyclohexanes exist: in the case of the sugars, values of J_{ea}^{vic} and J_{ee}^{vic} of 2–4 cycles sec^{-1} and values of J_{aa}^{vic} of 5–8 cycles sec^{-1} were observed(97).

(c) *Configurational Effects in Acetylated Carbohydrates.* Lemieux and co-workers(41, 97, 103) have observed many interesting configurational effects in the ^{1}H resonance spectra of acetylated carbohydrates which show conformational behaviour similar to that of cyclohexanes. It was found convenient to examine acetylated derivatives since the acetoxy group does not complicate the ^{1}H spectra of the ring hydrogen nuclei with unwanted spin–spin interaction fine structure. The main points of interest which emerged from their studies are:

(1) They observed a chemical shift of 0·13–0·25 ppm between the absorption bands of methyl groups in *equatorial* and *axial* acetoxy substituents. For example, in the ^{1}H spectrum of the fixed molecule α-D-glucopyranose pentaacetate shown in Fig. 10.11c there are two high field methyl absorption signals separated by 0·15 ppm. The less intense signal at lower fields is assigned on intensity considerations to that belonging to the single *axial* acetoxy group while the methyl groups in the acetoxy groups at *equatorial* positions are assigned to the intense higher field band. This feature is apparent in the spectra of a large number of acetylated carbohydrates and, furthermore, 1,2,3,4,5,6-hexaacetoxy cyclohexanes of known configuration also show this behaviour.

(2) They found that the chemical shift of an *equatorial* hydrogen nucleus was ~0·20 ppm to low fields of that of an *axial* hydrogen nucleus. Evidence for this is found in the ^{1}H resonance spectra shown in Fig. 10.10.

(3) The pair of *geminal* hydrogen nuclei (AB) on the α-carbon atom to the ring oxygen atom in β-D-xylopyranose tetra-acetate are separated by a much larger chemical shift (0·61 ppm) than is normally observed for an *equatorial*/

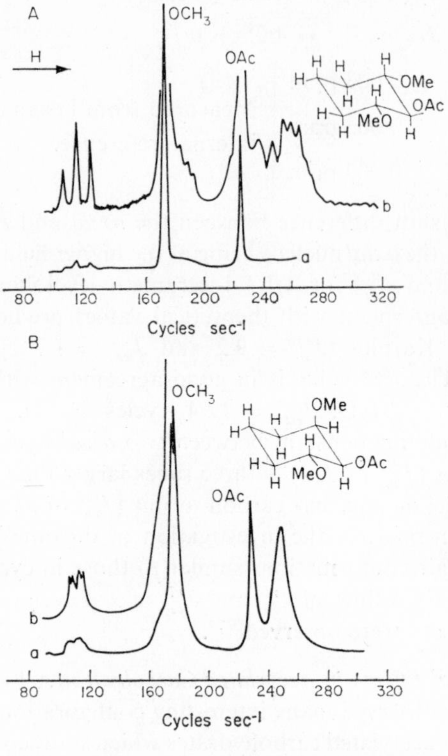

FIG. 10.10 The ^{1}H resonance spectra at 40 Mc sec^{-1} of (A) 1α, 3α-dimethoxy-2β-acetoxycyclohexane (B) 1α, 3β-dimethoxy-2α-acetoxycyclohexane. Both samples were examined as chloroform solutions. The solvent was used as internal reference. Lemieux, Kullnig, Bernstein and Schneider(97).

axial pair of hydrogen nuclei. It seems likely that the large differential shift is due to the magnetic anisotropic effects associated with the C—O bond.

Equatorial/axial differential chemical shifts of 0·25 to 0·65 ppm at the α-position to the ring oxygen atom have also been observed in the spectra of several anomeric pairs of acetylated aldopyranoses (the anomers differ in that the acetoxy substituent in the α-position to the ring oxygen atom is *axial* in one anomer and *equatorial* in the other).

(4) In cyclohexane type molecules which have a rigid structure, the spin–spin coupling constants between two *axial* hydrogen nuclei (*aa*) on adjacent carbon

atoms is observed to be 2 to 3 times larger than that between two hydrogen nuclei on adjacent carbon atoms having any other orientation (*ae* or *ee*).

Much useful information concerning both the configurational and conformational aspects of cyclohexane-type derivatives can be obtained by using the above empirical principles. Another useful observation in this respect, based on the significance of relative line widths in the ^{1}H spectra of cyclohexane derivatives, has been discussed by several workers[(23, 104, 105, 106)]. In molecules which are undergoing rapid interconversion, the coupling constants between the ring hydrogen nuclei are averaged values of those in the fixed conformations and this results in the absorption bands of the former being much narrower than those of the latter. In some spectra the broad absorption bands of the rigid conformer are due to overlapping absorption bands of similar chemical shifts. Rapid interconversion of the molecules can average out the chemical shifts of *equatorial* and *axial* hydrogen nuclei and this too will lead to line narrowing.

(d) *Cis- and Trans-4-t-Butylcyclohexyl Alcohols and Acetates.* Molecules of this type exist in known fixed conformations with the bulky t-butyl substituent preferentially occupying an *equatorial* position. Lemieux and co-workers[(97)] have examined the ^{1}H resonance spectra of this class of molecules and they have reported the line widths of the resonance band of the 1-hydrogen atom. It is observed that the half width of this signal in the *cis* alcohol and *cis* acetate ($\sim$ 7 cycles sec^{-1}) is only one-third of that observed for the *trans* isomers ($\sim$ 22 cycles sec^{-1} at 40 Mc sec^{-1}). The origin of the line broadening is thought to lie in unresolved multiplet structure arising from spin–spin coupling and since H—H spin–spin coupling constants are known to be appreciable for nuclei separated by up to three bonds it appears that the *axial* 1-hydrogen nuclei in the *trans* isomers are more strongly coupled with the neighbouring CH_2 groups than the *equatorial* 1-hydrogen nuclei of the *cis* isomers. This is a consequence of *axial* hydrogen nuclei on adjacent carbon atoms coupling much more strongly than hydrogen nuclei in other orientations.

(e) *Determination of the Configuration of Cyclohexane Derivatives Using NMR.* Examination of ring H—H coupling constants in the ^{1}H resonance spectra of two of the diastereomeric 1,3-dimethoxy-2-acetoxy cyclohexanes has enabled their configurational structure to be determined[(41, 97)].

1α, 3α-Dimethoxy-2β-acetoxycyclohexane. The ^{1}H resonance spectrum of this molecule is shown in Fig. 10.10A; it provides detailed information of the coupling constants between ring hydrogen nuclei in cyclohexane systems. The absorption bands for the 1- and 3-hydrogen nuclei are overlapped by the methoxy absorption band but the signal for the 2-hydrogen atom appears as a well-resolved triplet (J_{aa}^{vic} = 9 cycles sec^{-1}) resulting from spin–spin interaction with the hydrogen nuclei at positions 1 and 3.

1α, 3β-Dimethoxy-2α-acetoxycyclohexane. In the ^{1}H resonance spectrum of this molecule shown in Figure 10.10B the absorption multiplet for the 2-hydrogen nucleus appears as a quartet of bands at 107·5, 110·0, 113·8 and 116·5 cycles sec^{-1} from chloroform internal reference. The three hydrogen nuclei on adjacent carbon atoms constitute an ABX spin system and the quartet absorption of the 2-hydrogen nucleus is the X portion of the spectrum. Approximate values for the coupling constants between adjacent *axial–axial* (J_{aa} = 6·4 cycles sec^{-1}) and adjacent *axial–equatorial* (J_{ae} = 2·6 cycles sec^{-1}) hydrogen nuclei can be obtained by direct subtraction of appropriate bands in the quartet. In favourable cases, it is possible to use information of this kind to assign configurations of cyclohexane molecules.

(f) *Acetylated Aldopentapyranose Derivatives.* Figure 10.11 shows the hydrogen resonance spectra of several acetylated aldopentapyranose molecules. They can all be divided conveniently into four separate regions. An anomeric hydrogen nucleus (on the carbon substituted with an acetoxy group adjacent to the ring oxygen atom) gives rise to a low field signal of relative intensity 1 in the region ~ 3·9 to 4·7 τ. Its low shielding is due to the carbon atom to which

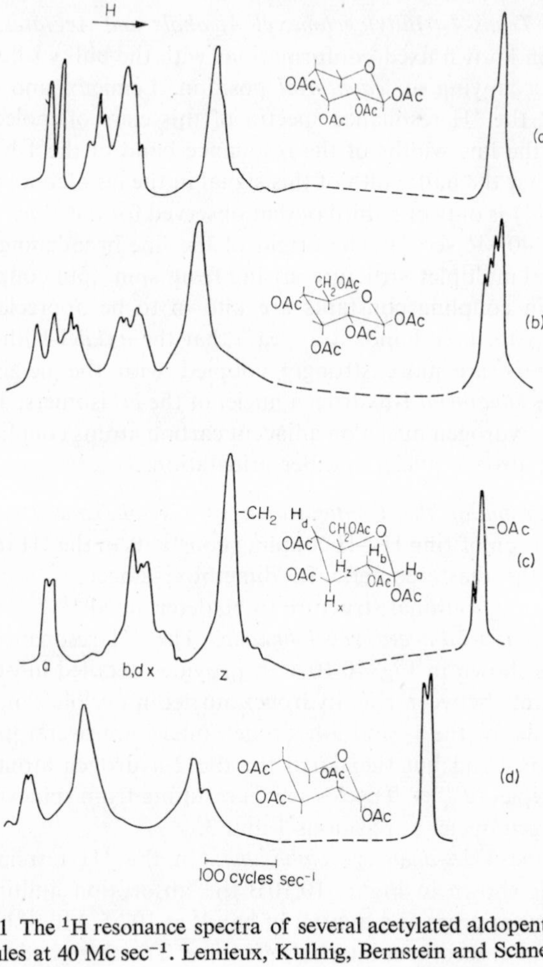

FIG. 10.11 The ^{1}H resonance spectra of several acetylated aldopentapyranose molecules at 40 Mc sec^{-1}. Lemieux, Kullnig, Bernstein and Schneider[97].

it is attached being bonded to two oxygen atoms. Further support for this assignment is found in the doublet splitting on the absorption band since the anomeric hydrogen nucleus would be expected to be strongly coupled with the single 2-hydrogen nucleus. In all cases, the magnitude of this coupling constant is in agreement with that predicted from the known orientations of the two nuclei. The three hydrogen nuclei on the secondary carbon atoms give rise to signals of the correct intensity in the region ~ 4·6 to 5·4 τ while the methylene hydrogen nuclei of the acetylated aldopentapyranose ring absorb in the region ~ 5·8 to 6·5 τ. Finally, the strong sharp signals in the ~ 8·0 to 8·5 τ region are assigned to the methyl groups of the acetoxy substituents. Thus, NMR supports the ring structures and anomeric configurations proposed for these molecules.

(g) *1,2,3,4,5,6-Hexachlorocyclohexanes.* Lemieux and co-workers[97] have examined the NMR spectra of five of the isomers of 1,2,3,4,5,6-hexachlorocyclohexane. All the hydrogen nuclei in the β-isomer are equivalent and thus a single resonance absorption band is observed. In the symmetrically substituted γ-isomer, rapid conformational interconversion averages the shielding of the hydrogen nuclei and a single absorption band is observed. Both the δ- and ε-isomers give simple spectra indicating the *equatorial* hydrogen nuclei to be less shielded than those in the *axial* positions. A very complex spectrum is obtained for the α-isomer (an AA′BB′CC′ system) with most of the fine structure on the *axial* hydrogen absorption bands. Similar spectra were obtained for the analogous hexa-acetates.

(h) *Tetra-O-Acetyl-1,4-Dideoxy-1,4-Dinitro-Neo-Inositols.* Lichtenthaler and Fischer[107] have used NMR to assign the configurations of several newly prepared cyclohexane derivatives related to the above compound. Examination

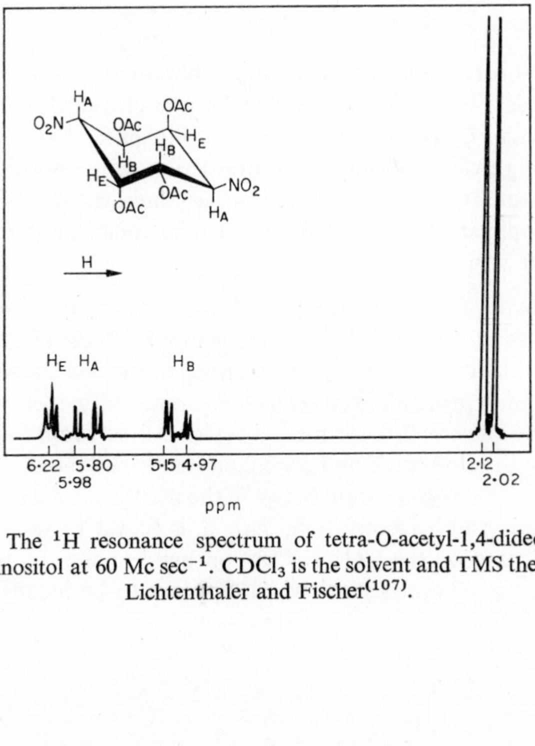

FIG. 10.12 The ^{1}H resonance spectrum of tetra-O-acetyl-1,4-dideoxy-1,4-dinitro-neo-inositol at 60 Mc sec^{-1}. $CDCl_3$ is the solvent and TMS the reference. Lichtenthaler and Fischer[107].

of the ^1H resonance spectrum of tetra-O-acetyl-1,4-dideoxy-1,4-dinitro-neo-inositol indicates that the molecule has the neo-1,4 configuration as shown in Fig. 10.12. The high field doublet is attributed to the two different types of methyl groups in the acetoxy groups, two being in *equatorial* and two in *axial* positions. The six ring hydrogen atoms form three pairs of equivalent hydrogen nuclei (H_A, H_B and H_E). H_A and H_B each give rise to a pair of equal intensity doublets; the larger doublet splitting features in each pair of doublets and is characteristic of *axial–axial* spin–spin coupling whilst the smaller coupling is due to interaction with adjacent *equatorial* hydrogen nuclei. This suggests that the H_A and H_B hydrogen nuclei occupy four *axial* positions while the H_E nuclei are in two *equatorial* positions. The absorption band of the two equivalent *equatorial* hydrogen nuclei (H_E) is a triplet due to spin–spin interaction with the two adjacent *axial* hydrogen nuclei H_A and H_B.

Configurational assignments have also been made for a series of deoxyadenosines on the basis of their ^1H resonance spectra[(108)].

(i) *Derivatives of Acetoxycholestanone.* Williamson and Johnson[(109)] have examined a series of isomeric α-acetoxy ketones (derivatives of acetoxycholestane-3-one and acetoxycholestane-2-one) and they have observed *cis* and *trans* J_{vic} coupling constants considerably larger than those previously reported for cyclohexane type derivatives. They measured J_{ae} values of up to 7·4 cycles sec^{-1} and J_{aa} values as large as 13·1 cycles sec^{-1}. They found it necessary to modify the parameters of the Karplus equations (10.4 and 10.5) relating J_{vic} coupling

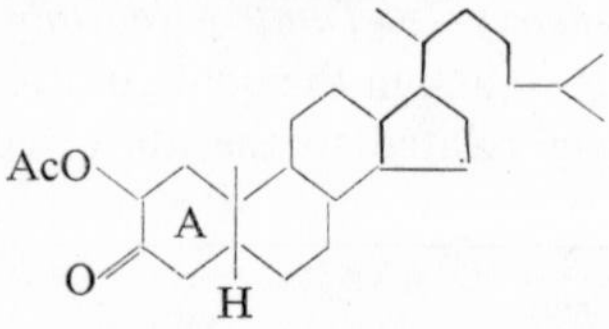

(I)

constants with dihedral bond angles in order to obtain mutually consistent values for the bond angles. In some of the molecules, the chemical shifts of the hydrogen nuclei in *equatorial* positions are found at higher field values than those in the corresponding *axial* positions, in contradiction to the normal shielding behaviour of such nuclei. This is attributed to the combined effects of ring rigidity and the anisotropic shielding contribution to the chemical shift from the carbonyl group (see structure I).

(j) *Monosubstituted Cyclohexane Derivatives.* At room temperature, the cyclohexyl halides exist as rapidly interconverting mixtures of their conformers with the bulky substituent spending most time in the *equatorial* position: the details of this dynamic process have already been discussed (see Section 9.7)[(110,111)]. A similar state of affairs exists for methyl cyclohexane. From the ^1H resonance spectra of methyl cyclohexane and its 2,2,6,6-tetradeuterated analogue shown in Fig. 10.13, the coupling constant between the methyl group and the hydrogen atom on the same ring carbon atom, J_{CH_3-H}, is found to be 6·8 cycles sec^{-1}. The doublet splitting on the CH_3 absorption band in the spectrum of methyl cyclohexane is only 4·7 cycles sec^{-1} which appears to be inconsistent with the remaining fine structure in the spectrum. Anet[112] has shown that in saturated compounds containing —$CHCH_3$ groups, very often the doublet splitting on the methyl absorption band is not equal to the J_{CH-CH_3} coupling constant even when the chemical shift between the two types of nuclei is large compared with the coupling constant involved. This arises because the effects of other magnetic nuclei in the molecule which are strongly coupled to either the CH or the CH_3 group must also be taken into consideration and a detailed analysis conducted.

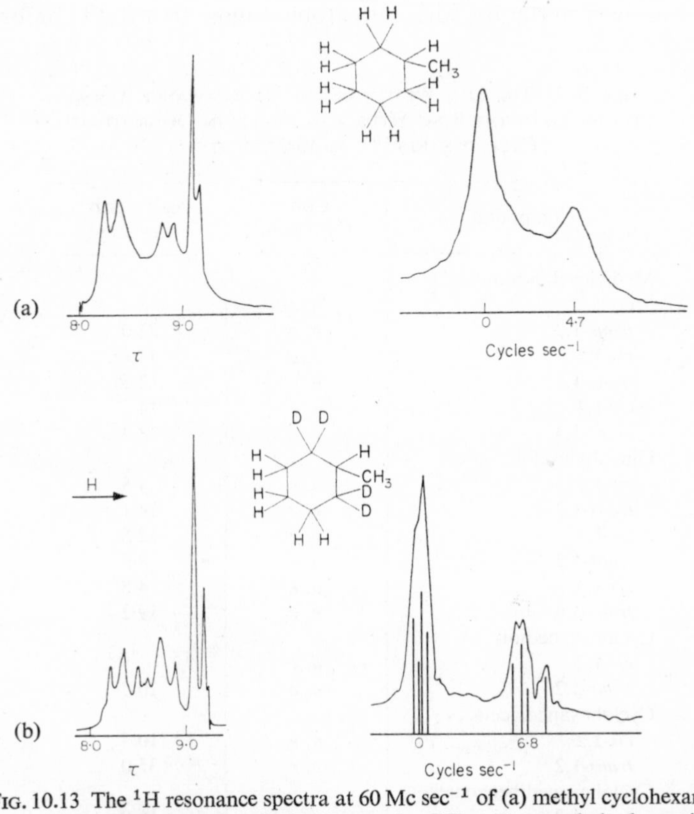

FIG. 10.13 The ^{1}H resonance spectra at 60 Mc sec^{-1} of (a) methyl cyclohexane, (b) 2,2,6,6-tetradeuteromethylcyclohexane in CCl_4. The methyl absorption bands were examined under the slow conditions shown on the right. Anet[112].

By appropriate deuterosubstitution of the molecule, the —$CHCH_3$ portion can be isolated from other hydrogen nuclei in the molecule and a much sharper doublet splitting on the methyl absorption is observed (see the ^{1}H resonance spectrum of 2,2,6,6-tetradeuteromethyl cyclohexane shown in Fig. 10.13). Musher[105] has reported unexpectedly low values of J_{CH-CH_3} in dimethylcyclohexanes and these can now be accounted for in the light of Anet's work. A similar effect is also observed in the resonance spectrum of 3-methylcyclohexanone where the broad high field CH_3 absorption band at 9·0τ becomes a sharp doublet upon suitable deuterosubstitution of the molecule[65, 112].

(k) *Disubstituted Cyclohexanes.* Brownstein and Miller[106] have demonstrated the possibility of determining by NMR the stereochemistry of a disubstituted cyclohexane molecule providing that the positions of substitution are known. Rapid interconversion of a cyclohexane derivative can result in averaging the magnetic environments of the ring hydrogen nuclei to the extent where a single absorption band is observed for nuclei which would undoubtedly be shielded differently in a fixed conformation. Another more subtle consequence of rapid interconversion is its effect on spin–spin coupling constants between hydrogen nuclei on adjacent carbon atoms. In a fixed conformation

TABLE 10.22 THE LINE WIDTHS OF THE ^{1}H RESONANCE ABSORPTION BANDS OF THE RING HYDROGEN NUCLEI IN DISUBSTITUTED CYCLOHEXANES[105] AT 40·00 Mc sec^{-1}

Compound	Conformation	Peak width cycles sec^{-1}
Methylcyclohexanols		
cis-1,2	*a, e*	8·4
trans-1,2	*e, e*	22·0
cis-1,3	*e, e*	37·8
trans-1,3	*a, e*	12·5
cis-1,4	*a, e*	14·3
trans-1,4	*e, e*	38·4
Dimethylcyclohexanes		
cis-1,2	*a, e*	4·8
trans-1,2	*e, e*	14·1
cis-1,3	*e, e*	12·8
trans-1,3	*a, e*	8·6
cis-1,4	*a, e*	4·8
trans-1,4	*e, e*	19·2
Cyclohexanediols		
cis-1,2	*a, e*	7·1
trans-1,2	*e, e*	20·2
Cyclohexanediacetates		
cis-1,2	*a, e*	10·3
trans-1,2	*e, e*	35·0
Cyclohexanedibenzoates		
trans-1,2	*e, e*	16·0

such coupling appears to be much greater than when the molecule is rapidly interconverting. Since the effect of the coupling (rarely resolvable) is mainly to broaden the absorption bands of the ring hydrogen nuclei, the net effect of rapid interconversion is to cause line narrowing of the absorption bands. Hence, if we examine the ^{1}H NMR spectra of *cis/trans* pairs of disubstituted cyclohexanes of known stereochemistry we always obtain much narrower line widths for the ring hydrogen nuclei in the molecules expected to interconvert. The disubstituted molecules most likely to show interconversion are those with the two substituents having an *axial/equatorial* (*a e*) relationship to each other

This is the case for the methyl substituents in *cis*-1,2, *trans*-1,3 and *cis*-1,4-dimethyl cyclohexanes and the rapidly interconverting molecules give rise to narrow absorption bands[105]. Conversely, the *trans*-1,2, *cis*-1,3 and *trans*-1,4 compounds will be expected to exist mainly with both methyl groups in *equatorial* positions (*e e*) and their ^{1}H resonance spectra will have broad absorption bands due to the absence of rapid interconversion. In the ^{1}H resonance spectra of the dimethyl cyclohexanes (not shown) the ring hydrogen nuclei of *e e* type molecules have broad low field absorption bands (line widths 10–15 cycles sec^{-1} at 40 Mc sec^{-1}) whilst the rapidly interconverting *a e* type molecules give relatively sharp absorption bands in this region (line widths 5–9 cycles sec^{-1} at 40 Mc sec^{-1}). It is obvious that if the positions of the substituents are known then from line width measurements one can make a *cis* or *trans* assignment. Table 10.22 summarises the line width measurements for the ring hydrogen nuclei signals for several disubstituted cyclohexanes of known configuration and the line widths are consistent with the above considerations in all cases. Muller and Tosch[352] have succeeded in freezing out the conformationally fixed molecules by cooling rapidly interconverting *a e* disubstituted cyclohexanes to temperatures below -100°C.

(l) *Decalins*. The conformational states of *cis*- and *trans*-decalin are reflected in their NMR spectra. *Cis*-decalin exists as a rapidly interconverting molecule and gives rise to a single sharp absorption band: *trans*-decalin has a rigid structure and gives rise to a broad poorly resolved absorption band as shown in Fig. 9.25. By cooling a solution of *cis*-decalin in carbon disulphide to -117°C, the single absorption band observed at room temperature becomes a doublet due to conformational "freezing"[95].

(m) *10-Methyl Decalols*. Musher[23] has examined the ^{1}H resonance spectra of four isomers of 10-methyl decalol-2 and his results, given in Table 10.23, clearly indicate that the shielding of the angular methyl groups is markedly dependent upon the configuration of the ring. The angular methyl resonance absorption in a *trans*-decalol has a chemical shift of 0·142 ppm to high field of the corresponding *cis*-decalol. This feature is of considerable assistance in assigning *C*-methyl groups in steroids.

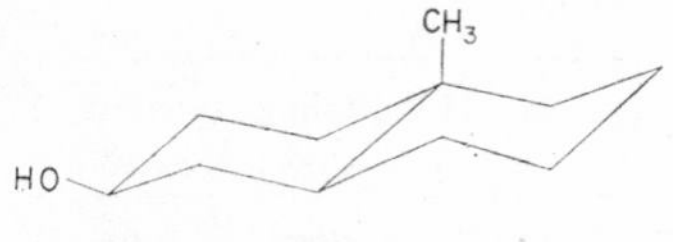

10-methyl-*trans*-decal-*cis*-2-ol

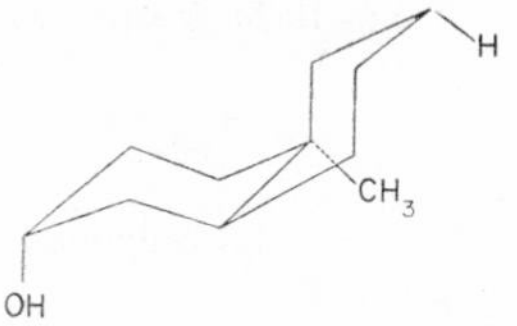

10-methyl-*cis*-decal-*cis*-2-ol

There is also an additional smaller effect on the shielding of the methyl group due to the hydroxyl group being in the *cis*- or *trans*-position with respect to the methyl group (when the 2-hydroxyl group is *cis* to the methyl group the CH_3 absorption is 0·026 ppm less shielded than when the two substituents are trans). Musher has observed similar behaviour for the shielding of methyl groups in methyl cyclohexanols.[105].

TABLE 10.23 ^{1}H CHEMICAL SHIFTS OF THE ANGULAR METHYL GROUPS
IN SOME 10-METHYL DECALOLS[23]

Compound	δ ppm	"τ"
10-Methyl-*cis*-decal-*cis*-2-ol	$-0\cdot927$	$9\cdot02$
10-Methyl-*cis*-decal-*trans*-2-ol	$-0\cdot900$	$9\cdot05$
10-Methyl-*trans*-decal-*cis*-2-ol	$-0\cdot784$	$9\cdot17$
10-Methyl-*trans*-decal-*trans*-2-ol	$-0\cdot758$	$9\cdot19$

Chemical shifts were measured in ppm from hexamethyldisiloxane (HMDS) internal reference
$$\text{"}\tau\text{"} = 9\cdot95 + \delta_{HMDS}$$

ALKENES

10.4 Vinyl Derivatives, $CH_2=CHX$

A great deal of interest has been focused on the NMR spectra of vinyl groups and several workers have reported correlations between their spectral constants and the molecular parameters of the system. A vinyl compound (I) possesses three magnetically non-equivalent hydrogen nuclei and constitutes a typical ABC spin system.

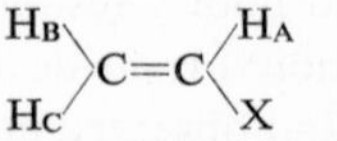

$$\begin{array}{cc} H_B & H_A \\ \diagdown & \diagup \\ C=C & \\ \diagup & \diagdown \\ H_C & X \end{array} \quad (I)$$

To achieve a complete analysis of this system is quite a difficult process but one is eventually rewarded with the knowledge of the magnitudes and relative signs of the three coupling constants J_{AB}, J_{BC} and J_{AC} in addition to the chemical shifts of the three nuclei. The ^{1}H resonance spectrum of pure vinyl bromide[113] shown in Fig. 10.14 is seen to be typical of an ABC system: 12 of the 15 possible transitions give rise to bands of measurable intensity at 60 Mc sec^{-1}. Without some knowledge of the typical values of coupling constants in unsaturated systems it is not possible to assign the bands in such a spectrum.

TABLE 10.24 SOME TYPICAL H—H COUPLING CONSTANTS IN OLEFINIC
COMPOUNDS[30, 114]

Compound	H—H Coupling constant (cycles sec^{-1})		
	J_{HH}^{gem}	J_{HH}^{trans}	J_{HH}^{cis}
trans-$C_6H_5CH=CHCHO$		$15\cdot6$	
trans-$CH_3CH=CHCHO$		$16\cdot2$	
$H_2C=CBrCH_2Br$	$2\cdot1$		
$H_2C=C(OCH_3)C(OCH_3)=CH_2$	$2\cdot1$		
cis-$C_6H_5CH=CHCOCH_3$			$12\cdot0$
[114]*cis*-$CH_3CO_2CH=CHCN$			$11\cdot5$
[114]*trans*-$CH_3CO_2CH=CHCN$		$15\cdot0$

By examining the spectra of various disubstituted olefines, one can deduce the relative magnitudes of the three coupling constants and it is found that for vinyl derivatives with non-metallic substituents the *geminal* coupling constant has the smallest value and the *trans* coupling constant the largest, that is J_{BC}^{gem} ($-3{\cdot}5$ to $+2{\cdot}5$ cycles sec^{-1}) $\ll J_{AB}^{cis}$ ($+4{\cdot}0$ to $+12{\cdot}0$ cycles sec^{-1}) $< J_{AC}^{trans}$ ($+12$ to $+19$ cycles sec^{-1}). The values for the *vicinal* coupling constants are

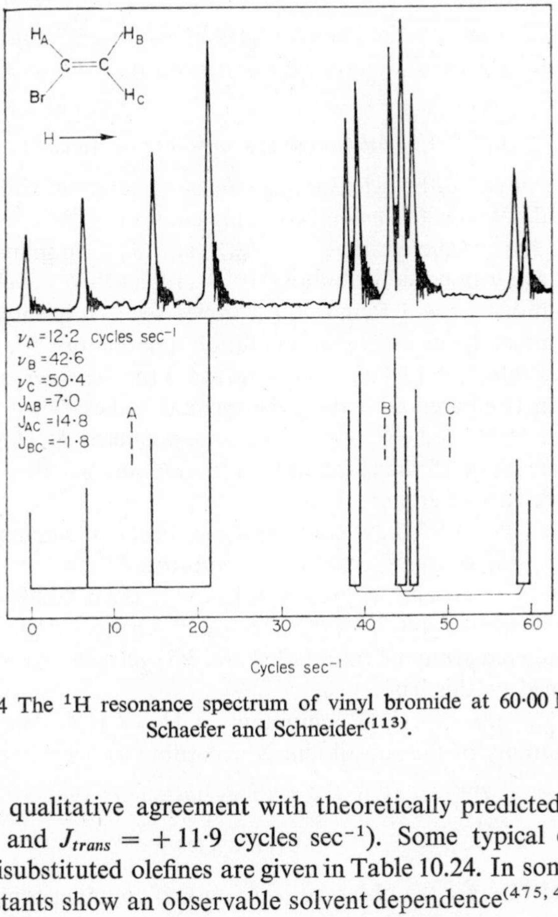

FIG. 10.14 The ^{1}H resonance spectrum of vinyl bromide at 60·00 Mc sec^{-1}. Schaefer and Schneider(113).

in fairly good qualitative agreement with theoretically predicted values(39, 62) ($J_{cis} = +6{\cdot}1$ and $J_{trans} = +11{\cdot}9$ cycles sec^{-1}). Some typical coupling constants(30) in disubstituted olefines are given in Table 10.24. In some systems the coupling constants show an observable solvent dependence(475, 476, 477, 478).

10.4.1 *Correlation Between Geminal Coupling Constants, J_{HH}^{gem}, and the H—C—H Bond Angles*

Gutowsky and co-workers(30) have shown that there should be a correlation between the J_{HH}^{gem} coupling constant and the H—C—H bond angle in a CH_2 group. Valence bond theory was applied to the problem and a curve of calculated J_{HH}^{gem} values against H—C—H bond angles was deduced. Using available experimental data for alkanes and alkenes it can be demonstrated that the theoretical curve is in poor agreement with the observed coupling constants.

This is particularly true for alkane derivatives where the theory predicts them to have large positive J_{HH}^{gem} values in contradiction to the experimentally determined negative values[32, 58]. For alkenes, the calculation appears to be reasonably successful, predicting that the J_{HH}^{gem} values decrease as the H—C—H bond angle increases and explaining the appearance of both negative and positive small coupling constants. However, in view of the obvious shortcomings of the theoretical treatment for the case of alkanes the calculation must be generally regarded as incorrect.

Accurate predictions of CH_2 bond angles based on J_{HH}^{gem} coupling constants must now await a general theoretical calculation of *geminal* H—H coupling constants.

10.4.2 Vicinal Coupling Constants in Alkenes

Calculations of *vicinal* H—H coupling constants have met with more success than similar calculations of *geminal* coupling constants[39].

Karplus[39] has predicted that the J_{HH}^{trans} and J_{HH}^{cis} coupling constants in ethylene will have σ bond contributions of + 11·9 and + 6·1 cycles sec^{-1} and π bond contributions of + 1·5 and + 1·5 cycles sec^{-1} respectively (the latter contribution arises from a σ–π configuration interaction)[62]. Although the total calculated values of 13·4 and 7·6 cycles sec^{-1} for the *trans* and *cis* coupling constants when compared with the experimental values[42] of 19·0 and 11·7 cycles sec^{-1} are found to be somewhat low, the predicted J_{cis}/J_{trans} ratio is correct. A similar state of affairs is found for the *trans* and *gauche vicinal* coupling constants in the case of ethane.

Gutowsky and Porte[116] have calculated the effect of changing the H—C—C angle on the *vicinal* coupling constants in substituted ethylenes. A change in this angle from 120° to 125° is predicted to lower the σ bond contribution to the J_{HH}^{cis} value from + 6·1 to + 4·0 cycles sec^{-1}. Ortho coupling constants in 7, 6 and 5-membered aromatic rings (12, 7 and 3·7 cycles sec^{-1} respectively[117]) can be explained on this basis.

J_{HH}^{trans} and J_{HH}^{cis} values in vinyl compounds, $CH_2{=}CHX$, depend linearly on the electronegativity of the substituent X according to the relationships

$$J_{HH}^{trans} = 19{\cdot}0 - 3{\cdot}3\Delta E \text{ cycles sec}^{-1} \quad (10{\cdot}8)$$

$$J_{HH}^{cis} = 11{\cdot}7 - 4{\cdot}0\Delta E \text{ cycles sec}^{-1} \quad (10{\cdot}9)$$

where 19·0 and 11·7 are the observed *trans* and *cis* coupling constants in cycles sec^{-1} in ethylene and ΔE is the difference in electronegativity between the substituent X and the hydrogen atom[34, 108, 119, 120].

The *trans* and *cis* H—H coupling constants in vinyl systems are much more sensitive to changes in the electronegativity of the substituent than are *vicinal* H—H coupling constants in saturated systems[34].

Signs of H—H *Coupling Constants in Unsaturated Systems.* By measuring the relative signs of H—H and ^{13}C–H spin coupling constants in alkene molecules, Lauterbur and Kurland[32] have been able to deduce the absolute signs of the H—H coupling constants (see Table 10.25).

Their conclusions are based on the assumption that $J_{13\text{C}-\text{H}}$ coupling constants between directly bonded nuclei are absolutely positive.

An interesting example of the complementary manner in which spectral analysis and double irradiation techniques can be used to determine relative signs of coupling constants is provided by such studies on 1-chlorobutadiene $-1, 2$ (I)

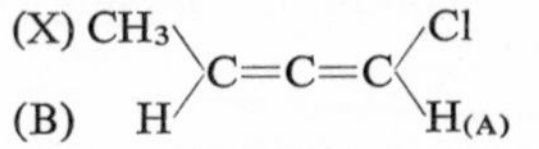

$$(X) \; CH_3 \qquad \qquad Cl$$
$$\underset{(B) \quad H}{} \; C{=}C{=}C \; \underset{H_{(A)}}{} \qquad (I)$$

A detailed analysis[176] of the ^1H resonance spectra at 40·00 and 60·00 Mc sec^{-1} yields only the relative signs of J_{AX} and J_{BX} while double irradiation experiments[177] give only the relative signs of J_{AB} and J_{BX}; hence all the relative signs are known ($+J_{AX}$, $+J_{BX}$ and $-J_{AB}$).

TABLE 10.25 ABSOLUTE SIGNS OF SOME H—H SPIN COUPLING CONSTANTS (CYCLES SEC^{-1}) IN UNSATURATED COMPOUNDS[32]

X	Signs of HH coupling constants in X—CH=CH$_2$			
	J			
	cis	*trans*	*gem*	Reference
H	+11·7	+19·1	+2·5	42
CH$_3$	+10·02	+16·81	+2·08	124
CH$_3$CH$_2$	+10·4	+17·4	+1·9	125
(CH$_3$)$_2$CH	+10·4	+17·3	+1·6	118
(CH$_3$)$_3$C	+10·8	+17·5	+1·4	125
CCl$_3$	+10·07	+16·05	−0·42	126
C$_6$H$_5$	+11·0	+17·8	+1·1	127
2,4,6-(CH$_3$)$_3$C$_6$H$_2$	+11·6	+18·0	+2·3	127
CN	+11·8	+18·0	+1·0	118
CH$_3$O	+ 6·8	+14·4	−2·2	118
CH$_2$=CHO	+ 6·4	+14·0	−1·8	118
CH$_3$COO	+ 6·5	+14·1	−1·5	127

HH Coupling Constants in —CH=CH—CH Systems.

Compound	J_a		J_b	J_c		Reference
	cis	*trans*		*cis*	*trans*	
CH$_3$—CH=CH$_2$	+10·02	+16·81	+6·40	−1·75	−1·33	124
trans-CH$_3$CH=CH—CHO		+15·3	+6·8	−1·6		128
trans-CH$_3$—CH=CH— —COOH		+	+	−		128
cis-CH$_2$Cl—CH=CHCl	+7·2		+7·2		−0·9	129, 130
trans-CH$_2$Cl—CH=CHCl		+13·1	+7·1	−0·5		129, 130
trans-CH$_3$—CH=CH— —C$_6$H$_5$			+6·6	−1·8		131

10.4.3 Correlation Between Coupling Constants and the Electronegativities of the Substituents in Vinyl Derivatives

Brügel and co-workers[132] have fully analysed the ^1H resonance spectra of 131 vinyl derivatives and their results have been used widely to demonstrate the existence of correlations between NMR spectral parameters and molecular structure. Table 10.26 gives the compiled coupling constant data for an ex-

TABLE 10.26 H—H SPIN COUPLING CONSTANTS IN VINYL DERIVATIVES[119]

X	E_X	No. of values	(cycles sec^{-1})			Reference
			J_{gem}	J_{cis}	J_{trans}	
1. —F	3·95*	3	−3·2	+4·65	+12·75	132, 133 30, 120
2. —Cl	3·2*	2	−1·4	+7·3	+14·6	132, 133
3. —Br	3·0*	4	−1·8	+7·1	+15·2	132, 133 113, 30
4. —OR (alkyl)	3·5*	17	−1·9	+6·7	+14·2	132, 133
5. —OR (aryl)	3·5*	13	−1·5	+6·5	+13·7	132
6. —OOCR	3·5†	12	−1·4	+6·3	+13·9	132
7. —Phosphates	3·5†	5	−2·3	+5·8	+13·2	132
8. —NO_2	3·35‡	1	−2·0	+7·6	+15·0	132
9. —NR	3·0†	5	0	+9·4	+16·1	132, 30
10. —COOR	2·5†	14	+1·7	+10·2	+17·2	132
11. —CN	2·5†	1	+1·3	+11·3	+18·2	134
12. —COR	2·5†	2	+1·8	+11·0	+18·0	132, 30
13. —R (alkyl)	2·5†	18	+1·6	+10·3	+17·3	132, 124
14. —R (aryl)	2·5†	9	+1·3	+11·0	+18·0	132
15. —Pyridyl	2·5†	3	+1·1	+10·8	+17·5	132
16. —Sulphones	3·0‡	9	−0·6	+ 9·9	+16·6	132
17. —Sn	1·9*	4	+2·8	+14·1	+20·3	132, 135
18. —As	2·1*	4	+1·7	+11·6	+19·1	132
19. —Sb	2·0*	1	+2·0	+12·6	+19·5	132
20. —Pb	1·9†	1	+2·0	+12·1	+19·6	132
21. —Hg	1·9†	1	+3·5	+13·1	+21·0	135
22. —Al etherate	1·5†	1	+6·3	+15·3	+21·4	135
23. —Li	1·0†	1	+7·1	+19·3	+23·9	136
24. —Ge	1·0	1	+10·0	+10·0	+10	428

* Reference 5.
† Reference 155.
‡ Reference 137.

tensive series of vinyl derivatives having substituents of widely differing electronegativity[119]. When any one of the three coupling constants, J_{HH}^{gem}, J_{HH}^{cis}, J_{HH}^{trans} is plotted against the electronegativity, E_X, of the substituent, an inverse proportionality between the two parameters is observed[118, 119]. Figure 10.15 shows the three roughly linear plots of J against E_X. Whether or not the overall relationship is in fact linear is doubtful. The J values for vinyl bromide are all much lower than such a linear correlation would predict. The scatter on the various plots might be due to inaccuracies in the determination of the coupling constants (it is necessary to proceed through a lengthy computational analysis to extract the coupling constants from an ABC analysis) and this idea is supported by the larger scatter found for the J_{HH}^{gem}/E_X plot where inaccuracies would be more obvious due to J_{HH}^{gem} being small. The best correlation is found between J_{HH}^{trans}

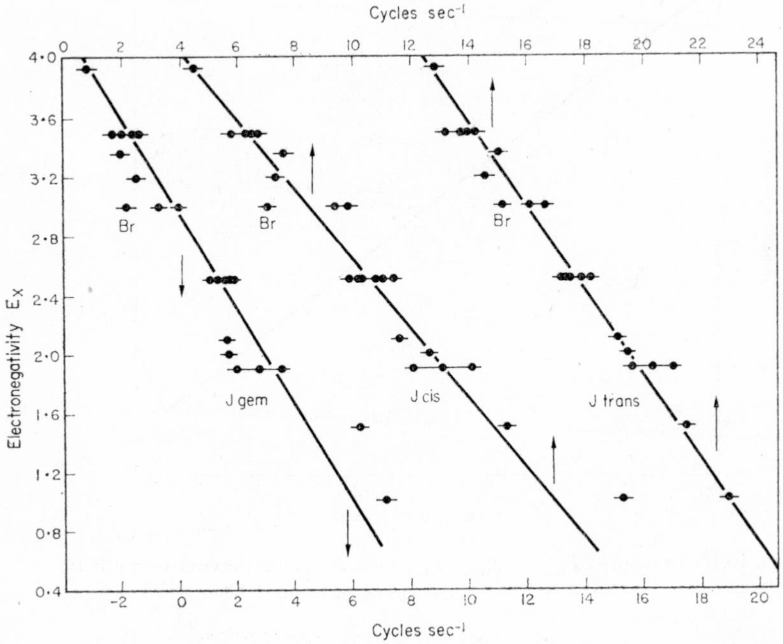

FIG. 10.15 Plots of J_{HH} coupling constants in vinyl systems, $CH_2{=}CHX$, against the electronegativities E_X of the substituent X. Schaefer[119].

and E_X where the errors will have least effect. However, strong evidence that the scatter in Fig. 10.15 is not caused by inaccuracies in measuring the coupling constants is obtained by plotting the sum of the three coupling constants in cycles sec^{-1} $\sum J = (J_{HH}^{gem} + J_{HH}^{cis} + J_{HH}^{trans})$ against the electronegativity of the substituents, E_X[30, 119, 132] (see Fig. 10.16). Despite the fact that $\sum J$ can be obtained accurately by direct measurement of the spectrum there is still an appreciable amount of scatter on the linear plot. The approximately linear relationship is a useful aid in deciding the correct value of $\sum J$ when some ambiguity exists (see tetravinylsilane[443, 132, 138]). A consequence of the three separate linear relationships between the coupling constants and the electronegativity of the substituent, E_X, is that there is also a linear relationship between the coupling constants themselves. In Figure 10.15, the three linear plots have similar gradients and Banwell and Sheppard[118] suggest that the three coupling constants are probably controlled by some common factor. Highly electronegative groups would be expected to reduce electron densities around the three hydrogen nuclei in a vinyl group and thus lead to reduced interaction between nuclear and electron spins which in turn would result in lower coupling constants[118]. J^{gem}_{HH} values in $H_2C{=}N{-}X$ systems have also been correlated with the electronegativity of the substituent X[455].

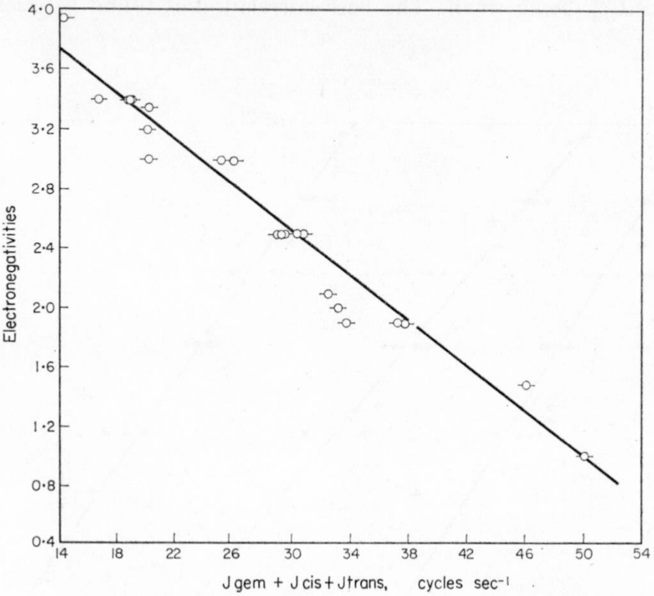

FIG. 10.16 The sum of $J^{gem}_{HH} + J^{cis}_{HH} + J^{trans}_{HH}$ plotted against the electronegativity, E_X, of the substituent atoms. Schaefer[119].

TABLE 10.27 ^{1}H CHEMICAL SHIFT PARAMETERS FOR A SERIES OF VINYL COMPOUNDS[118]

X atom	(A) H, X >C=C< H (B), H (C) Compound	Chemical shifts							
		δ_A†	"τ_A"	δ_B	"τ_B"	δ_C	"τ_C"	Δ_1	Δ_2
F	Vinyl fluoride	−0·84	3·83	+1·30	5·97	+0·96	5·63	+1·13	−1·96
O	Vinyl methyl ether	−1·10	3·57	+1·43	6·10	+1·29	5·96	+1·36	−2·46
	Divinyl ether	−1·06	3·61	+1·12	5·79	+0·81	5·48	+0·96	−2·02
Cl	Vinyl chloride	−0·97	3·70	−0·11	4·56	−0·19	4·48	−0·15	−0·82
Br	Vinyl bromide	−1·16	3·51	−0·70	3·97	−0·55	4·12	−0·63	−0·53
C	Vinyl benzene	−1·36	3·31	+0·12	4·79	−0·38	4·29	−0·13	−1·22
	Vinyl cyanide	−0·20	4·47	−0·72	3·95	−0·58	4·09	−0·65	+0·45
	Butene-1	—	—	—	—	—	—	—	−0·71
	3,3-dimethylbutene-1	—	—	—	—	—	—	—	−0·76
	3-methylbutene-1	−0·34	4·33	+0·56	5·23	+0·48	5·15	+0·52	−0·86

Notes: † In ppm relative to the resonance of ethylene as 0·00 which has the value of −3·9 ppm with respect to cyclohexane (τ value 4·67); errors ±0·05 ppm.
The compounds were examined as 10 molar per cent solutions in carbon tetrachloride.

$$\text{"}\tau\text{"} = 4{\cdot}67 + \delta_{C_2H_4}$$

10.4.4 *Changes in Chemical Shifts in Vinyl Groups with Changes in the Electronegativity of the Substituents*

Banwell and Sheppard [118] have correlated changes in various chemical shift parameters in vinyl systems, namely δ_A, $\Delta_1 = \frac{1}{2}(\delta_B + \delta_C)$, and $\Delta_2 = \delta_A - \frac{1}{2}(\delta_B + \delta_C)$ as the electronegativity of the substituent is varied. Table 10.27 gives the values of these parameters for the eight vinyl derivatives considered.

None of the vinyl chemical shift parameters correlates with the Huggins[5] electronegativity of the substituents. If we consider the carbon containing substituents i-propyl, cyanide and phenyl which are all expected to have similar electronegativities, we find them to have widely different values of δ_A (the $-$CN and $-C_6H_5$ groups both show strong neighbour diamagnetic anisotropic effects).

10.4.5 *Correlation of Chemical Shifts in Vinyl Systems with Hammett σ-Constants*

If we plot the parameters δ_A, Δ_1 and Δ_2 against the Taft[140] σ_I and σ_R constants (the contributions to the Hammett σ constants from inductive and resonance effects respectively) a fairly good linear correlation is found between the σ_R values and Δ_2 as shown in Fig. 10.17. Other correlations of chemical shift parameters with σ_I and σ_R were less satisfactory. Table 10.28 gives the Huggins electronegativities and the Taft σ_I and σ_R values for the substituents considered.

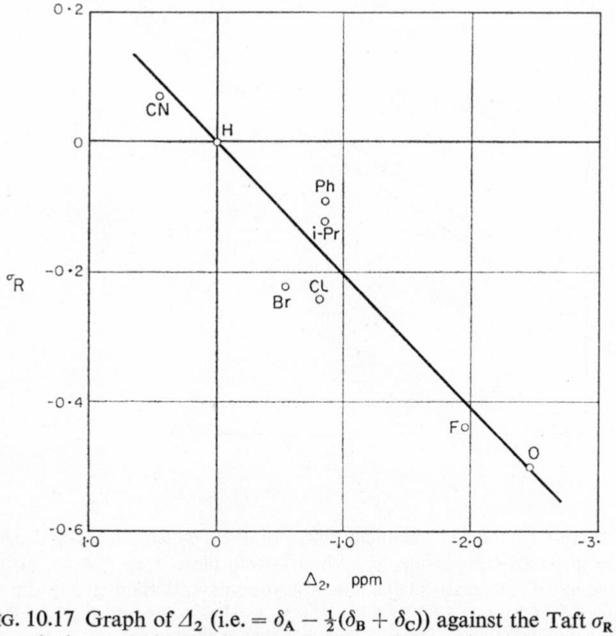

FIG. 10.17 Graph of Δ_2 (i.e. $= \delta_A - \frac{1}{2}(\delta_B + \delta_C)$) against the Taft σ_R values for the substituent X in vinyl systems $CH_2{=}CHX$. The point for phenyl (Ph) has been corrected for the diamagnetic anisotropy of the benzene ring. Banwell and Sheppard[118].

TABLE 10.28 THE HUGGINS ELECTRONEGATIVITIES E AND THE TAFT σ_I AND σ_R VALUES OF A SERIES OF SUBSTITUENTS[118]

(E)	F	> O	> Cl	> Br	> C			
	3·9	3·5	3·15	2·95	2·6			
(σ_I)	CN	> F	> Cl	> Br	> OCH_3	> Phenyl	> H	> t-butyl
	0·59	0·5	0·47	0·45	0·23	0·10	0·0	−0·17
(σ_R)	CN	> H	> Phenyl	> t-butyl	> Br	> Cl	> F	> OCH_3
	0·07	0·0	−0·09	−0·12	−0·22	−0·24	−0·44	−0·50

10.4.6 Correlation of Chemical Shifts in Vinyl Systems with Group Dipole Moments

A linear relationship between the ^1H chemical shifts of the terminal CH_2-group in a vinyl system and the group dipole moments[142] of the substituents has been pointed out by Reddy, Goldstein and Mandell[143]. Figure 10.18 shows the graphs illustrating this linear correlation.

Buckingham[27] has explained the solvent shifts observed for vinyl bromide and *cis*- and *trans*-1,2-dichloroethylene in terms of changes in dipolar effects accompanying changes in the dielectric constant of the solvent.

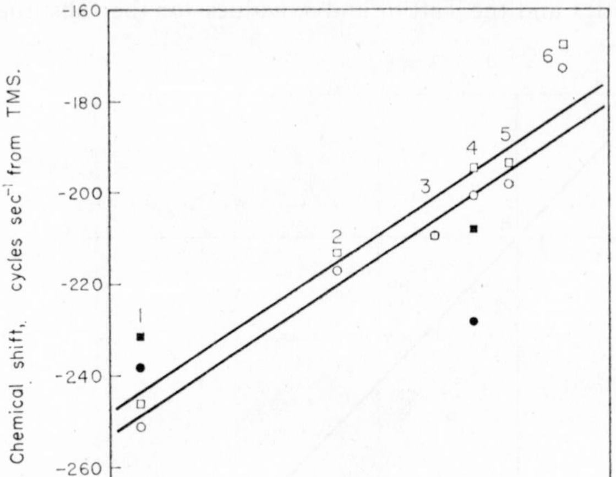

FIG. 10.18 Graph of the ^1H chemical shifts of the *cis*- and *trans*-hydrogen nuclei in the terminal CH_2 group of a vinyl system plotted against the group dipole moments of the substituents. The substituents and their group dipole moments are: 1, CN = −3·6; 2, Cl = −1·5; 3, H = −0·4; 4, C_6H_5 = 0·0; 5, CH_3 = +0·4; 6, OCH_3 = +1·16; □ are *cis* ^1H shifts, ○ are *trans* ^1H shifts and ■ and ● are shifts corrected for diamagnetic anisotropy of substituents. Reddy, Goldstein and Mandell[143].

10.4.7 Anomalous ^{1}H *Chemical Shifts in Vinyl Systems*

Certain substituents in vinyl derivatives have been observed to give rise to anomalous chemical shifts of the vinyl hydrogen nuclei which are inconsistent with the linear relationships already outlined. Three such substituents are —C≡N, —C_6H_5 and —OR groups and it is instructive to enquire into the reasons for their non-conformity.

Vinyl Cyanide, CH_2=CHCN. On simple electronegativity arguments, the —CN group (which is quite electronegative) would be expected to withdraw more electron density from around the hydrogen nucleus on the α-carbon atom than from the β-hydrogen nuclei thus causing the latter to be more shielded as is the case for vinyl chloride(138, 144). However, Goldstein and co-workers(143, 145) have observed the resonance absorption of the α-hydrogen nucleus in vinyl cyanide to be at higher fields than the β-hydrogen nuclei (that is the α-hydrogen nucleus is more shielded). Attempts to explain this anomaly in terms of resonance structures of the type I and II show that

$$\underset{\text{(I)}}{-\mathrm{C{\equiv}N}} \quad \text{and} \quad \underset{\text{(II)}}{-\overset{+}{\mathrm{C}}{=}\overset{-}{\mathrm{N}}}$$

this consideration would lead to the α-hydrogen nucleus being even less shielded. The explanation for the increased shielding of the α-nucleus is now thought to lie in the strong diamagnetic anisotropic effect expected to be associated with the triple bond of the cyanide group(143, 146). This effect will cause an increased shielding of all nuclei in the molecule and its magnitude depends on the distance of each hydrogen atom from the electrical centre of gravity of the —C≡N bond and the angle between the line joining the centre of the —C≡N bond and the hydrogen nucleus with the axis of the —C≡N bond. Whipple and co-workers(144) have calculated the contributions to the shielding from diamagnetic anisotropic effects of the —CN group for the three hydrogen nuclei in vinyl cyanide and when the observed shielding is corrected for this contribution, the chemical shifts are no longer anomalous. Table 10.29 gives the ^{1}H chemical shift parameters for vinyl cyanide and its methyl derivatives.

Styrene, CH_2=CHC_6H_5. Anomalous chemical shifts for the hydrogen nuclei of the vinyl system in styrene have been reported and it has been suggested that the shielding is largely influenced by the effects of diamagnetic circulations of electrons in the aromatic ring (ring currents)(147, 227). Conjugation within the styrene molecule is thought to maintain the vinyl group and the benzene ring in the same plane and based on this assumption the A, B and C nuclei

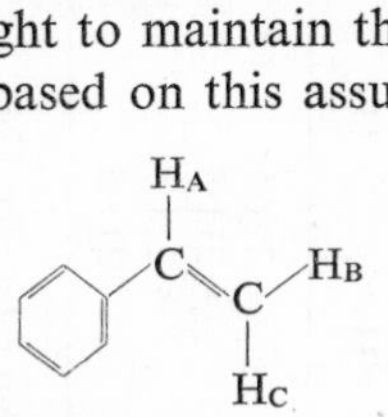

(I)

(see structure I) are calculated to be 3·5, 4·9 and 3·8 Å from the centre of the ring, respectively. Banwell and Sheppard(118) have estimated the necessary corrections to the vinyl chemical shifts in styrene using Pople's expression (see

TABLE 10.29 THE ^{1}H CHEMICAL SHIFTS (IN CYCLES SEC^{-1} AT 40 MC SEC^{-1}) FOR VINYL CYANIDE AND ITS METHYL DERIVATIVES[168]

	$(^1H)(^2H)C{=}C(H^3)(H_4)$	$(H)(H)C{=}C(H)(CH_3)$	$(H)(H)C{=}C(H)(CN)$	$(H)(H)C{=}C(CH_3)(CN)$	$(CH_3)(H)C{=}C(H)(CH)$	$(H)(CH_3)C{=}C(H)(CN)$
ω_1	−211·5	−198·5[a]	−231·6	−221·6		−251·0
ω_2	−211·5	−195·0[a]	−238·7	−225·8	−261·3	
ω_3	−211·5		−219·0		−208·7	−206·6
ω_4	−211·5	−229·3[a]				

[a] Taken from reference 124.
TMS used as an internal reference.

Section 3.7)[227]: the corrections to be applied are $\delta'_A = +0\cdot7$, $\delta'_B = +0\cdot2$ and $\delta'_C = +0\cdot55$ ppm. For α-methylstyrene the coplanarity of the vinyl and aromatic systems is destroyed somewhat by the steric interaction (evidence for this is found in the U.V. spectrum of α-methylstyrene)[148]. It was thought that this might result in the B nucleus of the olefinic system adopting a position nearer to the aromatic ring and becoming less shielded than the C nucleus (opposite to the styrene assignments (see Table 10.27)). Consistent with this assignment would be the larger H—CH$_3$ coupling fine structure observed on the C absorption band compared with that on the B band ($J^{trans}_{H-CH_3}$ is usually greater than $J^{cis}_{H-CH_3}$, but this is not always true). In the ^1H resonance spectrum of O-methyl nidulin[149, 150] there is other evidence that in α-substituted styrenes, nuclei in the B and C positions are shielded in the opposite manner to that found in styrene itself. However, specifically deuterated α-methyl styrene samples, (I)

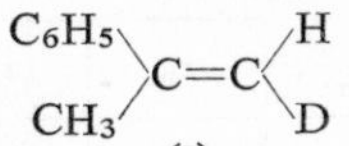

$$\underset{(I)}{\overset{\displaystyle C_6H_5}{\underset{\displaystyle CH_3}{\diagdown}}\!\!\!\!\diagup}C=C\underset{\displaystyle D}{\overset{\displaystyle H}{\diagup\!\!\!\!\diagdown}} \qquad \underset{(II)}{\overset{\displaystyle C_6H_5}{\underset{\displaystyle CH_3}{\diagdown}}\!\!\!\!\diagup}C=C\underset{\displaystyle H}{\overset{\displaystyle D}{\diagup\!\!\!\!\diagdown}}$$

and (II), have been examined by Roberts and Davis and the results of this investigation show that the olefinic H nucleus *trans* to the CH$_3$ group is less shielded than that in the *cis*-position[151]. The $J^{cis}_{H-CH_3}$ values are found to be larger than the $J^{trans}_{H-CH_3}$ values.

Vinyl Ethers, CH$_2$=CHOR. The ^1H resonance spectra of many vinyl ethers (I) have been examined and they are found to be characterised by anomalous high field chemical shifts of the hydrogen nuclei in the terminal ethylenic CH$_2$ group[118, 115, 153]. The increase in chemical shift is of the order of 0·5 ppm

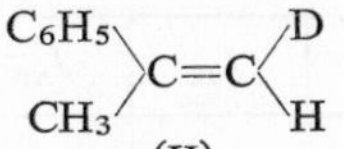

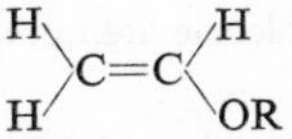

$$\underset{H}{\overset{H}{\diagdown}\!\!\!\!\diagup}C=C\underset{OR}{\overset{H}{\diagup\!\!\!\!\diagdown}} \quad (I)$$

compared with the chemical shifts of terminal ethylenic CH$_2$ groups in other vinyl derivatives[115]. This can be seen from examination of Table 10.30 which lists the spectral parameters observed in the NMR spectra of several vinyl ethers. The origin of the high shielding of the terminal ethylenic hydrogen nuclei is thought to lie in delocalisation effects involving the resonance forms

$$CH_3-O-CH=CH_2 \qquad\qquad CH_3-\overset{+}{O}=CH-\overset{-}{C}H_2$$

Such delocalisation would lead to the electron density of the terminal ethylenic carbon atom approaching that expected of an alkane carbon atom[118, 115]. However, no drastic changes to the stereochemistry of the vinyl group is envisaged since the observed coupling constants are all characteristic of a normal vinyl system (see Table 10.26). The substituents shown in Table 10.30 are arranged in increasing order of electronegativity and the J^{gem}_{HH} coupling constants can be seen to decrease as the electronegativity of the substituent increases as would be expected from empirical observations of J^{gem}_{HH} coupling constants in vinyl molecules (Section 10.4.3). Thus, the alkyl substituents of the alkoxy groups are considered to behave as electron repelling groups showing no hyperconjugative effects.

There is also a correlation between the electronegativity of the substituents in the alkoxy group and the chemical shift separation between the hydrogen nuclei in the terminal CH_2 (δ_{BC}) but no correlation was found between the actual chemical shifts, τ_B and τ_C, and the electronegativity of the substituents. It is probable that the internal chemical shift, δ_{BC}, arises mainly from the diamagnetic anisotropic shielding of the *β-cis* hydrogen nuclei by the C—O bond.

TABLE 10.30 THE ^{1}H CHEMICAL SHIFTS AND SPIN COUPLING CONSTANTS OF SOME VINYL ETHERS[115]

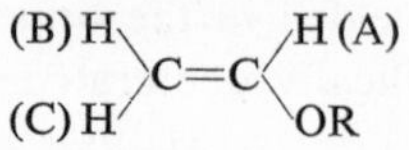

R	J_{BC}	J_{AB}	J_{AC}	τ_B	τ_C	τ_A	$\tau_B - \tau_C$
Decalyl†	±1·2	—	—	5·65	5·12	—	0·525
t-Butyl	−0·1	+6·2	+13·2	6·15	5·80	3·72	0·355
t-Propyl	−1·2	+6·9	+13·7	6·12	5·85	3·73	0·264
Cyclohexyl	−1·6	+5·7	+14·7	6·15	5·90	3·87	0·266
Furfuryl	−1·9	+6·6	+14·2	6·15	5·90	3·60	0·252
2-Ethylhexyl	−1·8	+6·1	+12·9	6·20	5·95	3·60	0·249
i-Butyl	−1·7	+6·3	+14·2	6·12	5·93	3·56	0·190
n-Butyl	−1·8	+6·9	+14·4	6·05	5·85	3·47	0·190
Ethyl	−1·7	+6·9	+14·9	6·12	5·93	3·55	0·187
Methyl	−2·2	+6·6	+14·4	6·15	6·00	3·62	0·154
2-Chloroethyl	−2·7	+6·6	+16·2	5·95	5·83	3·50	0·120

† The *trans* coupling constant, J_{AC}, is arbitrarily taken as positive, and the signs of the other two coupling constants in a particular molecule are quoted with reference to this.

10.4.8 Vinyl Chloride and Chloroethylenes

Comparing the chemical shifts found in vinyl chloride with that of ethylene ($\tau = 4{\cdot}71$) the effects of chlorine substitution on the chemical shifts of the three vinyl hydrogen nuclei are found to be −0·900, −0·12 and 0 ppm at the α,

TABLE 10.31 THE ^{1}H CHEMICAL SHIFTS AND SPIN COUPLING CONSTANTS OF A SERIES OF CHLOROETHYLENES[123]

Compound		τ	cycles sec^{-1}	
			J_{HH}	$J_{^{13}CH}$
cis-$C_2H_2Cl_2$		3·72	5·3	198·5
trans-$C_2H_2Cl_2$		3·76	12·1	199·1
1,1-$C_2H_2Cl_2$		4·62		166
C_2HCl_3		3·68		201·2
C_2H_3Cl	α	3·81	*gem* −1·3	α 195
	β-cis	4·59	*cis* 7·5	*β-cis* 160
	β-trans	4·71	*trans* 14·7	*β-trans* 161

β-cis and β-trans positions (τ values of 3·81, 4·59 and 4·71 ppm respectively)[123]. These results suggest that the inductive effect of the electronegative chlorine atom strongly withdraws electrons from the α-position causing it to become deshielded while at the β-positions there is possibly some cancellation of the inductive effects by lone pair conjugation[123].

Table 10.31 presents the measured chemical shifts and coupling constants observed in the complete series of chloroethylenes. Multiple chlorine substitution of the olefinic system seems to have only a small effect on the shielding of the α-position.

Examination of the ^{13}CH satellite spectra of the chloroethylenes can indicate the positions of chlorine substitution: hydrogen nuclei in the α-position to a chlorine substituent have J_{C-H} coupling constants in the region 195–201 cycles sec^{-1} whilst those in a β-position to a chlorine atom (but not α- to another) have J_{C-H} values in the region 160–166 cycles sec^{-1}.

10.4.9 Propene-1, Butene-1 and Hexene-1

Vinyl derivatives with alkyl groups as their substituents (i.e. alkene-1 compounds) have been examined by Bothner-By and Naar-Colin[124] as part of a more extensive study of olefinic compounds. They were particularly interested in (i) the effects of substitution on the chemical shifts of the hydrogen nuclei in the cis-, trans- and gem-positions to the substituent group and (ii) the part played by rotational isomerism about the bond between the trigonal and tetrahedral carbon atoms on the NMR spectral parameters. All the spectra observed for the alkene-1 derivatives are complex (see Fig. 10.19 for the ^1H resonance spectrum of propene-1 at 60·00 Mc sec^{-1}) and it is necessary to conduct a complete analysis of the spectra to extract exact values of the coupling constants and chemical shifts. Propene-1 constitutes an ABCD$_3$ system and to obtain agreement between the calculated and the observed spectrum of the molecule involves the use of computational techniques. Designating the molecule

$$\begin{array}{c} \text{(3) H} \\ \\ \text{(2) H} \end{array} \!\! \diagdown \!\!\! \diagup \begin{array}{c} \\ \text{C=C} \\ \end{array} \!\!\! \diagup \!\! \diagdown \begin{array}{c} \text{CH}_3 \ (4,4',4'') \\ \\ \text{H (1)} \end{array}$$

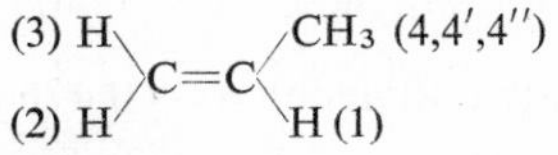

the assignments of the bands in the spectrum of propene-1 will be as shown in Fig. 10.19. The sixteen low field bands are due to the hydrogen nucleus H (1) and by using first order considerations, rough values of the coupling constants can be obtained: the sixteen bands can be sorted into a doublet ($J_{13} = \sim 17$ cycles sec^{-1}) of doublets ($J_{12} = \sim 10$ cycles sec^{-1}) of quartets ($J_{14} = \sim 6$ cycles sec^{-1}). Examination of the high field multiplets reveals them to be composed of a pair of doublets of quartets and from these, approximate values of J_{23}, J_{24}, J_{34} can be obtained. Approximate values of the chemical shifts of the nuclei can also be estimated by direct measurement of the spectrum. Using the approximate values of the parameters, a trial matrix is constructed (see Chapter 8) and a computer is employed to assist in modifying the trial matrix until it yields solutions which converge on to the measured eigenvalues. Accurate values of the chemical shift and coupling constant parameters are then available from the modified matrix elements. It is found that certain of the coupling constants must be postulated to have signs opposite to the others in order to obtain a theoretical spectrum in good agreement with the observed spectrum. Table 10.32 gives the chemical shifts and coupling constants for neat samples of propene-1, butene-1 and hexene-1. Dilute solutions of the compounds in carbon tetrachloride have also been examined and a very small (but nonetheless real) downfield shift of the more exposed hydrogen nucleus H(2) with respect to nuclei H(1) and H(3) is observed. These shifts are reported in Table 10.32 under the heading "standard" solution. Examination of Table 10.32 reveals that a change in the alkyl group has very little effect on the chemical shifts of

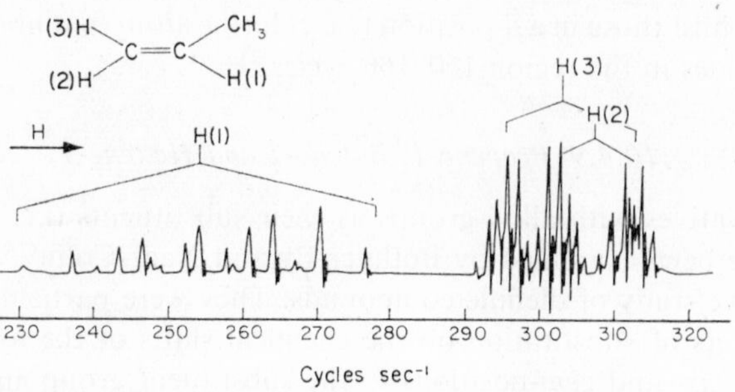

FIG. 10.19 The ^1H resonance spectrum of the olefinic hydrogen nuclei in propene-1 at 60·00 Mc sec^{-1}. CCl_4 is the solvent and TMS the internal reference. The latter was given a chemical shift of 600 cycles sec^{-1}. Bothner-By and Naar-Colin[124].

the hydrogen nuclei or on the coupling constants between them. Upon substituting an alkyl group into an ethylene molecule, the following chemical shift changes occur:

$$\tau(1) - \tau\,(\text{ethylene}) = -0{\cdot}402 \text{ ppm}$$

$$\tau(2) - \tau\,(\text{ethylene}) = +0{\cdot}476 \text{ ppm}$$

$$\tau(3) - \tau\,(\text{ethylene}) = +0{\cdot}399 \text{ ppm}$$

where τ (ethylene) = 4·650 ppm.

Bothner-By and Naar-Colin[124] have summarised the main factors controlling shielding in organic molecules: they are

(i) proximity of atoms or groups which donate or withdraw electrons by either an inductive or a resonance mechanism[9, 154, 156],

(ii) proximity of groups showing neighbour diamagnetic anisotropic effects[146, 157–160],

(iii) presence of permanent electric fields within the molecule which might distort the electronic orbitals near the hydrogen nuclei[8, 161],

(iv) near approach of polarisable groups which leads to a non-vanishing mean square electric field at the hydrogen nucleus and reduces its shielding[162]. There is also a paramagnetic contribution from within the C—H bonds but this is usually neglected since it represents a constant fraction of the diamagnetic contribution[141].

Bothner-By and Naar-Colin have conducted a detailed investigation of the relative importance of the various shielding factors in the case of 1-alkenes and it is instructive to examine their approach to the problem.

TABLE 10.32 THE ^1H CHEMICAL SHIFTS AND SPIN COUPLING CONSTANTS[124] FOR PROPENE-1, BUTENE-1 AND HEXENE-1

$$\begin{array}{c} (3)\,H \\ \diagdown \\ (2)\,H \diagup \end{array} C=C \begin{array}{c} (4) \\ \diagup CH_2R \\ \diagdown H\ (1) \end{array}$$

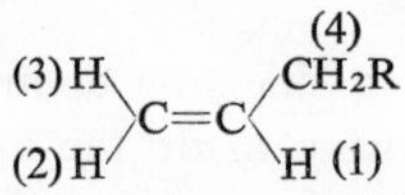

Chemical shift	Propene-1, R = H		Butene-1, R = CH$_3$		Hexene-1, R = C$_3$H$_7$	
	Neat	Standard	Neat	Standard	Neat	Standard
τ (1)	4·27	4·27	4·21	4·22	4·26	4·27
τ (2)	5·12	5·12	5·13	5·13	5·13	5·12
τ (3)	5·04	5·04	5·05	5·06	5·06	5·06
τ (4)	8·34	8·28	8·02	8·00	7·97	7·98
Terminal methyl τ_{CH_3}			9·02	9·01	9·14	9·10
Coupling constants	cycles sec^{-1}		cycles sec^{-1}		cycles sec^{-1}	
J_{12}	10·02		10·32		10·23	
J_{13}	16·81		17·23		17·03	
J_{14}	6·40		6·22		6·55	
J_{23}	2·08		1·96		2·23	
J_{24}	− 1·33		− 1·26		− 1·18	
J_{34}	− 1·75		− 1·66		− 1·51	

"Standard" solutions are dilute solutions of the alkene in carbon tetrachloride.

(i) The alkyl groups in alkenes can donate electrons to the double bond either by an inductive or a resonance (hyperconjugative) mechanism. If the inductive effect were the sole factor then because the influence of such an effect is greatly attenuated as the distance from the alkyl group increases, the greatest electron density would be on the nearest carbon atom resulting in the hydrogen nucleus on this carbon atom, H(1), being well shielded. However, it is observed experimentally that the hydrogen nuclei H(2) and H(3) are more shielded than H(1) indicating that the inductive effect is not the major factor controlling shielding in these molecules. A hyperconjugative mechanism involving the following resonance forms I and II

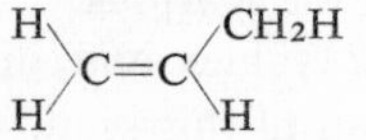

$$\begin{array}{c} H \\ \diagdown \\ H \diagup \end{array} C=C \begin{array}{c} \diagup CH_2H \\ \diagdown H \end{array} \quad (I) \qquad\qquad \begin{array}{c} H \\ \diagdown \\ H \diagup \end{array} \overset{-}{C}=C \begin{array}{c} \diagup CH_2H^+ \\ \diagdown H \end{array} \quad (II)$$

would result in the β-hydrogen nuclei being more shielded than the α-hydrogen nucleus.

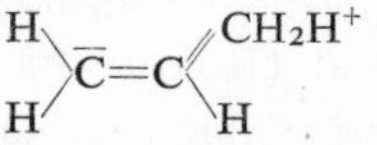

(ii) Another attempt to explain the observed chemical shifts in propene-1 is based on considerations of diamagnetic anisotropy of a single C—C bond. Such effects are thought to be unimportant since they predict a deshielding of the β-hydrogen nucleus, H(2), relative to the other two vinyl nuclei which is in contradiction with the experimental observations.

(iii) The dipole moment of 1-alkenes is thought to lie along the line indicated on the molecular structure[163] shown in structure III

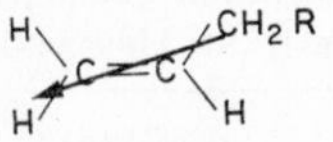

(III)

For the purpose of calculating shielding contributions for the vinyl nuclei, Bothner-By and Naar-Colin have made the approximation that this dipole moment can be replaced by a uniform electric field in the same direction. It is assumed that an electric field will push electron density along the bond and on to the hydrogen nuclei, thus increasing their shielding. Such an approach provides chemical shifts of the same magnitude and sign as the observed values and since the dipole moments of the various 1-alkenes are very similar one would also predict the observed invariance of the chemical shifts from one alkene to another.

(iv) To obtain the shielding contribution due to the approach of a polarisable group the following expression is used

$$\Delta\sigma = -1{\cdot}5 \times 10^{-18}\, \alpha\, \varepsilon / r^6$$

where $\Delta\sigma$ is the change in shielding (dimensionless), α is the polarisability of the group in cm^3, ε the ionisation energy in ergs and r is the distance of approach in cm (must be < 2 Å if this effect is to be appreciable). Although this effect leads to chemical shifts for the three vinyl hydrogen nuclei which are qualitatively in agreement with the observed values, any realistic choice of values for α and ε yield chemical shifts which are much too small.

It is concluded that the presence of a permanent dipole in the molecule (effect (iii)) appears to give the most consistent explanation of the observed chemical shifts in propene-1.

10.4.10 Spin Coupling Constants in Alkene-1 Derivatives

Examination of the coupling constants shown in Tables 10.32 and 10.33 reveals that the values obtained for alkene-1 derivatives show no exceptional variations from the characteristic values observed for vinyl systems. In butene-1 there is a possibility of rotational isomerism about the bond joining the sp^3 hybridised carbon atom and the sp^2 hybridised carbon atom. The coupling constants J_{14}, J_{24} and J_{34} will depend upon the isomeric state of the molecule and they should reflect whether or not a particular rotameric state is preferentially occupied at a particular temperature. Using the Karplus[39] relationships (equations (10.4) and (10.5)) which correlate J values and dihedral bond angles, it should be possible to obtain information of this kind. The coupling constants observed in liquid butene-1 at room temperature indicate that the three rotational isomeric states are equally populated[164].

Bothner-By and co-workers[165] have examined the ^{1}H resonance spectra of a series of alkyl ethylenes and a summary of their results is given in Table 10.34. For *trans* oriented hydrogen nuclei on adjacent trigonal and tetrahedral carbon atoms in alkyl ethylenes, the J_{HH} coupling constant appears to be about 11·5 cycles sec^{-1} whilst *gauche* oriented nuclei have a J_{HH} value near to 3·7 cycles sec^{-1}. Using these values it is possible to predict which rotameric

TABLE 10.33 SPIN–SPIN COUPLING CONSTANTS (IN CYCLES SEC^{-1}) REPORTED FOR SEVERAL OLEFINIC COMPOUNDS[124]

General structure: (3) H, (2) H on one carbon; CH_2R (4), H (1) on the other: $(3)H(2)H\,C{=}C\,(CH_2R)(4)\,H(1)$

Compound	$J_{1,2}$	$J_{1,3}$	$J_{1,4}$	$J_{2,3}$	$J_{2,4}$	$J_{3,4}$
$(H)(Cl)C{=}C(CH_2Cl)(H)$		13·1 13·1	7·1 7·3			0·5 −1·2
$(Cl)(H)C{=}C(CH_2Cl)(H)$	7·2 7·0		7·2 7·4		0·9 −1·2	
$(H)(H)C{=}C(CH_2Cl)(Cl)$				1·9 1·9	(0·3, 0·9) (0·3, 1·0)	
$(H)(H)C{=}C(CH_2Br)(H)$				2·2	(0·3, 1·0)	
$(H)(H)C{=}C(C_6H_5)(H)$	10·6 11·3	17·2 17·8		1·6 1·2		
$(H)(H)C{=}C(CN)(H)$	11·28	18·19		1·27		

† This table was compiled by A. A. Bothner-By and C. C. Naar-Colin from a survey of the literature.

forms of the various mono- and disubstituted propenes are occupied preferentially if the H—H spin coupling constants between nuclei on the adjacent trigonal and tetrahedral carbon atoms are known. The magnitude of the long range coupling constants between allylic hydrogen nuclei and the terminal ethylenic hydrogen nuclei also depend on the rotational conformation of the molecule, the values being smallest when the allylic hydrogen and the $=CH_2$ group are eclipsed.

10.5 DISUBSTITUTED OLEFINES

The characteristic values for the *gem-*, *cis-* and *trans-*coupling constants observed in vinyl systems are not changed appreciably in disubstituted olefines and consequently the problem of deciding the configurations of geometri-

TABLE 10.34 ^{1}H CHEMICAL SHIFTS AND SPIN COUPLING CONSTANTS OF SOME ALKYL SUBSTITUTED OLEFINES[(165)]

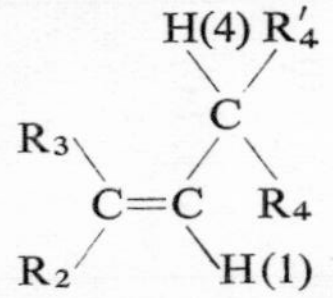

Substn. on olefine					Chemical shifts[b]				Coupling constants					
R_2	R_3	R_4	R'_4	State[a]	$\tau(1)$	$\tau(2)$	$\tau(3)$	$\tau(4)$	$J(1,2)$	$J(1,3)$	$J(1,4)$	$J(2,3)$	$J(2,4)$	$J(3,4)$
H	H	CH_3	CH_3	N	4·271	5·186	5·088	(8·170)[c]	10·37	17·22	6·41	1·74	− 1·17	− 1·43
				S	4·276	5·186	5·102	(8·170)[c]						
H	H	H	i-C_3H_7	N	4·280	5·075	5·058	(8·000)[c]	10·13	17·02	7·00	2·05	− 1·15	− 1·43
				S	4·295	5·074	5·064	(8·000)[c]						
H	H	H	t-C_4H_9	N	4·223	5·032	5·055	8·082	10·02	17·10	7·46	2·37	− 0·94	− 1·32
				S	4·231	5·036	5·061	8·075						
H	H	t-C_4H_9	t-C_4H_9	N	4·260	5·013	5·214	8·434	9·97	17·01	10·65	2·63	− 0·10	− 0·63
				S	4·262	5·020	5·221	8·435						
CH_3	CH_3	t-C_4H_9	t-C_4H_9	N	4·775	(8·443)[d]	(8·270)[d]	8·107	− 1·25[e]	− 1·25[e]	11·37	...[f]	...[f]	...[f]
				S	4·792	(8·438)[d]	(8·276)[d]	8·125						

[a] N = neat, S = 10 per cent (v./v.) in CCl_4. [b] Spectrometer frequency = 60·00 Mc sec^{-1}. [c] Assumed, not analysed. [d] Assignment not certain. [e] $J(H—CH_3)$. [f] Not resolved, probably less than 0·2 cycle sec^{-1}.

cal isomers can often be confidently solved using high resolution NMR. As the number of accurately measured spectra of olefinic compounds accumulates, the application of NMR to the study of geometrical isomerism about ethylenic double bonds is becoming increasingly useful. Stehling(379) has compiled chemical shift and coupling constant data (given in Appendix C) for an extensive series of mono olefines. Geometrical isomers of di- and tri-substituted olefines can be characterised by the chemical shifts of the β-CH_3 and α-CH groups(379).

10.5.1 Cis- and Trans-disubstituted Olefines

In molecules such as

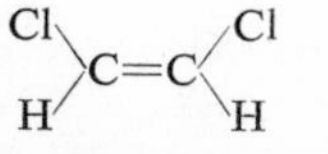

and

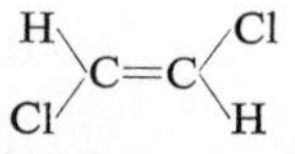

the chemical shifts of the hydrogen nuclei in the two molecules are different and the difference between them is referred to as the "differential shielding". For the molecules cited the "differential shielding", $\tau_{cis} - \tau_{trans} = -0{\cdot}08$ ppm. Jackman and Wiley have explained these differential shifts in terms of long range shielding contributions arising from neighbour diamagnetic anisotropic effects(166). Table 10.35 gives the differential shifts for four *cis/trans* pairs of $\alpha\beta$-disubstituted olefines.

TABLE 10.35 THE DIFFERENTIAL CHEMICAL SHIFTS ($\tau_{cis} - \tau_{trans}$) FOR FOUR *cis/trans* PAIRS OF $\alpha\beta$-DISUBSTITUTED OLEFINES, CHX=CHX(166)

X	CH_3	Cl	Br	CO_2Me
$\tau_{cis} - \tau_{trans}$ (ppm)	$-0{\cdot}03$	$-0{\cdot}08$	$-0{\cdot}38$	$+0{\cdot}525$

The contribution to the shielding from neighbour diamagnetic anisotropic effects is inversely dependent upon the cube of the distance (r) from the shielded nucleus to the electrical centre of gravity of the group of electrons involved (see Section 4.4). When this distance is greater than 3 Å long range shielding from this source can be neglected (excluding shielding in aromatic rings). For all *cis*-disubstituted olefines the β-hydrogen nucleus is too far from the centre of the carbon-substituent bond for it to experience a significant long-range shielding contribution of this type. In the case of *trans*-disubstituted olefines, the distance between the β-hydrogen nuclei and the centre of the carbon-substituent bond is much shorter ($\sim 2{\cdot}4$ Å) and thus a contribution to the shielding from the carbon-substituent bond is observed. The differential chemical shifts shown in Table 10.35 can be explained on this basis, the whole of the contribution arising in the *trans* isomer. The dimethyl derivatives have a very small differential shielding because the *trans* isomer has no long range contribution to the shielding as a result of the angle θ being very small for this molecule. For the dihalo-derivatives the carbon–halogen bond is electrically dipolar in nature and one must therefore measure the distance, r, from the halogen nucleus rather than from the centre of the carbon–halogen bond. This results in the term $(3\cos^2\theta - 1)$ being small and negative. Both the *trans*-dichloro and the *trans*-dibromo have a paramagnetic contribution to the shielding of their β-hydrogen nuclei.

Other disubstituted olefines which have been studied are *trans* styrenes[429], *trans* propenes[429] and α- and β-substituted cinnamic acids[430].

10.5.2 2-Substituted Propenes

Jackman and Wiley[166] have measured the 1H chemical shifts and the differential chemical shifts of the olefinic hydrogen nuclei in a series of 2-substituted propenes of general formula

$$\begin{array}{c} (A)\ H \\ \\ (B)\ H \end{array} \diagdown C=C \diagup \begin{array}{c} CH_3\ (X) \\ \\ R \end{array}$$

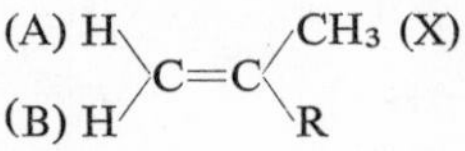

Table 10.36 gives the chemical shift data for several such molecules. Certain similarities are apparent between the measured differential shifts for this series of compounds and those observed in the analogous 1,2-disubstituted derivatives (for example when $R=Cl$, Br, $COOCH_3$). All the derivatives of methacrylic acid considered ($CONH_2$, $COCl$ and $COOCH_3$) have similar differential

TABLE 10.36 THE 1H CHEMICAL SHIFTS OF SEVERAL 2-SUBSTITUTED PROPENES[166]

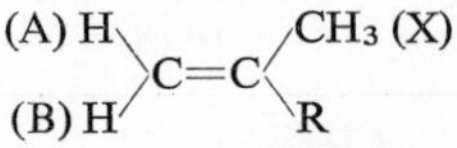

$$\begin{array}{c} (A)\ H \\ \\ (B)\ H \end{array} \diagdown C=C \diagup \begin{array}{c} CH_3\ (X) \\ \\ R \end{array}$$

R	Chemical shifts				R	Chemical shifts			
	$\tau(Me)$	τ_B	τ_A	$\tau_B - \tau_A$		$\tau(Me)$	τ_B	τ_A	$\tau_B - \tau_A$
$CH_2 \cdot C(CH_3)_3$	8·22	5·37†	5·20†	0·17	COCl	7·97	3·52	3·98	−0·46
Cl	7·85	4·92	4·92	0·00	COMe	8·20	3·96	4·16	−0·20
Br	7·70	4·67	4·47	0·20	CHO	7·90	3·62	3·92	−0·30
CN	7·97	4·28†	4·24†	0·04	Ph	7·86	4·72	4·98	−0·20
CO_2Me	8·10	3·96	4·51	−0·55	OAc	8·09	5·38	5·38	0·00
$CO \cdot NH_2$	8·06	4·24	4·63	−0·39					

† The assignment is uncertain.

shifts and fairly high values are also observed in the aldehyde and the methyl ketone derivative. In all cases the differential shielding is attributed to the deshielding of the β-hydrogen nuclei in the *cis* position to the carbonyl group due to the diamagnetic anisotropic effect of the latter.

Other substituents which exhibit differential shielding between the β-hydrogen nuclei in 2-substituted propenes are

(i) the neopentyl group, suggesting that the group spends appreciable periods of time in favourable conformations where the C—C bonds are effectively oriented to produce a significant diamagnetic anisotropic shielding of the *cis* β-hydrogen nucleus,

(ii) the phenyl group, where the aromatic ring currents influence the shielding of the β-hydrogen nuclei to differing extents. The nitrile and the acetoxy groups show only small differences in the shielding of their β-hydrogen nuclei; in both cases the effective centres of the electronic systems concerned are too far removed from the β-hydrogen nuclei for them to exert a long range anisotropic shielding influence. Other workers have studied the NMR spectra

TABLE 10.37 THE ^{1}H CHEMICAL SHIFTS (IN PPM) AND SPIN COUPLING CONSTANTS (IN CYCLES SEC^{-1}) OF SEVERAL 2-SUBSTITUTED PROPENES[145]

	Chemical shifts						Coupling constants		
R	δ_A^∞†	"τ"$_A$	δ_B^∞	"τ_B"	δ_X^∞	"τ_X"	J_{AX}	J_{BX}	J_{AB}
—Br	−0·42	4·54	−0·24	4·72	2·82	7·78	1·4	0·8	2·0
—Cl	0·03	4·99	0·00	4·96	2·99	7·95	1·38	0·65	1·25
—OCOCH$_3$	0·53	5·49	0·45	5·41	3·19	8·15	1·2	0·6	1·0
—OCH$_3$	1·3	5·26	1·3	6·26	3·31	8·27			
—CHO	−1·08	3·88	−0·78	4·18	3·27	8·23	1·6	1·0	1·1
—CN	−0·58	4·38	−0·47	4·49	3·15	8·11	1·7	1·15	1·0
—CH$_3$	0·42	5·38	0·42	5·38	3·36	8·32	1·25	1·25	
—CH$_2$Cl	0·20	5·16	0·05	5·01	3·24	8·20	1·5	0·85	1·6
—CH$_2$Br	0·20	5·16	0·01	4·97	3·21	8·17	1·5	0·8	1·5
—CH$_2$I	0·24	5·20	−0·09	4·87	3·17	8·13	1·5	0·8	1·5

† δ^∞ are chemical shifts measured relative to H_2O (liq.) external reference for the dilute solution in cyclohexane. Parameters listed according to ABX_3 notation with A defined by $|J_{AX}| > |J_{BX}|$.

$$\text{"}\tau\text{"} = 4{\cdot}96 + \delta_{H_2O}^\infty .$$

of 2-substituted propenes and in general their results agree with those of Jackman and Wiley[166]. Table 10.37 is a compilation of the chemical shift and coupling constant data obtained from detailed ABX_3 analyses of the spectra of the molecules in this series[145]. The value of $J^{cis}_{H-CH_3}$ is found to be greater than $J^{trans}_{H-CH_3}$ in the ^{1}H resonance spectrum of 2-chloropropene where the band assignments can be made with reasonable certainty based on the assignments of vinyl chloride (see Table 10.31). This finding indicates the same trend in J_{H-CH_3} values as was found by Alexander in butene-1[125]. In 2-chloropropene both long range J_{H-CH_3} coupling constants are shown to have the same sign[145] and there is some evidence to suggest that they are negative in sign (see Table 10.8). In all the molecules they examined, the two long range J_{H-CH_3} values differ by $\sim 0{\cdot}6$ cycles sec^{-1}.

As regards the shielding of the nuclei in the 2-substituted propenes listed in Table 10.37, it is found that the R substituent affects the shielding of the olefinic hydrogen nuclei to a greater extent than it does that of the methyl group hydrogen nuclei. Although most of the chemical shifts are qualitatively in agreement with the values predicted by simple inductive and mesomeric considerations, no precise correlation of the olefinic chemical shifts with Hammett constants of the substituents was observed. The shielding of the β-hydrogen nucleus *cis* to a CH_2X group is influenced to a greater extent than that in a β-*trans* position. This is consistent with the idea of contributions to the shielding from long range anisotropic effects as suggested by Jackman and Wiley[166].

For some of the 2-substituted propenes, specific medium effects were observed to accompany a change in solvent and this fact was used to assist in assigning the spectra.

10.5.3 2,3-Disubstituted Propenes

Whipple, Goldstein and McClure[167] have examined a series of 2,3-disubstituted propenes to assess the effects of allylic substitution on the NMR spectral parameters. These molecules have the general formula

$$\begin{array}{c} H \\ \diagdown \\ H \diagup \end{array} C{=}C \begin{array}{c} \diagup CH_2X \\ \diagdown Y \end{array}$$

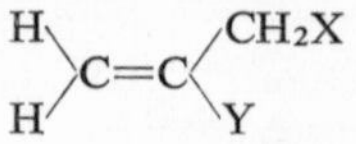

and their 1H resonance spectra can usually be analysed in terms of an ABX_2 system.

TABLE 10.38 THE 1H CHEMICAL SHIFTS AND SPIN COUPLING CONSTANTS OF SEVERAL 2,3-DISUBSTITUTED PROPENES[167]

$$\begin{array}{c} H \\ \diagdown \\ H \diagup \end{array} C{=}C \begin{array}{c} \diagup Y \\ \diagdown CH_2X \end{array}$$

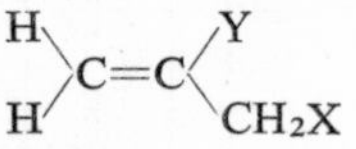

X Substituent	Chemical shifts (ppm)†						Coupling constants (cycles sec⁻¹)		
	δ_A^∞	"τ_A"	δ_B^∞	"τ_B"	δ_X^∞	"τ_X"	J_{AX}	J_{BX}	J_{AB}
	1. Y=Cl series								
—I	−0·44	4·52	−0·17	4·79	1·05	6·01	0·7		1·4
—Br	−0·45	4·51	−0·25	4·71	1·08	6·04	0·9		1·5
—Cl	−0·48	4·48	−0·27	4·69	1·01	5·97	1·2	0·6	1·5
—OH	−0·38	4·58	−0·19	4·77	0·96	5·92	1·5	1·0	1·4
	2. Y=Br series								
—Br	−0·91	4·05	−0·51	4·45	0·96	5·92	1·1		2·0
—Cl	−0·94	4·02	−0·51	4·45	0·92	5·88	1·5	0·9	1·9
	3. Y=CH₃ series								
—I	−0·09	4·87	0·24	5·20	1·25	6·21	0·8		1·5
—Br	0·01	4·97	0·20	5·16	1·25	6·21	0·9		1·5
—Cl	0·05	5·01	0·20	5·16	1·16	6·12	1·0		1·6

$$\text{"}\tau\text{"} = 4{\cdot}96 + \delta_{H_2O}^\infty.$$

† In ppm relative to an H_2O (liq.) external reference for the dilute solution in cyclohexane. Parameters listed according to ABX_2 notation with A nucleus defined by $|J_{AX}| < |J_{BX}|$.

In the methallyl halides, the olefinic hydrogen nucleus which couples more strongly with the methyl group has the weaker coupling interaction with the

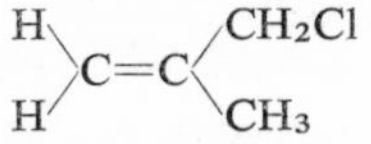

Methallyl chloride

halomethyl group and vice versa. The $J^{cis}_{H-CH_3}$ coupling constants are again found to be greater than the $J^{trans}_{H-CH_3}$ values in substituted propenes.

Table 10.38 gives the chemical shifts and the coupling constants for the 2,3-disubstituted propenes examined and it can be seen that the shielding of all the nuclei are influenced to a greater extent by the substituents in the 2-position than by those in the 3-position. This is to be expected for the olefinic hydrogen nuclei but the methylene group hydrogen nuclei are not shielded to the extent one would predict from the electronegative inductive effects of the allylic substituents. The effects of the 2-substituent on the olefinic chemical shifts and coupling constants are fairly independent of the extent of allylic substitution and are very similar to those observed in 2-substituted propenes. The long range coupling constants, J_{H-CH_2X}, are smaller in the allylic derivatives and decrease in the order, X=OH, Cl, Br, I. These long range coupling constants are solvent dependent, their values increasing as the solvents become less polar. Rotational isomers with differing dipole moments will be favoured to different extents in polar media and thus the variation in coupling constant with change of solvent might well originate in such conformational effects.

10.5.4 The Effects of Methyl Group Substitution on the ^{1}H *Resonance Spectra of Ethylenic Molecules*

Reddy and Goldstein[(168)] have measured the ^{1}H resonance spectra of ten methyl substituted ethylenic compounds in order to assess the effects of the methyl group substitution (see Tables 10.29, 10.39 and 10.40 for a summary of their

TABLE 10.39 PREDICTED AND OBSERVED CHEMICAL SHIFTS (CYCLES SEC^{-1} AT 40 MC SEC^{-1}) IN CYANOPROPENES[(168)]

Compound	Proton position with respect to the nitrile group	Chemical shifts in cycles sec^{-1} from TMS internal reference		
		Predicted[a]	Predicted[b]	Obsd.
α-Methacrylonitrile	*cis*	−222·2	−225·2	−225·8
	trans	−218·6	−221·6	−221·6
trans-Crotonitrile	α	−206·0	−209·0	−208·7
	β	−256·5	−259·5	−261·3
cis-Crotonitrile	α	−202·5	−205·5	−206·6
	β	−249·4	−252·4	−251·0

[a] Without the additional constitutive correction of −3·0 cycles sec^{-1}.
[b] With the additional constitutive correction of −3·0 cycles sec^{-1}.

results). The molecules examined are all derivatives of 1-propene and have one of the general formulae

$$CH_3 \diagdown C=C \diagup H \qquad CH_3 \diagdown C=C \diagup H \qquad CH_3 \diagdown C=C \diagup X$$
$$X \diagup \qquad \diagdown H \qquad H \diagup \qquad \diagdown X \qquad H \diagup \qquad \diagdown H$$

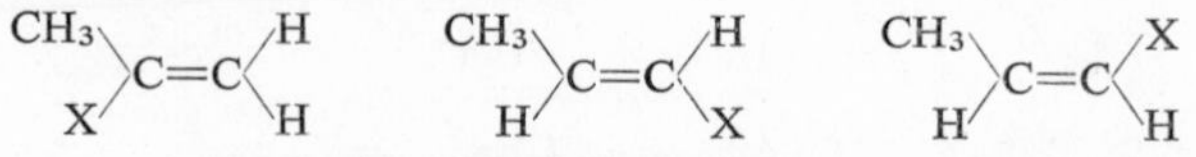

Care was taken to eliminate concentration shifts by extrapolating the chemical shifts to infinite dilution in an inert solvent in cases where there was any suspicion of such effects being present. It was found that substitution of a methyl group brings about a constant and characteristic shielding change at each of the positions in an ethylenic system. The significance of this can best be seen by considering a specific example in detail.

Vinyl Cyanide and Cyanopropenes. Table 10.29 gives the chemical shifts for ethylene, propylene, vinyl cyanide and the cyanopropenes (from TMS reference at 40 Mc sec^{-1}). For propylene, the *trans* hydrogen nucleus is 3·5 cycles sec^{-1} more shielded than that in the *cis* position, and in vinyl cyanide the *cis* hydrogen nucleus is 7·1 cycles sec^{-1} less shielded than that at the *trans* position. If these two effects are additive then for 2-cyanopropene the signal of the hydrogen nucleus in the *cis* position to the nitrile group would be 3·6 cycles sec^{-1} to lower field of that of the hydrogen in the *trans* position. Experimentally a difference of 4·2 cycles sec^{-1} in the same direction is observed which is in excellent agreement with the theoretical value (the error in the experimental value is $\pm 0·5$ cycles sec^{-1}).

A similar process of reasoning applied to the chemical shifts of the hydrogen nuclei in propylene, vinyl cyanide and *cis*- and *trans*-crotonitrile, shows that one can likewise predict the chemical shifts in the crotonitrilic compounds. In order to predict actual chemical shifts rather than internal chemical shifts we use the equation

$$\Delta_i = \Delta_i\,(Pr) - 211·5 \text{ cycles sec}^{-1} \qquad (10.10)$$

where Δ_i is the methyl substituent effect on the chemical shift of the ith hydrogen nucleus, $\Delta_i\,(Pr)$ the chemical shift of the hydrogen nucleus in the same position relative to the CH_3 group in propylene and 211·5 cycles sec^{-1} is the chemical shift of ethylene from tetramethylsilane at 40 Mc sec^{-1}. Thus for the methyl substituent effect we obtain the following values

α – position	$- 17·8$ cycles sec^{-1}
β – position (*trans* to CH_3 group)	$+ 16·5$
β – position (*cis* to CH_3 group)	$+ 13·0$

The chemical shifts of the hydrogen nuclei in cyanopropenes can now be predicted by adding the above terms on to the chemical shifts of the appropriate nuclei in vinyl cyanide to give the values shown in Table 10.39. All six predicted values are higher than expected by about 3 cycles sec^{-1} and to compensate for this discrepancy (assuming it to be a constitutive effect) we can modify equation (10.10) to

$$\Delta_i' = \Delta_i\,(Pr) - 214·5 \text{ cycles sec}^{-1}. \qquad (10.11)$$

Very good agreement between predicted and observed chemical shifts has also been obtained for the systems vinyl bromide/bromopropenes and vinyl chloride/chloropropenes (see Table 10.40) using this approach.

TABLE 10.40 PREDICTED AND OBSERVED CHEMICAL SHIFTS IN CYCLES SEC^{-1} AT 40 MC SEC^{-1} IN CHLOROPROPENES[168]

Compound	Proton position with respect to chlorine	Chemical shifts in cycles sec^{-1} from TMS internal reference	
		Predicted[a]	Obsd.
2-Chloropropene	*cis*	−200·0	−201·0
	trans	−198·5	−199·8
trans-1-Chloropropene-1	α	−234·8	−235·3
	β	−234·3	−232·8
cis-1-Chloropropene-1	α	−231·3	
	β	−229·3	

[a] No additional constitutive correction was necessary for these compounds.

10.6 TRISUBSTITUTED OLEFINES

10.6.1 1-Substituted Isobutenes

A series of compounds with the general formula

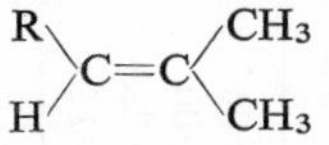

has been examined by high resolution NMR to evaluate the extent to which the chemical shifts of the allylic hydrogen nuclei can be used in assigning geometrical isomers of related molecules to their correct configuration[166].

Table 10.41 (see p. 736) lists the chemical shifts of the olefinic hydrogen nuclei and the two β-methyl groups for the compounds examined. The long range shielding effects of the freely rotating methyl groups will be small and can be neglected. If molecules containing groups which show large magnetic anisotropic effects are considered (such as those with carbonyl groups, R = $COOCH_3$, CHO, $COCH_3$) then the large long range shielding effects enable NMR to be used in assigning molecules of the type —$(CH_3)C:CR$— to their correct geometrical configurations[169].

The measured values of *cis* and *trans* H–CH_3 coupling constants in substituted propenes and isobutenes (see Table 10.42) indicate that the *cis* value is usually the larger but there are exceptions to this which prevent the use of empirical data of this kind for assignment of configurations.

10.6.2 αβ-Unsaturated Esters

A NMR examination of a large series of *cis*/*trans* isomeric pairs of αβ-unsaturated esters has served to emphasise the importance of long range anisotropic contributions to the shielding of nuclei in olefinic systems[169].

TABLE 10.41 THE ^{1}H CHEMICAL SHIFTS OF SOME 1-SUBSTITUTED ISOBUTENES[166]

R	τ(olefinic H)	τ(β-Me) cis[b]	trans[b]	$\tau_{cis} - \tau_{trans}$	R	τ(olefinic H)	τ(β-Me) cis[b]	trans[b]	$\tau_{cis} - \tau_{trans}$
$C(CH_3)_3$	4·87	8·38[a]	8·32[a]	0·06	COMe	4·03	7·94	8·14	−0·20
Br	4·22	8·25	8·25	0·00	CHO	4·37	7·89	8·09	−0·20
CO_2Me	4·38	7·88	8·16	−0·28	OAc	3·21	8·35	8·35	0·00
COCl	3·99	7·88	8·03	−0·15	C≡CH	4·83	8·12[a]	8·20[a]	−0·08

[a] The *cis* and *trans* assignment is uncertain.

[b] The isobutenes do not, of course, exist in separate *cis* and *trans* forms, but the methyl groups of $Me_2C{=}CHR$ give rise to two distinct shifts; these are labelled *cis* or *trans* according to whether they are ascribed to the methyl group *cis* or *trans* to the group R.

TABLE 10.42 *Cis*- AND *Trans*-H–CH_3 SPIN COUPLING CONSTANTS IN SUBSTITUTED PROPENES AND ISOBUTENES[166] (IN CYCLES SEC^{-1})

R · $C(CH_3)$:CH_2	J^{trans}_{H,CH_3}	J^{cis}_{H,CH_3}	J_{HH}	R · $C(CH_3)$:CH_2	J^{trans}_{H,CH_3}	J^{cis}_{H,CH_3}
R = Br	0·8	1·4	1·4	*R* = $C(CH_3)_3$	1·4	1·4
CO_3Me	0·9	1·45	1·8	Br	1·5	1·5
CO · NH_2	0·95	1·5	1·8	CO_2Me	1·3	1·3
COCl	0·90	1·5	0·0	COCl	1·4	1·2
COMe	0·7	1·3	0·7	OAc	1·55	1·55
CHO	1·5	1·0	1·0			

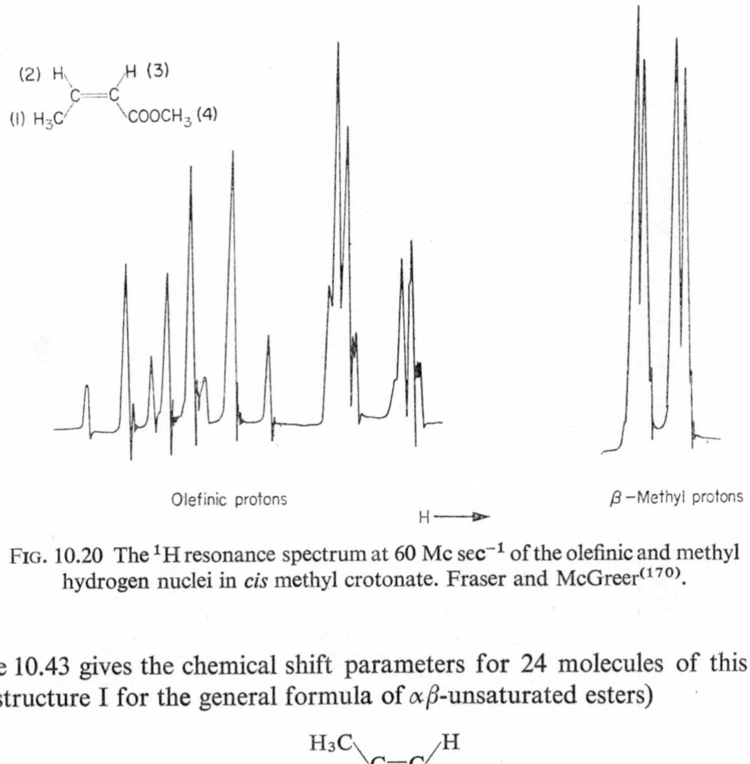

FIG. 10.20 The ¹H resonance spectrum at 60 Mc sec^{-1} of the olefinic and methyl hydrogen nuclei in *cis* methyl crotonate. Fraser and McGreer[170].

Table 10.43 gives the chemical shift parameters for 24 molecules of this type (see structure I for the general formula of $\alpha\beta$-unsaturated esters)

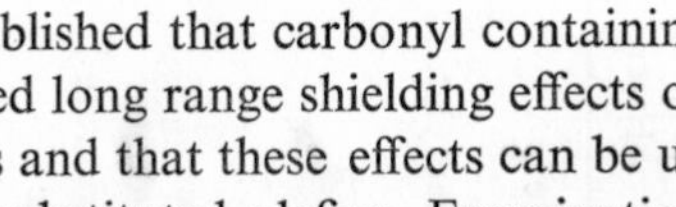

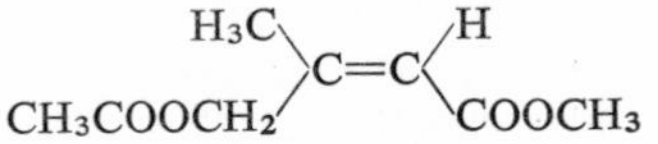

Structure I

It has already been established that carbonyl containing groups in substituted olefines have pronounced long range shielding effects on *cis*-β-hydrogen atoms and *cis*-β-methyl groups and that these effects can be used to assist in deciding the configuration of a substituted olefine. Examination of Table 10.43 shows that the τ values of the β-hydrogen nucleus in the various molecules are very sensitive to the stereochemistry of the substituents, the β-hydrogen being deshielded by 0·5 to 0·9 ppm in the isomer where it is *cis* to the alkoxy carbonyl substituent rather than in the *trans* position. For the *cis*-β-methyl group the

TABLE 10.43 THE ^{1}H CHEMICAL SHIFTS OF A SERIES OF *cis/trans* ISOMERIC PAIRS OF $\alpha\beta$-UNSATURATED ESTERS(169)

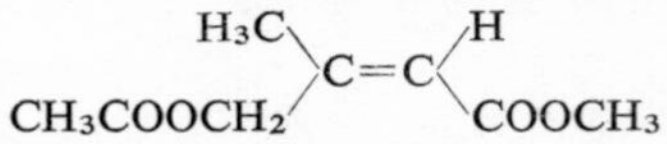

Ester	β-H	Δ	β-CH_3	Δ	Ester	β-CH_3	Δ
Me methacrylate	4·51	0·55			Me_2 *cis*-β-methylglutaconate	8·04	0·24*
	3·96				Me_2 *trans*-β-methylglutaconate	7·80	
Me $\beta\beta$-dimethylacrylate			8·16	0·28	Et *cis*-β-ionylideneacetate	7·98	0·27
			7·88		Et *trans*-β-ionylideneacetate	7·71	
Me_2 maleate	3·86	0·53			Me *cis*-geranate	8·27	0·25
Me_2 fumarate	3·33				Me *trans*-geranate	8·02	
Me_2 citraconate	4·25	0·94	7·96	0·24	Me *cis*-phytenoate	8·14	0·25
Me_2 mesaconate	3·31		7·72		Me *trans*-phytenoate	7·89	
Me_2 dimethylmaleate			8·11	0·10	Me *cis*-$\alpha\beta$-dimethylcinnamate	8·05	0·30
Me_2 dimethylfumarate			8·01		Me *trans*-$\alpha\beta$-dimethylcinnamate	7·75	
Me *cis*-crotonate	3·57	0·62	7·86	0·25	Me_2 *cis*($\alpha\beta$)-*trans*($\gamma\delta$)-β-methylmuconate	8·00	0·25
Me *trans*-crotonate	2·95		8·11				
Me angelate	4·02	0·85	8·03	0·25	Me_2 *trans*($\alpha\beta$)-*trans*($\gamma\delta$)-β-methylmuconate	7·75	
Me tiglate	3·27		8·27				

$\tau_{trans} - \tau_{cis} = \Delta$, where *cis* and *trans* refer to the relation of the proton(s) to the carboxylate group and not necessarily to the configuration of the ester.

* β-$CH_2 \cdot CO_2Me$ = 6·28 and 6·935, respectively; Δ = 0·655.

measured chemical shifts indicate a fairly constant deshielding of ~0·25 ppm on going from the *cis* to *trans* isomer in all the compounds examined. Hence, if both isomers of an $\alpha\beta$-unsaturated ester are available it is usually easy to decide their respective configurations from the ^{1}H resonance spectra of the compounds.

Fraser and McGreer[(170)] have also studied the NMR spectra of some $\alpha\beta$-unsaturated esters and their results are included in Table 10.44A. They adopted a more exact method of analysing the observed spectra which leads to more reliable values of the coupling constants involved. Figure 10.20 shows the hydrogen resonance spectrum of the olefinic and the methyl hydrogen nuclei in *cis*-methylcrotonate. An ABX_3 analysis of the spectrum gives nearly exact values for the chemical shift and coupling constant parameters featured in the spectrum. Attention is drawn to the appreciable error in the coupling constants obtained by assuming the spectrum to be completely first order: this is particularly important if one is attempting to attach significance to the small differences which are found between the various coupling constants. In the pairs of isomeric esters they examined it is found that the $J^{trans}_{H-CH_3}$ coupling constants can be less than, equal to or greater than the $J^{cis}_{H-CH_3}$ values and it would appear that such long range coupling constants will not be of great value in configurational analysis of geometrical isomers. Table 10.44B gives several long range H—H coupling constants measured in the spectra of olefinic molecules[(148)].

TABLE 10.44 THE ^{1}H CHEMICAL SHIFTS AND LONG RANGE SPIN COUPLING CONSTANTS OF (A) UNSATURATED ACIDS AND ESTERS[(148, 170)] (B) MISCELLANEOUS OLEFINIC COMPOUNDS[(148)]

TABLE 10.44 A

Compound	Coupling constants (cycles sec^{-1})			Chemical shifts (τ values)				
	$J_{1,3}$	$J_{1,2}$	$J_{2,3}$	τ_1	τ_2	τ_3	τ_4	τ_{C-CH_3}
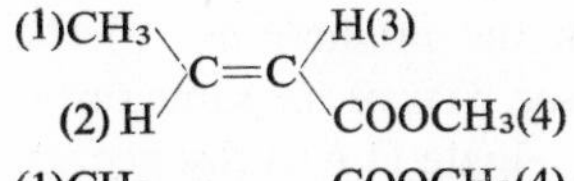 (1)CH_3(2)H>C=C<H(3) $COOCH_3$(4)	−1·67	6·85	15·5	8·12	3·10	4·24	6·33	
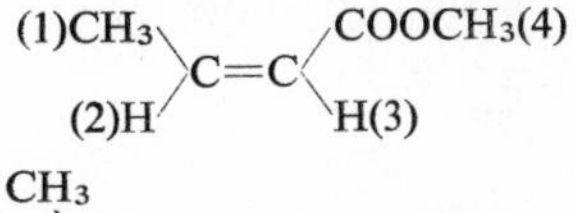 (1)CH_3(2)H>C=C<$COOCH_3$(4) H(3)	−1·82	7·27	11·4	7·86	3·72	4·28	6·36	
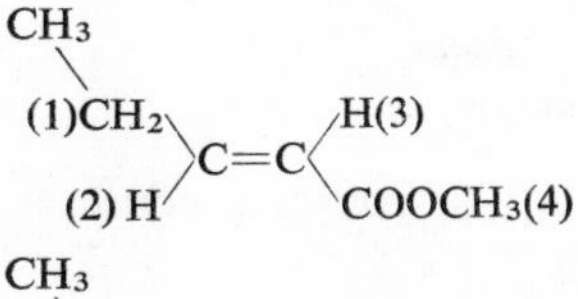 CH_3–(1)CH_2(2)H>C=C<H(3) $COOCH_3$(4)	−1·69	6·35	15·6	7·78	3·07	4·27	6·33	8·90
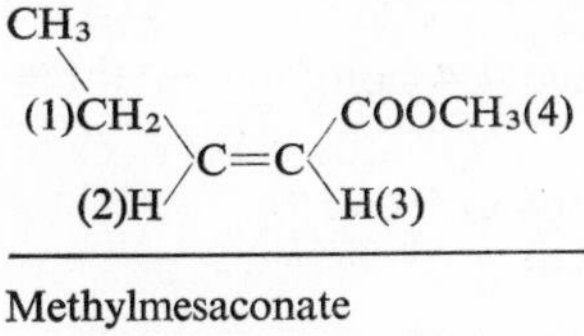 CH_3–(1)CH_2(2)H>C=C<$COOCH_3$(4) H(3)	−1·56	7·43	11·5	7·35	3·83	4·35	6·36	8·95
Methylmesaconate	$J^{trans}_{1,3}$ = 1·56							
Methylcitraconate	$J^{cis}_{1,3}$ = 1·64							

TABLE 10.44 B

1,3 coupling constants in cycles sec^{-1}

Compound	$J^{trans}_{1,3}$	$J^{cis}_{1,3}$	Reference
Butene-1	1·3	1·9	125
α-Methylstyrene	0·7	1·4	171
cis-Propenylbenzene	1·4		171
trans-Propenylbenzene		1·9	131
cis-cis-Dimethylmuconate	1·3		172
trans-trans-Dimethylmuconate		0·7	172
† *trans*-1,2,3-Trichloropropene-1	0·8		129
cis-1,2,3-Trichloropropene-1		0·4	129
‡ *cis*-1,3-Dichloropropene-1	0·9		129
	1·2		173
trans-1,3-Dichloropropene-1		0·5	129
		1·2	173

† *cis* and *trans* refer to the orientation of the two chlorine atoms on the double bond.
‡ *cis* and *trans* refer to the orientation of the two chlorine-containing groups.

10.7 LONG RANGE SPIN COUPLING VIA OLEFINIC SYSTEMS

Spin–spin interaction involving hydrogen nuclei separated by four bonds is frequently observed between methyl hydrogen nuclei and β-hydrogen nuclei in propenes and substituted propenes (see Table 10.44). Hoffman[174] has explained the occurrence of such long range coupling constants in terms of hyperconjugation between methyl group orbitals and π orbitals (see Section 5.5 on σ–π interactions). If such a mechanism is valid two predictions can be made about the coupling in the system: (i) the interaction of the π-electron on one of the unsaturated carbon atoms with the hydrogen nuclei in the attached methyl group will be approximately equal to its interaction with a hydrogen nucleus directly bonded to the unsaturated carbon atom: (ii) the $J_{H-C-C-CH_3}$ coupling constants via a triple bond should be about twice as large as those for a double bond[174, 175]. Experimental evidence supports both the predictions: (i) the $J_{CH_3-CH_3}$ coupling constant in tiglaldehyde (1·0 cycles sec^{-1}) is of the same order of magnitude as the $J^{cis}_{H-CH_3}$ value for *trans* crotonaldehyde (1·6 cycles sec^{-1}),

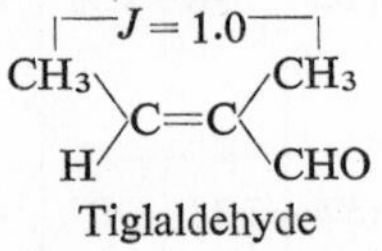

Tiglaldehyde

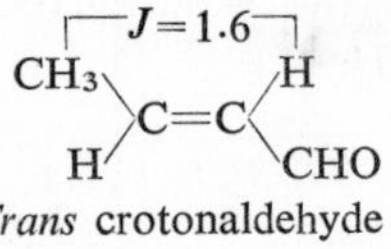

Trans crotonaldehyde

(ii) for propargyl chloride, H—C≡C—CH_2Cl, the J_{H-CH_2} coupling constant is 2·6 cycles sec^{-1}.

Snyder and Roberts[176] have observed long range 1,4 coupling in three substituted allenic derivatives

$(CH_3)_2C{=}C{=}CH_2$	$J_{1,4} = 3{\cdot}03 \pm 0{\cdot}06$ cycles sec^{-1}
$(CH_3)_2C{=}C{=}CHCl$	$J_{1,4} = 2{\cdot}14 \pm 0{\cdot}08$
$CH_3CH{=}C{=}CHCl$	$J_{1,3} = -\ 5{\cdot}8 \pm 0{\cdot}1$ (J_{AB})
X B A	$J_{1,4} = +\ 2{\cdot}4 \pm 0{\cdot}1$ (J_{AX})

The opposing signs of the 1,3 and the 1,4 coupling constants in the spectrum of $CH_3CH=C=CHCl$ are consistent with the theoretical predictions of Karplus[62] for long range coupling in π-electron systems. The magnitude of these coupling constants is explained in terms of hyperconjugation, structures II and III being considered important valence bond resonance structures

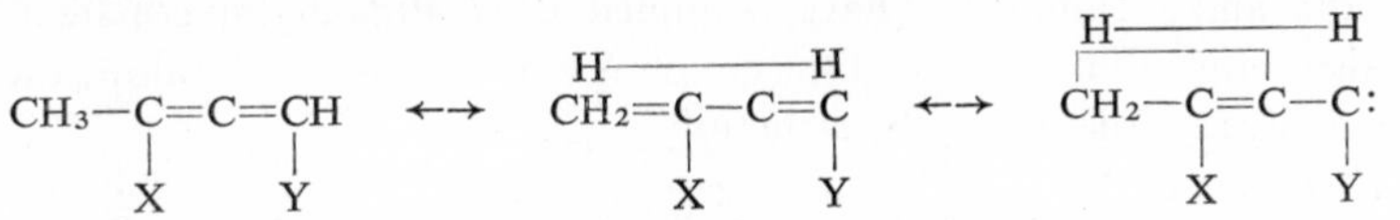

$$
\begin{array}{ccc}
CH_3-C=C=CH & \longleftrightarrow & CH_2=C-C=C & \longleftrightarrow & CH_2-C=C-C: \\
\quad|\quad\quad| & & \quad|\quad\quad| & & \quad|\quad\quad| \\
\quad X\quad\quad Y & & \quad X\quad\quad Y & & \quad X\quad\quad Y \\
(I) & & (II) & & (III)
\end{array}
$$

If these structures are considered then the predicted value for $J_{1,4}$ of 3·9 cycles sec^{-1} calculated by Karplus would be reduced and might agree more closely with the experimental value of $J_{1,4}$ (3·0 cycles sec^{-1})[176, 62].

In vinyl formate (IV) several long range H—H coupling constants have been detected[371]: $J_{14} = 0·6$, $J_{24} = 1·7$, $J_{34} = 0·8$ cycles sec^{-1}. The π-electron

$$
\begin{array}{c}
H_3 \\
\quad\quad C=C \\
H_2 \\
\end{array}
\begin{array}{c}
O \quad H_4 \\
\quad C \\
H_1 \quad || \\
O
\end{array}
\quad (IV)
$$

system appears to propagate such couplings and it should be noted that "*trans*" oriented hydrogen nuclei are coupled to a larger extent than "*cis*" oriented nuclei. Banwell and Sheppard[34] have noted that long range coupling in olefinic systems appears to operate most effectively between hydrogen nuclei separated by the "straightest" zigzag bond paths (as is the case in vinyl formate).

Double irradiation experiments have shown that the olefinic hydrogen nuclei in cyclohexene are coupled with the hydrogen nuclei in both the α- and β-methylene groups in the ring[372]. A similar state of affairs does not appear to exist in cyclopentene.

There are several examples of long range coupling constants which cannot be explained completely in terms of $\sigma-\pi$ interaction[34, 262] (see Section 5.5). Examples include the long range coupling constants observed in substituted furans (Section 10.16), quinolines (10.20) and pyridines (10.18).

10.8 MISCELLANEOUS OLEFINES

10.8.1 Conjugated Dienes[460]

We have already seen that the M.O. treatment of McConnell[33] for calculating spin–spin coupling constants between hydrogen nuclei (see Chapter 5) leads to positive signs for all long range H—H coupling constants. This is in contradiction with the results obtained using the Dirac vector model which predicts an alternation of sign of the coupling constant along a chain of carbon atoms[178, 35]. The results of valence bond theory[179] predict that spin–spin interactions via a π-electron system in an even alternate hydrocarbon chain will result in

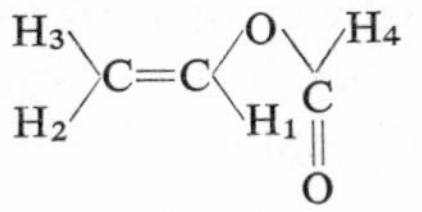

positive coupling constants between hydrogen nuclei separated by an odd number of C—C bonds and negative values for those separated by even numbers.

Alexander[125] and other workers[124] have fully analysed the ^1H resonance spectrum of butene-1 and they have found a negative coupling constant between the hydrogen nuclei on the 1- and 3-carbon atoms.

Elvidge and Jackman[172] have examined *cis-cis*-dimethylmuconate and they have also shown that the sign of the coupling constant alternates along the chain. This conjugated diene has the structure

$$CH_3OOC.\ \overset{1}{C}H{=}\overset{2}{C}H{-}\overset{3}{C}H{=}\overset{4}{C}H.\ COOCH_3$$

The coupling constants for this molecule are $J_{12} = +11{\cdot}8$, $J_{13} = -1{\cdot}3$ and $J_{23} = 11{\cdot}3$ cycles sec^{-1} and similar values of the coupling constants are observed in the other isomers of this molecule.

10.8.2 *Metal Alkene Derivatives*

Metal Vinyls. There has been considerable interest in the NMR spectra of metal alkyl compounds, especially in attempts to obtain information concerning the nature of the metal–carbon bonds in such compounds. Several metal vinyl derivatives have been examined and Tables 10.26 and 10.45 give the ob-

TABLE 10.45 THE ^1H CHEMICAL SHIFTS OF SOME METAL VINYL DERIVATIVES[135]

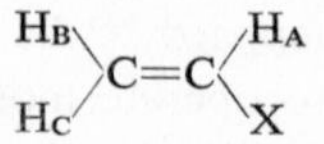

Compound	Chemical shifts† ppm		
	H_A	H_B	H_C
Divinylmercury	−5·87	−5·07	−4·53
Tetravinyltin	−4·79	−4·60	−4·15
Trivinylaluminium etherate	−4·79	−4·54	−4·18

† Chemical shifts measured relative to cyclohexane external reference.

served NMR parameters in some of these compounds[135, 136, 152]. It can be seen that the ^1H resonance chemical shifts show no simple correlation with the electronegativities of the metal concerned. The high shielding of the vinyl hydrogen nuclei in trivinylaluminium etherate is consistent with the low electronegativity of aluminium, but the large differences in chemical shifts in the vinyl groups of the tin and mercury derivatives (which have similar electronegativities in the Sn(IV) and the Hg(II) states) cannot be explained easily[135]. Variations in the diamagnetic susceptibilities of the metals could be a possible explanation of the anomalous shifts.

Metal alkenes of mercury[135], tin[135] and thallium[423] have been investigated by NMR and the following values for the metal hydrogen coupling constants have been obtained[135].

		Cycles sec^{-1}		
		$J^{cis}_{XH_1}$	$J^{trans}_{XH_2}$	$J^{gem}_{XH_3}$
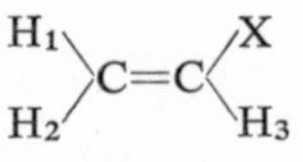	$(CH_2{=}CH)_2Hg$	159·6	295·5	128·5
	$(CH_2{=}CH)_2Sn$	90·6	183·1	98·3
	$(CH_2{=}CH)_2Tl^+$	805	1618	842
	$(CH_2{=}CH)Tl^{2+}$	1806	3750	2004

The *trans* X—H coupling constants are the largest, as are the *trans* H—H coupling constants in vinyl systems, but the *gem*- and *cis*-X–H coupling constants are of approximately the same value, unlike the analogous H—H coupling constants.

Vinyl lithium[136] gives rise to a conventional ABC type hydrogen resonance spectrum which has been assigned with the aid of empirical correlations relating the electronegativity of the vinyl substituent with the H—H spin coupling constants. The spectral parameters obtained from the analysis of the ^{1}H resonance spectrum are

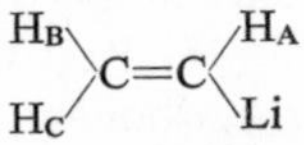

$\delta_A = 0 \quad \delta_B = +0{\cdot}511 \quad \delta_C = +1{\cdot}19$ ppm

$J_{AB} = 19{\cdot}3 \quad J_{AC} = 23{\cdot}9 \quad J_{BC} = 7{\cdot}1$ cycles sec^{-1}

This assignment implies that the vinyl hydrogen adjacent to the lithium (H_A) is the least shielded, which would not be expected on simple inductive grounds. Induced electronic currents might well play a major role in the shielding of the H_A hydrogen nucleus. The NMR spectrum of allyl lithium has been examined and reveals that the compound exists as a rapidly interconverting mixture of allylic isomers at room temperature. Similar behaviour is shown by allyl magnesium bromide (see Section 10.3.3).

Vinyl silicon derivatives have also been examined and the following are typical of the vinyl H—H coupling constants evaluated[180, 443].

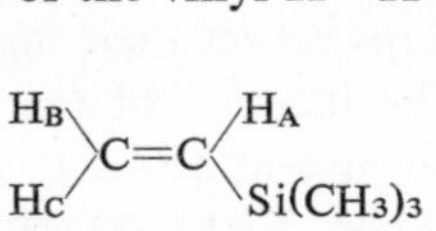

$J_{AB} = 14{\cdot}6 \quad J_{AC} = 20{\cdot}4 \quad J_{BC} = 3{\cdot}8$ cycles sec^{-1}

Cyclopentadienyl Derivatives. Ferrocene is known to have a sandwich structure (I) with both cyclopentadienyl rings freely rotating about the five-fold axis and this structure is consistent with the ^{1}H resonance spectrum which features one main absorption band[181]. The hydrogen resonance spectra of $Sn(C_5H_5)_2$ and $Pb(C_5H_5)_2$ similarly show only single absorption bands (4·38 and 4·83 ppm to low fields of cyclohexane reference respectively)[182]. If the molecules had a σ-bonded structure (II), the cyclopentadienyl rings might be expected to show complex spectra due to the presence of magnetically non-equivalent nuclei in the ring. However, a molecule such as π—$C_5H_5(\sigma$—$C_5H_5)Fe(CO)_2$ shows only two absorption bands in its hydrogen resonance spectrum—one for each type of C_5H_5 ring[181].

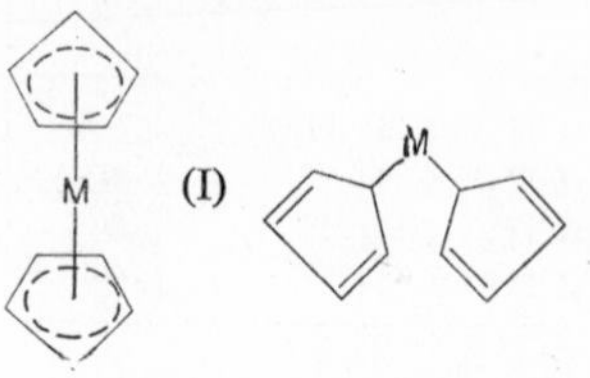

Likewise $Hg(C_5H_5)_2$, which is thought to have a linear σ-bonded structure also shows a single hydrogen resonance signal[183]. Hence the appearance of a single absorption band in the ^1H resonance spectrum of a cyclopentadienyl derivative cannot be taken as definite evidence of a π-bonded structure. The failure to observe a complex hydrogen resonance spectrum for some σ-bonded cyclopentadienyl derivatives could indicate that the metal atom is involved in a 1,2-rearrangement with the C_5H_5 ring at a rate sufficient to render the ring hydrogen nuclei equivalent[181]. Compounds which are known to have π-bonded C_5H_5 rings attached to a transition metal have a single absorption band in the range +2·5 to 3·1 ppm from a benzene reference signal: the hydrogen nuclei in σ-bonded C_5H_5 groups are less shielded[181]. The ^1H resonance spectrum of π-cyclopentadienyl cyclopentadiene rhenium dicarbonyl $C_{10}H_{10}Re(CO)_2$ is extremely complex, containing a single absorption band for the π-bonded C_5H_5 hydrogen nuclei and five multiplets for the remaining cyclopentadiene ring which is neither π- nor σ-bonded to the rhenium but is attached by virtue of the donor properties of one of its double bonds[184].

Several workers[185, 461, 483, 484] have examined many other transition metal cyclopentadienyl derivatives and they have shown their ^1H resonance spectra to be consistent with the structures indicated by other techniques.

10.8.3 Methyl Groups in Conjugated Polyenes

A comprehensive study of the methyl group ^1H resonance chemical shifts for 64 substituted conjugated polyenes has been undertaken by Barber and co-workers[186]. The band positions of the methyl groups reflect their molecular environments and useful information concerning the location of the methyl groups in the molecules can be obtained. Methyl groups attached to olefinic carbon atoms normally have tau values in the region 8·30–8·40. However, the methyl groups on non-terminal double bonded carbon atoms of a polyene chain absorb in the region $\tau = 7{\cdot}95$ to $8{\cdot}15$ (terminal methyl groups are slightly more shielded, $\tau = \sim 8{\cdot}2$). A good example of a polyene containing both terminal and in-chain methyl substituents is lycopene. The structure of lycopene (I) and the chemical shifts of the various methyl groups are indicated below.

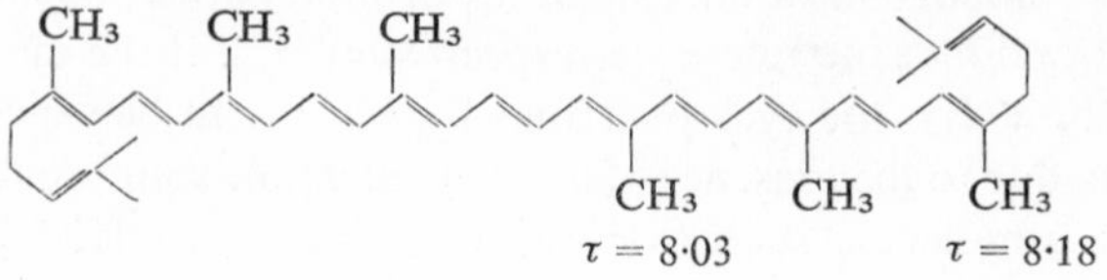

(I)

10.8.4 Induced Ring Currents in Annulenes

Annulenes are cyclic molecules having alternating single and double bonds in their ring skeleton. There is a possibility that molecules such as [14] annulene (I) might

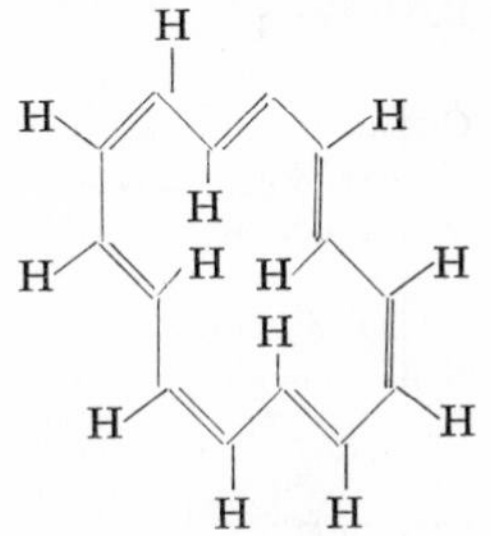

(I)

sustain a ring current around their cyclic conjugated structures thus showing aromatic behaviour (see Section 4.5). Such a ring current would result in the inner hydrogen nuclei being highly shielded and the outer hydrogen nuclei being at unusually low fields. The NMR ^{1}H spectrum of [14] annulene consists of a single absorption band with a chemical shift similar to that of the olefinic hydrogen nuclei in cyclo-octatriene, suggesting that the compound is not aromatic(366). However, in the ^{1}H resonance spectrum of [18] annulene (II) two broad absorption bands, one for the inner and one for the outer hydrogen nuclei are obtained ($\tau = 1{\cdot}1$ and $11{\cdot}8$) indicating this molecule to be aromatic in character(366).

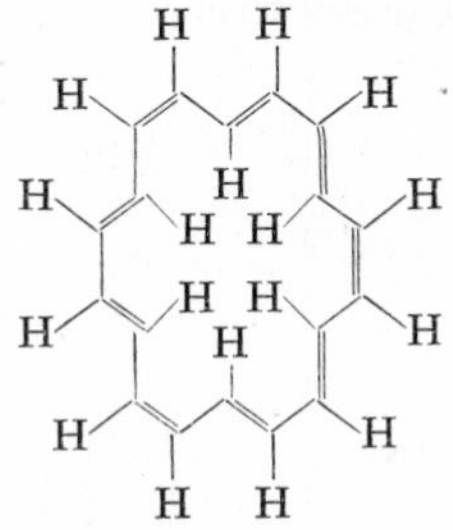

(II)

Some dehydro annulenes have also been shown to have aromatic character by means of their ^{1}H resonance spectra(366).

ACETYLENES

10.9 Acetylene and Related Molecules

The anomalously high shielding of acetylenic hydrogen nuclei—intermediate between paraffinic and ethylenic hydrogen shielding—has been the subject of several theoretical investigations and it is now well established that the neighbour diamagnetic anisotropic effect of the triple bond causes this increased shielding (see Section 4.4). Measurement of the τ-values of acetylenic hydrogen nuclei reveal them to have similar chemical shifts to methylene and methine hydrogen nuclei (see Table 10.46) and thus the NMR detection of acetylenic hydrogen nuclei can be a difficult process. Fortunately, however, acetylenic compounds show marked solvent shifts which can be used to characterise them. For example, the addition of pyridine to a dilute solution of a monosubstituted

TABLE 10.46 THE ^{1}H CHEMICAL SHIFTS OF SOME ACETYLENIC COMPOUNDS EXAMINED AS DILUTE SOLUTIONS IN CARBON TETRACHLORIDE AND CYCLOHEXANE[(189)]

Compound	Chemical shift		Coupling constant
	$\equiv$CH τ	—CH_2 τ	J_{HH} cycles sec^{-1}
$HC\equiv CCH_2Cl$ †	7·76	6·06	2·6
$HC\equiv CCH_2Br$ †	7·76	6·32	2·7
$HC\equiv CCH_2I$ †	7·81	6·48	2·8
$HC\equiv CCH_2OH$ ‡	7·67		
$HC\equiv CC(CH_3){=}CH_2$ ‡	7·29		
$HC\equiv CC_6H_5$ ‡	7·07		

† Examined as dilute solutions in cyclohexane (reference 189).
‡ Examined as dilute solutions in carbon tetrachloride (Appendix B).

TABLE 10.47 THE ^{1}H CHEMICAL SHIFTS AND SPIN COUPLING CONSTANTS OF SEVERAL MONOSUBSTITUTED ACETYLENES EXAMINED AS PURE LIQUIDS[(188)]

Compound	Cycles sec^{-1}	Chemical shift† of $\equiv$ CH ppm	"τ" ppm	State
$HC\equiv C\cdot CH_2Cl$	2·65	−1·19	7·37	liquid
$HC\equiv C\cdot CH_2Br$	2·70	−1·31	7·25	liquid
$HC\equiv C\cdot CH_2OH$	2·50	−1·32	7·24	liquid
$HC\equiv CCH_2$—N<CO—/CO— 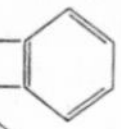	2·55	−0·375	8·18	dil. solution in benzene
$HC\equiv C\cdot CH_2$—O— 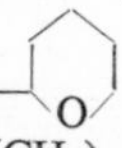	2·51	−1·19	7·37	liquid
$HC\equiv C\cdot CH_2$—$N(CH_3)_2$	2·51	−1·02	7·54	liquid
$HC\equiv C$—CH_2—$N(C_2H_5)_2$	2·55			liquid
$HC\equiv C\cdot CH_2\overset{+}{N}$(Me)(Me)(Et) I^-	2·60			solution in H_2O
$HC\equiv C\cdot CH(OH)\cdot CH_3$	2·15	−1·23	7·33	liquid
$HC\equiv C\cdot CH(OH)\cdot C_6H_5$	2·20	−1·02	7·54	CCl_4 solution
$HC\equiv C\cdot CH(CH_3)N(C_2H_5)_2$	2·20			liquid
$HC\equiv C$—$CH(CH_3)N$ 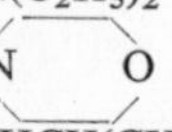 O	2·10			liquid
$HC\equiv C\cdot CH(CH_3)NHCH(CH_3)_2$	2·20	−1·21	7·35	liquid
$HC\equiv C\cdot CH(CH_3)NH$ n-C_4H_9	2·10			solution in CCl_4
$HC\equiv C\cdot CH(CH_3)N(CH_3)_2$	2·00			solution in CCl_4

† Chemical shifts were measured in ppm from cyclohexane internal reference.

$$"\tau" = 8{\cdot}56 + \delta_{C_6H_{12}}.$$

acetylene in carbon tetrachloride results in a deshielding of ~1 ppm of the acetylenic hydrogen nuclei in most cases[187].

Table 10.47 gives the chemical shifts of the acetylenic hydrogen nuclei in a series of monosubstituted acetylenes examined as pure liquids[188]: the variation in chemical shift extends over a very small range (~0·3 ppm) which indicates the acetylenic hydrogen shielding to be fairly insensitive to the nature of the substituent if the effects of intermolecular interaction are assumed to be similar in the different compounds. Only a limited amount of data is available for acetylenes examined in dilute solutions of inert solvents (see Table 10.46): the smallest chemical shifts appear to be in molecules where the triple bond is in conjugation with other electronic systems.

10.9.1 Propargyl Halides, $XCH_2C{\equiv}CH$

Propargyl halides give rise to two hydrogen resonance absorption multiplets, a doublet and a triplet in the intensity ratio 2 : 1. A typical example is the ^{1}H resonance spectrum of propargyl bromide shown in Fig. 10.21[189]. Table 10.46 includes the chemical shifts and coupling constants measured for three propargyl halides[189]. The chemical shifts of the halides were measured in dilute cyclohexane solutions from an internal tetramethylsilane reference and can reasonably be assumed to have negligible contributions from intermolecular effects. As might be expected from simple inductive considerations, the shielding of the $-CH_2X$ hydrogen nuclei decreases as the electronegativity of the halogen increases (similar behaviour to the α—CH_2 shielding in alkyl halides)[8]. Only small variations in the chemical shifts of the acetylenic hydrogen nuclei are observed when the halogen substituent is changed (~0·05 ppm). This effect is

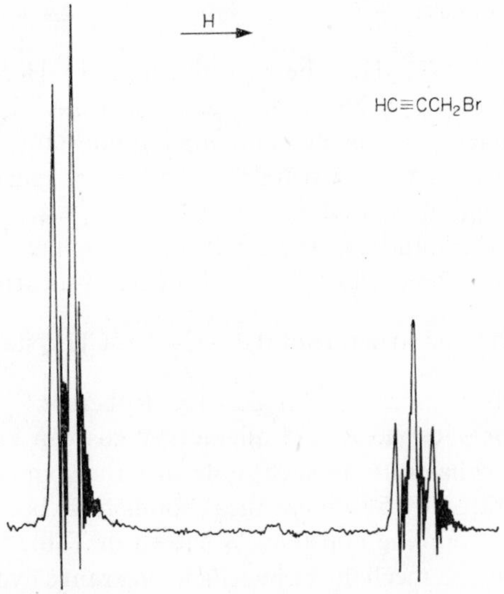

FIG. 10.21 The ^{1}H resonance spectrum of propargyl bromide at 40 Mc sec^{-1}. Whipple, Goldstein, Mandell, Reddy and McClure[189].

similar in magnitude to that caused by halogen atoms operating on the γ-hydrogen atoms in a series of n-propyl halides[8]. The three coupling constants are all equal to within the experimental error and no significance can be attached to the small differences between them.

10.10 Spin–spin Coupling Constants in Acetylenic Systems

Tables 10.46 and 10.47 list the long range H—H spin coupling constants measured in a series of acetylenic compounds (in all cases quoted the interacting nuclei are separated by four bonds). Generally, the coupling constants are found to be almost independent of the nature of saturated substituents. For example, molecules of general formula $RCH_2C{\equiv}CH$ all have J_{CH_2-CH} values of 2·5–2·7 cycles sec^{-1} whilst the spectra of $RR'CHC{\equiv}CH$ derivatives feature J_{CH-CH} values of 2·0–2·2 cycles sec^{-1}. The decrease in coupling constant upon introducing a further substituent might be due to the difference in bond angles[188]. Karplus[62] maintains that π-electrons play a significant role in H—H coupling in ethylenic, allenic and acetylenic hydrogen systems and he has shown that if π-electrons are involved appreciably in the coupling mechanism then the sign of the H—H spin coupling constants will be positive when the interacting nuclei are separated by an even number of carbon atoms and negative otherwise. For acetylenic systems there is quite reasonable agreement between observed long range H—H coupling constants and theoretical estimates made by Karplus, for example

	Theoretical J	Experimental J
$H{-}C{\equiv}C{-}H$	$+4{\cdot}6$	9·1
$H{-}C{\equiv}C{-}CH\!<$	$-3{\cdot}7$	$-2{\cdot}1$ to $-2{\cdot}9$
$HC{-}C{\equiv}C{-}CH\!<$	$+2{\cdot}9$	2·9 (unknown sign)

In ethyl acetylene, $HC{\equiv}CC_2H_5$, the two observed H—H coupling constants have been found to be opposite in sign, $J_{CH_3-CH_2} = +7{\cdot}2$, $J_{CH_2-CH} = -2{\cdot}4$ and $J_{CH_3-CH} = 0$ cycles sec^{-1} being the coupling constants extracted from a detailed A_2B_3C analysis of the spectrum[190]. The H—H spin coupling constant found in the spectrum of methyl acetylene[192], $J_{CH_3-CH} = 2{\cdot}8 \pm 0{\cdot}3$ cycles sec^{-1}, is similar in magnitude to the analogous coupling constant for ethyl acetylene ($J_{CH_2-CH} = -2{\cdot}4$ cycles sec^{-1}) and other substituted acetylenes. This suggests that the electronic structure of the $-\overset{|}{\underset{|}{C}}-C{\equiv}CH$ system does not change appreciably with substitution[190]. Snyder and Roberts[193] have shown that hydrogen nuclei in polyacetylenic and allenic systems can exhibit exceptional long range coupling behaviour: in such molecules the spin coupling constants between nuclei separated by 5 to 9 chemical bonds have been measured and a compilation of these coupling constants is shown in Table 5.9. There is good reason to believe that the mechanism by which long range hydrogen coupling is achieved in polyacetylenic systems depends upon hyperconjugation. This is simply an extension of the Karplus valence bond approach to the understanding of spin–spin coupling. To explain the larger long range H—H coupling constants it is postulated that in molecules of the type

$$>HC-(C\equiv C)_n-CH<$$

the following resonance structure is important

$$\begin{array}{c} H\text{————}H \\ >C=(C=C)_n=C< \end{array}$$

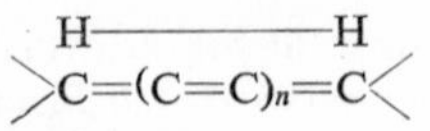

Hoffman and Gronowitz[174, 175] also believe that σ–π interactions make significant contributions to long range coupling constants and they have predicted that the coupling of methyl hydrogen nuclei to other hydrogen nuclei separated by a triple bond should be about twice the coupling between similar groups of nuclei separated by a double bond, if the hyperconjugative coupling mechanism is dominant. The prediction is in excellent agreement with the measured coupling constants. Observation of long range coupling constants in vinyl acetylenes has added further support to the theory that hyperconjugation is a major factor controlling H—H coupling in both acetylenic and olefinic systems[194, 195]. The possibility of establishing the concept

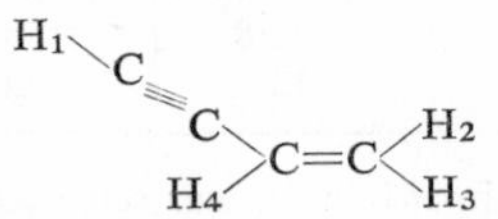

$$J_{14} = -2\cdot4 \text{ cycles sec}^{-1}$$
$$J_{12} = 0\cdot8$$
$$J_{13} = 1\cdot0$$

of hyperconjugation by NMR measurements will no doubt stimulate a more intense interest in long range coupling constants of this type.

10.11 SOLVENT EFFECTS ON THE CHEMICAL SHIFTS OF HYDROGEN NUCLEI IN ACETYLENIC MOLECULES

Acetylene is capable of self-association[196] and it can also form weak hydrogen bonds with molecules containing electronegative centres (such as acetone, acetonitrile and pyridine)[187, 189, 197]. It is not surprising, therefore, that the ¹H resonance spectra of acetylene and its derivatives are markedly dependent upon solvent effects. A detailed account of such effects is given in Section 10.39.

AROMATIC MOLECULES

10.12 BENZENE DERIVATIVES

10.12.1 The Effects of Solvents on the Resonance Spectra of Aromatic Compounds

Although a great deal of effort has been expended on the study of the shielding of ring hydrogen nuclei in substituted aromatic molecules many of the results are of little theoretical significance due to the fact that no attempt was made to eliminate intermolecular effects on the shielding. Such effects can be minimised by examining samples as infinitely dilute solutions in inert solvents. Before entering into a discussion of the NMR spectral parameters of aromatic molecules one should examine the extent to which intermolecular effects can influence the spectra of such molecules (see Section 10.39.2)[198–201, 207].

10.12.2 Monosubstituted Benzenes

Spiesecke and Schneider[208] have conducted a comprehensive study of the ^1H and ^{13}C resonance spectra of a series of monosubstituted benzenes with a view to reaching an understanding of the effects of substitution on the chemical

TABLE 10.48 ^1H CHEMICAL SHIFTS (IN CYCLES SEC^{-1} RELATIVE TO BENZENE) OF SOME MONOSUBSTITUTED BENZENES[208] EXAMINED AS 5 MOLE PER CENT SOLUTIONS IN CYCLOHEXANE AT 60 MC SEC^{-1}

Substituent	^1H shift relative to benzene		
	ortho	*meta*	*para*
F	+18·5	+ 1·4	+13·0
Cl	− 1·2	+ 1·5	+ 7·0
Br	−13·4	+ 5·1	+ 1·8
I	−24·0	+15·0	+ 2·0
OCH_3	+26·0	+ 2·4	+22·0
NH_2	+45·3	+12·2	+37·5
$N(CH_3)_2$	+36·0	+ 6·0	+36·9
CHO	−34·8	−12·8	−16·5
NO_2	−56·9	−12·5	−20·0

Positive shifts indicate greater hydrogen nuclear screening than that in benzene: negative shifts indicate lower screening.

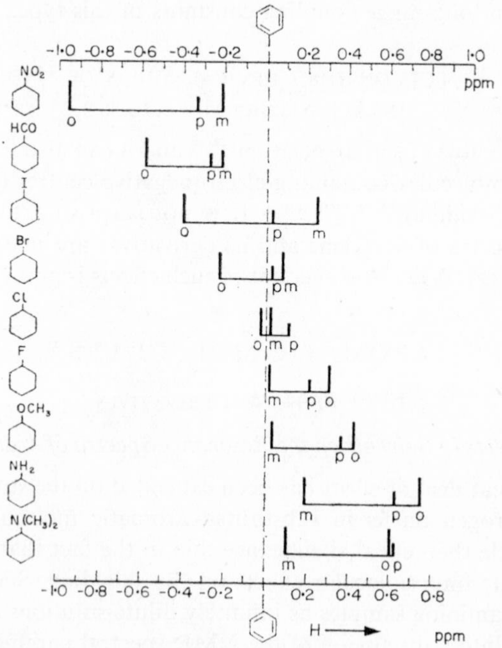

FIG. 10.22 ^1H chemical shifts in monosubstituted benzenes. Spiesecke and Schneider[208].

shifts of the molecules. By examining all molecules as 5 per cent solutions in cyclohexane they hoped to minimise any intermolecular effects. Earlier work on this class of compounds(154, 156, 198, 203, 204, 209, 210) suggested that the shielding of the ring hydrogen nuclei must be interpreted in terms of both inductive and resonance effects of the substituents. Spiesecke and Schneider(208) found it necessary to introduce considerations of magnetic anisotropy to explain fully their chemical shift data. Table 10.48 shows the ^{1}H chemical shifts for the *ortho-*, *meta-* and *para*-hydrogen nuclei in the monosubstituted benzenes

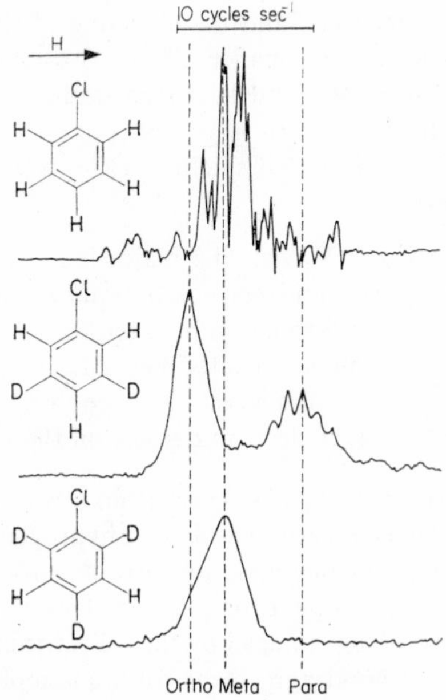

FIG. 10.23 The ^{1}H resonance spectra of chlorobenzene and two deuterated chlorobenzenes at 60 Mc sec^{-1}. Spiesecke and Schneider(208).

examined. The assignments of the ^{1}H chemical shifts were made with the assistance of specifically deuterated molecules. Table 12.14 gives the analogous list of ^{13}C chemical shifts for these molecules. The ^{1}H chemical shift data are presented in diagrammatic form in Fig. 10.22. A typical series of ^{1}H resonance spectra obtained for chlorobenzene and two deuterated chlorobenzenes is shown in Fig. 10.23(208). Deuteration results in a certain amount of line broadening due to unresolved spin–spin multiplet structure and also to quadrupole broadening effects.

From the ^{13}C resonance measurements one can deduce the relative electron densities at each carbon atom. Changes in the substituent will be accompanied by resonance effects which are thought mainly to influence the π electronic distribution of the system which in turn affects the electron density around the carbon atoms. The results of Spiesecke and Schneider allow one to estimate the extent to which changes in the electron density at the carbon atoms influence the shielding of hydrogen nuclei to which they are attached.

Shielding of ortho-Hydrogen Nuclei. The shielding of *ortho*-hydrogen nuclei in monohalobenzenes cannot be explained in terms of inductive and resonance effects alone and it is thought that the shielding is appreciably influenced by diamagnetic anisotropy effects of the substituent group, especially for the bromo- and iododerivatives where such shielding effects are expected to be large. When substituents other than the halogens are considered the diamagnetic anisotropy contribution is usually much less and the shielding of the hydrogen nuclei is then dominated by π-electron resonance effects. Strong electron-withdrawing groups cause the *ortho*-hydrogen nuclei to be deshielded (when $X = NO_2$, the *ortho*-hydrogen chemical shift is $-0{\cdot}95$ ppm) while strong electron-releasing substituents cause increased shielding ($X = NH_2$, $\delta_{ortho} = +0{\cdot}75$ ppm from benzene reference).

Shielding of para-Hydrogen Nuclei. The major factor controlling the shielding of both the *para*-hydrogen and *para*-carbon nuclei appears to be the resonance effect. A marked linear correlation between the *para*-hydrogen and *para*-carbon chemical shifts in monosubstituted benzenes has been pointed out by Spiesecke and Schneider[(208)]. This suggests that they are controlled by the same factor, namely changes in the π-electron density on the *para*-carbon atom.

Shielding of meta-Hydrogen Nuclei. There is no obvious correlation between the chemical shifts of the *meta*-carbon and *meta*-hydrogen nuclei and it appears that inductive, resonance and magnetic anisotropic effects are all of some importance in the shielding of *meta*-hydrogen nuclei. Estimates of the contribution to the shielding of *meta*-hydrogen nuclei by the "electric field" effect postulated by Buckingham[(27)] are in good agreement for some molecules (nitrobenzene) but poor in others (iodo- and bromobenzene). Spiesecke and Schneider consider that for the *ortho*- and *para*-hydrogen nuclei, the shielding from the "electric field" effect will be overshadowed by other effects. Although the *meta*-hydrogen nuclei are shielded to some extent by the electric field effect, this effect will have negligible influence on the shielding of the *meta*-carbon nuclei.

10.12.3 Correlation of ^{1}H *Chemical Shifts in Monosubstituted Benzenes with Hammett* σ*-Constants*

The chemical reactivity at *meta*- and *para*-positions in various substituted benzenes can be expressed in terms of Hammett σ-constants[(202)]. If these constants are related in any way to the electron densities at the *meta*- and *para*-carbon atoms one might expect Hammett σ constants (or the modified resonance and inductive components of the σ constants as proposed by Taft[(140)]) to show a correlation with the ^{13}C and ^{1}H chemical shifts of the nuclei involved. Many investigators have attempted to show that such a correlation exists[(140, 154, 156, 203–206)]. Spiesecke and Schneider have considered critically the extent to which a correlation of this type is to be expected in monosubstituted benzenes. Hammett constants are obtained using disubstituted benzenes and would therefore not be strictly applicable to the monosubstituted derivatives. Furthermore, Hammett constants are derived from kinetic data and would be expected to be related to the electron distribution in some transition-state complex rather than that in the unperturbed ground-state molecule. Finally, contributions to the shielding of hydrogen and carbon nuclei need not necessarily have their origin in the electron density around the nuclei (for example, diamagnetic an-

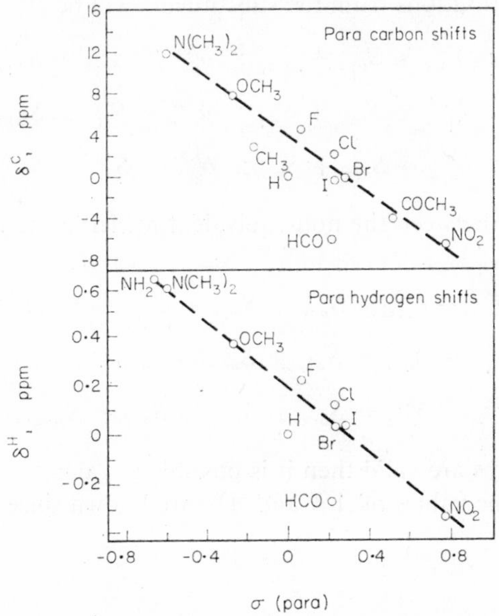

FIG. 10.24 Graphs of the *para*-^{1}H and *para*-^{13}C chemical shifts for monosubstituted benzenes against the Hammett σ-constants. Spiesecke and Schneider[(208)].

isotropic and paramagnetic contributions are possible and these will not show a correlation with chemical reactivity parameters). Despite these objections it is observed that both the *para*-^{13}C and *para*-^{1}H chemical shifts in monosubstituted benzenes show a roughly linear correlation with the Hammett σ-constants (see Fig. 10.24). The chemical shifts of nuclei at the *meta*-position show a very poor correlation with Hammett and Taft σ-constants.

Previous to the study of Spiesecke and Schneider, Corio and Dailey[(156)] had examined an extensive series of monosubstituted benzenes in an attempt to evaluate the relative electron densities at the *ortho*-, *meta*- and *para*-positions to the various substituents. Unfortunately, no account was taken of the effects of intermolecular interactions in this work and it is difficult to assess the theoretical significance of their measurements.

10.12.4 Disubstituted Benzene Derivatives

Diehl(211) has shown that the ^{1}H chemical shifts of the ring hydrogen nuclei in *meta*- and *para*-disubstituted benzenes measured in dilute hexane solution (5 mole per cent) can be calculated empirically by assuming the substituent effects on the chemical shifts to be additive. The substituent effects of a single substituent X (in the molecule C_6H_5X) at the *ortho*-, *meta*- and *para*-positions are respectively denoted by $S_{o;x}$, $S_{m;x}$ and $S_{p;x}$. Similarly for a substituent Y, (C_6H_5Y), the effects are $S_{o;y}$ $S_{m;y}$ and $S_{p;y}$. If these effects are additive then for the three *para*-disubstituted benzenes involving the substituents X, Y and Z the chemical shift contributions from the substituents will be

$$p\text{-}C_6H_4XY: \ \delta^{XY}_{o;x} = S_{o;x} + S_{m;y}; \quad \delta^{XY}_{o;y} = S_{o;y} + S_{m;x} \tag{10.12}$$

$$p\text{-}C_6H_4YZ: \ \delta^{YZ}_{o;y} = S_{o;y} + S_{m;z}; \quad \delta^{YZ}_{o;z} = S_{o;z} + S_{m;y} \tag{10.13}$$

$$p\text{-}C_6H_4XZ: \ \delta^{XZ}_{o;x} = S_{o;x} + S_{m;z}; \quad \delta^{XZ}_{o;z} = S_{o;z} + S_{m;x} \tag{10.14}$$

and the chemical shifts between the non-equivalent nuclei in the molecule can be written as

$$\Delta^{XY} = \delta^{XY}_{o;x} - \delta^{XY}_{o;y} = S_{o;x} + S_{m;y} - S_{o;y} - S_{m;x}.$$

$$\Delta^{YZ} = \delta^{YZ}_{o;y} - \delta^{YZ}_{o;z} = S_{o;y} + S_{m;z} - S_{o;z} - S_{m;y}.$$

$$\Delta^{XZ} = \delta^{XZ}_{o;x} - \delta^{XZ}_{o;z} = S_{o;x} + S_{m;z} - S_{o;z} - S_{m;x}.$$

If the above relationships are valid then it is possible to calculate the chemical shift difference Δ^{XY} if the values of Δ^{XZ} and Δ^{YZ} are known since

$$\Delta^{XY} = \Delta^{XZ} - \Delta^{YZ}$$

TABLE 10.49 OBSERVED AND CALCULATED ^{1}H CHEMICAL SHIFT DIFFERENCES (ppm) BETWEEN THE NON-EQUIVALENT HYDROGEN NUCLEI IN A SERIES OF *para*-DISUBSTITUTED BENZENES(211), p—C_6H_4XY

Substituent		Δ^{XY} (observed)	Δ^{XY} (calculated)	Substituent		Δ^{XY} (observed)	Δ^{XY} (calculated)
X	Y			X	Y		
Cl	F	−0·32	−0·31	CN	CH_3	−0·23	−0·26
Br	F	−0·52	−0·53	NO_2	F	−1·10	−1·00
Br	Cl	−0·22	−0·21	NO_2	CH_3	−0·82	−0·83
I	F	−0·85	−0·86	OCH_3	F	+0·11	+0·10
I	Cl	−0·53	−0·53	OCH_3	Br	+0·62	+0·63
I	Br	−0·33	−0·33	NH_2	F	+0·30	+0·22
CH_3	F	−0·18	−0·17	NH_2	Cl	+0·58	+0·54
CH_3	Br	+0·37	+0·35	NH_2	Br	+0·76	+0·68
CH_3	Cl	+0·15	+0·14	NH_2	I	+1·04	+1·10
CH_3	I	+0·68	+0·69	OH	Cl	+0·45	+0·48
CN	F	−0·52	−0·42	OH	Br	+0·67	+0·66
CN	Cl	−0·11	−0·09	OH	CH_3	+0·22	+0·29

Table 10.49 gives a list of the observed and calculated chemical shift differences between the non-equivalent hydrogen nuclei in a series of *para*-disubstituted benzenes: the agreement is seen to be excellent for most of the molecules examined[(211)]. The observed ^{1}H chemical shifts are all quoted with reference to the absorption signal from a 5 mole per cent solution of benzene in hexane. (The actual chemical shifts were measured from a chloroform external reference and the chemical shifts then transferred to a scale corresponding to benzene internal reference. Although this involves making bulk diamagnetic susceptibility corrections, it avoids the danger of intermolecular interactions which would be present if benzene is used directly as an internal reference.)

It is not possible to calculate absolute values for the substituent effects from a consideration of *para*-disubstituted benzenes alone. To do this, one needs to consider the chemical shifts in *meta*-disubstituted benzenes in terms of substituent effects $S_{o;x}$, $S_{m;y}$ etc. If the *meta*-disubstituted molecule, m—$C_6H_4X_2$, is designated

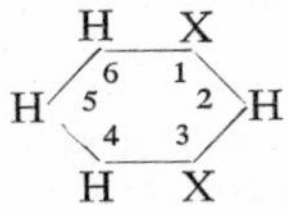

then the chemical shift contributions due to substituent effects can be written

$$\delta_2 = 2S_{o;x}$$

$$\delta_4 = \delta_6 = S_{o;x} + S_{p;x}$$

$$\delta_5 = 2S_{m;x}$$

If we consider the *para*-disubstituted molecule, p—$C_6H_4X_2$

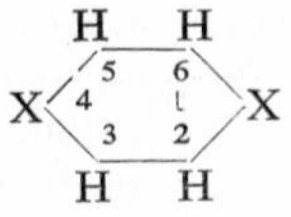

then the chemical shifts of the ring hydrogen nuclei in terms of the previously discussed contributions will be

$$\delta_2 = \delta_3 = \delta_5 = \delta_6 = S_{o;x} + S_{m;x} = \delta_H.$$

Hence, these relationships provide a simple check on the additivity concept since the chemical shift of the hydrogen nuclei in p—$C_6H_4X_2$ should be equal to the mean of the chemical shifts δ_2 and δ_5 in the m—$C_6H_4X_2$ molecule if the additivity concept is correct. Examination of Table 10.50 clearly indicates that this state of affairs prevails in the molecules examined.

To calculate absolute values of the substituent chemical shift contributions it is necessary to examine *meta*-disubstituted molecules of the type m—$C_6H_4X_2$ and m—$C_6H_4Y_2$; $S_{o;x}$ and $S_{m;x}$ values can then be obtained directly from the chemical shifts δ_2 and δ_5. Knowing a value for $S_{o;x}$, the chemical shift contribution $S_{p;x}$ can be derived from δ_4. In Table 10.51 the absolute chemical shift contributions $S_{o;Br}$, $S_{m;Br}$ and $S_{p;Br}$, calculated from the measured chemical shifts in *m*-dibromobenzene are given: a brief examination of the values will clarify the simple arithmetical manipulation involved.

Table 10.52 lists the chemical shifts of an extensive series of p—C_6H_4XY derivatives which can be used in conjunction with the absolute values of sub-

TABLE 10.50 OBSERVED AND CALCULATED ^{1}H CHEMICAL SHIFTS (ppm) IN *para*-$C_6H_4X_2$ MOLECULES (5 mole per cent IN HEXANE)[211]

Substituent	$m-C_6H_4X_2$ $\frac{1}{2}(\delta_2 + \delta_5)$ ppm	$p-C_6H_4X_2$ δ_H ppm
Br	$(-0{\cdot}44 + 0{\cdot}21)/2 = -0{\cdot}115$	$-0{\cdot}09$
Cl	$(-0{\cdot}10 + 0{\cdot}08)/2 = -0{\cdot}01$	$+0{\cdot}01$
OCH_3	$(+0{\cdot}76 + 0{\cdot}17)/2 = +0{\cdot}465$	$+0{\cdot}49$
CO_2CH_3	$(-1{\cdot}49 - 0{\cdot}19)/2 = -0{\cdot}84$	$-0{\cdot}86$

TABLE 10.51 ABSOLUTE CONTRIBUTIONS TO THE ^{1}H CHEMICAL SHIFTS OF THE RING HYDROGEN NUCLEI FOR $S_{o;\,Br}$, $S_{m;\,Br}$ AND $S_{p;\,Br}$

Observed chemical shifts (ppm)	Calculated substituent effect (ppm)
$\delta_2 = -0{\cdot}44$	$S_{o;\,Br} = -0{\cdot}22$
$\delta_4 = \delta_6 = -0{\cdot}16$	$S_{p;\,Br} = +0{\cdot}06$
$\delta_5 = +0{\cdot}21$	$S_{m;\,Br} = +0{\cdot}11$

TABLE 10.52 ^{1}H CHEMICAL SHIFTS (ppm) OF SEVERAL *para*-C_6H_4XY TYPE COMPOUNDS (5 mole per cent IN HEXANE[211])

Substituent X	Substituent Y	$\delta^{xy}_{o;\,x}$	$\delta^{xy}_{o;\,y}$	Substituent X	Substituent Y	$\delta^{xy}_{o;\,x}$	$\delta^{xy}_{o;\,y}$
F	F	+0·31	+0·31	Br	OCH_3	−0·08	+0·54
F	Cl	+0·25	−0·07	I	I	−0·14	−0·14
F	Br	+0·36	−0·16	I	CH_3	−0·30	+0·38
F	I	+0·41	−0·44	CH_3	CH_3	+0·24	+0·24
F	CH_3	+0·41	+0·23	CH_3	CN	+0·05	−0·18
F	CN	+0·12	−0·40	CH_3	NO_2	−0·03	−0·85
F	NO_2	+0·11	−0·99	OCH_3	OCH_3	+0·49	+0·49
F	OCH_3	+0·35	+0·46	F	NH_2	+0·51	+0·81
Cl	Cl	+0·01	+0·01	Cl	NH_2	+0·16	+0·74
Cl	Br	+0·08	−0·14	Br	NH_2	−0·03	+0·73
Cl	I	+0·19	−0·34	I	NH_2	−0·19	+0·85
Cl	CH_3	+0·09	+0·24	OH	Cl	+0·55	+0·10
Cl	CN	−0·17	−0·28	OH	Br	+0·62	−0·05
Br	Br	−0·09	−0·09	OH	CH_3	+0·55	+0·33
Br	I	+0·02	−0·31	CO_2–CH_3	CO_2–CH_3	−0·86	−0·86
Br	CH_3	−0·08	+0·29				

stituent effects found from the m—$C_6H_4X_2$ molecules and equations (10.12), (10.13) and (10.14), to predict the absolute values for the chemical shift contributions for many more substituents. In Table 10.53 a list of calculated values of the absolute contributions to the chemical shifts of aromatic ring hydrogen chemical shifts for various substituents is presented. Using these values, surprisingly good agreement between calculated and observed chemical shifts for *meta*-disubstituted derivatives has been obtained. This can best be demonstrated by considering the molecule *m*-chloronitrobenzene

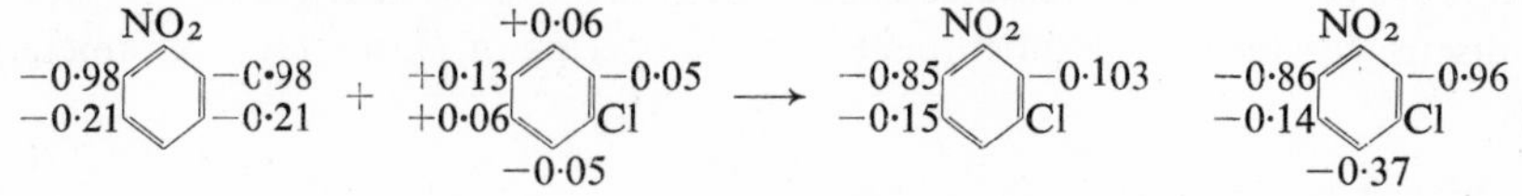

Calculated Observed

TABLE 10.53 ABSOLUTE CONTRIBUTIONS TO THE ^{1}H CHEMICAL SHIFTS (ppm) OF THE RING HYDROGEN NUCLEI FOR SOME SUBSTITUENTS[211]

Sub-stituent	S_o	S_m	S_p	Sub-stituent	S_o	S_m	S_p
NH_2	+0·68	+0·22		Br	−0·22	+0·11	+0·06
OH	+0·50	+0·16		CN	−0·35	−0·13	
OCH_3	+0·42	+0·10	+0·33	I	−0·41	+0·22	
F	+0·25	+0·01		CO_2CH_3	−0·74	−0·10	−0·20
CH_3	+0·17	+0·13	+0·17	NO_2	−0·98	−0·21	
Cl	−0·05	+0·06	+0·13				

For *ortho*-disubstituted benzenes the agreement is much poorer and this is found to be the case in all substituted benzenes with appreciable permanent dipole moments. For example, in the compound 1,2,3-trichlorobenzene (0·8 Debyes) the calculated chemical shifts are quite different from the measured values

Calculated Observed

Conversely, in the symmetrical molecule 1,2,4,5-tetrachlorobenzene (which has no dipole moment) there is excellent agreement between observed and calculated chemical shift values

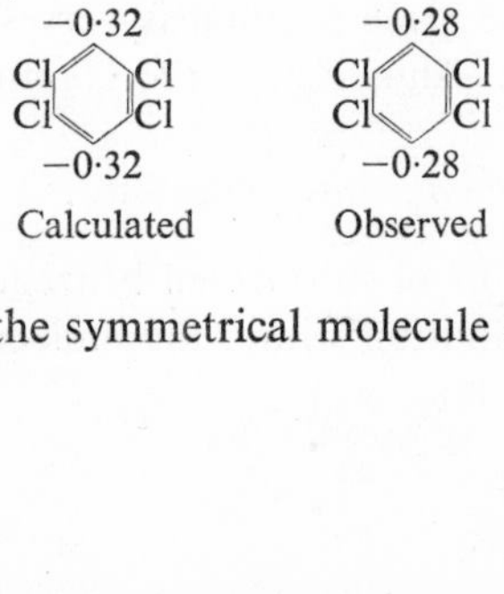

Calculated Observed

The same is also true for the symmetrical molecule mesitylene.

Diehl[211] made no attempt to interpret the benzene substituent effects in terms of the electric field produced by the permanent dipole of the aromatic molecule since this approach is known to give poor results for some substituted benzenes (e.g. halobenzenes) and furthermore does not reflect resonance effects in the benzene rings. The Buckingham approach[481] appears to be valid only if resonance effects are not large: thus, in nitrobenzene where this is the case, the values of the chemical shifts predicted by the electric field effect are in good agreement with the measured values, while in fluorobenzene—where resonance effects are large—poor predicted chemical shifts are obtained. Diehl[211] prefers to discuss his measured substituent effects in terms of Hammett σ parameters:

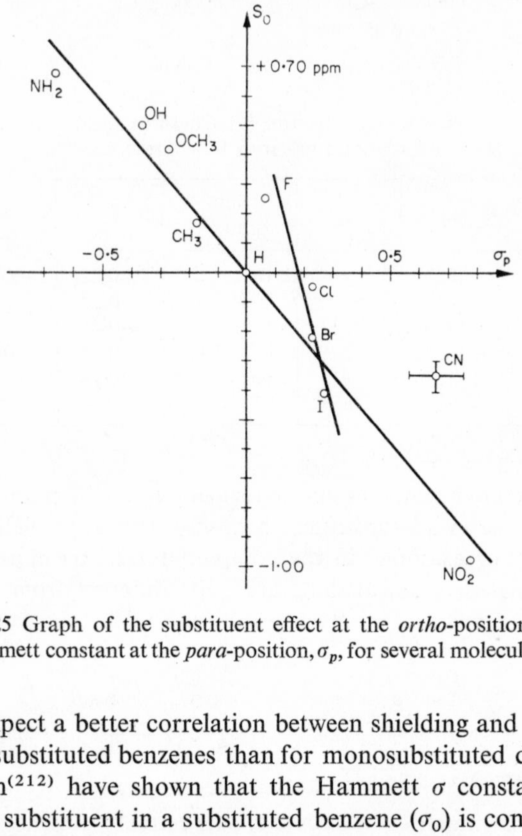

FIG. 10.25 Graph of the substituent effect at the *ortho*-position, S_0, against the Hammett constant at the *para*-position, σ_p, for several molecules. Diehl[211].

one would expect a better correlation between shielding and Hammett σ parameters for disubstituted benzenes than for monosubstituted derivatives. Farthing and Nam[212] have shown that the Hammett σ constant for the *ortho*-position to a substituent in a substituted benzene (σ_0) is composed of an electronic (σ_E) and a steric contribution (σ_S). The electronic portion (σ_E) has been shown to have its origin in both inductive (σ_I) and resonance (σ_R) effects. The electron distribution at the *ortho*-position is very similar to that at the *para*-position to the substituent. Thus if σ_p is the Hammett constant for the *para*-position then

$$\sigma_p = \sigma_E = \sigma_I + \sigma_R.$$

The chemical shift behaviour in substituted benzenes supports this interpretation of the electronic distribution within the molecules. When the substituent effect at the *ortho*-position, S_o, is plotted against σ_p most of the substituents have contributions which lie on a straight line as shown in Fig. 10.25. The halogens do not conform to this general relationship although they show a linear correlation among themselves (the gradients of the two straight lines are seen to be widely different). Another group which does not fit into the general correlation is the CN group. This behaviour is not surprising since all the groups which do not conform are those expected to show strong neighbour diamagnetic anisotropic effects at the *ortho*-position. The linear relationship for ordinary substituents can be represented by the equation

$$S_o = -1{\cdot}17\,\sigma_p.$$

Similar linear correlations are found between the substituent effects at the *meta*- and *para*-positions, S_m and S_p, and the Hammett σ_p contribution according to the equations

$$S_m = -0{\cdot}30\,\sigma_p + 0{\cdot}06$$

$$S_p = -0{\cdot}49\,\sigma_p + 0{\cdot}10.$$

Brey and Lawson[(213)] have made an attempt similar to that of Diehl to devise a scheme for predicting the chemical shifts of aromatic hydrogen nuclei in polysubstituted benzenes. Their results differ from those of Diehl[(211)] in several ways. Halogen substituents were found generally to give unsatisfactory agreement between predicted and measured chemical shifts and *meta*-disubstituted compounds were also found not to conform to the predicted additivity behaviour.

TABLE 10.54 OBSERVED AND CALCULATED ^{1}H CHEMICAL SHIFTS OF SOME SUBSTITUTED PHENOLS[(213)]

	Ring Position	Observed (ppm)	Calculated (ppm)
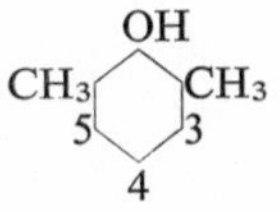	3,5	0·35	0·50
	4	0·53	0·54
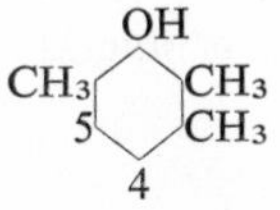	5	0·53	0·59
	4	0·75	0·77
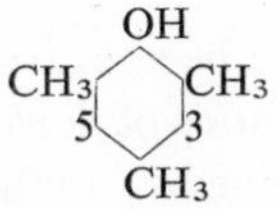	3,5	0·69	0·73
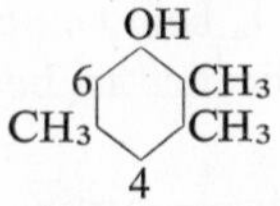	6	1·00	1·03
	4	0·85	0·91

Chemical shifts were measured in ppm from benzene external reference. Both sample and reference were examined at low dilution in CCl_4.

In many other instances the additivity approach gives excellent agreement between calculated and measured chemical shifts as can be seen from examination of Table 10.54 (the chemical shifts are referred to benzene external reference in infinitely dilute solution). They found that the chemical shifts of pentasubstituted benzenes and 2,6-disubstituted phenols cannot be predicted by the additivity method. Surprisingly, further substitution of the latter compounds seems to decrease the deviations (see Table 10.54). Smith[214] has also obtained values of S_o and S_m using a similar approach to that of Diehl: Appendix E is a collection of such values obtained by various workers.

Martin[215] has accurately measured the ^{1}H chemical shifts of a large series of *para*-disubstituted benzenes and he has found that the measured shifts obey the relation

$$\delta = d_o(R_1) + \gamma(R_1)\, d_m(R_4)$$

where δ is the chemical shift of the hydrogen nucleus *ortho* to substituent R_1 and *meta* to substituent R_4, d_o and d_m are characteristic *ortho* and *meta* shielding parameters and γ's are empirical constants. This is a refinement on the work of Diehl and other workers in that γ is not always unity. Table 10.55 lists some of Martin's shielding parameters for *para*-disubstituted benzenes.

TABLE 10.55 SUBSTITUENT PARAMETERS IN *para*-DISUBSTITUTED BENZENES[215]

Substituent	d_o, ppm	d_m, ppm	γ
NH_2	0·768	0·271	0·70
OCH_3	0·477	0·108	0·67
CH_3	0·183	0·107	0·91
Cl	0·000	0·065	1·00
Br	−0·159	0·134	1·03
I	−0·363	0·265	1·10
NO_2	−0·955	−0·155	1·20
CN	−0·27	−0·100	
CHO	−0·54	−0·195	
$COCH_3$	−0·64	−0·091	
COCl	−0·83	−0·156	

Dailey and co-workers[486, 488] have interpreted chemical shifts in substituted benzenes in terms of ring currents and pi-electron densities.

10.12.5 *Halogenated Benzene Derivatives*

The ^{1}H resonance spectra of 55 halogenated molecules have been examined by Stehling[216] as part of a more general investigation of methods of detecting such molecules. Unfortunately, the molecules were not examined as infinitely dilute solutions in an inert solvent (50 per cent solutions in CCl_4 being employed) a factor which does not allow their full theoretical significance to be discerned.

Despite this limitation several generalisations can be made regarding the chemical shift data which are given in chart form in Fig. 10.26. As regards the ring hydrogen nuclei, the chemical shifts appear to be mainly controlled by substituents in the *ortho*-position to the nucleus being considered and the effects are roughly additive.

The chemical shift of the methylene (—CH_2) hydrogen nuclei in $C_6H_5CH_2X$ derivatives was found to be almost independent of the nature of the halogen, X. *Ortho*-substituents, such as halogen atoms X, CH_2X and CH_3 groups, all

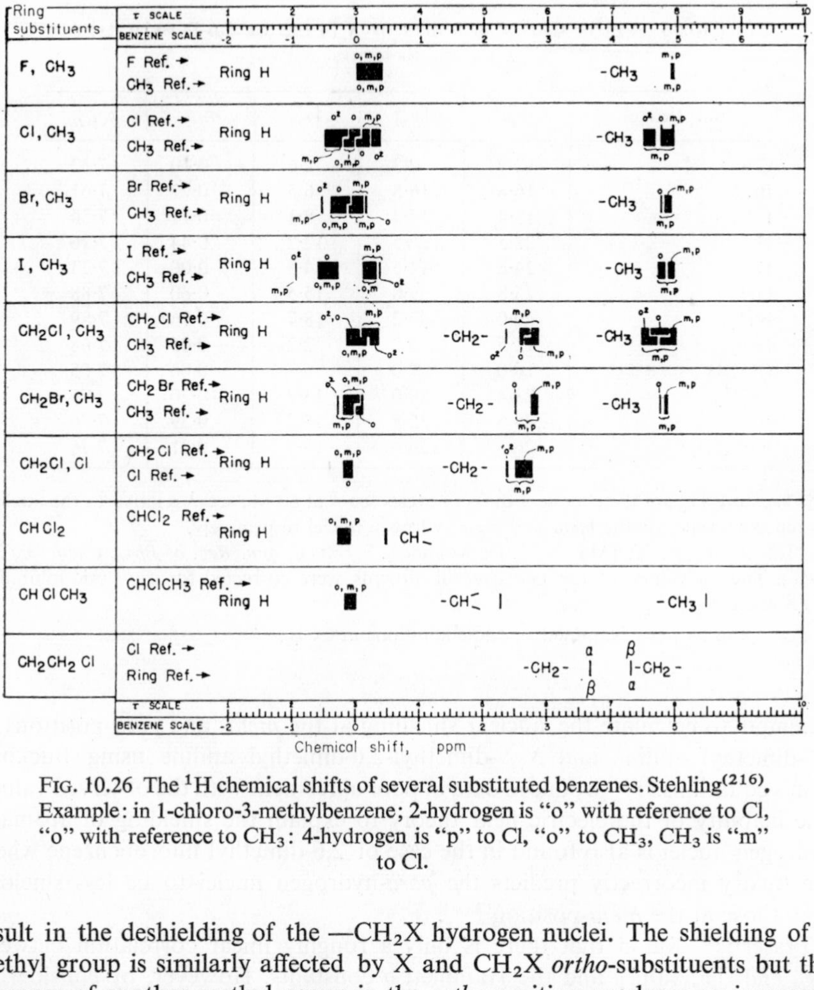

FIG. 10.26 The ¹H chemical shifts of several substituted benzenes. Stehling[216]. Example: in 1-chloro-3-methylbenzene; 2-hydrogen is "o" with reference to Cl, "o" with reference to CH_3: 4-hydrogen is "p" to Cl, "o" to CH_3, CH_3 is "m" to Cl.

result in the deshielding of the —CH_2X hydrogen nuclei. The shielding of a methyl group is similarly affected by X and CH_2X *ortho*-substituents but the presence of another methyl group in the *ortho*-position produces an increased shielding[217]. This is due to the neighbour diamagnetic anisotropic effects of halogen containing substituents.

10.12.6 Substituted Xylenes

Fraser[210] has measured the ¹H resonance chemical shifts in a series of 2,6-dimethyl-1-substituted benzenes examined as dilute solutions in carbon tetrachloride, and his results are given in Table 10.56. From the spectrum of

2,6-dimethyl deutero-benzene it is found that the chemical shifts of the *meta*-hydrogen nuclei are displaced 0·17 ppm to high fields of those in the *para*-positions by the introduction of the methyl substituents. Hence, the $\Delta\nu_m$ values given in Table 10.56 are corrected by this amount to make them more meaningful and the corrected values, $\Delta\nu'_m$, are also given in Table 10.56.

TABLE 10.56 THE ^{1}H CHEMICAL SHIFTS OF A SERIES OF 2,6-DIMETHYL-1-SUBSTITUTED BENZENES(210)

Substituent	$\Delta\nu_m$†	$\Delta\nu_p$†	$\Delta\nu'_m$	σ_R‡	τ_{CH_3}
CN	12·9	0·3	2·6	0·10	7·52
Br	16·8	16·8	6·5	−0·22	7·61
I	18·4	14·4	8·1	−0·11	7·54
F	22·5	26·5	12·2	−0·44	7·76
D	24·8	14·5	14·5	0·00	7·73
OH	25·8	39·0	15·5	−0·60	7·88
NH_2	29·0	47·2	18·7	−0·76	7·89
NO_2	12·5	5·2	2·2	+0·05	7·68
COOH	16·0	7·0	5·7	+0·06	7·55
OCH_3	23·5	29·0	13·2	−0·20	7·75
$NHCH_3$	25·5	35·8	15·2	−0·39	7·76
$N(CH_3)_2$	26	26	15·7	−0·21	7·76

† $\Delta\nu_m$ and $\Delta\nu_p$ are the chemical shifts in cycles sec^{-1} at 60 Mc sec^{-1} relative to the internal reference benzene for the *meta* and *para* hydrogen nuclei respectively.

‡ Taken from R. W. TAFT, N. C. DENO and A. S. SKELL, *Ann. Rev. of Phys. Chem.*, **9**, 292 (1958). The σ_R values of the last five substituents were corrected for the steric inhibition of resonance.

The compounds were examined as dilute solutions in CCl_4.

Attempts to calculate the nuclear shielding at the *meta*- and *para*-positions of 2,6-dimethyl aniline and *N,N*-dimethyl-2,6-dimethyl aniline using Buckingham's equations(481) produced data in poor agreement with the observed values. The inability of the electric field theory to explain the shielding of aromatic hydrogen nuclei is also found in the case of 2,6-dimethyl fluorobenzene where the theory incorrectly predicts the *para*-hydrogen nuclei to be less shielded than those at the *meta*-position(210).

Fraser(210) found that there is only a roughly linear correlation between $\Delta\nu'_m$ and $\Delta\nu_p$ values and the Hammett σ constants. However, by considering only those molecules which possess groups showing no steric inhibition of resonance, it is possible to obtain very good linear correlations of $\Delta\nu'_m$ and $\Delta\nu_p$ values with the Taft inductive (σ_I) and resonance (σ_R) contributions to the Hammett σ constants. The observed chemical shifts satisfy the simple equations

$$\Delta\nu'_m = 14{\cdot}5 - 17\sigma_I - 10\sigma_R \quad \text{cycles sec}^{-1} \text{ at 60 Mc sec}^{-1}$$

$$\Delta\nu_p = 14{\cdot}5 - 17\sigma_I - 46\sigma_R$$

From these equations one would expect a linear relationship between the difference in shielding between the *para-* and *meta-*hydrogen nuclei ($\Delta\nu_p - \Delta\nu'_m$) and the Taft resonance contribution σ_R: Fig. 10.27 shows that such a relationship does in fact prevail. Hence, the observed *meta-* and *para-*hydrogen chemical shifts in substituted xylenes are seen to depend mainly on inductive and resonance effects of the substituents.

Characteristic ^{1}H chemical shifts for the methyl and ethyl substituted derivatives of benzene and of some fused aromatic molecules have been reported(364).

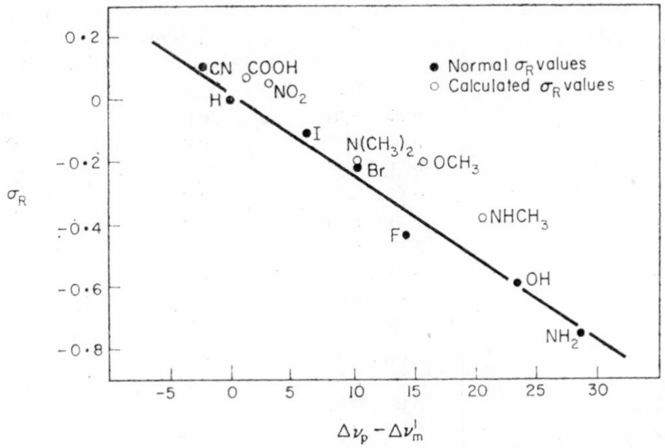

FIG. 10.27 Linear correlation of the separation in cycles sec^{-1} (at 60 Mc sec^{-1}) between the *meta-* and *para-*hydrogen nuclei with Hammett σ_R parameters. Fraser(210).

These are useful in structural determinations where the position of alkyl substitution is uncertain.

10.12.7 Hydroxy Benzenes

The ^{1}H resonance spectra of phenol, hydroquinone, catechol, resorcinol and pyrogallol have been examined, and the ^{1}H chemical shifts of the ring hydrogen nuclei have been measured from benzene external reference with a view to estimating the π-electron distributions in hydroxy benzenes(374). Intermolecular electric field effects were eliminated by measuring the chemical shifts in two different solvents and extrapolating to a medium of unit dielectric constant. Intramolecular electric fields at the ring hydrogen nuclei associated with the C—O and the O—H bond dipoles were calculated and the chemical shift contributions from this source evaluated(27) and subtracted from the measured chemical shifts. Variations in the corrected chemical shifts were attributed solely to changes in the π-electron distributions (see Section 4.5.5).

10.12.8 Aromatic Alkoxy Compounds

Heathcock[218] has reported the ^1H chemical shifts of an extensive series of anisole and phenetole derivatives and these are given in Tables 10.57 and 10.58. The chemical shifts of the methyl resonance in *meta*- and *para*-substituted anisoles show an approximately linear correlation with the corresponding Hammett σ parameters. Solvent effects were found to be appreciable for this

TABLE 10.57 ^1H CHEMICAL SHIFTS OF ANISOLE AND RELATED MOLECULES[218]

Compound[a]	Ring	Methoxy	Methyl
Anisole	2·88—3·3	6·34	
o-Methylanisole	3·08—3·36	6·35	7·86
m-Methylanisole	3·03—3·55	6·38	7·77
p-Methylanisole	3·03, 3·35	6·38	7·80
o-Aminoanisole	3·48	6·34	
o-Nitroanisole	2·30—3·00	6·16	
m-Nitroanisole	2·25—2·85	6·16	
p-Nitroanisole	1·92, 2·82	6·16	
p-Chloroanisole	2·88, 3·35	6·36	
o-Bromoanisole	2·50—3·25	6·18	
p-Bromoanisole	2·74, 3·35	6·36	
o-Iodoanisole	2·28—3·36	6·22	
o-Methoxybenzoic acid[b]	2·30—3·20	6·22	
p-Methoxybenzoic acid[b]	2·58, 3·17	6·24	
Methyl *o*-methoxy benzoate	2·30—3·15	6·20	6·20
Methyl-*p*-methoxy benzoate	2·13, 3·20	6·22	6·24
o-Acetamidoanisole[c]	3·2	6·24	7·95
p-Acetamidoanisole[c]	2·65, 3·20	6·30	7·95
p-Methoxybenzaldehyde	2·32, 3·12	6·21	
o-Phenylanisole	2·55—3·23	6·37	
m-Dimethoxybenzene	3·05—3·75	6·37	
p-Dimethoxybenzene	3·32	6·43	
p-Cyanoanisole	2·53, 3·12	6·18	
p-Methoxybenzyl alcohol	2·95, 3·36	6·39	
2,4-Dinitroanisole[d]		5·90	
2,4-Dichloroanisole	2·75, 2·90, 3·30	6·23	
2,5-Dimethoxytoluene	3·48	6·33, 6·37	7·87
2,3-Dimethoxybenzaldehyde	2·70—3·30	6·22	
2-Amino-5-nitroanisole[e]	2·25, 2·35, 3·40	6·13	
2-Iodo-5-nitroanisole[e]	2·12, 2·45, 2·50	6·11	
2-Hydroxy-5-formylanisole	2·65, 3·00	6·13	
2-Hydroxy-5-propenylanisole	3·35	6·26	

[a] All spectra were run at a concentration of 10 per cent in CCl_4 unless otherwise noted. The chemical shifts of the ring hydrogens are given as ranges where spin-coupling patterns were not readily interpretable. Resonance positions are expressed on the "tau" scale.

[b] 10 per cent hexamethylphosphoramide added as a solubiliser.

[c] 5 per cent in $CDCl_3$.

[d] 0·5 per cent in CCl_4. Poor signal-to-noise ratio did not permit the location of the ring resonances.

[e] 2 per cent in $CDCl_3$.

class of molecules and consequently the shifts were measured for dilute solutions of the samples in inert solvents. Kun and Cassidy(219) have also measured the NMR spectra of aromatic alkoxy compounds.

TABLE 10.58 ^{1}H CHEMICAL SHIFTS OF PHENETOLE AND RELATED MOLECULES(218)

Compound †	Ring	Methylene	Methyl	Ring methyl
Phenetole	2·88—3·3	6·13	8·68	
o-Methylphenetole	3·18—3·42	6·11	8·66	7·86
m-Methylphenetole	3·03—3·50	6·13	8·68	7·77
p-Methylphenetole	3·10, 3·36	6·15	8·69	7·80
o-Aminophenetole	3·48	6·10	8·68	
m-Aminophenetole	3·15—4·02	6·20	8·73	
p-Aminophenetole	3·50, 3·65	6·20	8·73	
o-Diethoxybenzene	3·30	6·07	8·65	
m-Diethoxybenzene	3·05—3·77	6·13	8·67	
p-Diethoxybenzene	3·35	6·15	8·70	
p-Nitrophenetole	1·85, 3·10	2·93	8·57	

† All samples were at a concentration of 10 per cent in CCl_4. The chemical shifts of the ring hydrogens are given as ranges where spin-coupling patterns were not readily interpretable. Resonance positions are expressed on the "tau" scale.

10.12.9 Aromatic Aldehydes

Tables 10.59 and 10.60 contain the chemical shifts of the formyl hydrogen nuclei in an extensive series of aromatic aldehydes(220). The shielding of the formyl hydrogen is controlled largely by the magnetic anisotropic effects of both the carbonyl group and the aromatic ring, and also by the polarisation of the C—H bond which reduces the electron density around the formyl hydrogen nucleus. In explaining the observed shielding constants for the aromatic aldehydic hydrogen nuclei it is assumed that the magnetic anisotropic deshielding associated with the carbonyl group is the same in all the molecules and that the variations in shielding are determined by the relative magnitudes of two opposing effects—namely the deshielding by induced ring currents and the shielding from changes in the polarisation of the C—H bond. The —CHO group in acetaldehyde has a τ value of $+0{\cdot}27$ while for benzaldehyde the value is $+0{\cdot}04$ which suggests that the ring current effect is greater than the conjugative shielding effect from the polarisation of the C—H bond. The induced ring current effect is thought to remain fairly constant for this series of molecules and thus variations in the polarisation of the C—H bond caused by the different electronic effects of the various substituents will control the shielding variations. An electron releasing substituent decreases the electropositive nature of the carbonyl group and increases the shielding of the formyl hydrogen nuclei.

For *meta*- and *para*-substituted benzaldehydes, the formyl hydrogen nuclei have τ values in the region $+0{\cdot}35$ to $-0{\cdot}20$ and the shifts have an approximately linear relationship with Hammett's σ constants. *Ortho*-substituted derivatives have corresponding τ values in the region $-0{\cdot}20$ to $-0{\cdot}50$ and there is some evidence for steric inhibition of resonance in these molecules. The aromatic aldehydes show solvent effects similar to those observed by Schaefer and Schneider(201) for other aromatic molecules. In carbon tetrachloride solutions of the molecules, the —CHO chemical shifts show only a

TABLE 10.59 ^{1}H CHEMICAL SHIFTS OF THE FORMYL HYDROGEN NUCLEUS IN SOME *meta*- AND *para*-SUBSTITUTED BENZALDEHYDES(220)

Aldehyde	τ†
Benzaldehyde	0·04 (+0·02)
m-Tolualdehyde	0·10 (+0·03)
p-Tolualdehyde	0·11 (+0·03)
p-Anisaldehyde	0·19 (+0·02)
m-Chlorobenzaldehyde	0·06 (+0·02)
p-Chlorobenzaldehyde	0·06 (0·00)
3,4-Dichlorobenzaldehyde	0·09 (—)
m-Bromobenzaldehyde	0·09 (+0·01)
p-Dimethylaminobenzaldehyde	0·35 (+0·05)
m-Fluorobenzaldehyde	0·05‡ (+0·02)
p-Fluorobenzaldehyde	0·08 (+0·01)
m-Benzyloxybenzaldehyde	0·12 (+0·05)
3,5-Dimethoxybenzaldehyde	0·18 (+0·04)
3,4,5-Trimethoxybenzaldehyde	0·27 (+0·02)
Piperonal	0·26 (+0·02)

† The bracketed quantity is the shift (in ppm) observed upon dilution of 20 per cent CCl_4 solutions.

‡ This is the centre of the observed doublet. $J = 1{\cdot}8$ cycles sec^{-1}. Shifts measured in ppm for 5 per cent w/v solutions using tetramethylsilane as internal reference (τ values)(220).

TABLE 10.60 ^{1}H CHEMICAL SHIFTS (IN ppm) OF THE FORMYL HYDROGEN NUCLEUS IN SOME *ortho*-SUBSTITUTED BENZENES AND IN SOME POLYCYCLIC ALDEHYDES(220)

Aldehyde	τ†
Salicylaldehyde	0·14 (+0·05)
Benzaldehyde	0·04 (+0·02)
o-Tolualdehyde	−0·18 (+0·03)
o-Nitrobenzaldehyde	−0·37 (+0·03)
o-Anisaldehyde	−0·39 (+0·01)‡
o-Chlorobenzaldehyde	−0·45 (+0·04)
Mesitylaldehyde	−0·49 (+0·04)
1-Naphthaldehyde	−0·31 (+0·07)

† Bracketed quantity is dilution shift for 20—5 per cent CCl_4 solution.

‡ This is the centre of the observed doublet. $J = 0{\cdot}8$ cycles sec^{-1}, due to coupling with one of the ring protons.

Shifts measured for 5 per cent w/v solutions using tetramethylsilane as internal reference (τ values)(220).

slight concentration dependence suggesting the absence of strong intermolecular hydrogen bonding.

Long range H—H coupling constants have been observed in the spectra of *ortho*-substituted benzaldehydes[373]: the formyl hydrogen nucleus couples with ring hydrogen nuclei in the 3- or 5-position (see Section 10.14). This is clearly indicated in the ^{1}H resonance spectrum of 2,4-dichlorobenzaldehyde shown in Fig. 10.28 where the formyl hydrogen nucleus gives rise to a low field doublet.

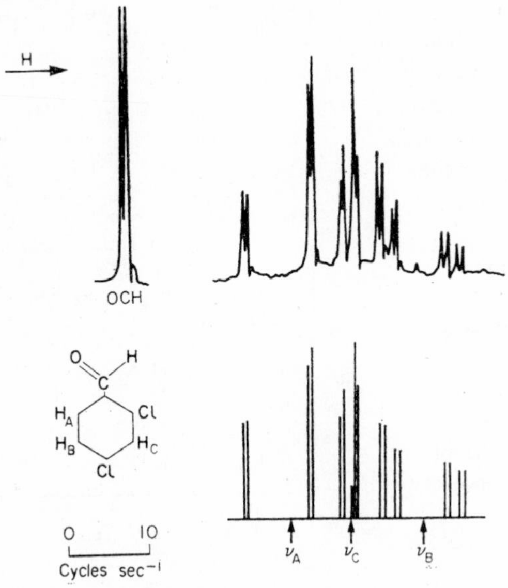

FIG. 10.28 The ^{1}H resonance spectrum of 2,4-dichlorobenzaldehyde at 60 Mc sec^{-1}. Kowalewski and de Kowalewski[373].

10.12.10 Trisubstituted Benzenes

Leane and Richards[221] have measured the ^{1}H resonance chemical shifts in a large series of trisubstituted benzene derivatives. The shifts, measured from a water external reference and corrected for bulk diamagnetic susceptibility effects, are shown in Fig. 10.29. Because the molecules were not examined at low dilution in an inert solvent the full significance of the data cannot be assessed since there will be some contribution to the shielding of the ring hydrogen nuclei from intermolecular effects. However, it is apparent that an increase in the proportion of electronegative substituents decreases the shielding of the aromatic hydrogen nuclei. In some molecules the contributions to the shielding of a nucleus from the three substituents appear to be additive.

10.12.11 Biphenyls

Brownstein[222] has examined the NMR spectra of several 2- and 4-halobiphenyls. Some of the absorption bands in the 2-halobiphenyl hydrogen resonance spectra are at higher fields than those of the parent biphenyl molecule and this is interpreted in terms of steric interactions between the halogen atom and the *ortho*-hydrogen atoms of the unsubstituted ring.

Hoffman and co-workers(223) have measured the ^1H resonance spectra of biphenyl, *ortho*-terphenyl and *meta*-terphenyl. Biphenyl and *meta*-terphenyl give complex AA′BB′C type spectra but *ortho*-terphenyl gives rise to a very simple spectrum(223) consisting of two narrow absorption bands in the intensity ratio 4 : 10 (see Fig. 10.30). The only possible explanation of this spectrum

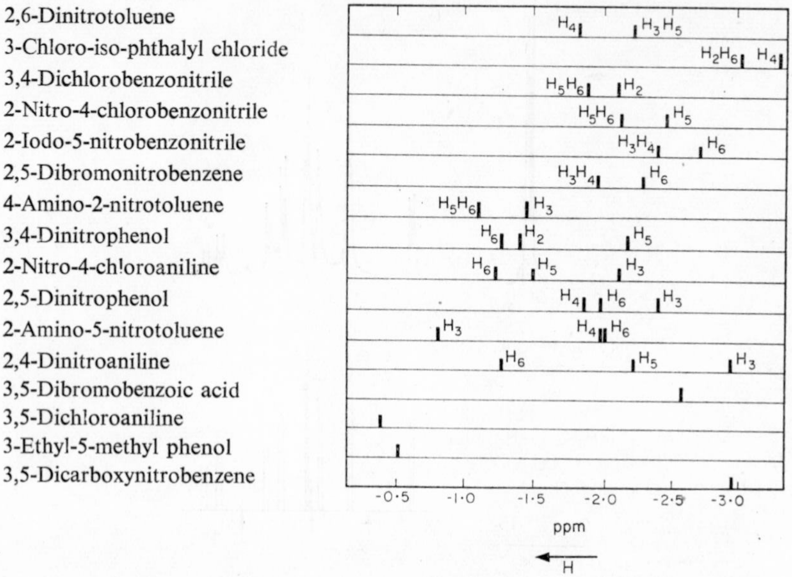

FIG. 10.29 ^1H chemical shifts (from external H_2O) of some trisubstituted benzene derivatives examined as liquids or as solutions in acetone or dimethyl sulphoxide. Shifts were corrected for bulk diamagnetic susceptibility effects. "τ" $= 5{\cdot}2 + \delta_{H_2O\,ext}$ (very approx.). Leane and Richards(221).

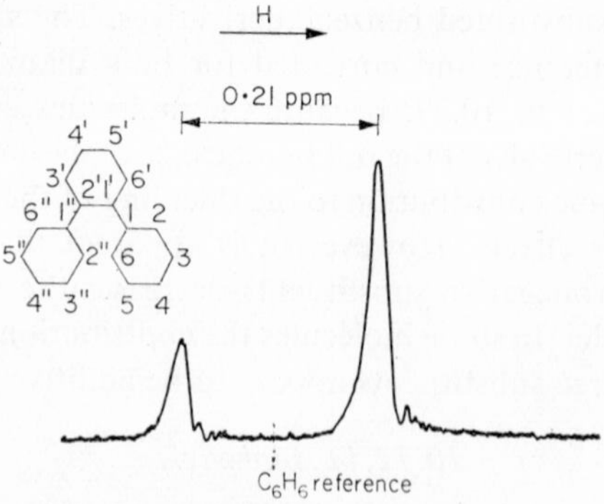

FIG. 10.30 The ^1H resonance spectrum of *ortho*-terphenyl in carbon tetrachloride at 40·00 Mc sec^{-1}. Hoffman, Kinell and Bergstrom(223).

is that all the hydrogen nuclei in any one ring are equivalent and the ten hydrogen nuclei of the lateral rings are more shielded than the four nuclei of the central ring. Hoffman has pointed out that because of the large coupling constants involved in aromatic systems the equivalence of nuclei need not be complete for a single absorption band to appear. By calculating the contributions to the shielding of the ring hydrogen nuclei from the induced aromatic ring currents assuming various configurations of the three rings, it was shown that *ortho*-terphenyl probably exists with the lateral phenyl groups perpendicular to the central ring. The results for biphenyl and *meta*-terphenyl would not allow of a conclusive conformational analysis of this type.

10.12.12 Indene

In the ^{1}H resonance spectrum of indene shown in Fig. 10.31 it is apparent that the ring hydrogen nuclei in the 5-membered ring of the molecule give rise to a first order spectrum(224). Because these hydrogen nuclei are only weakly

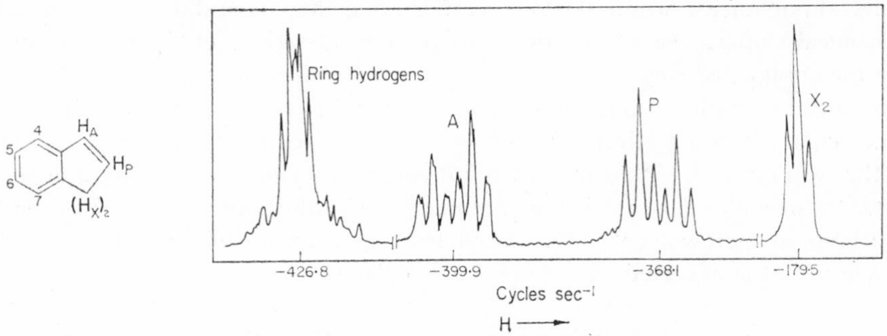

FIG. 10.31 The ^{1}H resonance spectrum of indene measured in cycles sec^{-1} from TMS internal reference at 60 Mc sec^{-1}. The A and P regions of the spectrum were run at twice the gain of the aromatic hydrogen and X_2 regions of the spectrum. Elleman and Manatt(224).

coupled to each other (an APX_2 spin system), the relative signs of the coupling constants cannot be extracted from an analysis of the ^{1}H resonance spectrum. Elleman and Manatt(224) have used a spin decoupling technique to show that J_{AX} is opposite in sign to both J_{AP} and J_{PX}. The chemical shifts and coupling constants for the hydrogen nuclei of the five-membered ring are

$$\tau_A = 3{\cdot}334 \qquad \tau_P = 3{\cdot}865 \qquad \tau_X = 7{\cdot}008$$

$$J_{AP} = +5{\cdot}58 \quad J_{AX} = -1{\cdot}98 \quad J_{PX} = +2{\cdot}02 \text{ cycles sec}^{-1}$$

A long range coupling constant (0·52 cycles sec^{-1}) which features in the A multiplet in Fig. 10.31 has been assigned to coupling between the A hydrogen nucleus and the aromatic hydrogen nucleus in position 7(451). Two long range coupling constants are detectable in the X_2 region of the spectrum because of coupling of the methylene hydrogen with aromatic hydrogen nuclei.

10.12.13 Aromatic Ring Currents

In Sections 4.3 and 4.5 a detailed account of the manner in which aromatic diamagnetic ring currents can shield or deshield hydrogen nuclei depending upon their situation with respect to the aromatic ring, has been given for many aromatic molecules. Several workers(225, 226) have modified the original expression used by Pople(227) for calculating the magnitude of the induced ring current effect by considering the magnetic field arising from n electrons circulating in a loop of radius a rather than approximating the system to a magnetic dipole. Using this approach (see Section 3.8) Johnson and Bovey(225) have calculated the contributions to the shielding of a hydrogen nucleus at various positions near an aromatic ring and a tabulation of their results for a wide range of parameters is given in Appendix B of Volume 1.

10.13 Polynuclear Aromatic Molecules

Bernstein, Schneider and Pople(228) have examined the NMR spectra of several polynuclear aromatic hydrocarbons and they have shown the observed chemical shifts to be those expected from considerations of the ring currents in the conjugated ring systems (see Section 4.3). Most of the compounds were examined as molten samples since at the time the importance of strong intermolecular shielding effects in such systems was not realised. More recently, other workers(229, 438) have carried out complete analyses of the ^{1}H resonance spectra of molecules of this type obtained using dilute solutions of the hydrocarbons in inert solvents. The calculated ring current shifts are in fair agreement with the observed values (see Table 4.9).

10.14 Spin–Spin Coupling in Aromatic Molecules

Hydrogen nuclei in benzene derivatives are spin coupled to each other with characteristic values of coupling constants depending upon their relative positions in the molecule. The range of values for the spin–spin coupling constants are shown below

$$J_{\mathrm{HH}}^{ortho} \sim 7{\cdot}0 \text{ to } 9{\cdot}2 \quad \text{cycles sec}^{-1}$$

$$J_{\mathrm{HH}}^{meta} \sim 1{\cdot}1 \text{ to } 3{\cdot}1 \quad \text{cycles sec}^{-1}$$

$$J_{\mathrm{HH}}^{para} \sim 0{\cdot}0 \text{ to } 0{\cdot}7 \quad \text{cycles sec}^{-1}$$

and they are found to be fairly independent of the substituents(221). Such characteristic values of the coupling constants will have obvious applications in the NMR determination of the nature of substitution in aromatic systems. Although the variation in coupling constants with change in substituents is small, a linear correlation has been observed between the coupling constants and the sum of the electronegativities of the substituents attached to the ring for various series of substituted benzenes(407).

Extraction of the coupling constants from the complex hydrogen resonance spectra often obtained for substituted benzenes, necessitates detailed spectral analysis. Table 10.61 is a compilation of aromatic H—H coupling constants which have been obtained in this manner[234]: they are seen to fall within the characteristic range of values expected for *ortho-*, *meta-* and *para*-coupling constants[221, 230–233].

TABLE 10.61 COMPILATION OF J_{HH} SPIN COUPLING CONSTANTS BETWEEN RING HYDROGEN NUCLEI IN AROMATIC MOLECULES[234]

para-disubstituted benzenes	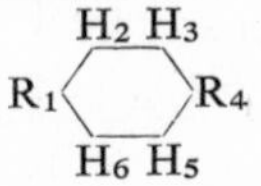			
Substituents	J_{23}	J_{25}	J_{26}	J_{35}
NH_2, OMe	+8·5	+0·5	+2·8	+2·8
NH_2, Cl	+8·6	+0·4	+2·8	+2·5
NH_2, Br	+8·5	+0·3	+2·9	+2·3
NH_2, I	+8·5	+0·3	+2·9	+2·2
NH_2, NO_2	+9·0	+0·3	+2·6	+2·3
OMe, Cl	+8·8	+0·3	+3·1	+2·5
OMe, Br	+8·7	+0·3	+3·1	+2·5
OMe, I	+8·9	+0·4	+3·0	+2·4
OMe, NO_2	+9·0	+0·3	+2·7	+2·7
Cl, Br	+8·4	+0·4	+2·5	+2·5
Cl, I	+8·4	+0·4	+2·4	+2·4
Cl, NO_2	+8·7	+0·3	+2·8	+2·2
Br, I	+8·6	+0·3	+2·5	+2·2
Br, NO_2	+8·9	+0·4	+2·6	+2·2
CN, OMe	+8·8	+0·4	+2·2	+2·7
CN, Cl	+8·4	+0·4	+2·1	+2·1
COMe, OMe	+8·7	+0·4	+2·6	+2·3
COMe, Cl	+8·4	+0·5	+2·2	+2·2
COCl, OMe	+8·9	+0·3	+2·7	+2·4
COCl, Cl	+8·5	+0·5	+2·3	+2·3
CHO, OMe	+8·6	+0·4	+2·5	+2·1
CHO, Cl	+8·3	+0·4	+2·1	+2·1
CH_3, NH_2	+8·1	+0·5	+2·4	+2·4
CH_3, OMe	+8·3	+0·4	+2·7	+2·4
CH_3, Cl	+8·4	+0·4		
CH_3, Br	+8·1	+0·6	+2·3	+2·3
CH_3, I	+7·9	+0·6	+2·4	+2·0
CH_3, NO_2	+8·5	+0·4	+2·3	+2·1
Symmetrically *meta*-disubstituted benzenes	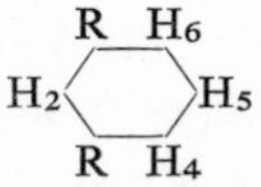			
Compound	J_{45}	J_{25}	J_{24}	
m-Dibromobenzene	8·1	0·4	1·8	
m-Di-iodobenzene	7·7	0·3	1·6	
m-Dinitrobenzene	+8·3	0·5	+2·2	
Isophthaloyl chloride	7·9	0·6	1·9	

(continued)

Symmetrically *ortho*-disubstituted benzenes

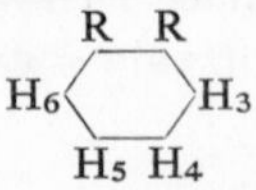

Compound	J_{34}	J_{35}	J_{36}	J_{45}
o-Dichlorobenzene	7·9	1·7	0·5	7·5
o-Dibromobenzene	8·1	1·5	0·3	7·3
o-Di-iodobenzene	7·9	1·5	0·3	7·3
Phthaloyl chloride	7·8	1·1	0·6	7·6

The relative signs of the three coupling constants are the same in all the molecules considered: Buckingham and McLauchlan(38) have shown that the J_{HH}^{ortho} value in *p*-nitrotoluene is absolutely positive and it appears likely that all H—H coupling constants between ring hydrogen nuclei in benzenes are positive.

McConnell(179, 191) has used a valence bond method to estimate the relative importance of the π-electron contribution to the H—H spin coupling mechanism in aromatic systems. He concludes that in naphthalene and substituted benzenes the *ortho* and *meta* H—H coupling operates mainly via the σ-electronic system while the *para* H—H coupling constant and longer range coupling constants (1–6, 1–7, 2–6, 2–7 in naphthalene—not observable) are thought to be controlled by the π-electronic system (see Section 5.6). The calculated π-electron contributions to H—H coupling constants in benzene and naphthalene are shown to give small positive coupling constants for hydrogen nuclei separated by an odd number of C—C bonds, and small negative values otherwise.

Spin coupling between hydrogen nuclei in separate rings has not been observed directly for any fused aromatic hydrocarbon system (unlike quinolines, see Section 10.20). However, there is some indirect evidence for such coupling in the ^{1}H resonance spectrum of anthracene(229), shown in Fig. 10.32, where the absorption bands of the "adjacent" A and X nuclei are considerably broadened, presumably due to inter-ring coupling. In the absence of spin coupling between the A and X nuclei, the A multiplet would have been expected to be a perfect mirror image of the B multiplet (typical of an AA'BB' system). A double irradiation experiment could probably be used to confirm the presence of spin coupling between the A and X nuclei. The ^{1}H spectrum of naphthalene (Fig. 10.32A) also deviates from the symmetrical AA'BB' type spectrum.

The observed *ortho* H—H coupling constants for several fused aromatic hydrocarbons are found to show a simple linear relationship

$$J = 12{\cdot}7\,P - 1{\cdot}1$$

where P is the π bond order of the appropriate C—C bond and can be calculated using simple molecular orbital theory. This is surprising in view of McConnell's prediction that *ortho* H—H spin coupling in aromatic molecules is maintained largely by the σ-electrons.

A long range H—H coupling constant has been observed in the spectra of *ortho* substituted benzaldehydes (I) where the —CHO absorption band[373] appears as a doublet due to coupling with a ring hydrogen nucleus situated

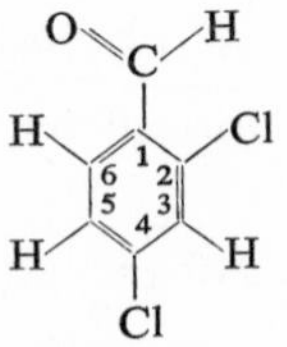

(I)

five bonds away (J = 0·31 to 0·83 cycles sec^{-1}). From a study of various substituted aromatic aldehydes it was shown that in some molecules the ring hydrogen nucleus in position 5 is involved in long range coupling with the aldehydic hydrogen nucleus while in other molecules the 3-hydrogen nucleus is responsible for the coupling. To observe this long range coupling it is necessary to have a substituent in the *ortho* position to the aldehyde group.

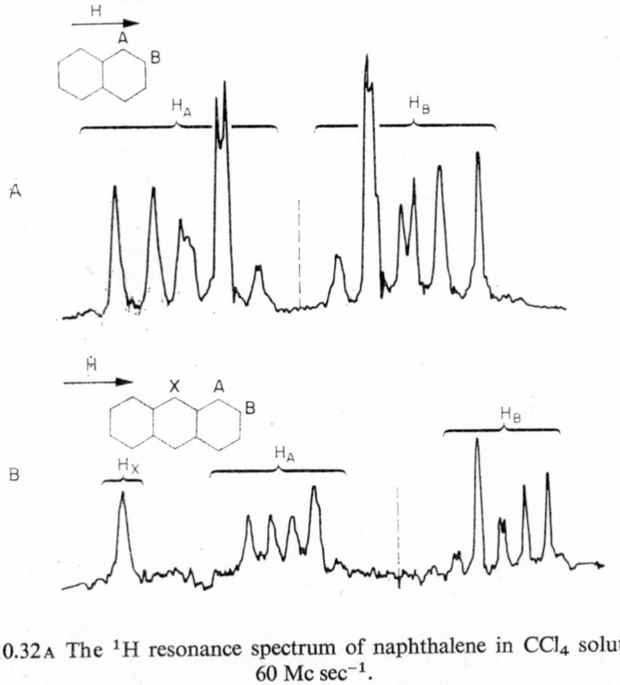

FIG. 10.32A The ^{1}H resonance spectrum of naphthalene in CCl_4 solution at 60 Mc sec^{-1}.

FIG. 10.32B The ^{1}H resonance spectrum of anthracene in CS_2 solution at 60 Mc sec^{-1}. Jonathan, Gordon and Dailey[229].

10.15 Aromatic Ions

Several interesting studies of the NMR spectra of aromatic ions have revealed features of their structures which hitherto could only be indirectly inferred[83, 208, 229, 235–246, 248, 250, 251]. To illustrate the scope of such studies a few typical examples will be discussed.

10.15.1 Triaryl Carbonium Ions

Triaryl carbonium ions can be formed by the action of a strong acid on a triaryl carbinol

$$Ar_3COH + 2H^+ \rightleftharpoons Ar_3C^+ + H_3O^+$$

The substitution of the aryl group greatly affects the stability of the ion and thus the tri-*p*-anisyl carbinol has an ionisation equilibrium constant which is 3×10^7 larger than that of the unsubstituted triphenyl carbinol. There is considerable doubt about the structure of the triaryl carbonium ion; some evidence suggests that only one or two of the rings are conjugated with the

Table 10.62 The ^1H Chemical Shifts of some Substituted Aryl Carbonium Ions[236]

Compound from which cation was derived	Aromatic shift (to main peak)	Substituent shift
Triphenylcarbinol	−101·0	—
p-Tolyl diphenylcarbinol	−98·0	+102·5
Di-*p*-tolyl phenylcarbinol	−94·75	+104·5
Tri-*p*-tolylcarbinol	−93·5	+105·5
m-Tolyl diphenylcarbinol	−95·5	+112·5
Tri-*m*-tolylcarbinol	−89·0	+112·5
p-Anisyl diphenylcarbinol	−96·0	+42·0
Tri-*p*-anisylcarbinol	−87·5	+47·0
p-t-Butylphenyl diphenylchloromethane	−101·0	+151·0
t-Butylbenzene	−76·0	+161·5
Anisole	−68·0	+59·5
Toluene	−69·0	+124·5

Chemical shifts were measured in cycles sec^{-1} at 40 Mc sec^{-1} from a water external reference: no bulk diamagnetic susceptibility correction was made.

The compounds were examined as 10 per cent solutions in a solvent mixture containing 1·5 M trifluoroacetic acid (TFA) in TFA anhydride.

$$\text{“}\tau\text{”} = 5{\cdot}2 + \frac{\nu_{H_2O\,ext}}{40}$$

central carbon atom, while other evidence favours a symmetrical "propeller" structure in which the π orbitals of the rings overlap the p orbitals of the central carbon atom to the same extent[235]. Table 10.62 contains the chemical shifts of the hydrogen nuclei in a series of substituted aryl carbonium ions[236]. For the molecules with a hydrogen containing substituent group, in no instance was there evidence for multiple absorption bands for the substituent group. While this is to be expected for the symmetrical propeller molecule, it does not preclude the possibility of the one-ring conjugated molecules being present as a rapidly interconverting mixture of isomers. Cooling solutions of tri-*p*-anisylmethyl and tri-*p*-tolylmethyl cations to $-80°C$ brought about no change in the absorption bands of the substituents. A single peak was observed for the substituent absorption band in all cases, while the ring hydrogen nuclei gave rise to well-resolved multiplet absorption bands. Both the ring hydrogen nuclei and the substituent hydrogen nuclei are deshielded in the carbonium ions compared with the analogous hydrogen nuclei in the parent molecule.

O'Reilly and Leftin(237) have also studied the ^{1}H resonance spectra of the triphenylcarbonium ion and their results indicate all rings to be equivalent for life-times longer than 10^{-2} sec. The observed chemical shifts for the ring hydrogen nuclei in both triphenyl- and methyldiphenyl-carbonium ions were explained in terms of induced ring current effects and electronic structures of the species.

Dehl, Vaughan and Berry(238) have examined several deuterated triphenyl-carbonium ions in order to establish the equivalence of the three aromatic rings in the ion. By examining the 3,5-d- and 3,4,5-d-species with all rings similarly deuterated it was possible to decide that the three rings are in fact equivalent on the NMR time scale (lifetime greater than 0·01 sec). The ^{1}H resonance spectrum of the 3,5-deutero derivative consists of two absorption bands in the intensity ratio of 1:2 with the less intense band at the lower field value while the 3,4,5-deutero derivative gives only a single absorption signal. The *para*-hydrogen nuclei are shown to be least shielded and those in the *ortho*-position are shielded the most: *meta*-hydrogen nuclei are slightly less shielded than the *ortho*-hydrogen nuclei. Tentative values of the coupling constants between the aromatic ion ring hydrogen nuclei of $J_{o-m} = 1{\cdot}8$ and $J_{m-p} = 3{\cdot}0$ cycles sec^{-1} have also been measured but a value for J_{o-p} could not be detected.

10.15.2 9,10-Dimethyl-1,2-benzanthracene Carbonium Ion and Other Aromatic Carbonium Ions

This aromatic carbonium ion was obtained by dissolving 9,10-dimethyl-1,2-benzanthracene in a mixture of either $CF_3COOH + H_2O \cdot BF_3$ or $HF + BF_3$(239). Addition of the proton to the basic polyaromatic molecule has been shown by NMR measurements to result in the formation of a —$CHCH_3$ group at the 9-position

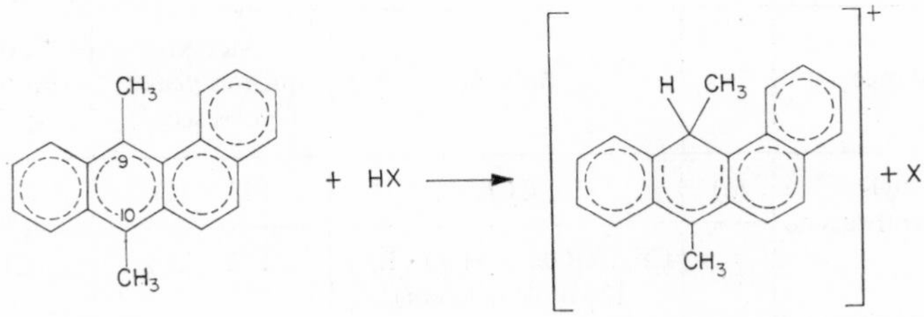

Figure 10.33 (b) clearly shows the appearance of a quartet CH absorption band at + 1·73 ppm from benzene internal reference with the characteristic splittings expected from coupling with an adjacent CH_3 group. The chemical shifts of the hydrogen nuclei in the two systems are given in Table 10.63. In the parent molecule the two methyl groups are non-equivalent and the formation of the carbonium ion increases the chemical shift difference between them: the high field doublet in Fig. 10.33 (b) has been assigned to the methyl group in the 9-position which couples with the added proton. When the carbonium ion is formed using fully deuterated acid as the solvent, the carbon atom at the

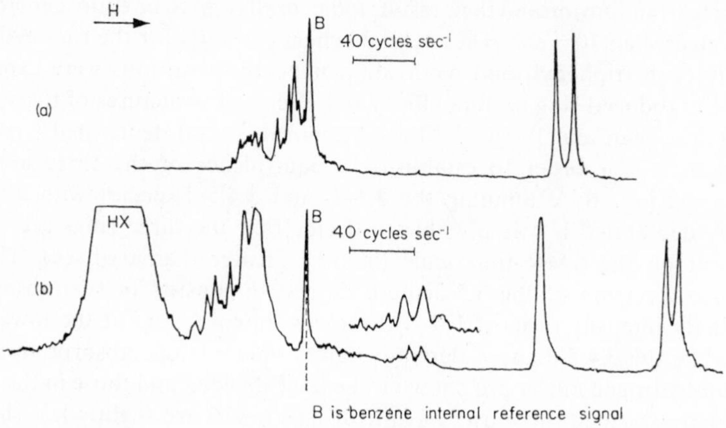

FIG. 10.33 The ¹H resonance spectrum of 9,10-dimethyl-1,2-benzanthracene (a) in CCl_4 and (b) in $CF_3COOH + 27$ mole % $H_2O \cdot BF_3$ at 40 Mc sec^{-1}. MacLean, van der Waals and Mackor[239].

9-position is substituted with deuterium $\left(D\diagdown_{C}\diagup CH_3\right)$ and the CH quartet no longer features in the spectrum.

Other aromatic ions have been made in a similar fashion and the presence of the "aliphatic" hydrogen nuclei detected by NMR measurements. A summary

TABLE 10.63 THE ¹H CHEMICAL SHIFTS[239] OF 9,10-DIMETHYL-1,2-BENZANTHRACENE (a) IN CCl_4 AND (b) IN $CF_3COOH + 27$ MOLE PER CENT $H_2O \cdot BF_3$ AT 40 MC SEC^{-1}

Substance		Solvent	Methyl proton peaks (cycles sec^{-1})	"Aliphatic" proton peaks (cycles sec^{-1})
9,10-Dimethyl-1,2-benzanthracene	(*a*)	CCl_4	158 171	
	(*b*)	$CF_3COOH + H_2O \cdot BF_3$ (27 mole per cent)	142 216 223	CHR : 69

Chemical shifts are measured in cycles sec^{-1} from a benzene internal reference.

of the NMR results for several such species is given in Table 10.64. In some cases, the presence of exchange equilibria of the type

$$AH^+ + A \rightleftharpoons A + AH^+ \qquad (10.15a)$$

$$AH^+ + X^- \rightleftharpoons A + HX \qquad (10.15b)$$

TABLE 10.64 THE ^{1}H CHEMICAL SHIFTS MEASURED IN CYCLES SEC^{-1} AT 40 MC SEC^{-1} (FROM A BENZENE INTERNAL REFERENCE) OF SEVERAL CARBONIUM IONS[239]

Substance	Solvent	Methyl proton peaks cycles sec^{-1}	"Aliphatic" proton peaks cycles sec^{-1}
Pentamethylbenzene	CCl_4	202	
	$CF_3COOH + H_2O \cdot BF_3$ (30 mole per cent)	196, 199, 204	not observed
	$HF + BF_3$	180, 187, 198	CH_2 : 102
Hexamethylbenzene	$HF + BF_3$	193	CHR : 131
Hexaethylbenzene	CCl_4	CH_2 : 193 CH_3 : 246	
	$HF + BF_3$	CH_2 : 185 CH_3 : 254	CHR : 120
9,10-Dimethylanthracene	CCl_4	166	
	$CF_3COOH + H_2O \cdot BF_3$ (17 mole per cent)	148 223 231	CHR : 102
Pyrene	$HF + BF_3$		CH_2 : 122
3,4-Benzopyrene	$CF_3COOH + H_2O \cdot BF_3$ (19 mole per cent)		CH_2 : 160

influences the observed NMR spectra by producing a broad absorption band for the aliphatic CH_2 group. Thus, the pentamethyl benzenium ion in $HF + BF_3$ shows a broad aliphatic CH_2 absorption band in its ^{1}H resonance spectrum.

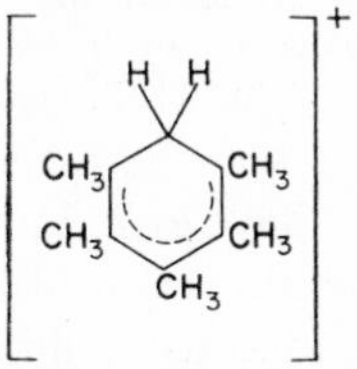

Equilibrium (10.15a) predominates for a strongly basic aromatic molecule in strong acid solution and it is possible to affect the equilibrium by varying the solvent acidity.

Other molecules which have been protonated using a $HF \cdot BF_3$ mixture are mesitylene, anisole, *m*-dimethoxybenzene and *m*-xylene[365]. At low temperatures the ^{1}H resonance spectra of mesitylene and *m*-xylene in $HF \cdot BF_3$ solution indicate clearly the presence of protonated complexes and from examination of the spectra one is able to determine the position of protonation. Similar information can be obtained from the room temperature spectra of anisole and *m*-dimethoxybenzene in $HF \cdot BF_3$ solution. It is also possible to obtain kinetic information about the various types of proton transfer in such systems (see Section 9.3.1).

10.15.3 Azulinium Ion and Related Species

When azulene is introduced into strongly acid media, protonation at the 1-position is thought to occur

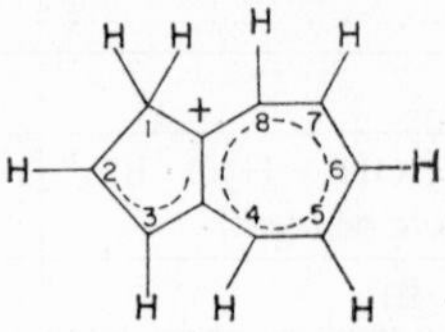

(I)

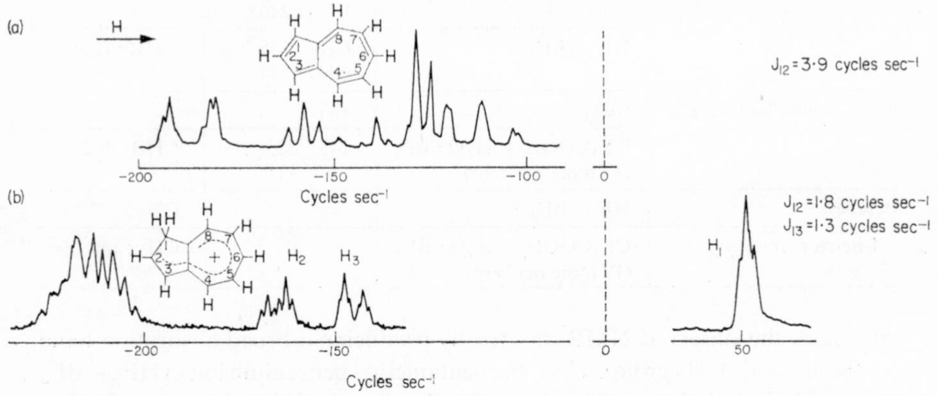

FIG. 10.34 The ^1H resonance spectra at 60 Mc sec^{-1} of (a) 7 mole per cent azulene in CH_2Cl_2, (b) the azulinium ion (7 mole per cent azulene in CF_3COOH). CH_2Cl_2 was used as an internal reference, its signal being 320 cycles sec^{-1} to low fields of TMS. Danyluk and Schneider[(240)].

Danyluk and Schneider[(240, 241)] have examined the ^1H resonance spectrum of azulene in trifluoroacetic acid solution and by comparing it with the spectrum of azulene[(117)] itself they were able to confirm that protonation takes place as shown above. The ^1H resonance spectra of azulene and the azulinium ion, together with their assignments are shown in Fig. 10.34. In Fig. 10.34(b) the high field absorption at + 53 cycles sec^{-1} from CH_2Cl_2 external reference is assigned to the aliphatic CH_2 group at the 1-position: the remaining ring hydrogen nuclei at positions 2 and 3 of the azulinium ion give rise to a symmetrical pair of AB type doublets of multiplets which have a similar chemical shift to the analogous hydrogen nuclei in azulene. The triplet fine structure on the components of the AB doublets (H_2 and H_3) arises from spin coupling of the two H_1 nuclei with H_2 and H_3. The 7-membered ring hydrogen nuclei are all seen to be markedly deshielded in the azulinium ion compared with the parent molecule and this is consistent with the positive charge mainly residing on the carbon atoms of the 7-membered ring. NMR studies of deuterated azulinium ions have established the assignments(242) shown in Fig. 10.34(b).

The ^{1}H resonance spectra of 4,6,8-trimethylazulene and guaiazulene and their conjugate acids have also been studied; in both cases monoprotonation of the 5-membered ring occurs(241).

An extremely large long range spin coupling constant has been observed in the ^{1}H spectrum of the guaiazulenium ion (II) between the CH_2 hydrogen

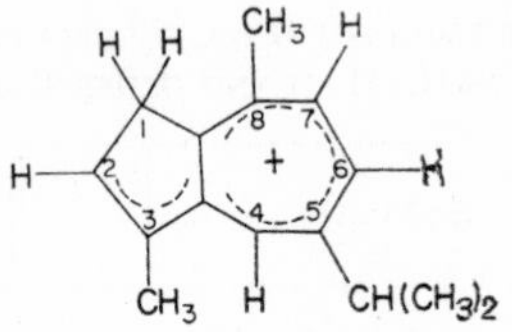

(II)

nuclei at position 1 of the 5-membered ring and the CH_3 group at position 3 ($J_{H_2C-C-C-CH_3} \doteq 2{\cdot}0$ cycles sec^{-1})(241). The large value is probably due to delocalisation of the electrons in the C—H bond by a hyperconjugative mechanism. When the 3-methyl group is replaced by a hydrogen atom as in the azulenium ion, the $J_{1,3}$ coupling constant is 1·3 cycles sec^{-1}. This strongly suggests that the long range coupling in these ions proceeds via a σ–π interaction mechanism(241) (see Section 10.7).

10.15.4 Cyclopentadienyl Anion ($C_5H_5^-$) *and Tropylinium Cation* ($C_7H_7^+$)

The ^{1}H resonance spectra of the $C_5H_5^-$ and $C_7H_7^+$ species have been measured independently by several workers(99, 239, 248). It was found that the single sharp absorption band of $C_5H_5^-Na^+$ has a chemical shift of $+1{\cdot}85$ ppm to high fields of an internal reference benzene signal while that of the tropylinium salt is $-1{\cdot}9$ ppm to low fields in the same reference solvent. Cyclopentadiene itself gives rise to a very complex NMR spectrum consisting of two multiplet absorption bands at $+0{\cdot}84$ and $+4{\cdot}4$ ppm from benzene internal reference. When a mixture of cyclopentadiene and the cyclopentadienyl anion is examined the NMR spectrum is a superposition of the two component spectra with no indication that rapid exchange is taking place between the anion and the parent molecule.

Table 10.65 lists the observed chemical shifts in a series of salts of $C_5H_5^-$ and $C_7H_7^+$; in all cases the ions give a single absorption band(248). Also included in Table 10.65 are the sandwich compounds—ferrocene, ruthenocene, osmocene and magnesocene.

Other NMR studies have established that positive charges on the atom to which hydrogen nuclei are attached generally result in decreased shielding of the hydrogen nuclei (see Table 10.66)(248). Thus the observed chemical shifts in the $C_5H_5^-$ and the $C_7H_7^+$ species can be accounted for on the basis of a simple electrostatic interaction between the charge localised in the π-orbital of the carbon atom with the electrons in the C—H bond. Fraenkel and co-workers(248) have used an electrostatic model to explain the chemical shifts of these ions and they have extended their results to predict charge distributions within other aromatic molecules.

Dailey, Gawer and Neikam(83) have studied the extent to which ^1H chemical shifts can be related to electron densities in the aromatic hydrocarbon ions

TABLE 10.65 ^1H CHEMICAL SHIFTS OF THE CYCLOPENTADIENYL ANION ($C_5H_5^-$), THE TROPYLINIUM CATION ($C_7H_7^+$) AND OTHER RELATED MOLECULES(248)

Compound	Solvent	Concn., %	Chemical shift $\delta \pm 0{\cdot}004$ ppm
$C_7H_7^+ClO_4^-$	Dimethyl sulphoxide	2	−1·938
$C_7H_7^+ClO_4^-$	Acetonitrile	2	−1·873
$C_7H_7^+BF_4^-$	Dimethyl sulphoxide	2	−1·934
$C_7H_7^+BF_4^-$	Acetonitrile	2	−1·873
$C_5H_5^-Na^+$	Dimethyl sulphoxide	2	1·970
$C_5H_5^-Na^+$	Acetonitrile	2	1·785
$C_5H_5^-Na^+$	Tetrahydrofuran	2	1·724
$C_5H_5^-Li^+$	Tetrahydrofuran	2	1·738
$(C_5H_5)_2Mg$	Tetrahydrofuran	2	1·494
$(C_5H_5)_2Mg$	Ethyl ether	1	1·089
$(C_5H_5)_2Mg$	Benzene	1	0·819
$(C_5H_5)_2Mg$	Cyclohexane	1	1·185
$(C_5H_5)_2Os$	Tetrahydrofuran	2	2·696
$(C_5H_5)_2Ru$	Tetrahydrofuran	2	2·805
$(C_5H_5)_2Fe$	Tetrahydrofuran	2	3·200

Chemical shifts were measured in ppm from a benzene internal reference.

TABLE 10.66 ^1H CHEMICAL SHIFTS OF SOME SPECIES WITH A POSITIVE CHARGE(248)

Final state (A)	Initial state (B)	Proton	Shift (δ_{A-B} ppm)
$CH_3NH_3^+$	CH_3NH_2	CH_3	−0·30†
$(CH_3)_2NH_2^+$	$(CH_3)_2NH$	CH_3	−0·44†
$(CH_3)_2NH^+$	$(CH_3)_2N$	CH_3	−0·70†
$NH_3^+CH_2CO_2^-$	$NH_2CH_2CO_2^-$	CH_2	−0·29‡
$\overset{+}{N}H_3CH_2CO_2H$	$\overset{+}{N}H_3CH_2CO_2^-$	CH_2	−0·50‡
$CH_3COHNHCH_3^+$	$CH_3CONHCH_3$	HCH_3	−0·37††

† E. Grunwald, H. Loewenstein and S. Meiboom, *J. Chem. Phys.*, **27**, 641 (1957).
‡ M. Takeda and O. Jardetzky, *J. Chem. Phys.*, **26**, 1346 (1957).
†† G. Fraenkel and C. Niemann, *Proc. Natl. Acad. Sci. U.S.*, **44**, 688 (1958).

$C_5H_5^-$, $C_7H_7^+$, and $C_8H_8^{2-}$. These systems are suitable for such an investigation since they have a known amount of charge distributed symmetrically about the ring. Before any correlation of chemical shift with electron density can be attempted, two additional effects must be taken into account, namely, the shielding contributions from induced ring currents and those from solvent effects. For aromatic ions the ring current shifts will be different from those observed in benzene. The magnitude of the shielding contribution from induced ring currents in aromatic ions has been estimated by using the relationship

$$\sigma_1 = 0{\cdot}63\, K_b \left(\frac{a_1}{a_b}\right)^2 \mathrm{I}_1$$

where K_b is the shielding constant value given in the table of Johnson and Bovey[225] (Appendix B, Volume 1) for the appropriate separation between the centre of the ring and the hydrogen nucleus, a_1 is the radius of the ring in question, a_b is the radius of the benzene ring, I_1 is the ratio of the ring current intensities for the ion and benzene and 0·63 is an empirical constant found by Jonathan and co-workers[229]. This relationship has been used to find the ring current corrections for 5-, 6-, 7- and 8-membered aromatic ions[229]. Solvent effects were eliminated by subtracting from the chemical shift at infinite dilution in the individual solvent, the chemical shift in the gas phase corrected for the van der Waal's shift (taken to be the average chemical shift of methane and ethane at infinite dilution in the solvent). Table 10.67 summarises the observed

TABLE 10.67 CHEMICAL SHIFT/ELECTRON DENSITY RATIOS FOR HYDROCARBON AROMATIC IONS[83]

Ion	Observed chemical shift from benzene reference	δ corrected for solvent shift	δ corrected for ring current	π Charge difference from benzene	Chemical shift / electron density ratio
$C_5H_5^-$	+1·731	+1·60	+1·43	+0·200	7·15
$C_7H_7^+$	−1·87	−1·70	−1·59	−0·143	11·13
$C_8H_8^{2-}$	+1·575	+1·48	+2·42	+0·250	9·70
					av. 9·3

chemical shifts for three aromatic hydrocarbon ions: it contains the corrections for induced ring currents and solvent effects for the ions and indicates that the average chemical shift per electron density ratio is 9·3 ppm per electron charge. Other workers have also conducted similar investigations and they have obtained results which are in reasonable agreement with the above [99, 243, 244]. By dividing the observed chemical shifts[208] in the non-alternant hydrocarbon, azulene (corrected for ring current effects), by 9·3, the differences in electron densities from those in benzene have been determined for the various positions in the molecules[83]: there is rough qualitative agreement between these values and those calculated by other methods[245, 246].

Similar calculations have been successfully carried out on the corrected chemical shift data for pyridine, quinoline, isoquinoline and pyrimidine(83). Schaefer and Schneider(99) have also estimated electron densities in aromatic ions from NMR spectra (see Section 4.5.5).

Although there is reasonable agreement between observed and calculated "electron densities", in view of the many uncertainties involved in such complex systems it is far from being an established fact that chemical shift measurements can yield accurate and unambiguous estimates of electron densities.

HETEROCYCLIC COMPOUNDS

10.16 Furan and Substituted Furans

The ^{1}H resonance spectrum of furan, examined as a pure liquid, consists of a pair of triplets and this led early investigators to conclude that the two cross-ring coupling constants, J_{AB} and $J_{AB'}$, are equal. Reddy and Goldstein(249) have shown since that the spectrum of furan in acetone consists of a pair of quartets, and furthermore, from an examination of the ^{13}CH satellites in the spectrum it has been possible to extract two different cross-ring coupling constants. The coupling constants deduced in this way are consistent with an AA′BB′ analysis of the deceptively simple spectrum previously obtained (see Section 8.16.2). The coupling constants and chemical shifts for furan and two methyl substituted derivatives(252) are shown in Table 10.68. As might be

Table 10.68 ^{1}H Chemical Shifts and Spin Coupling Constants for Furan and Two Methyl Substituted Furans(252)

	τ_2	τ_3	τ_4	τ_5	J_{23}	J_{24}	J_{25}	J_{34}	J_{35}	J_{45}
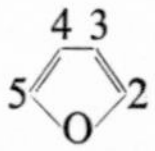	2·702	3·750	3·750	2·702	1·4	1·2			1·2	1·4
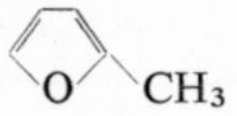	7·827	4·175	3·880	2·852	1·1	0·4	0·35	3·4	1·0	1·9
	7·864	4·307	4·307	7·864	0·4	0·3			0·3	0·4

expected on simple electronegativity grounds, the hydrogen nuclei on the α-carbon to the oxygen of the furan ring are less shielded than those on the β-carbon atom. Methyl substitution results in increased shielding of the ring hydrogen nuclei as would be predicted for an electron releasing substituent. In 2-methylfuran, the methyl group is coupled almost as strongly to the adjacent ring hydrogen nucleus (J_{23} = 1·1 cycles sec^{-1}) as are the 4 and 5 ring hydrogen nuclei to each other (J_{45} = 1·9 cycles sec^{-1}).

Leane and Richards[253] had examined previously a series of substituted furans and shown that fairly characteristic values of coupling constants between ring hydrogen nuclei exist, namely

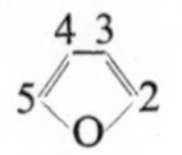

$$J_{34} = 3{\cdot}1 \text{ to } 3{\cdot}8 \text{ cycles sec}^{-1}$$
$$J_{45} = 1{\cdot}7 \text{ to } 2{\cdot}0 \text{ cycles sec}^{-1}$$
$$J_{35} = 0{\cdot}7 \text{ to } 1{\cdot}0 \text{ cycles sec}^{-1}$$

Thus the coupling constants are seen to be much smaller than those observed for benzene derivatives.

A double irradiation experiment has shown that the three coupling constants between the ring hydrogen nuclei in 2-furoic acid (I) all have the same sign[368].

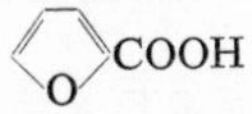 (I)

Table 10.69 lists the chemical shifts of an extensive series of furan derivatives measured from water used as an external reference[254]. Hydrogen nuclei attached to the ring carbon atoms are found at lower field values than those

TABLE 10.69 THE ^{1}H CHEMICAL SHIFTS OF SOME SUBSTITUTED FURANS[254]

Compound	δ_α	δ_β	Signal ratio $\alpha:\beta$	Solvent
Furan	−2·45 (t)	−1·38 (t)	1 : 1	CCl_4
Furan	−2·80 (t)	−1·75 (t)	1 : 1	$Cl_2CHCHCl_2$
Furan	−2·83 (t)	−1·78 (t)	1 : 1	CH_2Cl_2
2-Methylfuran	−2·60 (m)	−1·63, −1·35 (m)	1 : 2	CH_2Cl_2
2,5-Dimethylfuran		−0·875 (s)		CCl_4
2,5-Dimethylfuran		−1·21 (s)		CH_2Cl_2
Menthofuran	−2·13			CCl_4
Menthofuran	−2·40			CH_2Cl_2
Furfurol	−2·53	−1·41	1 : 2	CCl_4
Furfurol	−2·78	−1·63	1 : 2	CH_2Cl_2
Furfural	−2·90 (s)	−2·40, −1·78 (d, q)	1 : 2	CCl_4
Furfural	−3·05 (s)	−2·60, −1·93 (d, q)	1 : 2	CH_2Cl_2
2-Furoic acid	−2·90 (q)	−2·65, −1·88 (q, q)	1 : 2	CH_2Cl_2
3-Furoic acid	−3·40, −2·73	−2·08	2 : 1	$CDCl_3$
2-Methyl-3-furoic acid	−2·53	−1·98	1 : 1	$CDCl_3$
4-Methyl-3-furoic acid	−3·40, −2·58			$CDCl_3$
Cafestol	−2·60 (d)	−1·58 (d)	1 : 1	CH_2Cl_2
Columbin	−2·83	−1·73	2 : 1	CH_2Cl_2
Limonin	−2·83	−1·75	2 : 1	$CDCl_3$ or CH_2Cl_2

Resonance bands marked s, d, t, q, m, appeared as singlets, doublets, triplets, quartets and higher multiplets, respectively. Bands not marked appeared as a single unresolved (but possibly multiplet) band.

δ measured in ppm from H_2O external reference.

"τ" $= 5{\cdot}2 + \delta_{H_2O\,ext}$ (very approximate conversion)

TABLE 10.70 H–H COUPLING CONSTANTS IN CYCLES SEC^{-1} FOR SOME SUBSTITUTED FURANS[256]

Substance	J_{24}	J_{25}	J_{34}	J_{35}	J_{45}	
2-Methylfuran			3·12 (0·10)	1·03 (0·07)	1·90 (0·08)	$J_{CH_3-3} = 0{\cdot}91$
2-Furanmethanethiol			3·25	0·73	1·91	$J_{CH_2-3} = 0{\cdot}79$
2-Furfurylamine			3·18 (0·10)	0·76 (0·10)	1·94 (0·10)	$J_{CH_2-3} = 0{\cdot}84$
2-Furfurol			3·17 (0·05)	0·84 (0·07)	1·90 (0·05)	
2-Furanacrylic acid			3·44 (0·07)		1·84 (0·08)	
2-Furanacrolein			3·46 (0·08)		1·83 (0·04)	
2-Furamide			3·57 (0·07)	0·72 (0·07)	1·76 (0·04)	
Ethyl 2-furoate			3·47 (0·09)	0·91 (0·06)	1·76 (0·05)	
2-Furoic acid			3·51 (0·07)	0·86 (0·09)	1·73 (0·08)	
Ethyl 2-furoylacetate			3·60 (0·09)	0·82 (0·10)	1·72 (0·05)	
2-Furfural			3·62 (0·05)	0·82 (0·06)	1·65 (0·08)	$J_{CH-5} = 0{\cdot}81$
2-Nitro furan			3·66 (0·10)	0·98 (0·07)	1·92 (0·07)	
2-Furoyl trifluoromethyl ketone			3·70 (0·06)	0·76 (0·06)	1·70 (0·04)	
2-Furoyl chloride			3·79 (0·07)	0·79 (0·07)	1·70 (0·05)	
5-Chloromethyl furfural			3·67 (0·07)			
3-Furoic acid	0·8 (0·1)	1·5 (0·1)			1·8 (0·1)	
2-Methyl-3-furoic acid					1·94 (0·1)	
4-Methyl-3-furoic acid		1·6 (0·1)				$J_{CH_3-5} = 1{\cdot}4$
2,3-Difuroic acid					1·83 (0·1)	

TABLE 10.71 SUBSTITUENT EFFECTS ON THE RING HYDROGEN CHEMICAL SHIFTS (ppm) OF SUBSTITUTED FURANS[256]

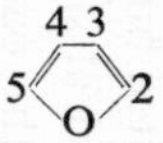

Compound	(*a*) Pure liquids			(*b*) In 10% acetone solution				(*c*) 10% CH_2Cl_2 solution		
	δ_3	δ_4	δ_5	δ_2	δ_3	δ_4	δ_5	δ_3	δ_4	δ_5
2-Methylfuran	+0·38	+0·08	+0·10		+0·435	+0·153	+0·205	+0·43	+0·15	+0·23
2-Furanmethanethiol	+0·15	+0·03	+0·03							
2-Furfurylamine	+0·13	−0·05	−0·08		+0·242	+0·100	+0·137			
2-Furfurol	−0·04	−0·01	−0·05		+0·151	+0·076	+0·089	+0·15	+0·15	+0·05
Furan	0·00	0·00	0·00	0·00	0·000	0·000	0·000	0·00	0·00	0·00
2-Furanacrylic acid					−0·408	−0·144	−0·136			
2-Furanacrolein					−0·551	−0·209	−0·226			
Ethyl 2-furoate	−0·85	−0·18	−0·33		−0·774	−0·183	−0·226			
2-Furoic acid					−0·795	−0·181	−0·220	−0·88	−0·10	−0·08
Ethyl 2-furoylacetate	−1·13	−0·35	−0·33		−0·959	−0·255	−0·298			
Furfural	−1·10	−0·35	−0·48		−0·987	−0·294	−0·366	−0·83	−0·15	−0·23
2-Nitro furan	−1·08	−0·43	−0·33		−1·065	−0·402	−0·318			
2-Furoyl trifluoromethyl ketone					−1·198	−0·373	−0·454			
2-Furoyl chloride	−1·20	−0·38	−0·48							
5-Chloromethyl furfural	−1·10	−0·45								
2,5-Dimethyl furan	+0·50	+0·50								
3-Furoic acid†				−0·70		−0·39	−0·17			
2-Methyl-3-furoic acid†						−0·29	+0·08			
4-Methyl-3-furoic acid†				−0·52			+0·20			
2,3-Difuroic acid†						−0·64	−0·42			

Chemical shifts measured in ppm from the corresponding absorption band in furan.
(*a*) Actual furan values from dioxane internal reference are $H_2 = -3{\cdot}83$, $H_3 = -2{\cdot}75$ ppm.
(*b*) Actual furan values from acetone internal reference are $H_2 = -5{\cdot}48$, $H_3 = -4{\cdot}36$ ppm.
† Unknown concentration, very dilute.

attached to ethylenic carbon atoms and this is thought to be due to ring current effects. This is illustrated by comparing the τ-values in furan and dihydropyran

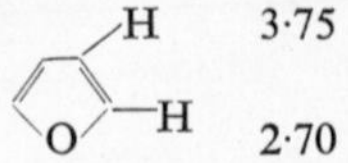

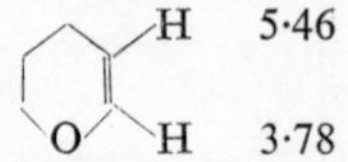

Abraham and Bernstein[255, 256] have examined a large number of substituted furans and their results are summarised in Tables 10.70 and 10.71. Examination of Table 10.70 reveals that the coupling constant J_{34} increases significantly as the electronegativity of the substituent in the 2-position is increased (the compounds are arranged in order of increasing electronegativity of substituent). A similar, though less well-defined, correlation has also been observed for substituted pyrroles[256]. Interesting linear correlations between the J_{34} coupling constants and the sum of the angles $(\theta_1 + \theta_2)$, and between J_{23} values and the sum of the angles $(\theta_2 + \theta_3)$ have been found by Abraham and Bernstein.

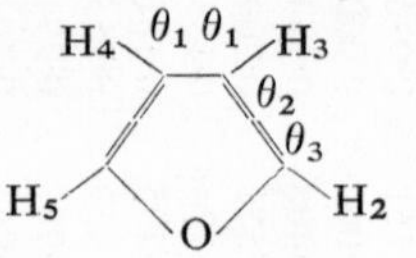

In many cases hydrogen nuclei in the substituent group couple with the adjacent ring hydrogen nucleus: similar long range coupling is observed in simple olefinic systems. The hydrogen resonance chemical shifts for substituted furans are found to be solvent dependent (see Table 10.71 where the chemical shifts are reported in ppm from the corresponding resonance band of the parent compound) and this seriously limits the extent to which correlations between chemical shifts and the nature of the substituents can be expected[256]. Nevertheless, from the data for 2-substituted furans in acetone solution mutual linear relationships between the chemical shifts are obtained and can be represented by the equations

$$\delta_3 = 3{\cdot}08\,\delta_4 - 0{\cdot}42$$

$$\delta_5 = 1{\cdot}23\,\delta_4 + 0{\cdot}10$$

2-substituted furans are seen to show different substitution effects from those observed in the spectra of substituted benzenes. Two factors appear to be operating in the shielding of the furan hydrogen nuclei (i) the electronegativity of the substituents and (ii) conjugation of the substituents with the electron system of the ring. An increase in electronegativity of the substituent causes an overall deshielding of the ring hydrogen nuclei, the nearest nuclei being influenced the most. Conjugation effects will disturb the π-electron system of the ring and thus influence the shielding of the ring hydrogen nuclei. Although no account was taken of neighbour anisotropic effects in this investigation, the observed chemical shifts were explained qualitatively using the above considerations. It was also found that for multiply-substituted furans, the chemical shifts of the ring hydrogen nuclei can be predicted approximately by assuming the shielding contributions from various substituents to be additive.

10.17 Pyrrole and Substituted Pyrroles

The ^{1}H resonance spectrum of the ring hydrogen nuclei in pyrrole shown in both Fig. 10.35 and 8.52 is seen to be composed of two chemically shifted multiplets, the low field multiplet being assigned to the α-hydrogen nuclei [257] (see also Section 8.19.5). Although quadrupolar broadening effects associated with the nitrogen nucleus cause the NH absorption band to be very broad, they do not prevent the NH hydrogen nucleus from coupling with the ring hydrogen nuclei. This coupling gives rise to multiplet splittings comparable with those from

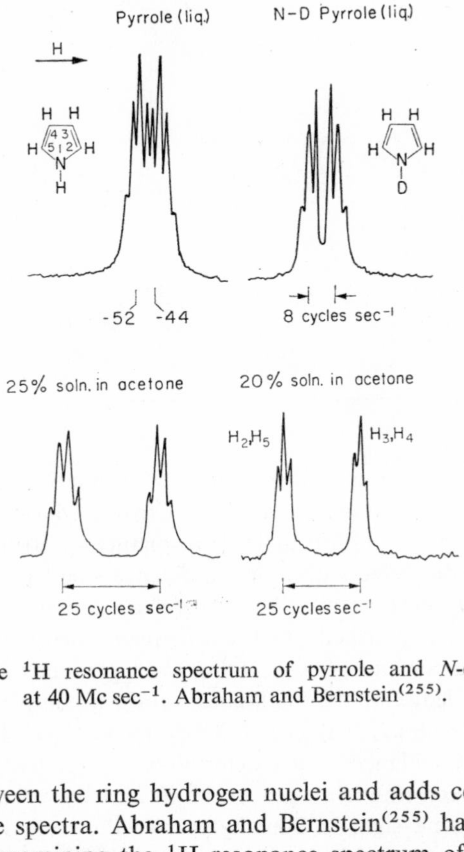

Fig. 10.35 The ^{1}H resonance spectrum of pyrrole and *N*-deuteropyrrole at 40 Mc sec^{-1}. Abraham and Bernstein[255].

the coupling between the ring hydrogen nuclei and adds considerably to the complexity of the spectra. Abraham and Bernstein[255] have eliminated this complication by examining the ^{1}H resonance spectrum of *N*-deuteropyrrole (see Fig. 10.35) where this coupling constant no longer features. It is also possible to remove the fine structure from this source by examining pyrrole in solvents such as *N,N*-dimethylformamide or dimethyl sulphoxide which promote the rapid exchange of NH hydrogen atoms by a base catalysed mechanism[258].

The ^{1}H resonance spectrum of pyrrole was explained originally by assuming the cross ring coupling constants J_{23} and J_{24} to be equal: subsequent examination of the spectra of substituted pyrroles showed this not to be the case[256, 258].

A list of coupling constants found in the spectra of substituted pyrroles is given in Table 10.72. Gronowitz and his co-workers[258] give the following average values for the ring coupling constants: $J_{34} = 3{\cdot}40$ to $3{\cdot}80$, $J_{45} = 2{\cdot}40$ to $3{\cdot}10$, $J_{25} = 1{\cdot}95$ to $2{\cdot}20$ and $J_{24} = 1{\cdot}35$ to $1{\cdot}50$ cycles sec^{-1}. The deceptively simple spectrum for pyrrole (Fig. 10.35) can be shown to be consistent with these average values[256]. The characteristic values of coupling constants between the ring hydrogen nuclei can often be used to assist in the assignment of the spectra

TABLE 10.72 ^{1}H SPIN COUPLING CONSTANTS (CYCLES SEC^{-1}) IN SUBSTITUTED PYRROLES[258]

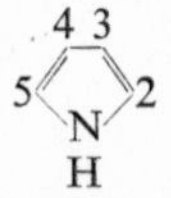

Substituents	J_{34}	J_{45}	J_{35}/J_{24}	J_{25}	Other couplings
3-CH_3, 4-$CO_2C_2H_5$				2·20	$J_{15} = 3{\cdot}05$; $J_{CH_3-2} = 1{\cdot}00$
2-CH_3, 3-$CO_2C_2H_5$		3·10			
2-CHO, 5-CH_3	3·75				$J_{CH_3-4} = 0{\cdot}65$; $J_{CH_3-3} = 0{\cdot}45$
2-CHO	3·80	2·40	1·40		$J_{14} \sim J_{45}$; $J_{CHO-5} = 1{\cdot}15$
2-$COCH_3$	3·75	2·40	1·35		$J_{13} = 2{\cdot}50$; $J_{14} \sim J_{45}$; $J_{15} = 3{\cdot}00$
2-CH_3	3·40	2·45	1·50		
3-CO_2CH_3		2·80	1·40	1·95	

of substituted pyrroles. A monosubstituted thiocyanation product of pyrrole has been shown to be a 2-substituted derivative from a consideration of the coupling constants and chemical shifts in its ^{1}H resonance spectrum[259]. Such determinations will be conducted with more confidence when a larger range of substituted pyrroles has been examined and the characteristic values of the coupling constants firmly established. It should be mentioned that it is not possible to predict coupling constants between ring hydrogen nuclei in condensed pyrroles from a knowledge of the analogous values in simple pyrroles since in some condensed pyrroles J_{45} values of $\sim 3{\cdot}5$ cycles sec^{-1} have been reported[260].

Cohen and McLauchlan[261] have determined the relative signs of the coupling constants between ring hydrogen nuclei in 2-carboxypyrrole and find that they all have the same sign. In 2-methylpyrrole the methyl group is coupled with the 3-hydrogen ($J_{23} = 0{\cdot}65$ cycles sec^{-1}) and the 4-hydrogen nuclei ($J_{24} = 0{\cdot}45$ cycles sec^{-1}): an independent investigation of the 2,3- and 2,5-dimethyl derivatives failed to detect any coupling of this type.

Hoffman and Gronowitz[262] have drawn attention to the similar values of J_{34} coupling constants between ring hydrogen nuclei in furans, pyrroles and thiophenes. Table 10.73 summarises the typical values of H—H coupling constants found in aromatic-type molecules. An attempt has been made to explain the magnitude of the J_{24} and J_{25} coupling constants in pyrroles in terms of the hybridisation of the nitrogen atom[262].

TABLE 10.73 TYPICAL H–H SPIN COUPLING CONSTANTS (CYCLES SEC^{-1}) IN MONOCYCLIC AROMATIC MOLECULES

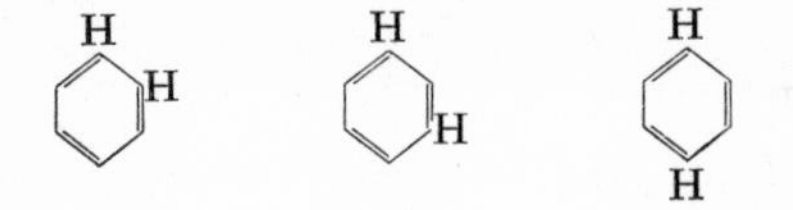

7·0 to 9·2	1·1 to 3·1	0·0 to 0·7
+	+	+

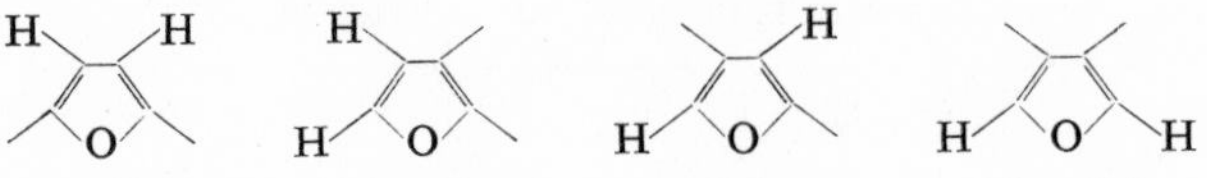

3·2 to 3·8	1·8 to 2·0	~0·7	1·3 ~ 1·5
+	+	+	

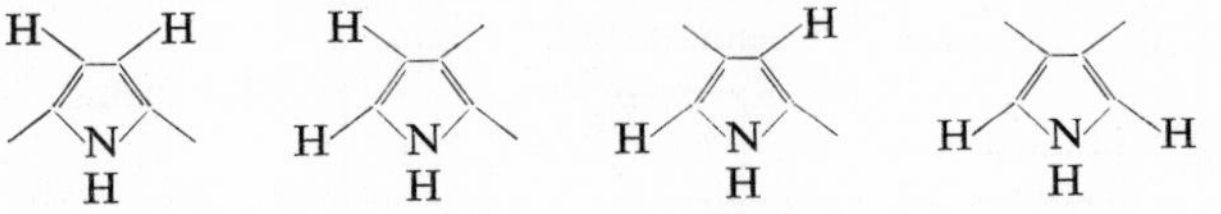

3·4 to 3·8	2·4 to 3·1	1·3 to 1·5	1·9 to 2·2
+	+	+	

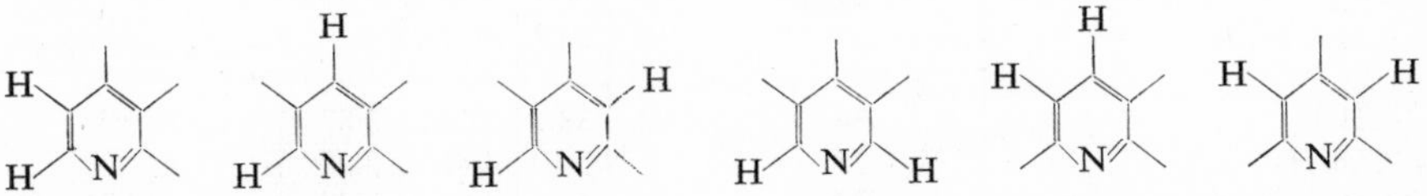

3·9 to 5·1	1·4 to 2·5	0·6 to 1·2	0·0 to 0·3	7·4 to 8·6	1·0 to 1·6

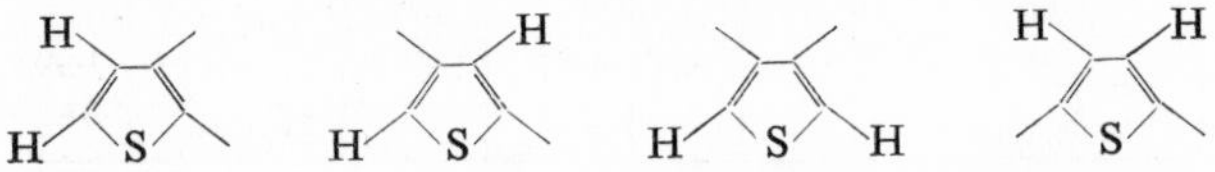

4·9 to 5·8	1·2 to 1·7	3·2 to 3·7	3·4 to 4·3
+	+	+	+

Only the relative signs of the coupling constants have been determined for furans, thiophenes and pyrroles but they are likely to be absolutely positive.

The limits given for the coupling constants were obtained from the values of the coupling constants quoted elsewhere in this chapter.

10.17.1 Chemical Shifts in Pyrroles

At the present time, the effects of solvents on the shielding of hydrogen nuclei in pyrroles have not been fully determined and therefore it is not possible to reach a detailed understanding of the factors influencing shielding in these molecules. Table 10.74 gives a list of τ-values for a series of pyrroles examined in dioxane solution[258]. By comparing the chemical shifts of the substituted derivatives with those of pyrrole itself one finds that electron withdrawing substituents have a deshielding effect on the ring hydrogen nuclei, while electron donating groups have the opposite effect. Abraham and his co-workers[263] have measured the chemical shifts of several methyl pyrroles as part of a wider study of the effects of hydrochloric acid on the compounds. The ions formed by this procedure have been shown by NMR to be protonated at the α-carbon atom as shown in (I)

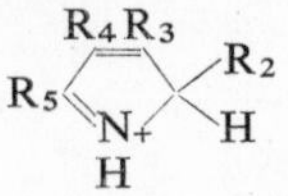

(I)

TABLE 10.74 THE ^{1}H CHEMICAL SHIFTS OF SOME SUBSTITUTED PYRROLES[258]

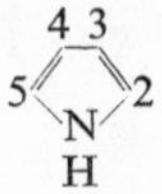

Substituents	Concentration % in dioxane	Chemical shifts †† ppm				Side chains
		"τ_2"	"τ_3"	"τ_4"	"τ_5"	
None	34	3·27	3·83	3·83	3·27	
3-CH_3, 4-$CO_2C_2H_5$	22	3·53			2·70	τ_{3-CH_3} = 7·76
2-CH_3, 3-$CO_2C_2H_5$	27			3·56†	3·50†	
2-CHO, 5-CH_3	29		3·07	4·01		τ_{CHO} = 0·70; τ_{CH_3} = 7·72
2-CHO	34		3·07	3·74	2·87	τ_{CHO} = 0·53
2-$COCH_3$	29		3·10	3·81	2·98	
2-CH_3	32		4·25	4·06	3·48	τ_{CH_3} = 7·76
3-CO_2CH_3	26	2·56		3·43	3·24	
2,5-$(CH_3)_2$; 3,4-$(SCN)_2$	10					τ_{CH_3} = 7·70
1-CH_3, 2,5-$(CH_3)_2$	39‡		4·41	4·41		$\tau_{2,5-CH_3}$ = 7·99; τ_{1-CH_3} = 6·95

† The assignment is uncertain.
‡ These shifts were obtained in cyclohexane solution.
†† Chemical shifts were measured from the solvent dioxane and converted to the τ scale

$$\text{“}\tau\text{”} = \delta^{\text{nt}}_{\text{Dioxane}} + 6{\cdot}43$$

Table 10.75 compares the chemical shifts of analogous hydrogen nuclei in monosubstituted pyrroles and thiophenes[258]. Although different solvents were used for the two series of compounds, the agreement between the shielding contributions is surprisingly good.

The total effect of methyl substitution on the chemical shifts of the ring hydrogen nuclei of thiophene, furan and pyrrole has been shown to be ~ +0·75 ppm. This is essentially similar to the total effect for both β-hydrogen nuclei in ethylenic systems of general formula $CH_2{=}CXCH_3$ and would appear to be characteristic of systems with sp^2 hybridised carbon atoms. In propylene, where the effect of methyl substitution can be estimated by comparing its chemical shifts with that of ethylene[265], the contributions to the shielding of a β-hydrogen nucleus *trans* to the CH_3 group is +0·425 ppm and for one in the β-*cis* position, +0·325 ppm (total contribution 0·75 ppm). Table 10.76 gives the observed chemical shift data for the methyl substituted derivatives of furan, pyrrole and thiophene[264]. All samples were examined as dilute solutions in tetramethylsilane. Reddy and Goldstein[264] consider that the total contribution to the shielding of the hydrogen nuclei in an ethylenic system by a methyl group is a measure of the charge transferred from the substituent to the ethylenic systems by some long range process which probably has its origin in hyperconjugation effects. By replacing the ethylenic system with a conjugated structure it is possible that the total transferred charge might be redistributed over the conjugated system. Some justification for this hypothesis is provided by the

TABLE 10.75 ^{1}H CHEMICAL SHIFTS (ppm) OF RING HYDROGEN NUCLEI IN RELATED PYRROLES AND THIOPHENES[258]

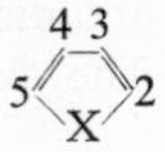

Compound	Chemical shifts (ppm)			
	δ_2	δ_3	δ_4	δ_5
2-Methylpyrrole		+0·42	+0·23	+0·21
2-Methylthiophene		+0·37	+0·24	+0·28
2-Pyrrolealdehyde		−0·76	−0·09	−0·40
2-Thiophenealdehyde		−0·65	−0·10	−0·45
2-Acetylpyrrole		−0·73	−0·02	−0·29
2-Acetylthiophene		−0·57	0·00	−0·28
3-Carbomethoxypyrrole	−0·71		−0·40	−0·03
3-Carbomethoxythiophene	−0·78		−0·47	+0·05

Chemical shifts measured in ppm relative to the signals from the corresponding α- and β-hydrogens in the parent compounds pyrrole and thiophene.

TABLE 10.76 THE ^{1}H CHEMICAL SHIFTS OF METHYL SUBSTITUTED DERIVATIVES OF FURAN, PYRROLE AND THIOPHENE[264]

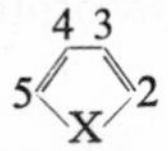

Compound	τ_2	τ_3	τ_4	τ_5	$\tau_{Me(2)}$	$\tau_{Me(3)}$
Furan	2·7	3·75	3·75	2·70		
2-Methylfuran		4·19	3·90	2·87	7·83	
2,5-Dimethylfuran		4·31	4·31		7·86	
Thiophene	2·85	3·02	3·02	2·85		
2-Methylthiophene		3·37	3·25	3·11	7·62	
3-Methylthiophene	3·29		3·25	2·97		7·83
2,5-Dimethylthiophene		3·61	3·61		7·70	
Pyrrole	3·49	3·85	3·85	3·49		
2-Methylpyrrole		4·24	4·02	3·66		

Tetramethylsilane was used as both a solvent and reference material.

chemical shift of the aromatic hydrogen atoms in toluene which are shielded to the extent of 0·15 ppm compared with those in benzene: for five aromatic hydrogen nuclei the total shift will be 0·75 ppm which compares very well with the total contribution observed in ethylenic systems. All the molecules considered in Table 10.76 are known to show some aromatic character and they lend themselves to an investigation of this effect. From an examination of the data in the table it would appear that such an effect is in operation. The manner in which the effect is distributed over the ring hydrogen nuclei depends to some extent on the heteroatom and the observed chemical shifts are roughly as expected from our knowledge of conjugation in the various molecules[264].

10.17.2 Porphyrins

Porphyrins are a class of complex organic molecules which have been studied extensively by NMR[267, 268, 271]. The skeleton of these molecules has the general form

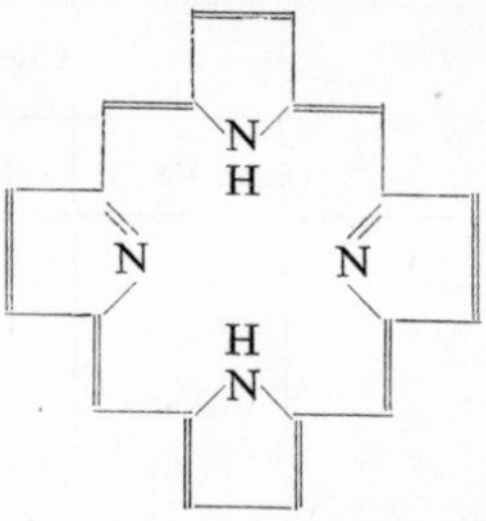

and is seen to contain a closed conjugated system. The resulting induced ring current of the porphyrin system influences markedly the chemical shifts of all hydrogen nuclei on or near the porphyrin ring. Figure 10.36 shows the ^{1}H resonance spectrum of a typical porphyrin, coproporphyrin – 1, where the substituents are P = $CH_2CH_2COOCH_3$ and M=CH_3[269]. The band at very low field (τ = 0·04 ppm) has been assigned to the four methine hydrogen nuclei: thus, as a result of the ring current effect, the methine hydrogen nuclei are deshielded 2·7 ppm to low fields of the absorption bands of the analogous benzene

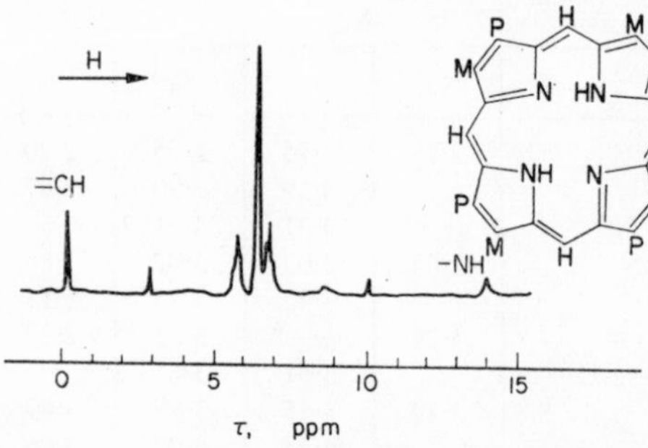

FIG. 10.36 The ^{1}H resonance spectrum of coproporphyrin – 1 in $CDCl_3$ at 60 Mc sec^{-1}. Becker, Bradley and Watson[269].

hydrogen nuclei. The broad absorption band at very high fields ($\tau = 13{\cdot}89$) is attributed to the NH hydrogen nuclei, which are shielded by the ring current effect (13·00 ppm to high fields of the NH absorption of pyrrole). Also influenced by the aromatic ring currents are the ring methyl substituents, which have a chemical shift ($\tau = 6{\cdot}45$) indicating them to be less shielded than a normal methyl group on an unsaturated carbon atom. Attempts to give a quantitative description to the effects of ring currents on the shielding of hydrogen nuclei in porphyrins have not proved completely successful but the relative shielding of the nuclei can be predicted[268]. The NMR hydrogen resonance spectrum of coproporphyrin − 1 confirms that the four pyrrole rings are equivalent due to a tautomeric equilibrium involving exchange of NH protons at a rate greater than 200 cycles sec^{-1}. Many substituted porphyrins have been examined by NMR and the effects of the substituents on the chemical shifts have been measured[269, 270].

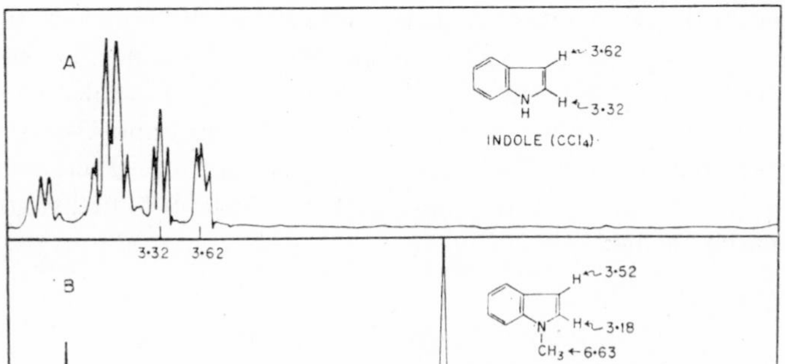

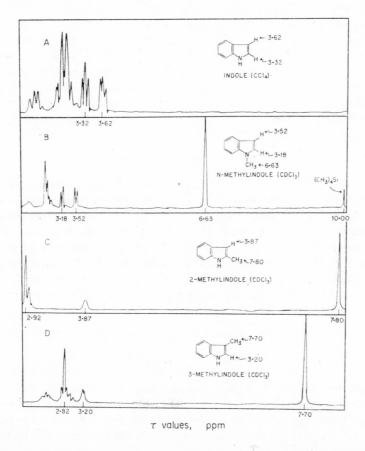

FIG. 10.37 The ¹H resonance spectra of indole and some methyl substituted indoles at 60 Mc sec^{-1} (τ values are marked on the spectra). Cohen, Daly, Kny and Witkop[272].

10.17.3 Indoles

Cohen and his co-workers[272] have demonstrated that NMR can be used successfully to determine the extent of substitution at the 2- and 3-positions of the indole molecule (structure I)

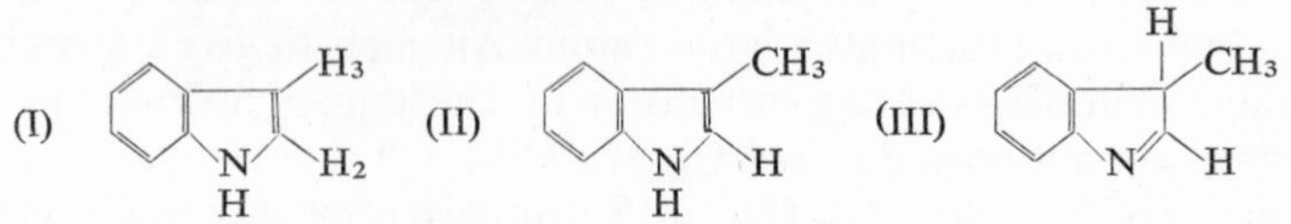

Figure 10.37 shows the ^{1}H resonance spectrum of indole and from examination of the spectra of methyl substituted indoles of known structure (Fig. 10.37) one can assign the two high field triplets in the indole spectra to the H_2- ($\tau = 3{\cdot}32$ ppm) and H_3-hydrogen atoms ($\tau = 3{\cdot}62$ ppm). The triplet splitting arises because the α- and β-hydrogen nuclei couple not only with each other but also with the NH hydrogen nucleus. This is confirmed by the removal of the splitting in the spectrum of *N*-methylindole (Fig. 10.37) where the 2- and 3-hydrogen nuclei appear as a pair of doublet absorption bands. From the spectra shown in Fig. 10.37 one can exclude the possibility of indolenine tautomerism in the ground state of the indole derivatives. For example, 3-methyl indole shows the spectrum expected for structure II and not for structure III which would have an absorption band in the region $\tau = 8{\cdot}60$ for a methyl group on a saturated carbon atom.

10.18 Pyridine and Related Molecules

Bernstein, Pople and Schneider[273] have given a detailed analysis of the complex NMR spectrum of pyridine (Fig. 10.38 shows part of the spectrum recorded at 100 Mc sec^{-1}). The assignments of bands to the 2- and 3-hydrogen nuclei were made with the aid of specifically deuterated pyridines. It is found that the 2-hydrogen nuclei are the least shielded and that the 4-hydrogen nucleus is less shielded than the 3-hydrogen nuclei: a similar order for the shielding of the 2, 3 and 4-carbon atoms is observed in the ^{13}C spectrum of pyridine[205]. From the analysis of the ^{1}H resonance spectrum of pyridine the H—H coupling constants were calculated to be

$$J_{23} = 5{\cdot}5 \quad J_{24} = 1{\cdot}9 \quad J_{34} = 7{\cdot}5 \text{ cycles sec}^{-1}.$$

$$J_{25} = 0{\cdot}9 \quad J_{35} = 1{\cdot}6 \quad J_{26} = 0{\cdot}4$$

Pyridines are known to show pronounced solvent effects in their NMR spectra[275] and since none of the reported investigations of such systems has made allowance for solvent effects (by examining the molecules at low dilution in an inert solvent) the available chemical shift data do not lend themselves to a quantitative evaluation.

Contributions to the shielding of the ring hydrogen nuclei from induced ring current effects must also be taken into account. Hall, Hardisson and Jackman have attempted to estimate the magnitude of the ring current shielding contributions in several heterocyclic molecules, using an extension of the self-consistent form of the molecular orbital theory[247, 367]. Their results serve to indicate the effect of ring substitution on the induced ring current. If the electronegativity of a group attached to a ring is increased there is a corresponding increase in the ring current due to this electronegative centre increasingly counteracting the localising effect of the nitrogen in the ring.

Brügel[274] has measured the ^{1}H resonance spectra of more than 150 pyridine derivatives and Table 10.77 gives a selection of the observed chemical shifts. Generally speaking, the chemical shifts reflect the electronegativity of

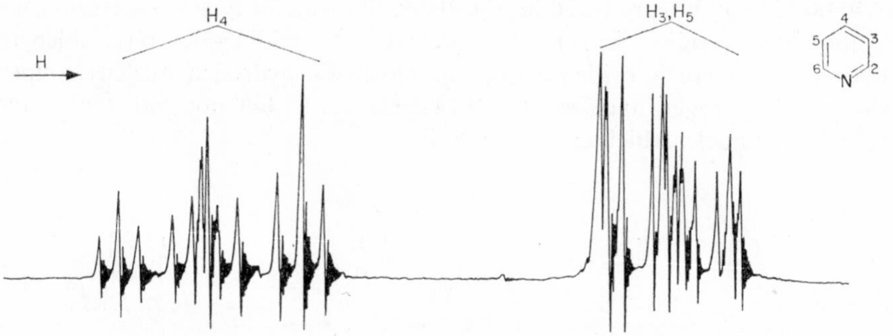

FIG. 10.38 The ^{1}H resonance spectrum of the H_3, H_4 and H_5 hydrogen nuclei of pyridine at 100 Mc sec^{-1}. By courtesy of Varian Associates.

TABLE 10.77 THE ^{1}H CHEMICAL SHIFTS OF SOME MONOSUBSTITUTED PYRIDINES[274]

Compound [a]	Chemical shifts ppm [b]				
	"τ_2"	"τ_3"	"τ_4"	"τ_5"	"τ_6"
Pyridine	1·71 [c]	3·23	2·85		
4-Methylpyridine	1·45	2·96			
4-Chloropyridine	1·38	2·73			
4-Cyanopyridine	0·95	2·00			
4-Aminopyridine	1·56	3·36			
3-Methylpyridine	1·46		2·55	2·87	1·46
3-Chloropyridine	1·27		2·27	2·71	1·38
3-Cyanopyridine	0·78		1·53	2·19	0·91
2-Methylpyridine		3·00	2·57	3·08	1·49
2-Chloropyridine		2·51	2·17	2·61	1·42
2-Aminopyridine		3·30	2·56	3·40	1·89

[a] Compounds examined as pure liquids if possible: if solid, they were examined in dimethylsulphoxide solution.

[b] The chemical shifts are τ values extrapolated from chemical shifts measured from water used as an external reference.

[c] The low field shift of the H_2 nuclei has been explained in terms of the magnetic anisotropic effects of the nitrogen atom and intramolecular electric field effects associated with the local dipole moment from the nitrogen lone pair[466].

the substituents but in some cases anisotropic effects are important. In the spectra of the 2-substituted derivatives it is found that CH_3 and NH_2 substituents cause an increase in shielding of the ring hydrogen nuclei while the CN group causes a deshielding[276-278]. These effects can be interpreted in terms of the inductive and mesomeric tendencies of the substituent groups[276].

The observed coupling constants in substituted pyridines are similar to those in pyridine with the exception of compounds having strong electron donors in the 3-position[274].

Kowalewski and de Kowalewski[279] have made a detailed ABCD analysis of the ^1H spectra of several 3-substituted pyridines examined as pure liquids and their results are given in Table 10.78. The spectrum of 3-bromopyridine at 40·00 Mc sec^{-1} reproduced in Fig. 10.39, illustrates a typical spectrum for a 3-substituted pyridine[279]. In the spectrum of pyridine-3-carboxy-aldehyde (not shown) there is evidence that the aldehydic hydrogen nucleus couples with the β-hydrogen nucleus (J = 0·44 cycles sec^{-1}) but not with the α- and γ- hydrogen nuclei which are nearer to it.

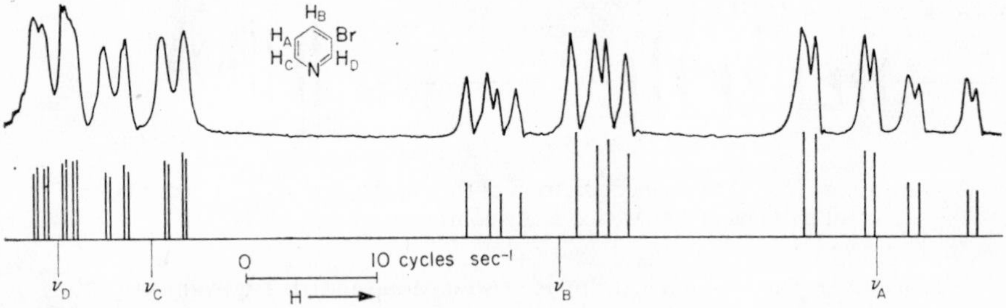

FIG. 10.39 The ^1H resonance spectrum of 3-bromopyridine at 40·00 Mc sec^{-1}. Kowalewski and de Kowalewski[279].

Kowalewski and co-workers[363] have also examined the complex ABCD type spectra given by several 2-pyridines. An indication of the magnitudes of the typical coupling constants in such compounds can be obtained by considering

TABLE 10.78 ^1H SPIN COUPLING CONSTANTS (CYCLES SEC^{-1}) OF SEVERAL 3-SUBSTITUTED PYRIDINES[279]

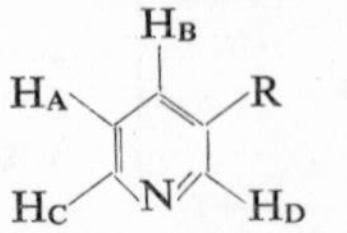

R	J_{AB}	J_{AC}	J_{BC}	J_{AD}	J_{BD}	J_{CD}
$COCH_3$	7·99	4·87	1·79	0·83	2·12	0·00
COH	7·85	5·00	1·81	0·88	2·02	0·00
Br	7·81	4·76	1·44	0·81	2·39	0·30
Cl	8·22	4·69	1·52	0·71	2·49	0·30

the values obtained from an ABCD analysis of the ¹H spectrum of 2-chloropyridine

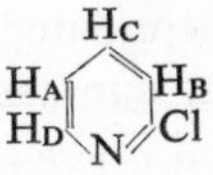

	J_{AB}	J_{AC}	J_{AD}	J_{BC}	J_{BD}	J_{CD}	
	0·96	7·22	4·67	7·75	0·75	1·98	cycles sec^{-1}

The α-, β- and γ-picolines have also been investigated by NMR and the effects of the methyl substitution on both the chemical shifts and the coupling constants are shown to be small[280, 281]. Coupling between the methyl groups and the ring hydrogen nuclei was not observed in the spectra of the picolines. Table 10.79 gives the spectral parameters deduced from an exact analysis of the picoline spectra.

For complicated spectra some assistance in making band assignments is often available from the results of multiple spin decoupling experiments.

TABLE 10.79 THE ¹H SPIN COUPLING CONSTANTS (CYCLES SEC^{-1}) OF METHYL SUBSTITUTED PYRIDINES[281]

Compound	J_{35}	J_{34}	J_{45}	J_{56}	J_{36}	J_{46}	J_{23}	J_{24}	J_{25}	J_{26}
α-Picoline 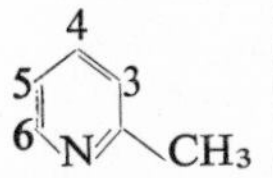	1·0	7·4	7·4	4·5	0·6	2·0				
β-Picoline 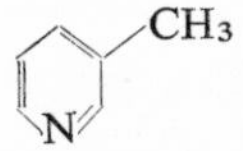			7·9	4·8		1·7		2·5	1·2	0·0
γ-Picoline 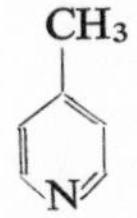	1·6			5·1	0·9		5·1		0·9	0·0

Figure 10.40 shows the "uncoupled" ¹H resonance spectrum of 1, 2, 5, 6-tetrahydropyridine and several spectra which indicate the spectral changes occurring when certain hydrogen nuclei are decoupled by double irradiation[282]. By examining the decoupled spectra, the olefinic hydrogen nuclei on C_3 and C_4 can be assigned to their respective absorption bands. The multiplet at 575 cycles sec^{-1} ($\tau = 4{\cdot}25$) is in the olefinic region of the spectrum and consists basically of an AB quartet with additional fine structure due to spin interaction with the hydrogen nuclei on the C_2 and C_5 atoms. The AB quartet arises from the resonance bands of the two olefinic hydrogen nuclei being separated by a chemical shift small compared with the coupling constant between them. In Fig. 10.40 the high field portion of the AB multiplet is shown to sharpen when the C_2

hydrogen nuclei are irradiated and if it is assumed that $J_{23} > J_{35}$ then this implies that the hydrogen nucleus on C_3 is more shielded than that on C_4. This is further supported when the hydrogen nuclei at C_5 are irradiated and the low field part of the AB multiplet sharpens. The spectrum can be further simplified by multiple irradiations. Shoolery[282] has discussed other examples of how the spin decoupling double irradiation technique can be used to support spectral assignments.

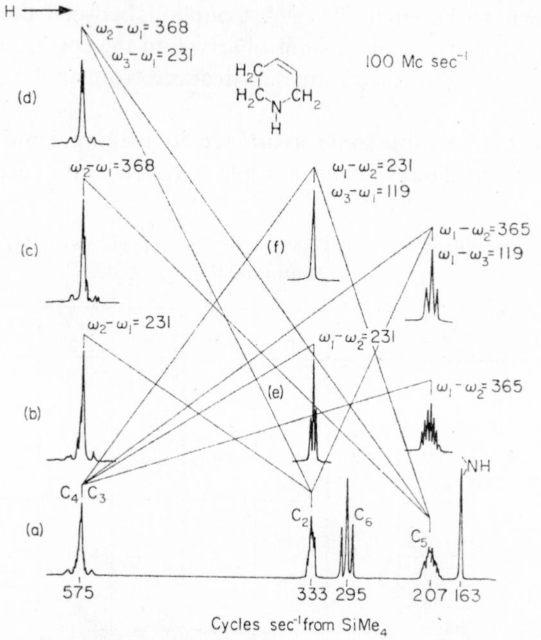

FIG. 10.40 (a) Uncoupled ^1H resonance spectrum of 1,2,5,6-tetrahydropyridine at 100 Mc sec^{-1}; (b) olefinic hydrogen nuclei observed while decoupling hydrogen nuclei on C_2; (c) olefinic hydrogen nuclei observed while decoupling hydrogen nuclei on C_5; (d) olefinic hydrogen nuclei observed while decoupling hydrogen nuclei at both C_2 and C_5; (e) C_2 hydrogen nuclei observed while decoupling olefinic hydrogen nuclei; (f) C_2 hydrogen nuclei observed while decoupling both the olefinic and the C_5 hydrogen nuclei. Shoolery[282].

10.19 THE EFFECTS OF SOLVENTS ON THE ^1H RESONANCE SPECTRA OF UNSATURATED HETEROCYCLIC RING COMPOUNDS

Schaefer and Schneider[275] have found that the shielding of ring hydrogen nuclei in unsaturated heterocyclic compounds depends to a large extent on solvent effects: these effects are discussed in Section 10.39.3.

10.20 QUINOLINES

Table 10.80 gives the chemical shifts of the ring hydrogen nuclei in a series of alkyl substituted quinolines dissolved in hexane, acetone and benzene solvents[283]. Examination of Table 10.80 shows that large specific solvent effects are operating, particularly in the benzene solutions. Although no satisfactory explanation has been suggested for the preferential solvent shifts found for certain positions in the molecules, it can be seen that the solvent effects increase as the distance between the nitrogen and hydrogen atoms increases. However,

TABLE 10.80 ^{1}H CHEMICAL SHIFTS OF A SERIES OF ALKYL SUBSTITUTED QUINOLINES IN HEXANE, ACETONE AND BENZENE[283]

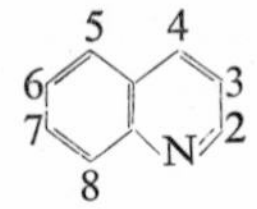

Compound	Solvent 5 mole % solution in	H_2	H_3	H_4	H_5	H_6	H_7	H_8
Quinoline	n-Hexane	−1·32	0·33	−0·45				−0·60
	Acetone	−1·42	0·02	−0·62				−0·80
	Benzene	−0·88	1·10	0·35				−0·42
7-Ethylquinoline	n-Hexane	−1·30	0·38	−0·40	−0·07	0·22		−0·43
	Acetone	−1·42	0·07	−0·77	−0·37	0·00		−0·43
	Benzene	−0·98	1·02	0·22	0·42			−0·35
6,8-Dimethyl-quinoline	n-Hexane	−1·28	0·33	−0·33	0·20		0·20	
	Acetone	−1·35	0·10	−0·62	0·07		0·07	
	Benzene	−0·95	0·98	0·25				
5,8-Dimethyl-quinoline	n-Hexane	−1·32	0·32	−0·60		0·38	0·18	
	Acetone	−1·43	0·02	−0·85		0·22	0·03	
	Benzene	−1·02	0·97	0·05				
5,7-Dimethyl-quinoline	n-Hexane	−1·27	0·37	−0·57		0·43		−0·25
	Acetone	−1·38	0·08	−0·85		0·25		−0·23
	Benzene	−0·98	0·95	0·05		0·93		−0·20
4,6-Dimethyl-quinoline	n-Hexane	−1·10	0·52		−0·13		0·12	−0·50
	Acetone	−1·18	0·25		−0·33		−0·05	−0·45
	Benzene	−0·88	1·13		0·38		0·62	−0·45
3,8-Dimethyl-quinoline	n-Hexane	−1·20		−0·17				
	Acetone	−1·30		−0·48				
	Benzene	−0·97		0·47				
2,8-Dimethyl-quinoline	n-Hexane		0·38	−0·32				
	Acetone		0·13	−0·60				
	Benzene		0·10	0·27				

Chemical shifts were measured in ppm from $CHCl_3$ external reference: corrections for bulk diamagnetic susceptibility effects were made.
"τ" $= 3{\cdot}5 + \delta_{CHCl_3 ext.}$ (very approximate conversion).

no simple relationship is evident, H_5, H_6 and H_7 being shifted less than H_3 and H_4 in benzene solutions. The large preferential solvent shifts can be put to good use in assisting in the assignment of the complex spectra observed for substituted quinolines. Table 10.81 gives the coupling constants featured in the spectra of alkyl quinolines[283]. The *ortho* coupling constant J_{23} (4·0 ± 0·2

TABLE 10.81 THE ^{1}H SPIN COUPLING CONSTANTS (CYCLES SEC^{-1}) BETWEEN THE RING HYDROGEN NUCLEI OF SOME ALKYL SUBSTITUTED QUINOLINES[283]

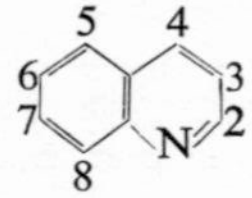

Compound	J_{23}	J_{24}	J_{34}	J_{48}	J_{56}	J_{57}	J_{67}	J_{78}	J_{68}
Quinoline	4·1 ± 0·2	1·8 ± 0·2	8·5 ± 0·3	1·0 ± 0·2				8·2 ± 0·3	2·1 ± 0·2
2,8-Dimethylquinoline	4·2 ± 0·2	2·2 ± 0·2							
4,6-Dimethylquinoline						1·8 ± 0·2		8·5 ± 0·2	
5,7-Dimethylquinoline	4·0 ± 0·1	1·6 ± 0·1	8·4 ± 0·1	0·5					
5,8-Dimethylquinoline	4·1 ± 0·1	1·7 ± 0·1	8·4 ± 0·2				7·2 ± 0·3		
6,8-Dimethylquinoline	4·1 ± 0·1	1·8 ± 0·1	8·2 ± 0·2						
7-Ethylquinoline	4·1 ± 0·1	1·8 ± 0·1	8·3 ± 0·2	0·8 ± 0·2	8·4 ± 0·1				

J_{23}, J_{34} and J_{24} have the same relative sign in quinoline[427].

cycles sec^{-1}) is much smaller than the *ortho* coupling constant in benzene derivatives ($\sim$ 8 cycles sec^{-1}).

Spin coupling between hydrogen nuclei in different rings in fused ring systems has been observed in the hydrogen resonance spectra of 5,7-dichloro- and 5,7-dimethylquinoline[(284)]. The ^{1}H resonance spectra of 8-methylquinoline, 5,7-dimethylquinoline and 5,7-dichloroquinoline are shown in Fig. 10.41 and the

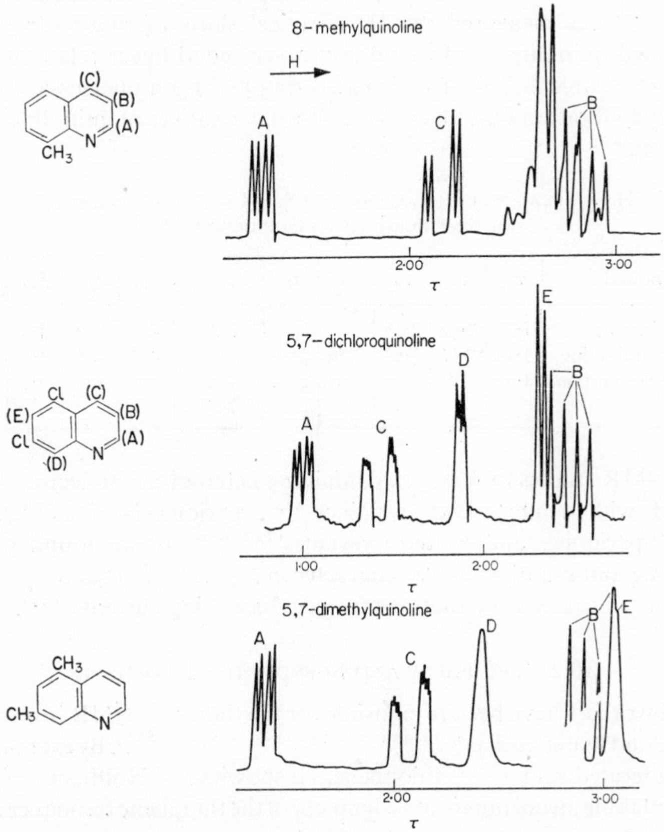

FIG. 10.41 The ^{1}H resonance spectra at 60 Mc sec^{-1} of (a) 8-methylquinoline, (b) 5,7-dichloroquinoline, (c) 5,7-dimethylquinoline. The CH_3 group resonances are not shown in (a) and (c). Anet[(284)].

chemical shifts and coupling constants deduced from the spectra are given in Table 10.82. For all the spectra, the quartets A and B have been assigned to the 2- and 3-hydrogen atoms respectively: band C (assigned to the 4-hydrogen atom) shows common splittings with bands A and B showing that H_2, H_3 and H_4 are all coupled with each other. However, band C in the spectra of the disubstituted quinolines is seen to be an octet which means that H_4 must be coupled to another hydrogen nucleus in addition to H_2 and H_3. Since there are no more hydrogen nuclei in the pyridine ring the additional splitting must arise from coupling with a hydrogen nucleus in the other ring. Other assignments indicated on the spectra are based on empirical considerations of the effects of CH_3 and Cl substitution (band D to H_8 and band E to H_6). Hence, in the dichloro compound it appears that H_8 is coupled with the H_4 hydrogen nucleus while in the dimethyl derivative it cannot be decided whether the 4-hydrogen nucleus is coupled to the 6- or the 8-hydrogen nucleus because of the broad unresolved nature of their absorption bands. Schaefer also observed a weak J_{48} coupling constant ($\sim$ 1·0 cycles sec^{-1}) in the spectra of methyl quinolines(283).

Seiffert(356) has measured the ^{1}H chemical shifts of ring hydrogen nuclei in substituted quinolines and found that a very good linear relationship exists between the chemical shift of an isolated ring hydrogen nucleus and its C—H out-of-plane vibration frequency. Mononitro derivatives of quinoline have also been studied(490).

TABLE 10.82 ^{1}H CHEMICAL SHIFTS (τ VALUES) AND SPIN COUPLING CONSTANTS (CYCLES SEC^{-1}) OF SOME SUBSTITUTED QUINOLINES(284)

Compound	τ_2	τ_3	τ_4	τ_6	τ_8	τ_{methyl}	J_{23}	J_{34}	J_{24}	J_{48}	J_{68}
8-Methylquinoline	1·28	2·88	2·18			7·23	4·1	7·9	1·8		
5,7-Dichloroquinoline	1·18	2·66	1·61	2·50	2·05		4·2	8·5	1·6	0·8	2·0
5,7-Dimethylquinoline	1·38	2·95	2·09	3·08	2·43	7·65 7·57	3·9	8·6	1·7	0·8	

Other NMR studies of nitrogen containing heterocyclic molecules have been concerned with 4-substituted pyridines(285), pyridine-1-oxides(285), pyrrolines(286), 2-pyridones and related molecules(287, 426). It was found possible to estimate the amount of aromatic character in 2-pyridone rings from considerations of the shielding contributions from induced ring currents(287).

10.21 THIOPHENE AND SUBSTITUTED THIOPHENES

Several workers have been responsible for the thorough NMR investigation of thiophene and its derivatives(174, 233, 253, 262, 288–298, 469, 471). By examining specifically deuterated samples of thiophene, Gronowitz and Hoffman(289) have succeeded in making an unequivocal assignment of the thiophene resonance spectrum.

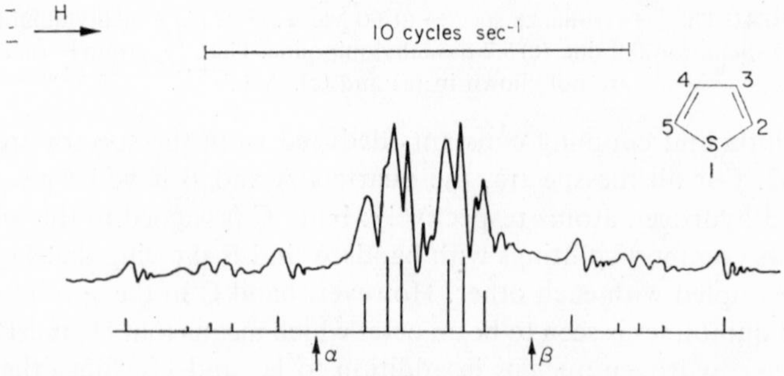

FIG. 10.42 The ^{1}H resonance spectrum of thiophene at 40 Mc sec^{-1}. Gronowitz and Hoffman(289).

The coupling constants in thiophene have the same sign[261] and are calculated to be $J_{23} = 5{\cdot}15$, $J_{24} = 1{\cdot}05$, $J_{25} = 2{\cdot}75$ and $J_{34} = 3{\cdot}45$ cycles sec^{-1} (all values accurate to $\pm 0{\cdot}2$ cycles sec^{-1}). Pure thiophene gives rise to a complex AA′BB′ spectrum as shown in Fig. 10.42, the α-hydrogen multiplet being 0·125 ppm

TABLE 10.83 CHEMICAL SHIFTS (ppm) OF SUBSTITUTED THIOPHENES, RELATIVE TO THE SHIFTS OF THE α- AND β-HYDROGENS IN THIOPHENE[293]

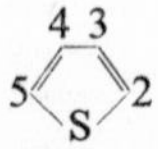

Substituent	2-substituted thiophenes			3-substituted thiophenes		
	δ_3	δ_4	δ_5	δ_2	δ_4	δ_5
NO_2	−0·82	+0·03	−0·30	−0·95	−0·60	−0·03
SO_2Cl	−0·73	−0·06	−0·45			
CN	−0·47	0·00	−0·28	−0·63	−0·20	−0·15
CHO	−0·65	−0·10	−0·45	−0·79	−0·45	−0·03
$COCH_3$	−0·57	0·00	−0·28	−0·68	−0·47	+0·02
COC_2H_5	−0·55	0·00	−0·28	−0·70	−0·48	+0·04
COCl	−0·88	−0·06	−0·44	−1·05	−0·50	−0·03
CO_2CH_3	−0·70	+0·05	−0·20	−0·78	−0·47	+0·05
SCN	−0·30	+0·05	−0·28	−0·25	−0·05	−0·05
C≡CH	−0·15	+0·16	+0·12			
I	−0·13	+0·33	−0·01	−0·06	0·00	+0·19
Br	+0·05	+0·27	+0·11	+0·12	+0·08	+0·10
2-Thienyl	−0·08	+0·11	+0·15			
SH	0·00	+0·20	+0·07	+0·22	+0·20	+0·10
SCH_3	+0·03	+0·18	+0·05	+0·33	+0·10	+0·03
CH_3	+0·37	+0·24	+0·28	+0·45	+0·22	+0·14
OCH_3	+0·94	+0·43	+0·82	+1·10	+0·38	+0·20
OC_2H_5	+0·92	+0·43	+0·81			
$OC(CH_3)_3$	+0·77	+0·38	+0·65	+0·78	+0·36	+0·22
NH_2	+0·95	+0·45	+0·85	+1·25	+0·53	+0·25

Chemical shifts measured in ppm from the α- and β-hydrogen resonances in thiophene: the measurements have been extrapolated to infinite dilution in cyclohexane solution

$$``\tau_2" = 2{\cdot}84 + \delta_2$$

$$``\tau_3" = 3{\cdot}03 + \delta_3$$

The actual τ values for the α- and β-hydrogen nuclei are 2·81 and 2·96 respectively (Appendix B).

to low fields of that of the β-hydrogen nuclei[289]. Mono- and dideuterated thiophenes have simpler NMR spectra which allow of a less ambiguous assignment than does the spectrum of thiophene (see Fig. 10.43)[289]. In Tables 10.83 and 10·84 extensive lists of chemical shifts and spin coupling constants found in monosubstituted thiophenes are reproduced[293]. All shifts were measured at infinite dilution in cyclohexane solution where the effects of intermolecular interactions would be expected to be eliminated. The chemical shifts given in

Table 10·83 have been measured with respect to the absorption band of the α- and β-hydrogen nuclei in thiophene: the extrapolated "τ" values are also given. Detailed estimations of the effect of the diamagnetic anisotropy of the substituent group on the shielding of the ring hydrogen nuclei have shown these effects to play only a minor part in the overall shielding; consequently, the

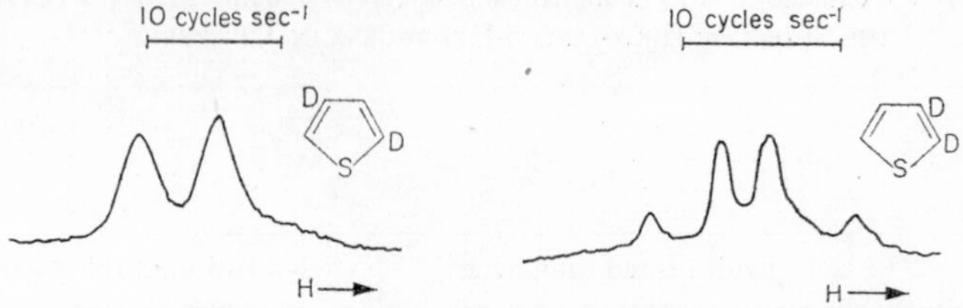

FIG. 10.43 The ^{1}H resonance spectra of two dideuterated thiophenes at 40 Mc sec^{-1}. Gronowitz and Hoffman[289].

TABLE 10.84 H—H COUPLING CONSTANTS (CYCLES SEC^{-1}) IN MONOSUBSTITUTED THIOPHENES[292]

2-substituted thiophenes 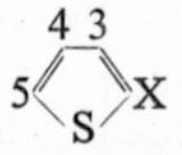

Substituents	J_{34}	J_{35}	J_{45}	Side-chain couplings
NO_2	4·0	1·7	5·1	
SO_2Cl	3·8	1·4	5·1	
CN	4·5		4·5	
CHO	3·8		5·0	$J_{5-X} = 0{\cdot}9$
$COCH_3$	3·6	1·1	5·0	
COC_2H_5	3·6	1·2	5·0	
COCl	3·4	1·4	5·0	
CO_2CH_3	3·6	1·3	5·0	
SCN	3·7	1·4	5·2	
C≡CH	3·5	1·4	5·1	$J_{3-X} \approx 0{\cdot}4$
I	3·8	1·3	5·0	
Br	4·0	1·7	5·0	

3-substituted thiophenes 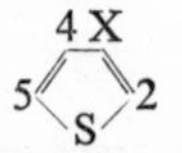

Substituents	J_{24}	J_{25}	J_{45}	Side-chain couplings
NO_2	1·5	3·2	5·4	
CN	1·4	2·8	5·1	
CHO	1·4	2·7	5·2	$J_{5-X} = 0{\cdot}7$
$COCH_3$	1·3	2·8	5·1	
COCl	1·4	2·9	5·1	
CO_2CH_3	1·3	2·9	5·1	
SCN	1·5	3·0	5·0	
I	1·2	2·9	4·9	

chemical shifts of the various ring hydrogen nuclei are determined largely by the electron density surrounding them. Such chemical shifts have been shown to be consistent with the expected inductive and resonance effects on the electron densities. For 3-substituted thiophenes, smaller values of chemical shift are measured for hydrogen nuclei in the 4-position compared with the 2-position nuclei while the chemical shifts of the 2-position hydrogen nuclei in 3-substituted thiophenes are larger than those of the 3-position nuclei in 2-substituted thiophenes.

In 2-methyl thiophene[262] the hydrogen nucleus at the 3-position is coupled to the methyl group, with a spin coupling constant of 1·00 to 1·15 cycles sec^{-1}, and the hydrogen in the 4-position is likewise coupled, with a J_{H-CH_3} value of 0·2–0·5 cycles sec^{-1}, the two coupling constants being opposite in sign. Similarly in 3-methyl thiophene, the methyl group couples with the 2-hydrogen nucleus (0·9–1·25 cycles sec^{-1}) and with the 4- and 5-hydrogen nuclei (0·4 to 0·5 cycles sec^{-1}). A great deal of interest has been centred on these long range coupling constants due to their proposed hyperconjugative origin[174, 297]. It has been estimated that if hyperconjugation is responsible for such long range coupling constants then the two methyl groups in a 2,3-dimethyl thiophene should show a $J_{CH_3-CH_3}$ value of about 1 cycle sec^{-1}[297]; a $J_{CH_3-CH_3}$ value of this order of magnitude has been observed in the hydrogen resonance spectrum

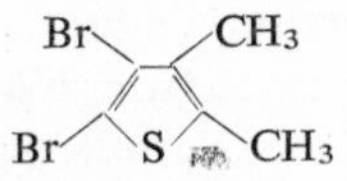

of 2,3-dimethyl-4,5-dibromothiophene[406]. The ^{1}H spectrum consists of two chemically shifted quartets ($J_{CH_3-CH_3}$ = 0·75 cycles sec^{-1}).

10.22 Thiazole and Methyl Substituted Thiazoles

Thiazole is a 5-membered ring compound containing both nitrogen and sulphur as hetero atoms

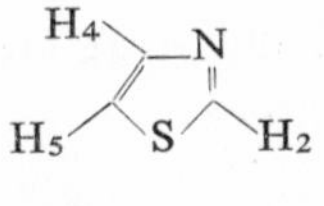

Table 10.85 ^{1}H Chemical Shifts and Spin Coupling Constants of some Substituted Thiazoles[266]

Compound	Chemical shifts† (ppm)						Coupling constants (cycles sec^{-1})		
	δ_2	"τ_2"	δ_4	"τ_4"	δ_5	"τ_5"	J_{24}	J_{45}	J_{25}
Thiazole	−3·85	1·4	−2·83	2·4	−2·25	3·0	0	3·1	1·8
2-CH_3-thiazole			−2·53	2·7	−2·08	3·1		3·6	
4-CH_3-thiazole	−3·67	1·5			−1·80	3·4			2·0
2,4-di-CH_3-thiazole					−1·57	3·6			

† δ refers to the chemical shift measured in ppm from a water external reference.
"τ" = 5·2 + $\delta_{H_2O\,ext.}$

By examining the hydrogen resonance spectra of a series of methyl substituted thiazoles it was possible to assign unequivocally the spectrum of thiazole itself(266). Table 10.85 summarises the chemical shift and coupling constant data for the thiazoles examined in this study. Ring hydrogen nuclei in the 2- and 4-positions give rise to broader signals than the hydrogen nucleus at the 5-position due to the quadrupolar broadening effects of the adjacent nitrogen atom. The effect of the nitrogen atom on its immediate neighbours is also reflected in the J_{24} and J_{25} coupling constant values: although the 2-hydrogen nucleus is separated from the 4- and 5-hydrogen nuclei by the same number of bonds the coupling across the sulphur atom (J_{25} = 2·0 cycles sec^{-1}) is much larger than that across the nitrogen atom (J_{24} is too small to be detected).

LARGE COMPLEX ORGANIC MOLECULES

Although NMR measurements can reveal many important structural features of complex organic molecules of unknown structure, alone they can never lead to a complete structural analysis. The technique is most valuable (i) in the early stages of an investigation when it can both characterise and estimate the relative amounts of various nuclei in the molecule and (ii) in the final stages of an analysis when one is trying to decide which of several structural possibilities prevails in the molecule. Very little information concerning the overall skeleton of the molecule can be obtained from NMR evidence but it is sometimes possible to indicate the presence of various types of component rings within the molecule (such as aromatic, cyclohexane, oxygen and nitrogen heterocyclic rings). In favourable cases conformational information can also be deduced from the NMR spectra. It is intended to discuss a few examples of the application of this technique to the determination of molecular structure of complex organic molecules.

10.23 Alkaloids

The ^1H resonance spectra of the alkaloids lunacrine and lunine(299) have shown the molecular structures to be

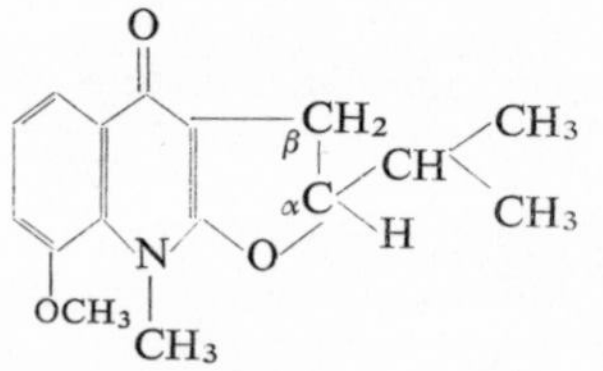

(I) Lunacrine

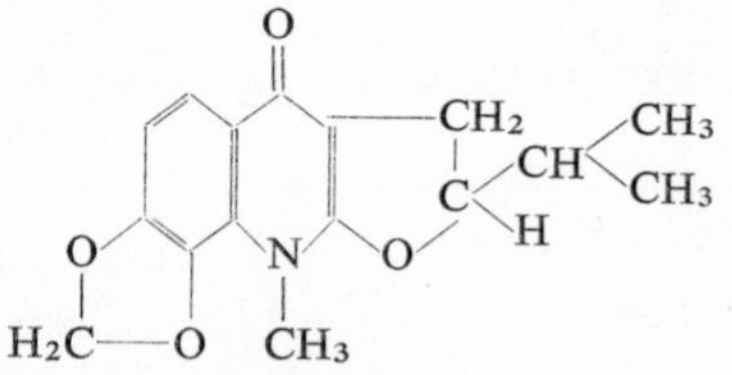

(II) Lunine

Figure 10.44 shows the NMR spectra of the two alkaloids and it is instructive to examine the assignments of the absorption bands in the spectra in some detail.

Lunacrine. The spectrum of lunacrine is composed of seven fairly well-resolved regions and these are labelled *a* to *g* on the spectrum shown in Fig. 10.44. On the basis of chemical shifts, the absorption bands in the regions *a* and *b* are assigned to the aromatic ring hydrogen nuclei, the multiplet *c* to the α-hydrogen atom of the dihydrofurano ring, the two strong bands at *d* to the *N*-methyl and the methoxyl nuclei, the complex multiplet at *e* to the β-hydrogen atoms of the dihydrofuran ring and multiplets *f* and *g* to the side chain hydrogen atoms. The group of lines in regions *e* and *c* constitute an ABX spectrum from the two β-hydrogen nuclei (A, B) which have bands well-shifted from the absorption band of the α-hydrogen nucleus (X) of the furan ring. A detailed analysis of this

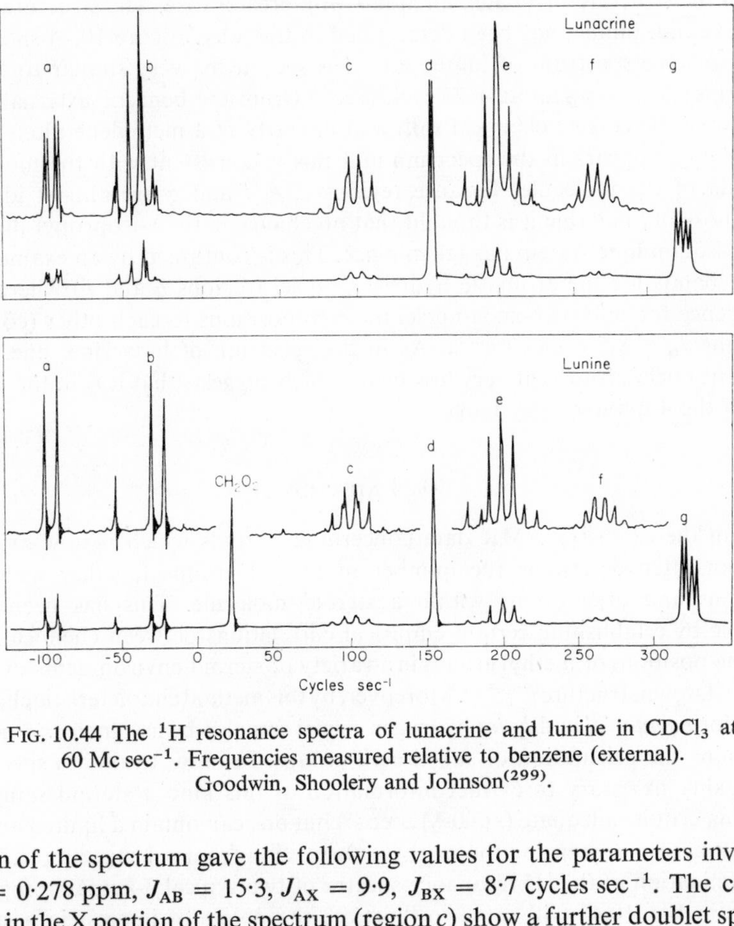

FIG. 10.44 The ^{1}H resonance spectra of lunacrine and lunine in $CDCl_3$ at 60 Mc sec^{-1}. Frequencies measured relative to benzene (external). Goodwin, Shoolery and Johnson(299).

region of the spectrum gave the following values for the parameters involved: $\delta_{AB} = 0{\cdot}278$ ppm, $J_{AB} = 15{\cdot}3$, $J_{AX} = 9{\cdot}9$, $J_{BX} = 8{\cdot}7$ cycles sec^{-1}. The components in the X portion of the spectrum (region *c*) show a further doublet splitting due to coupling with another nucleus Y of spin $I = \frac{1}{2}$ ($J_{XY} = 7$ cycles sec^{-1}). This suggests that the side chain alkyl group is an isopropyl group and the high field absorption bands *f* and *g* support this conclusion. An interesting feature of the spectrum is provided by the methyl groups of the isopropyl side chain: molecular asymmetry causes them to be non-equivalent as evidenced by the two chemically-shifted doublets in the spectrum (region *g*). The groups of bands in region *a* and *b* originate from the three non-equivalent aromatic hydrogen nuclei (an ABX system). Analysis of the ABX spectrum leads to the values

$J_{AX} = 7$, $J_{AB} = 7$, $J_{BX} = 2$ cycles sec^{-1} and $\delta_{AB} = 0{\cdot}15$ ppm. From a knowledge of the characteristic values of coupling constants in aromatic systems it can be deduced that the three aromatic hydrogen nuclei must be adjacent to each other. The final assignment of the methoxy group to its position adjacent to the nitrogen of the quinoline ring was made from chemical shift data obtained on substituted quinolines of known structure.

Lunine. The elucidation of the NMR spectrum of lunacrine enables one to obtain the structure of related alkaloids with greater ease. The structure of the leaf alkaloid, lunine, has been determined in this way. Figure 10.44 shows the ^{1}H resonance spectrum of lunine and it is seen to be very similar to that of lunacrine. A new signal at $+23$ cycles sec^{-1} (from the benzene external reference) with the correct chemical shift and intensity of a methylene dioxy group ($-CH_2O_2$) appears in the spectrum and this is consistent with the molecular formula of the molecule. Because regions *c*, *e*, *f* and *g* are almost identical with those of lunacrine it is thought that no change in the α-isopropyl-dihydrofuran-4-quinolone system has taken place. This is confirmed by an examination of the bands for the aromatic hydrogen nuclei (regions *a* and *b*) where there is evidence for only two such nuclei in *ortho* positions to each other (coupling constant $J_0 = 8{\cdot}5$ cycles sec^{-1}). As in the spectrum of lunacrine, one of the aromatic nuclei absorbs at very low fields which suggests that it is in the 5-position of the 4-quinolone system.

10.24 Steroids

From the extensive NMR data concerning steroids which is now available one can often determine the number of methyl groups together with their positions and orientations within a steroid molecule. This has been made possible by establishing certain empirical correlations between chemical shifts and the positions of methyl groups in a variety of steroid environments in molecules of known structure[98,492]. Moreover, by this method characteristic chemical shifts for *equatorial* and *axial* hydrogen nuclei can also be assigned and used to determine the orientation of substituent groups. In order to obtain spectra of the quality necessary to extract information of this kind a steroid sample of 5–25 mg is quite adequate (at 60 Mc sec^{-1}) but one can obtain a limited amount of information concerning the methyl substitution from a 1 mg sample.

Examination of the ^{1}H resonance spectra of two typical 3-ketoallopregnanes shown in Fig. 10.45 will serve to illustrate the points of interest in a steroid resonance spectrum[301, 303]. In the high field region of the spectrum ($\tau = 7{\cdot}3$ to $9{\cdot}3$) we observe a complex broad absorption band surmounted by several sharp narrow absorption bands. The broad band is attributed to hydrogen atoms attached directly to the ring skeleton: the broadening is due to (i) the short relaxation times of such nuclei in the absence of rapid molecular motion and (ii) unresolved spin–spin interactions between the similarly shielded nuclei. Conversely, the angular methyl groups, which have long relaxation times due to their rapid free rotation, show intense sharp signals. Other absorption bands distinguishable from the broad envelope are those for methylene groups adjacent to double bonded systems, to olefinic hydrogen atoms, or to hydroxyl groups, and for hydrogen atoms on the same carbon atom as an oxygen, fluorine, chlorine or nitrogen atom[301]. Because of the complexity of the broad absorption envelope only limited information can be obtained from this part of the

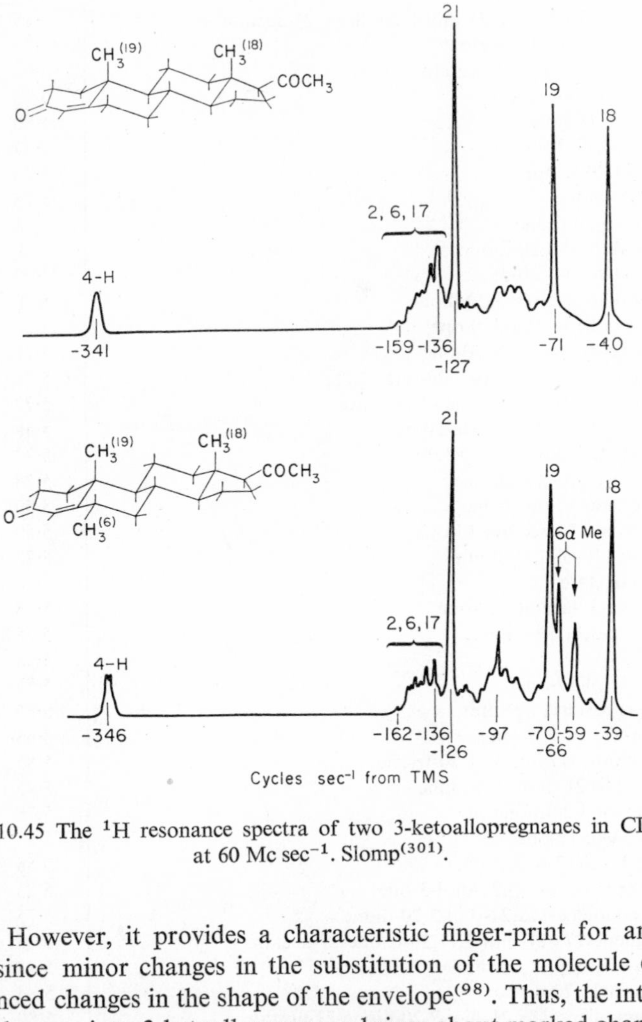

FIG. 10.45 The ^{1}H resonance spectra of two 3-ketoallopregnanes in $CDCl_3$ at 60 Mc sec^{-1}. Slomp[301].

spectrum. However, it provides a characteristic finger-print for any steroid molecule since minor changes in the substitution of the molecule can result in pronounced changes in the shape of the envelope[98]. Thus, the introduction of a methyl group into 3-ketoallopregnane brings about marked changes in the unresolved region of the spectrum (see Fig. 10.45).

Undoubtedly, the most valuable NMR contribution to the determination of steroid structures is found in the characteristic chemical shifts of the angular methyl groups at C–18 and C–19[98, 302]. These chemical shifts are quite sensitive to the nature and position of other substituents[98] as can be seen by examining Table 10.86 which lists the measured chemical shifts for 18–CH_3

TABLE 10.86 ^{1}H CHEMICAL SHIFTS OF THE 18–CH_3 AND 19–CH_3 GROUPS IN SEVERAL STEROIDS[98]

Steroid[a]	$\delta_{C_{18}}$ ppm	$\delta_{C_{19}}$ ppm
$\Delta^{5(6)}$-Cholestene-3β-acetate	5·70	5·38
Δ^4-Androstene-17β-ol-3-one	5·60	5·20
Δ^4-Androstene-17β-ol-17α-methyl-3-one	5·50	5·20
19-Nortestosterone	5·58	—
Δ^4-Pregnene-9α-fluoro-11β,21-diol-3,20-dione-21-acetate	5·45	4·83
Δ^4-Pregnene-21-ol-3,11,20-trione	5·73	5·00
Δ^4-Pregnene-3,20-dione-21-acetate	5·70	5·20
$\Delta^{5(6)}$-Pregnene-3β-ol-20-one	5·75	5·38
Δ^4-Pregnene-3,20-dione	5·80	5·25
Allopregnane-3,11,20-trione	5·83	5·20
Pregnane-3,11,20-trione	5·78	5·18
Pregnane-3,20-dione	5·75	5·38
Allopregnane-3,20-dione	5·78	5·38
Δ^4-Pregnene-11β-ol-3,20-dione	5·50	4·93
Δ^4-Pregnene-11α-ol-3,20-dione	5·70	5·10
Δ^4-Pregnene-11α-acetoxy-3,20-dione	5·70	5·15
$\Delta^{5(6),16}$-Pregnadiene-3β-ol-20-one	5·50	5·35
$\Delta^{5(6)}$-Pregnene-3β-methoxy-20-one	5·78	5·40
$\Delta^{5(6)}$-Pregnene-3β,21-diacetoxy-20-one	5·73	5·38
$\Delta^{5(6)}$-Pregnene-3β,21-diol-20-one-21-acetate	5·73	5·38
$\Delta^{5(6),16}$-Pregnadiene-3β-acetate-20-one	5·48	5·35
Allopregnane-3,20-dione-21-acetate	5·73	5·38
Δ^4-Pregnene-3,11,20-trione	5·78	5·00
$\Delta^{5(6)}$-Androstene-3β-ol-17-one	5·50	5·38
$\Delta^{5(6)}$-Androstene-3β-acetate-17-one	5·50	5·35
Allopregnane-11α-ol-3,20-dione	5·73	5·25
Stigmasteryl acetate	5·70	5·40
$\Delta^{5(6)}$-Pregnene-3β-acetate-20-one	5·78	5·38
Δ^4-Androstene-3,11,17-trione	5·55	4·98
Estrone	5·55	—
Androstane-3β-ol-17-one	5·55	5·53
5,6-Dihydroergosteryl acetate	5·85	5·58
Δ^4-Pregnene-17α-ol-3,20-dione	5·68	5·18
Pregnane-4-chloro-17α-ol-3,11,20-trione	5·85	5·20
Δ^4-Pregnene-11β,21-diol-3,20-dione	5·45	4·93
Pregnane-11α-ol-3,20-dione	5·78	5·28
Androstane-3α-ol-17-one	5·58	5·53
Etiocholane-3α-ol-17-one	5·58	5·48
$\Delta^{4,17(20)}$-Pregnadiene-11β,21-diol-3-one	5·23	4·93
$\Delta^{4,9(11)}$-Pregnadiene-17α,21-diol-3,20-dione	5·75	5·08
Δ^1-Allopregnene-17α,21-diol-3,11,20-trione-21-acetate	5·75	5·13
Pregnane-3α-acetoxy-11,20-dione	5·83	5·25
Pregnane-3α-ol-11,20-dione	5·83	5·30
$\Delta^{4,9(11)}$-Pregnadiene-17α,21-diol-3,20-dione-21-acetate	5·80	5·05
Ergosterol	5·78	5·45
Δ^5-Cholestene-3-one	5·70	5·23
$\Delta^{5(6),7}$-Cholestadiene-3β-acetate	5·78	5·48

Benzene external reference used.

[a] Solutions in $CDCl_3$.

Approximate "τ" = 3·5 + $\delta_{C_6H_6ext.}$

and 19–CH_3 groups reported in the literature. The differences in shielding of the methyl groups are thought to be largely due to neighbour anisotropic effects[(23)]. Several workers have pointed out that it is possible to calculate the chemical shifts of C–18 and C–19 angular methyl groups by assuming the contributions to the methyl hydrogen shielding from the various substituents to be additive[(301, 304)]. Slomp and MacKellar[(302)] have examined a series of steroids with hydrocarbon side chains and despite the complexity of the spectra in the methyl region they were able to assign the angular methyl group absorption bands.

Usually the conformation of any particular skeletal hydrogen atom cannot be decided since its absorption band is invariably submerged in the broad unresolved region of the spectrum. However, if an oxygen atom is attached to the same carbon atom as the hydrogen atom, then the resonance signal of the latter is displaced to low fields and is readily detectable. Shoolery and Rogers[(98)] have examined the ^{1}H resonance spectra of a series of hydroxylated steroids (see Table 10.87) and have shown that the chemical shifts of such hydrogen

TABLE 10.87 ^{1}H CHEMICAL SHIFTS OF HYDROGEN NUCLEI ON THE SUBSTITUTED CARBON ATOM IN A SERIES OF HYDROXYLATED STEROIDS[(98)]

Compound	Proton location	Substituent and orientation	Proton conformation	Chemical shift† ppm
Androsterone	C_3	3α-OH	*Equatorial*	2·28
Epiandrosterone	C_3	3β-OH	*Axial*	2·83
5-Isoandrosterone	C_3	3α-OH	*Axial*	2·83
3α-Hydroxypregnane-11,20-dione	C_3	3α-OH	*Axial*	2·90
11β-Hydroxyprogesterone	C_{11}	11β-OH	*Equatorial*	1·95
9α-Fluorocorticosterone acetate	C_{11}	11β-OH	*Equatorial*	1·93
Corticosterone	C_{11}	11β-OH	*Equatorial*	2·05
11β-21-Dihydroxy-4,17-(20)-pregnadiene-3-one	C_{11}	11β-OH	*Equatorial*	1·95
11α-Hydroxyprogesterone	C_{11}	11α-OH	*Axial*	2·38
11α-Hydroxypregnane-3,20-dione	C_{11}	11α-OH	*Axial*	2·38
11α-Hydroxyallopregnane-3,20-dione	C_{11}	11α-OH	*Axial*	2·50
19-Nortestosterone	C_{17}	17β-OH	*Axial*	2·75

† Chemical shifts were measured in ppm from benzene external reference. The steroids were examined as solutions in $CDCl_3$. "τ" $= 3{\cdot}5 + \delta_{C_6H_6ext.}$

nuclei, for any particular position in the molecule, depend on whether the hydrogen nuclei are in *axial* or *equatorial* positions[(98)]. Using empirical data of this type it is often possible to obtain valuable conformational information for steroid molecules of unknown structure.

Richards and co-workers[(351)] have characterised several 11-keto steroids using the NMR technique.

10.25 Fatty Acids

Hopkins and Bernstein have applied the NMR technique to characterise a large series of fatty acids[305]. Chemical groups in fatty acids such as hydroxy, acetoxy, epoxy, isolated, and conjugated and methylene interrupted double bonds each give hydrogen resonance absorption signals with characteristic chemical shifts. Using the observed chemical shifts shown in Table 10.88 the structures of several fatty acids in natural glyceride oils have been determined.

Table 10.88 ^{1}H Chemical Shifts of Groups in Fatty Acids[305]

Type of hydrogen nuclei	Chemical shift† δ ppm
Terminal-CH_3	+0·43
Chain-CH_2	0·00
CH_2 α-to-COOH group	−1·00
—OCH_2—	−3·00
—O—CH (with bonds above and below CH)	−4·00
—CH=CH—	−4·1
CH_2—CH=CH	−0·75
Conjugated CH=CH	−4·6
CH_3 in ester group	−2·3

† Measured from the signal of the long chain-CH_2 group in the spectra of the fatty acids. "τ" = 8·75 + δ (very approximate conversion).

10.26 Amino Acids and Peptides

Several workers[306–308] have examined the NMR spectra of numerous amino acids in either aqueous or trifluoroacetic acid solution with a view to applying the observed characteristic absorption frequencies to the structural analysis of proteins. A selection of typical chemical shifts measured in these compounds is given in Table 10.89. From considerations of the spectral parameters, information concerning the distribution of charge within the molecules, inductive effects of polar groups and positive charges, rates of proton exchange with solvent, base strength, and in favourable cases the conformation of the molecule, can be obtained[308].

10.27 Miscellaneous Studies

The ^{1}H resonance spectrum of pterocarpin at 100 Mc sec^{-1} is shown in Fig. 10.46 together with two alternative structures for the molecule[282]. An analysis of the spectrum strongly supports structure (II)[283, 353, 354]. The three aromatic hydrogen nuclei, H_5, H_6 and H_8 constitute an ABX system which can be assigned readily as shown in Fig. 10.46. The remaining aromatic hydrogen absorption bands (H'_3 and H'_6) show no trace of spin coupling, which

TABLE 10.89 ^{1}H CHEMICAL SHIFTS OF AMINO ACIDS AND PEPTIDES IN TRIFLUOROACETIC ACID SOLUTIONS[308]

Compound	τ_{CONH}		$\tau_{NH_3^+}$	τ_{CH_2, CH_3}	
Glycine	—		2·46 (m, b)	5·80 (q, J = 6)	
Diglycine	2·05 (d, J = 6)		2·46 (m, b)	5·71 (m, b)	
Tetraglycine	2·05 (m) 2·25 (m)		2·49 (m, b)	5·68 (m, b)	
	τ_{CONH}	**$\tau_{NH_3^+}$**	**$\tau_{\alpha-CH}$**	**τ_{CH, CH_2}**	**τ_{CH_3}**
DL-Alanine		2·52 (m, b)	5·54 (m, J = 5)		8·15 (d, J = 7)
DL-Valylglycine	1·97	2·58 (m, b)	5·64 (m, b)	7·55 (m)	8·75 (d, J = 6)
L-Valyl-L-valine (2) (1)	2·15 (d, J = 4)	2·52 (m, b)	(1) 5·64 (m, b) (2) 5·26 (m, b)	7·61 (m)	(1) 8·91 (d, J = 7) (2) 8·52 (d, J = 7)
	τ_{CONH}	**τ_{aryl}**	**$\tau_{NH_3^+}$**	**$\tau_{\alpha CH}$**	**τ_{CH, CH_2, CH_3}**
DL-Phenylalanine		2·60	2·60	5·40 (m, b)	6·56 (d, J = 7)
N-Acetyl-L-tyrosine ethyl ester	1·63 (d, J = 8·5)	3·00		5·03 (q, J = 7)	Ac 8·01 CH_2 6·80 (d, J = 6) CH_2O 5·63 (q, J = 7·5) CH_3 8·66 (t, J = 7·5)
	τ_{SH}	**$\tau_{NH_3^+}$**	**$\tau_{\alpha CH}$**	**τ_{CH_2, CH_3}**	
L-Cysteine	8·06 (t, J = 9)	2·34 (m, b)	5·22 (q, J = 5)	6·54 (d, d, J = 5, J = 9)	

The multiplet structure on the absorption band is denoted as follows: d = doublet, t = triplet, q = quartet, m = unresolved multiplet. If the absorption band is greater than 10 cycles sec^{-1} in width it is designated b = broad.

suggests that they are in *para* positions to each other as in structure (II) (coupling between *ortho* hydrogen nuclei would have been ~8 cycles sec^{-1}).

The semicarbazones and 2,4-dinitrophenyl hydrazones of aldehydes and ketones can be conveniently characterised by the chemical shifts of the N=C—H hydrogen absorption signals(309, 310). In some cases information concerning the stereoisomerism associated with the —C≡N bond was obtainable and values for the *syn–anti* isomeric ratios could be estimated from the NMR spectra(310). Purines(311, 312) and rotenones(313) are two classes of natural

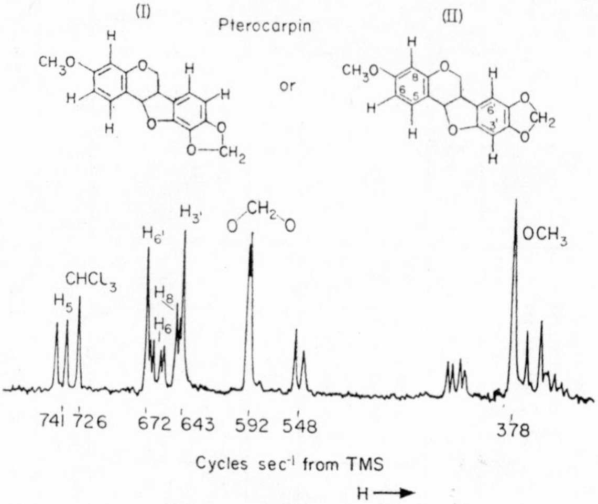

FIG. 10.46 The ^1H resonance spectrum of pterocarpin at 100 Mc sec^{-1}. Shoolery(282).

products which have been advantageously studied. Glycerides(408), substituted naphthalenes(409), carbohydrates(491), norbornenes(480), and [1–*n*] paracyclophanes(410) have also been examined by NMR methods.

10.28 Detection of *C*-Methyl Groups by NMR

Anet(112) has drawn attention to the problems encountered in the detection of *C*-methyl groups by high resolution magnetic resonance methods. A methyl group attached directly to a saturated carbon atom gives rise to a strong absorption signal with a characteristic tau value, $\tau \sim 9{\cdot}0$ ppm. When the saturated carbon atom to which it is attached is also bonded to one or more hydrogen atoms, the methyl absorption band will show fine structure due to spin–spin interaction between the hydrogen nuclei. *C*-methyl groups on carbon atoms which carry no hydrogen atoms usually give single line absorption bands but for some molecules weak coupling between the methyl group and remote hydrogen nuclei (four bonds removed) is observed(59). For example, the two non-equivalent *geminal* methyl groups in structure I are found to be weakly coupled together. Molecules which contain a $>CHCH_3$ group would be expected to show a strong doublet splitting (6–8 cycles sec^{-1}) on the methyl absorption

(I) 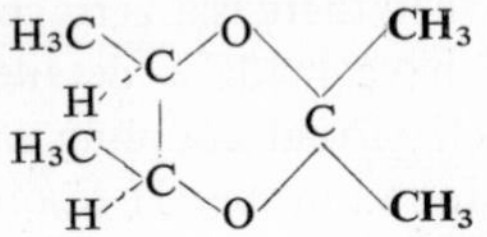

$$J_{CH_3-CH_3} = 0{\cdot}5 \text{ cycles sec}^{-1}$$

band due to J_{H-CH_3} spin coupling. However, if the two groups of nuclei are strongly coupled (see Section 8.13.3) the molecule gives rise to the spectrum expected of an AB_3 system, and a simple doublet absorption for the methyl

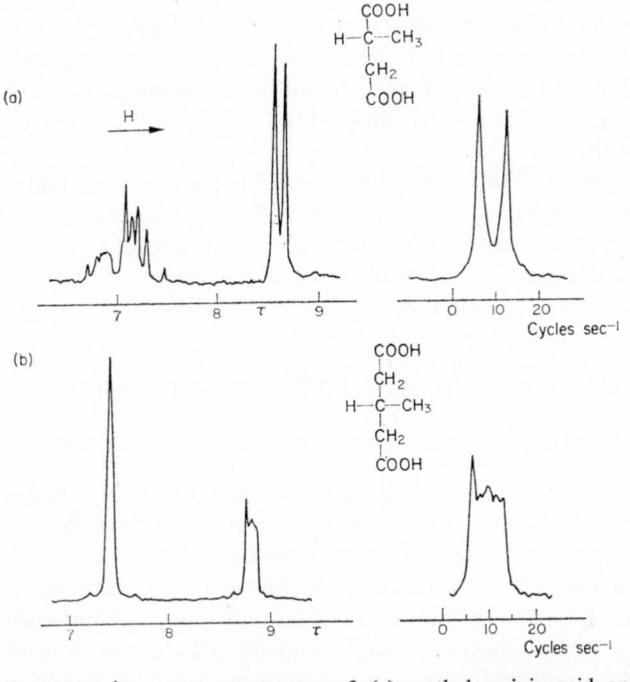

FIG. 10.47 The ¹H resonance spectra of (a) methylsuccinic acid and (b) β-methyl glutaric acid in CF_3COOH at 60 Mc sec^{-1}. The bands from COOH groups are not shown. Methyl group bands at slow sweeps are shown on the right. Anet[112].

group is no longer observed. It is necessary to carry out a full analysis of such a spectrum to obtain accurate values for the spectral parameters.

Quite frequently, molecules containing $>CHCH_3$ groups give rise to complex methyl absorption spectra even when the two groups of nuclei are only weakly coupled to each other (that is the chemical shift difference between the —CH and CH_3 absorption band is much larger than the coupling constant between them). This is due to the —CH hydrogen nucleus being coupled strongly to another group of hydrogen nuclei in the molecule. Even though this third group of nuclei does not couple with the methyl group it is necessary, in order to completely analyse the system, to consider all nuclei which are strongly coupled to any nucleus interacting with the methyl group. Hence there can be virtual coupling between nuclei even when there is a zero coupling constant between them. (Musher and Corey[314] have made a detailed investigation of the implications of the effects of such virtual coupling in the three spin system.) Examples of this behaviour are found in the ^1H resonance spectra of methyl succinic acid and β-methyl glutaric acid shown in Fig. 10.47. Although these molecules are structurally very similar, the form of the high field methyl absorption band is quite different in the two spectra. The methyl absorption of methyl succinic acid is a sharp doublet: the chemical shift difference between the α- and the two α'-hydrogen atoms is sufficiently large to prevent the methyl absorption from being affected by nuclei other than the tertiary hydrogen nucleus. In β-methyl glutaric acid the α-, α'- and β-hydrogen nuclei are only slightly chemically shifted from one another and thus give rise to a single broad absorption band. A complex methyl absorption band is observed in this case[112].

A consequence of this behaviour in $>CHCH_3$ groups is that the splitting observed on a methyl absorption band is often smaller than the actual J_{H-CH_3} coupling constant. Anet[112] has explained the anomalous coupling constants in methylcyclohexane on this basis and also the widely varying values of coupling constants reported in the spectra of 6α- and 6β-methyl steroids[303].

HYDROGEN ATTACHED TO ATOMS OTHER THAN CARBON

10.29 Hydrogen Attached to Oxygen Atoms

In Section 9.4 it was seen that such hydrogen atoms are often involved in the formation of hydrogen bonds with the result that the observed shielding of the hydrogen nuclei has an appreciable contribution from the intermolecular interaction. The only meaningful chemical shifts of nuclei of this type will be those measured at infinite dilution in an inert solvent such as carbon tetrachloride or cyclohexane where it can often be assumed reasonably that the molecule is present in the monomeric form. A further factor complicating the study of OH systems is the possibility of exchange phenomena involving the hydrogen attached to the oxygen atom. In addition to displacing the resonance signal this also results in the loss of fine structure on the hydrogen absorption signal. Because of these difficulties very little work has been expended on attempts to correlate the chemical shifts of nuclei of this type with molecular parameters. The main NMR interest in OH systems has been in the study of their hydrogen bonding and exchange behaviour[315-317] (see Section 9.4.4). Table 10.90 summarises the chemical shifts extrapolated to infinite dilution in an inert solvent for a series of molecules containing hydrogen attached to oxygen atoms. One noteworthy aspect of the chemical shifts of substituted phenols is that they have a fairly constant value ($\tau \sim 5{\cdot}5$) in all but the molecules where strong intramolecular hydrogen bonding would be expected to be present (for example *o*-chlorophenol) where an appreciable decrease in shielding is observed. Dilution in an inert solvent will not break down intramolecular hydrogen bonds.

Paterson and Tipman[(361)], have measured the OH chemical shifts extrapolated to infinite dilution in carbon tetrachloride for a series of *para* substituted phenols. Their results are given in Table 10.91 and the extrapolations can be considered to be reliable in view of the low concentrations examined. No correlation between the —OH shielding and the nature of the ring substituents was observed.

TABLE 10.90 ^{1}H CHEMICAL SHIFTS OF —OH SYSTEMS AT INFINITE DILUTION IN CARBON TETRACHLORIDE SOLUTION

Compound	"τ" ppm	Reference
CH_3OH	9·5	
C_2H_5OH	9·3	
t-C_4H_9OH	9·3	
Phenol	5·8	315
o-Cresol	5·5	315
p-Chlorophenol	5·3	315
m-Chlorophenol	5·5	315
o-Chlorophenol	4·4	315
Methylsalicylate	−0·58	
Salicylaldehyde	−0·95	
Carboxylic acids (dimers)	−2·2	315, 316, 319

These chemical shifts were measured originally from cyclohexane internal reference in CCl_4 solutions. They have been converted to the τ scale[(85)].

Gutowsky and co-workers[(318)] have measured the OH chemical shifts extrapolated to infinite dilution in carbon tetrachloride for phenol, β-naphthol, 9-phenanthrol and for several chelated *ortho*-substituted derivatives of each of these molecules. They interpret the difference in shielding of the OH hydrogen nuclei in the chelated and the parent molecules ($\Delta\delta$) in terms of the strengths of the intramolecular hydrogen bonds. The $\Delta\delta$ values are shown to be proportional to the bond multiplicity of the bonds in the aromatic ring between the carbon atoms attached to the chelating substituents[(318)].

In carboxylic acids, the carboxyl hydrogen resonance signal was found to depend on dilution only in solutions of concentration less than 25 mole per cent: this is consistent with the known tendency for such molecules to form stable dimers with appreciable amounts of monomer only appearing at low dilution. Reeves[(319)] has measured the —COOH hydrogen chemical shifts for several simple carboxylic acids present in the dimeric state (pure liquids) and he has found that the chemical shift is similar for all the molecules ($\tau = -2{\cdot}2 \pm 0{\cdot}1$) indicating that the environment of the hydrogen nucleus in various hydrogen bonded situations is very similar. Acetic acid itself is known to contain higher polymers than dimers in the liquid state and this is reflected in the tau value of the —COOH absorption ($\tau = -1{\cdot}55$): upon dilution in carbon tetrachloride the shielding decreases to $\tau = -2{\cdot}1$, the value expected for the dimeric state.

TABLE 10.91 THE OH CHEMICAL SHIFTS OF A SERIES OF *para*-SUBSTITUTED PHENOLS[361]

Compound	OH Chemical shift (ppm)†
C_6H_5OH	−2·84
p-ClC_6H_4OH	−2·90
p-BrC_6H_4OH	−2·91
p-IC_6H_4OH	−2·92

† OH chemical shifts measured in ppm from cyclohexane internal reference and extrapolated to infinite dilution in CCl_4. "τ" $= 8{\cdot}564 + \delta_{C_6H_{12}int.}$

10.30 HYDROGEN ATTACHED TO NITROGEN ATOMS

Nitrogen-14 has a spin number $I = 1$ and thus possesses a quadrupole moment. A consequence of this is that the absorption bands for hydrogen nuclei attached directly to nitrogen atoms are generally broadened due to quadrupolar relaxation effects. These effects can be removed either by double irradiation techniques[257] or by examining symmetrical species such as the ammonium ion where there are no electrical field gradients[320]. If the NH hydrogen atoms are in rapid equilibrium with other hydrogen atoms in the system (such is the case for amines in the presence of trace amounts of water) then sharp absorption bands are obtained. A hydrogen atom attached to nitrogen is also involved in the formation of hydrogen bonds, and the monomer

TABLE 10.92 THE "ASSOCIATION SHIFT" OF SOME AMINE DERIVATIVES[322]

	Association shift (ppm)	Reference
Monoethylamine	0·995	322
Diethylamine	0·990	322
Isobutylamine	>0·87	322
Ammonia	1·05	161

chemical shifts can only be obtained by examining dilute solutions of the sample in inert solvents[161, 321, 322] (Section 9.4.4). The tau value for the NH hydrogen nuclei in monomeric monoethylamine molecules dissolved in carbon tetrachloride solution is $9{\cdot}17\tau$ (carbon tetrachloride reacts with amines and the above measurements were made before the reaction had progressed appreciably)[321, 322]. By cooling the amines, the NH hydrogen chemical shift becomes constant just above the melting point: this has been taken as the chemical shift of the *n*-mer and a list of such values is given in Table 10.92. The association shift (the difference between the monomer and *n*-mer chemical shifts) was found to be about 1·0 ppm in all cases. This is in good agreement with the observed association shift for ammonia obtained by examining liquid and gaseous ammonia samples[(161)]. In view of the many factors complicating the NMR study of NH hydrogen nuclei it is not surprising that no correlations of NH chemical shifts with molecular structure have so far been attempted. Kern and Lipscomb[(323)] have calculated a shielding value for NH hydrogen nuclei but there is poor agreement with the experimental values.

TABLE 10.93 THE EFFECTS OF TEMPERATURE ON THE NMR SPECTRAL PARAMETERS OF SEVERAL —NH CONTAINING MOLECULES[(326)]

Compound	N–H absorption at 35°C	Approx. transition temp., singlet to triplet absorption, °C	*J* of triplet absorption, cycles sec^{-1}
Formamide	Broad singlet	50 ± 10	60 ± 4
Acetamide	Broad singlet	175 ± 10	56 ± 5
N-Methylformamide	Broad singlet	Not obsd. to 250	
N-Methylacetamide	Broad singlet	225 ± 20	60 ± 5
Succinimide		>250	
Pyrrole	Very broad singlet	50 ± 25	55 ± 5
Methylammonium chloride†	Broad triplet	<0	49 ± 2
Ethylammonium chloride†	Broad triplet	<0	50 ± 2
Dimethylammonium chloride†	Very broad triplet	≦0	53 ± 3
Pyrrolidine hydrochloride†	Very broad triplet	25 ± 5	52 ± 4

† Approximately 50 per cent aqueous solutions containing two drops of concentrated hydrochloric acid per 0·5 ml.

We have already seen that hydrogen attached to nitrogen atoms can give broad absorption signals due to quadrupolar relaxation effects (formamides and pyrroles have line widths of 10–75 cycles sec^{-1} at 40 Mc sec^{-1}) or narrow signals due to exchange phenomena: a further possibility is that the NH absorption band can exhibit triplet fine structure from spin–spin interaction with the ^{14}N nucleus (I = 1). Such triplet splittings have been observed in the ^{1}H resonance spectra of anhydrous ammonia[(324)] and of ammonium ions in acid solution[(325)].

By observing a decrease in line widths on raising the temperature, Roberts[(326)] has demonstrated that the line broadening often observed for the NH hydrogen absorption signals is in fact due to quadrupole relaxation and not to intermediate rates of proton exchange. For many nitrogen-containing molecules the broad NH absorption resolves itself into a triplet at some elevated temperature. Table 10.93 gives an indication of the temperature behaviour and the NH coupling constants for several NH type molecules. The use of the double irradiation technique has since proved unequivocally the origin of line broadening of NH absorption bands.

To identify OH and NH type hydrogen by NMR it is necessary to examine solutions of low concentration in inert solvents. However, the presence in a resonance spectrum of an absorption band which is extremely sensitive to both solvent concentration and temperature is invariably due to hydrogen nuclei of this type. The addition of a small amount of acid to the sample will bring about a drastic change in the chemical shift of these absorption bands and this feature can be used to assist in assigning spectra. Another rapid method of identifying a —OH or —NH absorption band is to shake the sample with a small amount of deuterium oxide (D_2O): rapid exchange of deuterium for the hydrogen attached to the O or N atom will cause a diminution in the intensity of the band in question.

10.31 Hydrogen Attached to Boron Atoms

Very few examples of ^1H chemical shifts for BH type groups have been reported. In diborane[(437)], $\tau_{BH_2} = 6{\cdot}05$ ppm and $\tau_{BHB} = 10{\cdot}53$ ppm: a coupling constant between the bridge and terminal hydrogen nuclei of diborane has been measured (7 cycles sec^{-1}).

The ^1H chemical shift measured for BH type hydrogen nuclei in borazoles and related molecules is $5{\cdot}5\tau$. It is thought that aromatic type ring currents make an appreciable contribution to the shielding of the ring hydrogen nuclei in borazoles[(327)].

Kern and Lipscomb[(323, 328)] have calculated the shielding of the hydrogen nuclei in diborane: their results agree roughly with the experimentally observed shielding values for the bridge and terminal BH hydrogen nuclei (see Section 12.1.3).

10.32 Hydrogen Attached to Sulphur Atoms

It has been shown that the SH hydrogen absorption band in ethyl mercaptan is displaced to higher field values when the pure liquid is diluted with carbon tetrachloride. This is taken as evidence for the presence of hydrogen bonding in the pure liquid state. The difference in chemical shift between the SH absorption in the pure liquid and that in a dilute carbon tetrachloride solution was found to be $0{\cdot}38 \pm 0{\cdot}015$ ppm[(329)]. There are very few reported NMR studies of hydrogen atoms attached directly to sulphur[(217, 329–331)] and only in the case of ethyl mercaptan has an estimate of the hydrogen bonding effect been made. However, in view of the small value of the dilution shift for this molecule, the range of chemical shift values given by Chamberlain[(217)] for aliphatic thiols ($\tau = 8{\cdot}4$ to $8{\cdot}8$) need only be slightly modified (τ values from $8{\cdot}4$ to $9{\cdot}2$ will be observed at low dilution in CCl_4). In thiophenol, a much lower SH chemical shift value is observed ($\tau = 6{\cdot}4$) but no correction was made for the contribution of intermolecular effects to the shielding of the SH nuclei in this molecule[(217)].

More recently, the ^{1}H chemical shifts of the SH nuclei in several aliphatic ($\tau_{SH} = 7{\cdot}8$ to $9{\cdot}0$) and aromatic ($\tau_{SH} = 6{\cdot}3$ to $7{\cdot}0$) thiols in dilute solutions in carbon tetrachloride have been reported(463).

10.33 Hydrogen Attached to Silicon Atoms

A study of the effects of organic groups and chlorine atoms in several substituted silanes has indicated that shielding factors other than the electronegativity of the substituents must also be taken into consideration in order to explain the shielding of hydrogen nuclei in the molecules(332). Table 10.94 gives the chemical shifts for the Si—H hydrogen nuclei in a series of trisubstituted silanes(332). Generally, an increase in the electronegativity of the substituents is seen to cause a decrease in shielding of the hydrogen nuclei in the Si—H group. However, some of the shifts are anomalous; the vinyl and phenyl derivatives, for example, are predicted to have electronegativities in the order $C_2H_5 < CH_2{=}CH < C_6H_5$ whereas other studies predict the reverse order(333). The anomalous shielding in the vinyl derivative has been attributed to extra *p–d* π-bonding from the sp^2 hybridised carbon to the silicon(332, 180) while the results for the phenyl type derivatives have been interpreted in terms of valence bond contributions to the structure of the molecule of resonance forms such as

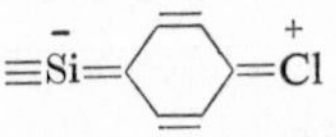

However, many of the anomalies found in the ^{1}H chemical shifts of substituted silanes are also observed in the spectra of analogous carbon compounds: thus the NMR evidence for the presence of *p–d* π-bonding in silicon compounds is far from conclusive(440). If the nature of the alkyl group is varied in the substituted silanes, the observed effect is to increase the shielding of the Si—H hydrogen nucleus according to the order Methyl = *i*-Butyl < n-Propyl = n-Butyl < Ethyl < *i*-Propyl. Thus only the portion of the series $CH_3 < < C_2H_5 <$ *i*-Propyl agrees with expected inductive effects. It has been tentatively suggested that the deviations from the expected inductive behaviour might originate in hyperconjugation effects. ^{1}H chemical shifts in silicon hydride derivatives are less sensitive to changes of substituent than are the chemical shifts in analogous carbon containing molecules(411).

A plot of τ values for Si—H hydrogen nuclei against the Si—H stretching frequencies proves to be linear for all the trisubstituted silanes except those containing phenyl or vinyl groups. Hence, it appears that both parameters are controlled by similar factors, which need not necessarily be simple inductive effects(332).

Webster(332) has extended his investigation to compounds with the general structure $Me_xCl_{3-x}SiH$, $Me_xCl_{3-x}CH$, $Me_xPh_{3-x}SiH$ and $Me_xPh_{3-x}CH$ and he finds that progressive replacement of methyl groups with electronegative chlorine atoms causes deshielding of both SiH and CH hydrogen nuclei. Each successive replacement has a smaller influence on the shielding than the preceding one and much larger changes are observed in the shielding of the CH than of

TABLE 10.94 ^{1}H CHEMICAL SHIFTS OF THE Si—H HYDROGEN IN TRISUBSTITUTED SILANES[332], R_3SiH

R	Peak multiplicity[a]	τ (ppm)	R	Peak multiplicity[a]	τ (ppm)	R	Peak multiplicity	τ (ppm)
Me	10	6·149 ± 0·014	Bu^n	m	6·336 ± 0·002	p-C_6H_4Cl	1	4·625 ± 0·014
Et	7	6·388 ± 0·012	Bu^i	7	6·151 ± 0·007	CH_2Ph	7	5·969 ± 0·014
Pr^n	7	6·316 ± 0·014	Vinyl	m	5·672 ± 0·012	p-$CH_2{\cdot}C_6H_4Me$	7	6·023 ± 0·014
Pr^i	m	6·701 ± 0·014	Ph	1	4·579 ± 0·005	p-$CH_2{\cdot}C_6H_4Cl$	7	6·013 ± 0·012
			p-C_6H_4Me	1	4·649 ± 0·012	Cl	1	3·848 ± 0·002

[a] m signifies a multiplet where the number of lines could not be counted accurately.
Additional Si—H ^{1}H chemical shifts are given in references 462, 489.

the SiH hydrogen nuclei. This latter effect is thought to be due to the double bonding tendencies of silicon which cause the electron density to be held on the silicon atom and thus diminishes the effect of replacing methyl groups by chlorine atoms. Similar effects are observed in the phenyl silane derivatives.

By examining the H—D coupling constants in deuterated silanes, SiH_3D and $SiHD_3$, the J_{HH}^{gem} value for SiH_4 has been estimated to have a value[(362)] of $2{\cdot}75 \pm 0{\cdot}15$ cycles sec^{-1}. Similarly, the *geminal* HH coupling constants have been measured for several substituted silanes and these values are given together with other coupling constants in Table 12.52. Attempts to explain the changes in *geminal* HH coupling constants in terms of variations in the H—Si—H bond angles using a simple valence bond approach were not successful. This was attributed to the influence of the silicon *d* orbitals on the coupling[(362)] but it is much more likely to be simply a reflection of the general inadequacy of this approach to the problem[(58, 56)].

10.34 Hydrogen Attached to Germanium, Tin and Lead Atoms

Drake and Jolly[(360)] have characterised several germanes using nuclear magnetic resonance spectroscopy. Hydrogen nuclei in —GeH_3 groups have chemical shifts of $-3{\cdot}3$ ppm from an external tetramethylsilane reference while the corresponding shifts for —SiH_3 groups are $\sim -3{\cdot}3$ to $-3{\cdot}6$ppm, and for —CH_3 groups $\sim -1{\cdot}1$ ppm. Hydrogen nuclei in $>GeH_2$ groups are more

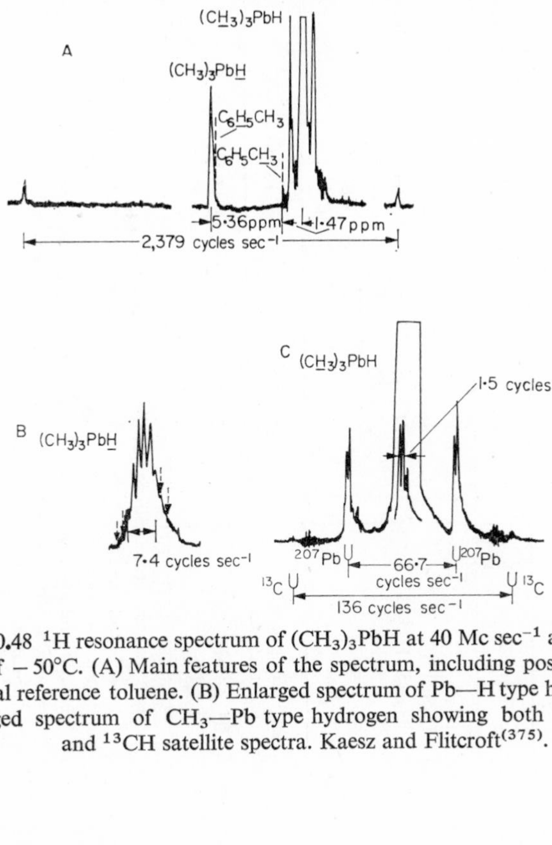

FIG. 10.48 ^{1}H resonance spectrum of $(CH_3)_3PbH$ at 40 Mc sec^{-1} at a temperature of -50°C. (A) Main features of the spectrum, including positions of the internal reference toluene. (B) Enlarged spectrum of Pb—H type hydrogen. (C) Enlarged spectrum of CH_3—Pb type hydrogen showing both the ^{207}PbH and ^{13}CH satellite spectra. Kaesz and Flitcroft[(375)].

TABLE 10.95 ^{1}H CHEMICAL SHIFTS AND SPIN COUPLING CONSTANTS OF SOME STANNANES AND RELATED COMPOUNDS(375)

	Chemical shifts (τ values) and H—H spin coupling constants (cycles sec^{-1})			Coupling constants (cycles sec^{-1})				
Tin compounds	τ_{Sn-H} [mult.][a]	τ_{SnCH_3} [mult.][a]	J_{HCSnH} (cycles sec^{-1})	^{119}Sn—H	^{117}Sn—H	^{13}C—H	^{119}SnCH$_3$	^{117}SnCH$_3$
SnH_4[b]	6·15 [1]			1931	1846			
CH_3SnH_3[c]	5·86 [4]	9·73 [4]	2·7	1852	1770	130	62	
$(CH_3)_2SnH_2$[c]	5·24 [7]	9·83 [3]	2·5$_5$	1758	1682	126·5	58·0	55·5
$(CH_3)_3SnH$[c]	5·27 [10]	9·82 [2]	2·3$_7$	1744	1664	128·5	56·5	54·5
$(CH_3)_4Sn$		9·86 [1]				128	54	51·5
$(CH_3)Sn^-$, Li^+[d]		10·4 [1]					14	
Lead compounds	τ_{PbH} [mult.][a]	τ_{PbCH_3} [mult.][a]	J_{HCPbH}	^{207}Pb—H		^{13}C—H	^{207}PbCH$_3$	
$(CH_3)_3PbH$[e]	2·32 [10]	9·15 [2]	1·4$_7$	2379		136	66·7	
$(CH_3)_4Pb$		9·13				132·5	60·5	

[a] Resonances were observed at the multiplicity given in brackets.

[b] Neat liquid at -50°C; chemical shift measured for 9 per cent solution in cyclopentane containing 9 per cent toluene internal standard whose methyl resonance was taken at $\tau = 7·68$ under these conditions.

[c] Neat liquid and solution at 40°C; chemical shift measured for 9 per cent solution in neopentane with 9 per cent toluene as internal standard, whose methyl resonance was taken at $\tau = 7·68$ under these conditions.

[d] Approximately 0·1 M solution in CH_3NH_2; methyl protons of solvent taken at $\tau = 7·77$.

[e] Neat liquid and solution at -50°C; chemical shift measured for 9 per cent solution in cyclopentane containing 9 per cent toluene as internal standard, whose methyl resonance is taken at $\tau = 7·68$ under these conditions.

shielded than those in —GeH_3 groups by 0·193 ppm. This behaviour is similar to that observed for silanes but opposite to that for alkanes which suggests the following order of electronegativities C > H > Si ~ Ge.

Kaesz and Flitcroft(375) have examined the ^{1}H resonance spectra of some stannanes and related compounds (including $(CH_3)_3PbH$) and their results are given in Table 10.95. Hydrogen nuclei attached to tin and lead (τ values ~ 6 and ~ 2 respectively) are less shielded than hydrogen attached to saturated carbon atoms in analogous carbon compounds. Figure 10.48 shows the ^{1}H resonance spectrum of trimethylplumbane, $(CH_3)_3PbH$: the methyl and hydridic hydrogen nuclei give rise to two separate absorption multiplets in the correct intensity ratio and both absorptions are accompanied by ^{207}PbH satellite spectra. The hydrogen nuclei in the methyl groups also couple with the hydridic hydrogen nucleus resulting in a decet multiplet structure on the hydridic absorption band and a doublet splitting on the methyl absorption band (J_{H-CH_3} = 1·47 cycles sec^{-1}).

The NMR parameters of mixed hydrides of silicon, germanium, arsenic and phosphorus have also been obtained (e.g. SiH_3PH_2, SiH_3AsH_2, GeH_3PH_2 and GeH_3AsH_2)(412).

Reeves and Wells(450) have pointed out the following correlation between J_{X-H} coupling constants and the atomic number Z_X for Group IV elements X = C, Si, Sn and Pb

$$(J_{X-H}/\mu_X)^{\frac{1}{2}} = 0{\cdot}676 Z_X + 8{\cdot}0$$

A similar relationship has been found for J_{X-CH} coupling constants(450).

10.35 Hydrogen Attached to Transition Metal Atoms

Hydrogen atoms attached directly to diamagnetic transition metal atoms are highly shielded (5·9–17·3 ppm to high fields of tetramethylsilane reference signal) and consequently they are readily characterised by NMR(323, 334–341). For example, biscyclopentadienyl rhenium hydride, $(C_5H_5)_2ReH$ shows two absorption bands in its ^{1}H resonance spectrum in the intensity ratio of 10:1(334).

Table 10.96 ^{1}H Chemical Shifts of the Hydridic Hydrogen Nuclei in Transition Metal Hydrides

Compound	Reference compound	Chemical shift ppm	"τ"	Reference
$(C_5H_5)_2ReH$	C_6H_5 in toluene	20·5	23·6	334
$HCo(CO)_4$	C_6H_5 in toluene	17·3 ± 2·0	20·4	335
$H_2Fe(CO)_4$	C_6H_5 in toluene	17·4	20·5	337
$HCr(CO)_3C_5H_5$	C_6H_5 in toluene	13·1	16·2	338
$HMo(CO)_3C_5H_5$	C_6H_5 in toluene	12·8	15·9	338
$HW(CO)_3C_5H_5$	C_6H_5 in toluene	14·7	17·8	338
$HPtCl(PEt_3)_2$	H_2O	22·0	27·2	339, 342
$[HCo(CN)_5]^{3-}$	H_2O	17·4	22·6	340
$[HRh(CN)_5]^{3-}$	H_2O	15·6	20·8	340
$HMn(CO)_5$	H_2O	13·0	18·2	341

"τ" = 5·2 + $\delta_{H_2O\,ext.}$

Table 10.96 gives a compilation of the hydridic chemical shifts for several molecules of this type. This high shielding of the hydridic hydrogen nuclei is thought to be due to the proton being submerged in the electron density of the metal[338]. Kern and Lipscomb[323, 336, 456] have developed a theory to explain the chemical shift of the hydridic hydrogen in $HCo(CO)_4$: the shielding is shown to depend on the electron density around the hydrogen nucleus and upon the electron populations in the large and diffuse $4s$ and $4p$ orbitals of the cobalt atom.

Several protonated transition metal carbonyl complexes (such as $[\pi\text{-}C_5H_5Mo(CO)_3]_2H^+$ and $[\pi\text{-}C_5H_5Ru(CO)_2]_2H^+$) have been characterised by their ^1H resonance spectra[355]: protonation results in the formation of a metal–hydrogen bond as evidenced by the appearance of a high field absorption band ($\tau = 28{\cdot}58$ to $38{\cdot}07$).

MISCELLANEOUS STUDIES

10.36 Contact Chemical Shifts in Paramagnetic Species

The ^1H resonance spectra of paramagnetic molecules often show very large variations in the shielding of the different hydrogen nuclei in the same molecule. The variations extend over a range of ~ 400 ppm which is considerably greater than that found for diamagnetic molecules (~ 20 ppm). Sometimes the absorption bands observed in the spectra of paramagnetic species are broad due to their short nuclear relaxation times resulting from the creation of large fluctuating magnetic fields by the paramagnetic moments in the system which promote rapid relaxation (see Section 2.5.1). The large differences in the nuclear shielding observed in such systems can be explained quantitatively in terms of isotropic contact interactions between the hydrogen nuclei and the unpaired spin density produced in the ligand molecule by the paramagnetic metal atom to which it is bonded (see Section 3.16)[343, 344, 458]. The presence of small amounts of unpaired electron spin density in the various parts of a ligand has been qualitatively explained by Milner and Pratt[343]. If one considers an ethylene diamine complex of nickel, the $3d$ orbitals of Ni(II) are split

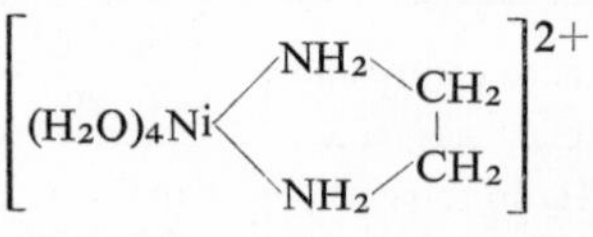

into two groups by the presence of the octahedral group of ligands, three t_{2g} orbitals and two e_g orbitals of higher energy. The eight available $3d$ electrons distribute themselves in such a manner as to fully occupy the t_{2g} orbitals and to singly occupy the two e_g orbitals. These latter two unpaired electrons will be polarised in a magnetic field so that their spins will tend to point in the field direction. The Ni—N bonds lie along the same axes as an e_g orbital, hence there is a possibility of transfer of electron density from the nitrogen to the nickel atoms. Because of the polarised nature of the single unpaired e_g electron in a magnetic field, the transfer process will preferentially involve the nitrogen electron in the Ni—N bond with a spin antiparallel to that of the nickel electron. This results in a slight excess of electron spin density remaining on the nitrogen orbitals in the same direction as the applied field. This is referred to as positive spin density and results in a decrease in the diamagnetic shielding of the nitrogen nucleus. By assuming that there can be a slight amount of unpairing of the electrons in bonding orbitals, the electrons associated with the hydrogen atoms bonded to the nitrogen would adopt an antiparallel orientation, and spin density can be transmitted to other parts of the molecule via a spin-polarisation mechanism. The negative spin density on the hydrogen atoms will cause increased shielding of their nuclei, thus explaining the higher field chemical shifts observed for such nuclei in the ^{1}H resonance spectra of ethylene diamine nickel complexes (see Fig. 10.49). Similar arguments predict negative spin densities on the α-carbon atoms and hence positive spin densities on their hydrogen atoms consistent with the low field chemical shifts observed for the methylene groups attached to nitrogen (see Figure 10.49). Many other complexes of Ni(II)

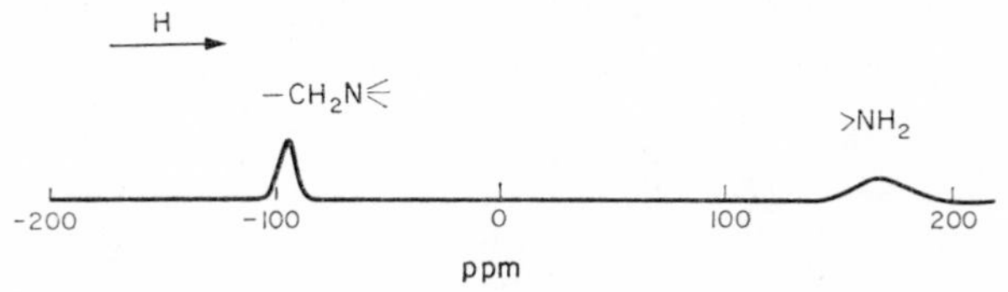

FIG. 10.49 The ^{1}H resonance spectrum of an aqueous solution of a 1:1 complex of nickel(II) and ethylene diamine at 56·4 Mc sec^{-1}. Milner and Pratt[343].

and Co(II) have been examined in this way, and in favourable cases information about the structures of the complex and the relative amounts of the different species present can be obtained.

Eaton and co-workers[344–346] have investigated the isotropic contact interactions in the NMR spectra of some Ni(II) aminotroponeimineates in deuterochloroform solution, and they observed bands of much narrower line widths than those found by Milner and Pratt. The Ni(II) ion in these molecules undergoes a rapid inversion between a square planar (diamagnetic) and a tetrahedral (paramagnetic) structure, which influences favourably the relaxation times of the hydrogen nuclei. Because of the narrow line widths it is possible to observe the presence of spin–spin interaction fine structure on the absorption bands and this enables the spectra to be assigned with confidence[465]. The values of the spin coupling constants are very similar to those in the parent quinoline molecule.

Figure 10.50 shows the ^{1}H resonance spectrum of nickel(II) *N*,*N*-di (6-quinolyl) aminotroponeimineate. There are nine contact interaction shifts involved in the spectrum and it is possible to calculate the spin densities at each position in the molecule from the measured chemical shifts (see Section 3.16). This method gives results in good agreement with valence bond calculated values. By examining a wide variety of molecules an estimate can be made of the relative ease of transmission of electron density through groups linking conjugated systems. It is found that electron density can be transmitted through the central metal atom.

By measuring contact shifts, the distribution of spin densities has also been estimated for Ni(II) chelates of *N-m*-tolylsalicylaldimines but the absorption bands are much broader and fine structure from spin–spin coupling could not be resolved(358). The contact chemical shifts for Ni(II) *N*-methylsalicylaldimine vary

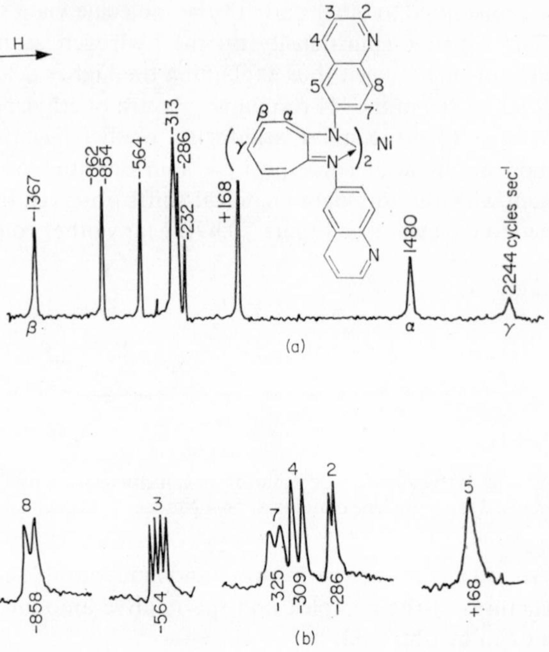

FIG. 10.50 (a) The ^{1}H resonance spectrum of Ni(II) *N,N'*-di (6-quinolyl) aminotroponeiminate. (b) The ^{1}H resonance spectrum of the 6-quinolyl group of Ni(II) *N,N'*-di (6-quinolyl) aminotroponeiminate. The spectra were obtained at 60 Mc sec^{-1} using $CDCl_3$ as solvent and $(CH_3)_4Si$ as internal reference. Eaton, Josey, Phillips and Benson(344).

with the concentration of the solvent and this is consistent with the changes in its magnetic susceptibility accompanying dilution(359).

The spin densities in some tetrahedral Co(II) complexes have been evaluated from the measurement of ^{1}H contact shifts(439). ^{19}F contact interaction constants for *ortho*-, *meta*- and *para*-substituted fluorobenzenes have been obtained by examining the ^{19}F resonance spectra of the appropriate fluoro derivatives of *N*-substituted Ni(II) aminotroponeimineates(357, 432). There is considerable π bonding between the fluorine atom and the aromatic system and this causes the simple proportionality existing between hydrogen contact interaction constants and spin densities on adjacent carbon atoms in aromatic molecules to be invalid for fluorine contact interaction constants.

10.37 NMR Studies of High Polymer Solutions

Several hundred published papers dealing with low resolution NMR studies of solid polymers have shown that such investigations are useful in determining the relative positions of hydrogen nuclei in the molecules, the extent of segmental molecular motion and the degree of crystallinity of polymer samples. Comprehensive reviews of this aspect of NMR have been written by Powles[(381)], Slichter[(382)] and Sauer and Woodward[(383)]. There have been comparatively few high resolution NMR investigations of polymers due mainly to the solubility requirements and the occurrence of broad resonance bands which often render a detailed analysis of the resonance spectrum impossible. Broad absorption lines are a consequence of the molecular motion of the polymer being insufficient to average out completely the dipolar broadening. Polymers in solutions are thus often examined by NMR at high temperatures to enable higher concentrations of solutions to be used, and to decrease the viscosity of the solution. However, it is usually the segmental motion within a polymer molecule which determines the line widths. If a suitable solvent can be found for a polymer, then high resolution NMR techniques can be applied to the determination of its molecular structure in much the same way as they can to the study of any large organic molecule. Because the shielding of a magnetic nucleus is sensitive to slight changes in its spatial environment, similar nuclei in polymeric chain sequences of different stereochemical configuration often give rise to separate absorption bands. Thus a 15 per cent solution in chloroform of a sample of polymethylmethacrylate (see Section 10.37.3) examined at 90°C shows three resolvable CH_3 resonance bands corresponding to α-CH_3 groups in isotactic, syndiotactic and heterotactic sequences in the polymer chain. Measurement of the intensities of such absorption bands enables the tacticities of various samples to be characterised with an accuracy of $\pm$ 5 per cent.

Ethylene polymers and copolymers have also been characterised by NMR[(444)]. Ten per cent solutions of the copolymers (for example, ethylene/ethylacrylate) in diphenyl ether were heated to 240°C and then introduced into a conventional NMR spectrometer with no thermostatted probe accessories: good quality ^{1}H resonance spectra were obtained by rapidly scanning the spectrum before appreciable cooling had taken place. This method has obvious limitations but it is adequate for qualitative or quantitative compositional determinations.

Useful information concerning segmental motion in polymer molecules is sometimes obtainable from studies of the line widths in their resonance spectra.

Several typical NMR investigations of polymers in solution will be discussed in order to illustrate the scope of the technique in this field. Section 11.24 contains some examples of NMR studies of fluorinated polymers.

10.37.1 Segmental Motion in Polymers

Figure 10.51 shows the high resolution ^{1}H resonance spectrum of a sample of polystyrene (molecular weight $\sim$ 30,000) dissolved in carbon tetrachloride[(384)]. Included in Fig. 10.51 is the ^{1}H resonance spectrum of the related small molecule, cumene, $C_6H_5 \cdot CH(CH_3)_2$. It is apparent that the line widths of the polymer spectrum are somewhat broader than those of the cumene spectrum as would be expected from the decrease in both inter- and intramolecular motion of the large polymer molecules in solution compared with that of the cumene molecules. However, the line width of the polymer phenyl band is considerably narrower (0·005 gauss) than the remaining bands in the spectrum, and furthermore, the line widths in the spectrum are independent of the molecular weight of the sample[384, 385] over the range 2000–1,000,000. The line widths are also independent of the concentration of the solution (below about 50 per cent) indicating that they are independent of the macroscopic viscosity of the solution. If the motion of the dissolved polymer as a whole determined the phenyl line width, then a much greater width would be observed and there would be an

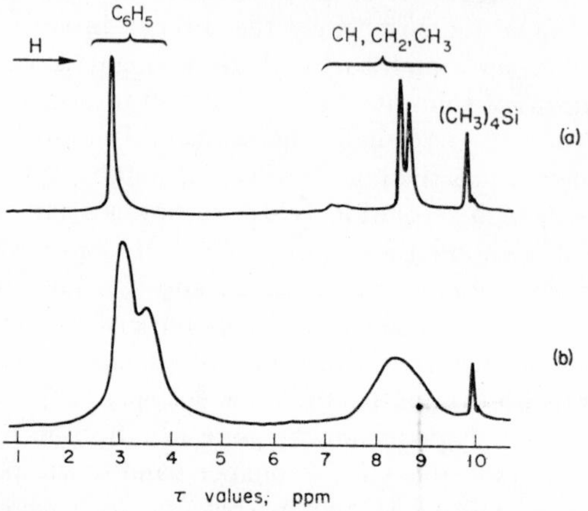

FIG. 10.51 The ^1H resonance spectra at 40 Mc sec^{-1} of (a) 10 per cent cumene in CCl_4 and (b) 15 per cent polystyrene in CCl_4. The band at 10 ppm is that of the internal reference tetramethylsilane. Bovey, Tiers and Filipovich[384].

appreciable increase of the line width on increasing the molecular weight. Hence, the narrow line resonance signals have been attributed to segmental motion within the polymer molecules. The band width is determined by the local viscosity in the immediate neighbourhood of each chain segment. If the neighbouring chain segments do not restrict the motion of each other, then the local viscosity is independent of both the molecular weight of polymer and the solution concentration. By contrast, the signal line widths of small molecules are viscosity dependent over the range of viscosities normally encountered (see Section 2.7). However, if the solvent has a resonance band, its line width is barely affected by the viscosity of the polymer solution, suggesting that the structure of the solution is such as to allow unhindered re-orientation of the solvent molecules. Odiyama[385] has also shown that the line widths of the phenyl and methylene absorption bands of polystyrene in a carbon tetrachloride solution are independent of the polymer chain length. Measurements of the line widths indicate that segmental motion in the chain is performed by segments containing about ten monomer units[385].

The rates, enthalpies and entropies of activation for the various motions of which polymer chains are capable may be determined directly by measuring spin lattice relaxation times, T_1, over a range of temperatures (see Section 2.4). For example it has been demonstrated that benzene rings attached to random coil polymer chains rotate 40 to 50 times more slowly than free benzene molecules[(384)].

Polymer molecules having little segmental motion give rise to broad absorption bands in their resonance spectra. Thus, the ^1H resonance spectra of natural proteins of high molecular weight ($\sim$ 65,000) are poorly resolved due to the presence of restricted segmental motion. The partly helical polypeptide chains are rather tightly intertwined to form compact spheres or ellipsoids. In such cases, the re-orientation of the molecule as a whole determines the line width and such a re-orientation is difficult for a molecule of high molecular weight. Protein molecules, such as bovine serum albumin, may be unfolded by dissolving them in deutero-urea in D_2O, or in trifluoroacetic acid where they exhibit well resolved ^1H NMR spectra[(386, 387)] due to adequate segmental motion.

Bovey and Tiers[(388)] have examined samples of polyacrylamide and polymethacrylamide in aqueous solutions, and surprisingly they find that the amide ^1H resonance bands are narrower for the polymer than for amides of low molecular weight. The line narrowing is attributed to the partial removal of the ^{14}N quadrupolar relaxation mechanism (i.e. the cause of the —NH line broadening). Apparently, the tumbling motions of the polymer segments are slow enough to allow the electric quadrupole moment of the ^{14}N nucleus to be coupled more effectively to the motions of the molecular framework. Thus, the ^1H resonance spectrum of polyacrylamide in aqueous solution shows a doublet resonance absorption in the amide hydrogen region of the spectrum, in contrast to the broad single absorption observed for low molecular weight amides. If a low molecular weight amide is examined in a very viscous solvent then two amide bands are also obtained. The two separate amide bands observed for the polymer correspond to two amide hydrogen nuclei rendered non-equivalent by the restricted rotation about the C—N bond. The two non-equivalent nuclei do not appear to be appreciably coupled by spin–spin interaction. By studying the collapse of the amide doublet with variation in temperature, the rate of rotation of the amide groups and the activation energy associated with the rotation have been estimated under various conditions of pH.

10.37.2 The Use of NMR in Determining the Molecular Structures of Polymers

Some of the NMR investigations of high molecular weight polymers in solution have much in common with conventional NMR studies of any large complex organic molecule. Two typical examples will be discussed to illustrate this point.

Butadiene–Isoprene Copolymers. The ^1H resonance spectra of butadiene–isoprene copolymers[(389)] (molecular weights $\sim$ 100,000 to 200,000) examined as 5 per cent solutions in CCl_4 can be used to characterise hydrogen nuclei in different molecular environments. By measuring the intensities of the absorption bands, the composition of the copolymer can be measured with an accuracy of ± 3 per cent. In such a copolymer the following forms are found:

$$-CH_2-\underset{\overset{\displaystyle |}{CH_3}}{\overset{\displaystyle |}{C}}-CH=CH_2 \qquad CH_2=\underset{\overset{\displaystyle |}{CH_3}}{\overset{\displaystyle |}{C}}-CH-CH_2- \qquad -CH_2-\underset{\overset{\displaystyle CH_3}{|}}{C}=CH-CH_2-$$

cis and trans

$$-CH_2-CH-CH=CH_2 \qquad -CH_2-CH=CH-CH_2-$$

cis and trans

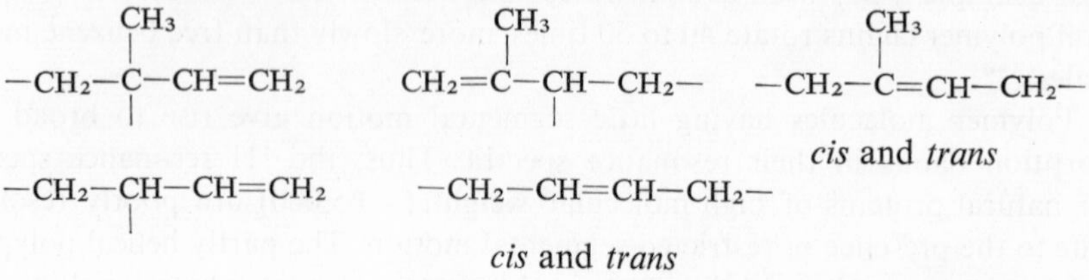

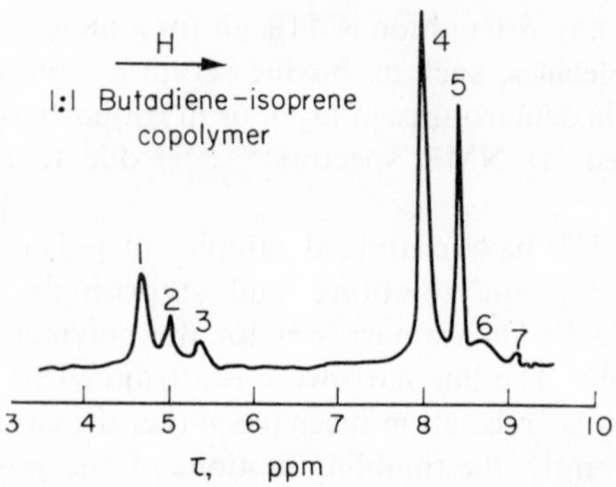

FIG. 10.52 The ^1H resonance spectrum at 60 Mc sec^{-1} of a 5 per cent solution in CCl$_4$ of a 1:1 butadiene-isoprene copolymer. Chen[389].

TABLE 10.97 ^1H CHEMICAL SHIFTS FOR HYDROGEN NUCLEI FOUND IN CHARACTERISTIC GROUPS IN A 1:1 COPOLYMER OF BUTADIENE AND ISOPRENE[389]

Band number†	Chemical shift‡ τ	Type of hydrogen		
1	4·70	—CH=CH$_2$ —CH=CH—		
2	4·97	—CH=CH$_2$ —CH=$\overset{\overset{\textstyle CH_3}{	}}{\underset{\underset{\textstyle CH_3}{	}}{C}}$—
3	5·35	CH$_2$=C—		
4	8·02	CH—C=C		
5	8·42	CH$_3$—C—C		
6	8·74	CH—C—C		
7	9·08	CH$_3$—C—C		

‡ Chemical shifts measured in ppm from TMS internal reference (10·0 ppm).
† The band numbers refer to the spectrum shown in Fig. 10.52.

Figure 10.52 shows the well resolved ^{1}H resonance spectrum of a 1:1 copolymer of butadiene and isoprene: seven distinct absorption bands are obtained corresponding to the various types of hydrogen nuclei as indicated in Table 10.97. The assignments are based on chemical shift measurements undertaken on small model compounds.

Polyisoprene, polybutadiene and copolymers of vinylidene-vinyl chloride[459] can also be examined in this way.

Poly(n-1)-methyl-1-alkenes. NMR has been used to examine the structure of samples of polymeric (*n*-1)-methyl-1-alkenes (such as polyisobutylene and poly-3-methyl-1-butene) prepared by cationic polymerisation in a homogeneous aluminium chloride catalyst system at different temperatures[390]. It is possible to detect *geminal* methyl groups $\left(-\overset{|}{C}(CH_3)_2\right)$ and isolated methylene groups $\left(-\underset{|}{\overset{|}{C}}-CH_2-\underset{|}{\overset{|}{C}}-\right)$ since these give rise to absorption bands having no fine structure. The appearance of a doublet absorption in the methyl region indicates the presence of a $>CH-CH_3$ group (including isopropyl). In molecules where there is a large amount of steric crowding around a *geminal* methyl group, the methyl hydrogen nuclei are appreciably deshielded compared with those in molecules where free rotation is possible (a similar deshielding of the crowded methylene groups is also observed). Introduction of two or more methylene groups between the *geminal* methyl groups is sufficient to relieve the steric strain and such methyl hydrogen nuclei have normal chemical shifts (this has been established by studying the ^{1}H spectra of small model compounds). Thus in the ^{1}H spectrum of polyisobutylene, the sterically crowded methyl groups have low chemical shifts ($\tau = 8{\cdot}9$) compared with the *geminal* methyl groups in poly-3-methyl-1-butene ($\tau = 9{\cdot}17$): this indicates that the *geminal* methyl groups of the latter are separated by more than one methylene group. When longer chain monomers (e.g. 5-methyl-1-hexene) are polymerised by cationic polymerisation at -73°C, there is a progressive increase in the number of terminal isopropyl groups in the polymer accompanying the increase in chain length of the monomer. This is shown by the appearance of a CH_3 doublet absorption in the spectrum in addition to the single sharp absorption of the *geminal* methyl groups. When the polymerisation is carried out at higher temperatures (0°C) the proportion of terminal isopropyl groups increases as evidenced by an increase in the relative intensity of the CH_3 doublet. It is necessary to postulate a re-arrangement of the carbonium ion intermediate in order to explain the structures of the polymers[390].

10.37.3 Determination of the Stereochemical Configurations of Polymers by NMR

Probably the most important application of high resolution NMR spectroscopy to the study of polymers in solution is to the determination of the stereochemical configurations of polymer molecules[384, 391, 392, 404]. A monomer unit which is flanked on both sides by monomer units of the same configuration as itself i.e. a *ddd* or *lll* sequence, is referred to as being in an *isotactic* configuration. If the monomer unit has the opposite configuration to the two flanking units, i.e. a *dld* or *ldl* sequence, the overall configuration is termed *syndiotactic*. *Heterotactic* configurations can have any one of the sequences *ldd*, *dll*, *ddl* or *lld* for the monomer units. These definitions of tacticity were proposed by Bovey and they are particularly convenient for NMR studies in this field. (See Section 9.5.5 for a discussion of the significance of *dextro* (*d*) and *laevo* (*l*) configurations in compounds containing single C—C bonds.) A general review of stereoregular polymerisation has been published[405].

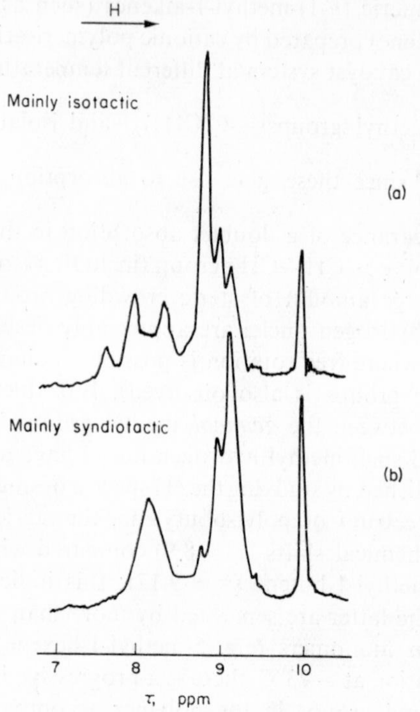

FIG. 10.53 The high field portion of the ^{1}H resonance spectrum at 40·00 Mc sec^{-1} of a solution in chloroform of polymethylmethacrylate prepared using (a) n-butyllithium in toluene at −62°C and (b) benzoyl peroxide in toluene at 100°C as initiators. Tetramethylsilane is used as an internal reference and the solutions were examined at 90°C. Bovey and Tiers[392].

Hydrogen nuclei in different spatial configurations often have different chemical shifts and consequently high resolution NMR spectroscopy can be used alongside X-ray crystallographic[393] and infrared[393] methods in the determination of the stereochemical configuration of polymers.

The first tacticity determinations by the NMR method were carried out on samples of polymethylmethacrylate[393, 394]. Suitable ^{1}H spectra can be obtained from 15 per cent solutions of the polymer in chloroform at ~90°C. Figure 10.53 shows the ^{1}H resonance spectra of two samples of polymethylmethacrylate prepared using two different methods of polymerisation. There are three α-methyl absorption bands clearly resolved in the spectra (τ values

8·78, 8·95 and 9·09) and the relative intensities of the bands vary widely with the method of preparation. A band at 6·4τ found in both spectra corresponds to the ester methyl group and this band is unaffected by the chain configuration. The polymer prepared by n-butyllithium initiation in hydrocarbon solvents appears to have a predominantly isotactic configuration and thus the most intense α-methyl band at 8·78τ in Fig. 10.53 (a) may be assigned to α-methyl groups of the central monomer units in isotactic sequences or triads (*ddd* or *lll*). The absorption band at 9·09τ is assigned to methyl groups in the central monomer units of syndiotactic sequences and that at 8·95τ to the α-methyl groups in heterotactic configurations. Measurement of the relative intensities of these absorption bands gives the proportions of the various units in the polymer chain. The methylene groups in syndiotactic polymer configurations give a single absorption band because, on a time average, both hydrogen nuclei experience the same chemical environment (see Fig. 10.53 (b)). In an isotactic sequence the two methylene hydrogen nuclei are usually shielded differently and give rise to a pair of AB type doublets (see Section 8.13.1). For isotactic polymethylmethacrylate, three bands of the isotactic methylene AB quartet are seen to be centred at 8·14τ: a fourth component of the quartet presumably lies under the α-methyl absorption bands. The chemical shift difference between the non-equivalent methylene hydrogen nuclei is 0·60 ppm and the coupling constant is 15·5 cycles sec^{-1} (see Fig. 10.53 (a)).

The NMR technique has also been used to determine the extent of geometrical isomerism in poly(ethylene-1, 4-cyclohexane dicarboxylate)[(377)] and the tacticities of polypropylene[(473)] and polyvinylethers[(474)].

10.37.4 The Use of Spin Decoupling in the Determination of Polymer Structures

For vinyl polymers having only a single α-substituent there is considerable H—H spin coupling between nuclei on the α- and β-carbon atoms. Such spin coupling often complicates the spectra to such an extent that it is not possible to observe clearly the different multiplets arising from the nuclei in various stereochemical sequences. Bovey and co-workers[(395)] have used the spin decoupling technique to decouple the α- and β-hydrogen nuclei in compounds such as polyvinyl chloride, polyvinyl fluoride and polyvinyl methyl ether, thus enabling the tacticities of the samples to be characterised successfully. Figure 10.54 (a) shows the ^{1}H resonance spectrum of a sample of polyvinyl chloride in chlorobenzene solution at 170°C and at 60 Mc sec^{-1}. Johnsen[(396)], in a previous examination of the spectrum, assigned the two overlapping high field triplets (τ values centred at 7·78 and 7·96) to *meso*- and *racemic*-methylene groups respectively and assumed that the hydrogen nuclei in each CH_2 group are magnetically equivalent. The high field triplet was arbitrarily assigned to the *racemic*-methylene hydrogens as found in syndiotactic sequences. The α-hydrogen nuclei give rise to a "quintet" centred at 5·53τ. Bovey and co-workers[(395)] have confirmed the methylene hydrogen assignments by decoupling the α- and β-hydrogen nuclei. When the β-hydrogen nuclei are decoupled from the α-hydrogen nuclei, the two high field triplets collapse to two single absorption bands separated by 0·20 ppm (see Fig. 10.54 (d)). The decoupled spectrum of the methylene absorption bands is similar to the ^{1}H spectrum of poly α-d_1-vinyl chloride[397] shown in Fig. 10.54 (b). When the CH_2 hydrogen nuclei are irradiated, three separate absorption bands are observed in the α-hydrogen region of the spectrum as shown in Fig. 10.54 (c) (τ values of 5·48, 5·59 and 5·71). By considering the effects on the α-hydrogen region of the spectrum of specifically irradiating the *meso*- and *racemic*-methylene nuclei in turn, the three low field bands can be attributed to syndiotactic, heterotactic and isotactic triads respectively (assuming that the β-hydrogen nuclei have been assigned correctly). Thus, the undecoupled α-hydrogen "quintet" is in fact three overlapping quintets. Intensity measurements can be made on the decoupled spectrum to ascertain the extent of stereoregularity in a particular sample.

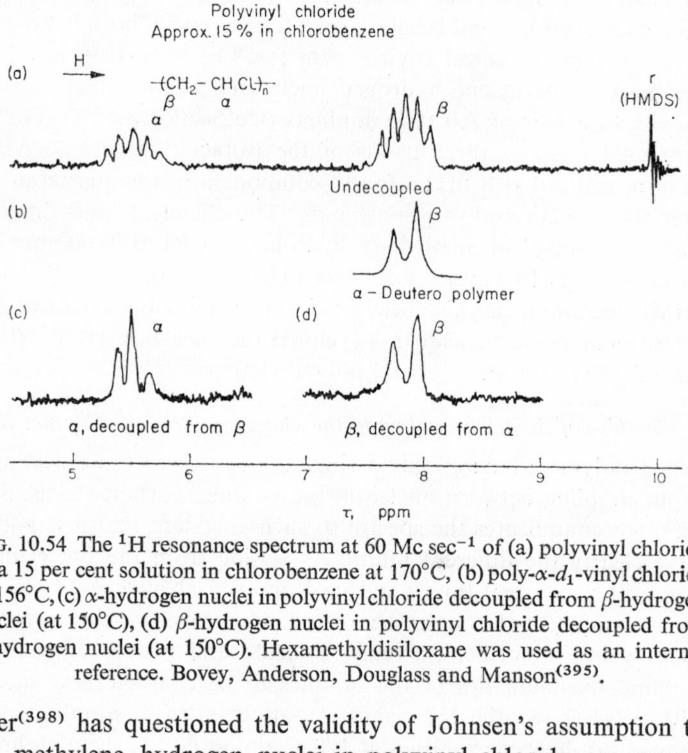

FIG. 10.54 The ^{1}H resonance spectrum at 60 Mc sec^{-1} of (a) polyvinyl chloride in a 15 per cent solution in chlorobenzene at 170°C, (b) poly-α-d_1-vinyl chloride at 156°C, (c) α-hydrogen nuclei in polyvinyl chloride decoupled from β-hydrogen nuclei (at 150°C), (d) β-hydrogen nuclei in polyvinyl chloride decoupled from α-hydrogen nuclei (at 150°C). Hexamethyldisiloxane was used as an internal reference. Bovey, Anderson, Douglass and Manson[395].

Tincher[398] has questioned the validity of Johnsen's assumption that the isotactic methylene hydrogen nuclei in polyvinyl chloride are magnetically equivalent and he has shown that the observed ^{1}H spectrum can be reconciled with non-equivalent methylene hydrogen nuclei. However, the spin decoupling experiments indicate that the two nuclei have the same chemical shift within the resolution of the experiment.

10.37.5 The Use of Deuteration in the Determination of Polymer Tacticities by NMR

Polypropylene. Spin coupling between hydrogen nuclei on adjacent carbon atoms in polymer chains such as those found in polypropylene causes the ^{1}H resonance spectrum to be extremely complex. Substitution in the molecule of some of the hydrogen atoms by deuterium atoms can simplify considerably the ^{1}H resonance spectrum since the magnitudes of the ^{1}H—D coupling constants are small and do not introduce any detectable splittings on the absorption bands[399]. Figure 10.55 (a) shows the complex ^{1}H resonance spectrum obtained

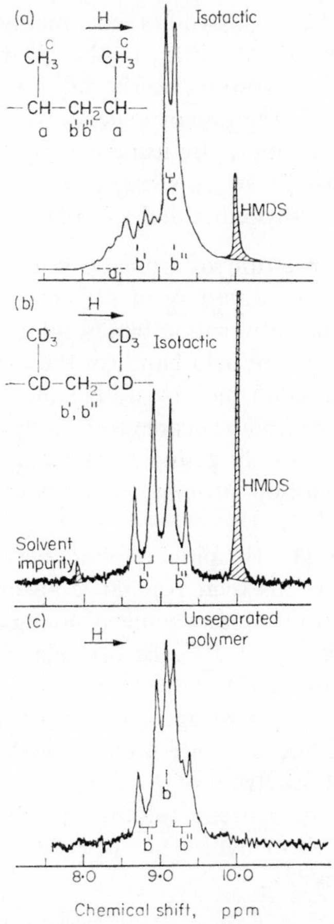

FIG. 10.55 The ^{1}H resonance spectra at 60 Mc sec^{-1} of (a) isotactic polypropylene in *p*-dichlorobenzene at 175°C, (b) isotactic polypropylene-2,3,3,3-d_4 in 2-chlorothiophene at 110°C. (c) a sample of unseparated polypropylene-2,3,3,3-d_4 in 2-chlorothiophene at 110°C. Hexamethyldisiloxane was used as an internal reference ($\tau = 9{\cdot}95$). Stehling[399].

for a sample of isotactic polypropylene[399]. Satoh and co-workers[400] have attempted a detailed analysis of spectra of this type and they were able to obtain the tacticities of various samples of polypropylene from NMR measurements. In contrast to Fig. 10.55 (a), the ^{1}H spectrum of isotactic polypropylene-2,3,3,3-d_4, shown in Fig. 10.55 (b), can readily be identified as typical of two non-equivalent interacting hydrogen nuclei forming an AB system (see Section 8.13.1). Each hydrogen nucleus in the methylene group gives rise to a doublet and because the nuclei are strongly coupled, the intensities of the components of the doublet are unequal. In the ^1H spectrum shown in Fig. 10.55(c) for a sample of unseparated polypropylene-2,3,3,3-d_4, in addition to the AB quartet of the isotactic methylene groups, an extra absorption band for syndiotactic methylene groups is observed. The single absorption is as expected since the hydrogen nuclei in a syndiotactic methylene are equivalent. By measuring appropriate band intensities in the ^1H resonance spectrum of a sample of the deuterated polypropylene the ratio of isotactic to syndiotactic sequences can be estimated. The polypropylenes used in this investigation[(399)] were prepared from the monomer by using a typical Ziegler catalyst and the various fractions of different stereoisomeric composition were separated by solvent extraction using diethyl ether and n-heptane.

Polystyrene. The ^1H spectrum of isotactic polystyrene (molecular weight 200,000) dissolved in any of a variety of solvents (CS_2, $CDCl_3$, C_6H_6 etc.) shows two separate aliphatic absorption bands, a low field band corresponding to α-hydrogen nuclei and a high field band for the β-hydrogen nuclei[(402, 403)]. This assignment has been confirmed by noting the disappearance of the low field band when the α-hydrogen nuclei are replaced by deuterium[(402)]. A sample of atactic polystyrene shows only a single ^1H resonance band in the aliphatic region of the spectrum in all but aromatic solvents where two bands are again resolvable[(402)].

Because the extensive H—H spin coupling between α- and β-hydrogen nuclei in polystyrene broadens their resonance absorptions it is not possible to detect readily the various stereochemical configurations in the molecule using the NMR method[(184, 401, 402)]. Brownstein and co-workers[(401)] have resorted to the deuterium substitution technique to study the tacticity of polydeuterostyrenes. When the β-hydrogen nuclei of styrene are replaced by deuterium, spin coupling fine structure on the α-hydrogen absorption band is removed. Thus in the ^1H spectrum of polydeuterostyrene prepared from this monomer and examined in benzene solution at 100°C, separate absorption bands are detectable for the α-hydrogen nuclei in isotactic, syndiotactic and heterotactic configurations[(401)].

10.38 Empirical Estimation of Chemical Shifts

We have already seen (Chapter 4) that quantum mechanics cannot be used to calculate the shielding of hydrogen nuclei in any but the simplest of molecules due to limited knowledge of the required wavefunctions. Since it is obviously desirable to be able to estimate the chemical shifts of hydrogen nuclei in molecules, an empirical method for predicting such shifts has been resorted to. Primas, Arndt and Ernst[(347)] have devised a simple scheme for predicting the chemical shifts of hydrogen atoms attached to carbon atoms, based on the assumption that the chemical shift of a particular nucleus can be considered as the sum of several characteristic contributions from the various groups and features in the molecule. Although there is no sound theoretical reason for assuming additivity behaviour, the success of the scheme in predicting chemical shifts cannot be denied. Thus, the τ value of a hydrogen nucleus in the molecule is given by the simple expression

$$\tau = T_0 + \sum c_j T_j$$

TABLE 10.98 CONTRIBUTIONS TO THE ^{1}H CHEMICAL SHIFTS FROM VARIOUS SUBSTITUENTS AND GROUPINGS[347]

		Characteristic contribution	Number of samples
		$T_0 = 9{\cdot}067$	284
No skeleton substituent		No contribution	21
Skeleton substituent no. 1		$T_1 = -0{\cdot}248$	96
Skeleton substituent no. 2		$T_2 = -0{\cdot}244$	137
Skeleton substituent no. 3		$T_3 = -0{\cdot}147$	56
Skeleton substituent no. 4		$T_4 = -0{\cdot}006$	10
Substituent	**Position**	**Characteristic contribution**	**Number of samples**
$—CR_3$	3	$T_5 = +0{\cdot}038$	110
Double bond	1	$T_6 = -3{\cdot}802$	21
	2	$T_7 = -0{\cdot}583$	31
	3	$T_8 = -0{\cdot}203$	7
Triple bond	1	$T_9 = -1{\cdot}032$	3
	2	$T_{10} = -0{\cdot}694$	4
$=O$	1	$T_{11} = -8{\cdot}536$†	7
	2	$T_{12} = -1{\cdot}021$	21
	3	$T_{13} = -0{\cdot}004$	11
$—OCH_3$	2	$T_{14} = +0{\cdot}373$	6
$—OCH_2—CR_3$	2	$T_{15} = +0{\cdot}237$	7
	3	$T_{16} = -0{\cdot}210$	6
$—OH$	1	$T_{17} = -2{\cdot}467$	8
	2	$T_{18} = -0{\cdot}048$	8
	3	$T_{19} = -0{\cdot}235$	5
$—O—CO—CR_3$	1	$T_{20} = -2{\cdot}931$	28
	2	$T_{21} = -0{\cdot}041$	11
	3	$T_{22} = +0{\cdot}086$	5
$—F$	2	$T_{23} = -0{\cdot}089$	9
	3	$T_{24} = -0{\cdot}131$	9
$—Cl$	1	$T_{25} = -2{\cdot}170$	29
	2	$T_{26} = -0{\cdot}254$	19
	3	$T_{27} = -0{\cdot}177$	12
$—Br$	1	$T_{28} = -1{\cdot}995$	24
	2	$T_{29} = +0{\cdot}363$	16
	3	$T_{30} = -0{\cdot}023$	7
$—I$	1	$T_{31} = -1{\cdot}846$	10
	2	$T_{32} = -0{\cdot}388$	5
$—NH_2$	2	$T_{33} = -0{\cdot}094$	3
$—O—CR_3$	1	$T_{34} = +1{\cdot}434$‡	

R may be any group, including R = H.

† By using this group the only allowed substituent in position 1 is T_{34}.
‡ Has only to be used in combination with T_{11}.

where $T_0 = 9 \cdot 067$, T_j is the chemical shift contribution from a group or feature, and c_j is the number of times it occurs in the molecule. Primas evaluated the contributions T_j by considering the extensive data of Tiers (see Appendix B) and subjecting them to a computer, programmed to solve the many linear equations involved.

For the purpose of the scheme, the carbon skeleton of the molecule is numbered starting with the carbon to which the hydrogen is attached (carbon 1) and numbering each of the others according to the number of bonds separating it from the hydrogen atom as shown: each carbon atom up to carbon 4 is considered to make a contribution to the chemical shift. The carbon atom in position 4 is treated as a substituent of carbon 3. Only contributions from

No.	Skeleton substituent	Characteristic contribution
1	$-C^2$	T_1
2	$-C^2-C^3$	T_2
3	$-C^2\Big\langle{}^{C^3}_{C^3}$	T_3
4	$-C^2\!\!-\!\!C^3\big\langle{}^{C^3}_{C^3}$	T_4

TABLE 10.99 OBSERVED AND CALCULATED ^1H CHEMICAL SHIFTS FOR A SERIES OF MOLECULES[347]

1) $CH_3CO-COCH_3$
$\tau = T_0 + T_2 + T_5 + T_{12} + T_{13} = 7 \cdot 83$
　　value measured by Tiers $\tau = 7 \cdot 77$

2) $CH_3CH_2\!\!\diagdown{}_{}\!\!C\!\!\diagup{}^{COOEt}$
　$CH_3CH_2\!\!\diagup{}^{}\!\!{}\diagdown{}_{COOEt}$
$\tau = T_0 + T_1 + T_4 + T_5 + 2T_{13} + 2T_{16} = 8 \cdot 42$
　　value measured by Tiers $\tau = 8 \cdot 16$

3) $CH_3CH_2\!\!\diagdown{}_{}\!\!C\!\!\diagup{}^{COOCH_2CH_3}$
　$CH_3CH_2\!\!\diagup{}^{}\!\!{}\diagdown{}_{COOCH_2CH_3}$
$\tau = T_0 + T_1 + T_{20} = 5 \cdot 89$
value measured by Tiers $\tau = 5 \cdot 85$

4) $HC{\equiv}CCH_2Br$
$\tau = T_0 + T_2 + T_{10} + T_{28} = 6 \cdot 13$
value measured by Tiers $\tau = 6 \cdot 18$

5) $Me_2C{=}CHCH_2CH_2CHCH_2CHO$
　　　　　　　　　　$|$
　　　　　　　　　CH_3
$\tau = T_0 + T_1 + T_3 + T_5 + T_{12} = 7 \cdot 69$
　　value measured by Tiers $\tau = 7 \cdot 81$

6) $CF_2ClCHCl_2$
$\tau = T_0 + T_1 + 2T_{23} + 2T_{25} + T_{26} = 4 \cdot 05$
　　value measured by Tiers $\tau = 4 \cdot 08$

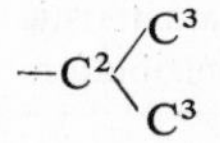

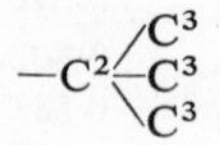

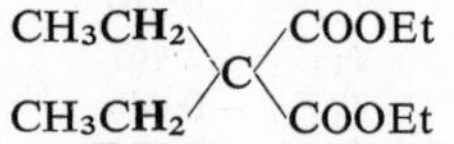

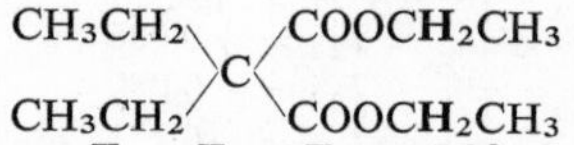

substituents on the first three carbon atoms are considered and these are given in Table 10.98. The manner in which the scheme operates can best be understood by examining the typical examples shown in Table 10.99. Excellent agreement between predicted and observed chemical shifts is obtained for most of the 284 compounds considered, the least reliable predictions being noted in halogenated molecules. The molecules investigated did not include cyclic molecules, acids or molecules containing hetero atoms in the skeleton (with the exception of ethers, esters, and acid anhydrides). For aldehydes, ketones, esters, ethers, acid anhydrides and acid halides the τ-values are assumed to be composed of contributions from the substituents R=O, —O—COR, OCH_3, OC_2H_5, etc.

Besides this general method for estimating chemical shifts, numerous other methods have been outlined for specific classes of molecules and some of these are discussed in the appropriate sections of this chapter. In the absence of suitable model compounds, such empirical calculations of chemical shifts can prove useful in the NMR determination of molecular structures.

10.39 Medium Effects in Liquids

The shielding constant of a nucleus in a particular molecule is determined by the electronic distribution within the molecule, and also by the nature of the surrounding medium (see Sections 3.9 and 3.10). The observed shielding constant, σ, is the sum of the value for the isolated molecule and a contribution arising from the surrounding medium, that is

$$\sigma = \sigma_{\text{medium}} + \sigma_{\text{mol}}$$

where σ_{mol} is the value for a gaseous sample at low pressures. σ_{medium} can be measured as the difference between the chemical shift of a gaseous sample at low pressures and that of the sample dissolved in a particular solvent, both measured with respect to the same external reference compound.

Buckingham, Schaefer and Schneider[200] have suggested that σ_{medium} has contributions from five sources:

$$\sigma_{\text{medium}} = \sigma_b + \sigma_a + \sigma_w + \sigma_E + \sigma_H. \qquad (10.16)$$

σ_b is proportional to the bulk diamagnetic susceptibility of the medium and has been discussed in Section 3.3. The magnitude of σ_b depends upon the shape of the sample container (see equation (3.6)) and is zero for a spherical sample. Most NMR measurements are made with the sample in a cylindrical tube and in this case σ_b is given by

$$\sigma_b = (2/3)\,\pi\,\chi_v \qquad (10.17)$$

where χ_v is the volume susceptibility of the medium.

σ_a is a consequence of the non-zero averaging of the anisotropy in the diamagnetic susceptibility of the solvent molecules. It is particularly important for disc-shaped solvents such as aromatic molecules, and rod-like solvents such as carbon disulphide. The magnitude of σ_a depends upon the nature of the anisotropy and has been discussed in Section 3.10 (where σ_a was referred to as $\Delta\sum^{(a)}$). For disc-shaped molecules σ_a can be described approximately by the equation

$$\sigma_a = -2n(\chi_\parallel - \chi_\perp)/(3R^3)$$

and for rod-shaped molecules

$$\sigma_a = n(\chi_\parallel - \chi_\perp)/(3R^3)$$

in which R is the distance between the nucleus in the solute molecule and the centre of the solvent molecule, and n is the number of solute molecules within this distance R. Benzene is an example of a disc-shaped solvent, and it is found that for methane dissolved in benzene $[(\chi_\parallel - \chi_\perp) = -9 \times 10^{-29}$, $n = 2$, $R \sim 4{\cdot}5$ Å], $\sigma_a = 1{\cdot}3$ ppm. For methane in carbon disulphide, a rod-shaped molecule $[(\chi_\parallel - \chi_\perp) = -5 \times 10^{-29}$, $n = 2$, $R \sim 4$ Å], $\sigma_a = -0{\cdot}5$ ppm. Abraham[420] has also calculated chemical shift contributions arising from the magnetic anisotropy of cylindrical solvents: for benzene, he obtained a value for σ_a in good agreement with that of Buckingham and co-workers while for carbon disulphide, the σ_a value was much smaller. Although the formulae predict the correct direction for the chemical shift contribution from this source, the observed values for non-polar solutes are always larger than the predicted values.

σ_w is a contribution arising from the weak Van der Waals forces between the solute and solvent molecules[200, 422]. Two effects may contribute to σ_w; (a) an interaction between the solute and the solvent (in its equilibrium configuration) leading to a distortion, probably an expansion, of the electronic environment of the solute nuclei. This leads to a reduction in the diamagnetic term in Ramsey's equation for σ (see Section 3.5) and hence to a negative value for σ_w; (b) departures from the equilibrium configuration of the solvent molecules lead to a time varying distortion of the electronic environment of the solute molecules. If the solute is an atom in an S state, the interaction will destroy the electronic symmetry and hence introduce a paramagnetic term into the shielding constant (see Section 3.5). This time dependent interaction will be most effective for nuclei of atoms but may also be important for nuclei in molecules with symmetrical environments, as in axially symmetric X—H bonds. Effect (a) is independent of temperature, but effect (b) should increase with temperature leading to an increased negative σ_w. Measurements on CH_4 in CCl_4 at -27°C and 95°C show that effect (b) is not important for this solute; however, atoms such as ^{129}Xe should show a large temperature dependent σ_w.

σ_E arises because of the effect of an electric field on the shielding constant[493]. Buckingham[481] has shown (see Section 3.9) that an applied electric field affects the shielding constant of a hydrogen atom in an X—H bond. Thus, when a polar molecule is dissolved in a medium of dielectric constant ε it induces a reaction field which then tends to reduce the value of the shielding constant producing a shift to lower applied magnetic fields. Even molecules which do not have a permanent dipole moment may still produce a reaction field provided that the molecule possesses polar groups (see Section 3.9). In both cases, if an Onsager model is used to calculate the reaction field then σ_E is proportional to $(\varepsilon - 1)/(\varepsilon + 1)$.

The last term in equation (10.16), σ_H, is the result of specific solvent–solute interactions, such as hydrogen bonding, and it is usually by far the largest term. Specific solvent effects of this type have been dealt with in Section 9.4 and will not be elaborated on here.

Buckingham *et al.*(200) have tested equation (10.16) for the cases of both a polar and non-polar solute dissolved in different liquid solvents. For a non-polar solute they chose methane, and the chemical shifts of this solute in a

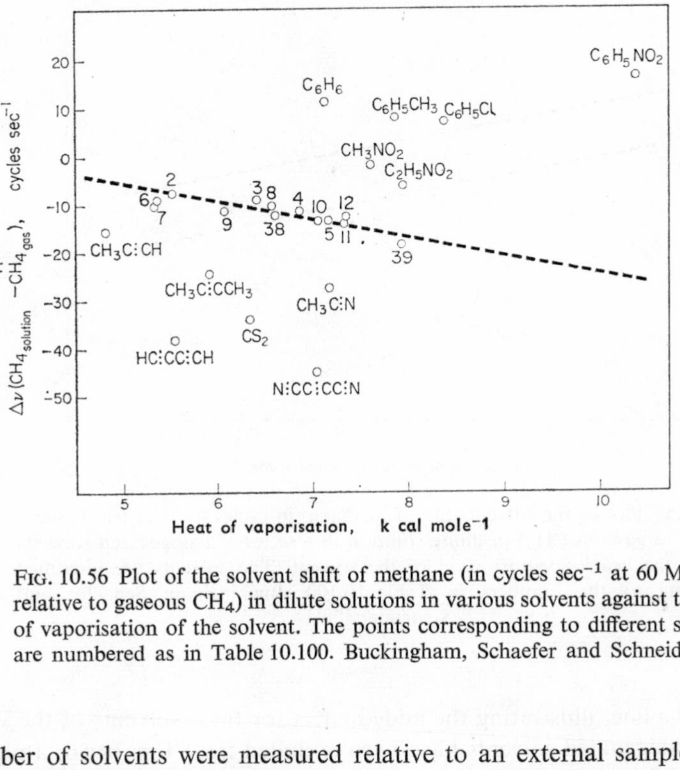

FIG. 10.56 Plot of the solvent shift of methane (in cycles sec^{-1} at 60 Mc sec^{-1} relative to gaseous CH_4) in dilute solutions in various solvents against the heat of vaporisation of the solvent. The points corresponding to different solvents are numbered as in Table 10.100. Buckingham, Schaefer and Schneider(200).

number of solvents were measured relative to an external sample of chloroform. The shifts were then referred to an external reference of gaseous CH_4 by applying equation (10.17) for the value of σ_b. Table 10.100 gives the chemical shift values obtained and the final column shows the shifts relative to CH_4 gas reference, this giving a measure of $(\sigma_{\text{medium}} - \sigma_b)$. For a symmetrical non-polar molecule like CH_4 the terms σ_H and σ_E are zero and only $(\sigma_a + \sigma_w)$ are likely to affect the magnitude of $\Delta\nu\ (CH_{4\text{solution}} - CH_{4\text{gas}})$. Rather than calculate a value of σ_w to compare with $\Delta\nu\ (CH_{4\text{solution}} - CH_{4\text{gas}})$, Buckingham *et al.*(200) used instead the value of the heat of vaporisation of the solvent at the boiling point as a measure of the van der Waals interaction. This is primarily a measure of the interaction between like solvent molecules but is also proportional to the interaction between the solvent molecules and the common solute molecule, provided that the interaction is of the simple van der Waals type. The heat of vaporisation H_b at the boiling point T_b was calculated from the empirical relation of Hildebrand and Scott[413] of

$$H_b = 17{\cdot}0T_b + 0{\cdot}009T_b^2$$

Figure 10.56 shows a plot of $\Delta\nu$ ($CH_{4\text{solution}} - CH_{4\text{gas}}$) against H_b for the solvents listed in Table 10.100. The diagram shows a linear plot for spherical solvents while disc-shaped and rod-shaped solvents have points displaced above

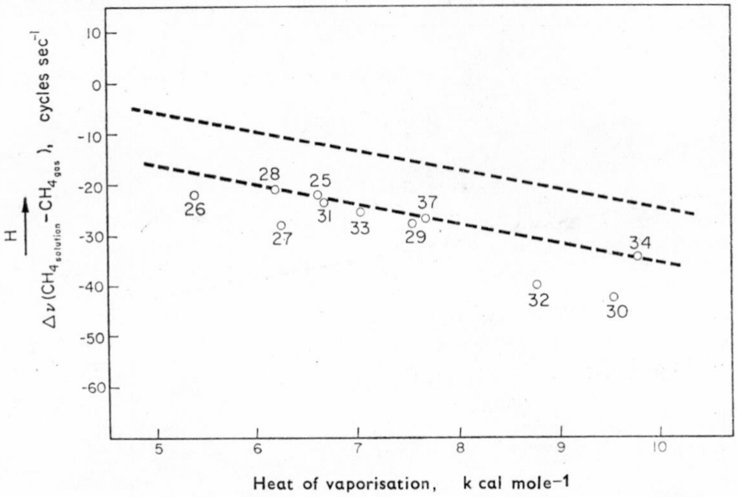

FIG. 10.57 Plot of the solvent shift of methane (in cycles sec^{-1} at 60 Mc sec^{-1} relative to gaseous CH_4) in dilute solution in a series of halogenated solvents against the heat of vaporisation of the solvent. The solvents are identified according to the numbers in Table 10.100. Buckingham, Schaefer and Schneider[200].

and below the line, illustrating the added effect for these solvents of the value of σ_a. The halogenated solvents have been excluded from Fig. 10.56; a plot of $\Delta\nu$ ($CH_{4\,\text{solution}} - CH_{4\,\text{gas}}$) for these solvents shows a linear variation with H_b, but the points lie consistently below the line for the other solvents (see Fig. 10.57). An explanation of this behaviour has not been put forward; it may indicate simply that the magnetic susceptibilities are incorrect.

To test the validity of equation (10.16) for a polar molecule, Buckingham *et al.*[200] measured the shifts of acetonitrile, CH_3CN, dissolved in various solvents. They attempted to isolate the polar effect σ_E from the rest by avoiding solvents which are expected to show large values of σ_a and σ_w, that is aromatic, rod-shaped and halogenated solvents, and by using a 5 mole per cent solution of CH_3CN in n-hexane as a reference state. The shifts measured relative to an external chloroform sample are shown in Table 10.101; the shifts being corrected for differences in bulk diamagnetic susceptibility. The quantity

TABLE 10.100 HYDROGEN CHEMICAL SHIFTS OF DILUTE SOLUTIONS OF CH_4 IN VARIOUS SOLVENTS (IN CYCLES SEC^{-1} at 60 Mc SEC^{-1})[(200)]

Solvent	$-\chi_v (\times 10^6)$	Chemical shifts (cycles sec^{-1})		
		Measured ($CHCl_3$ reference)	Corrected ($CHCl_3$ reference)	Corrected [CH_4 (gas) reference]
1. CH_4 (gas)	0	538·2	446·5	0
2. Neopentane	0·554[a]	460·9	438·7	−7·8
3. Cyclopentane	0·661[a]	445·9	437·1	−9·4
4. n-Hexane	0·586	452·9	434·7	−11·8
5. Cyclohexane	0·631	445·2	432·7	−13·8
6. *trans*-Butene-2	0·45[a]	469·4	437·3	−9·2
7. *cis*-Butene-2	0·475[a]	468·2	436·1	−10·4
8. Acetone	0·460	469·9	435·9	−10·6
9. Ethyl ether	0·547	458·1	435·0	−11·5
10. Ethyl acetate	0·547	455·9	432·9	−13·6
11. Ethyl nitrate	0·485[a]	463·4	432·7	−13·8
12. Triethylamine	0·610[a]	449·0	433·8	−12·7
13. Propyne	0·470[a]	460·6	427·9	−15·6
14. Acetonitrile	0·486[a]	449·6	418·9	−27·6
15. Butyne-2	0·519[a]	448·5	421·9	−24·6
16. Carbon disulphide	0·68[illegible]	418·8	412·5	−34·0
17. Diacetylene	0·401[a]	450·0	408·7	−37·8
18. Dicyanoacetylene	0·417[a]	440·5	401·2	−45·2
19. Benzene	0·626	470·5	457·3	+10·8
20. Toluene	0·631	466·8	454·3	+7·8
21. Chlorobenzene	0·707	456·3	453·3	+6·8
22. Nitrobenzene	0·598	479·3	462·6	+16·1
23. Nitromethane	0·473[a]	476·8	444·4	−2·1
24. Nitroethane	0·497	469·2	440·0	−6·5
25. Bromine	1·17[a]	369·4	424·6	−21·9
26. CH_3Br	0·73[b]	424·5	424·5	−22·0
27. CH_3I	0·918	395·2	418·6	−27·9
28. CH_2Cl_2	0·733	425·5	425·7	−20·8
29. CH_2Br_2	0·946	392·0	419·0	−27·5
30. CH_2I_2	1·16	350·2	404·1	−42·4
31. $CHCl_3$	0·731	423·1	423·1	−23·4
32. $CHBr_3$	0·913	383·9	406·7	−39·8
33. CCl_4	0·684	427·2	421·3	−25·2
34. CBr_4 (100°C)	0·863[c]	396·0	412·5	−34·0
35. CH_2ClBr	0·839[a]	408·4	421·9	−24·6
36. $CHClBr_2$	0·792[a]	396·8	404·4	−42·1
37. CCl_3Br	0·752[a]	415·5	418·1	−26·4
38. $SiCl_4$	0·796	426·1	434·2	−12·3
39. $SnCl_4$	0·986	395·8	427·8	−18·7

[a] Estimated from Pascal's constants and interpolation of data of related compounds.
[b] From A. A. Bothner-By and R. E. Glick, *J. Chem. Phys.*, **26**, 1647 (1957).
[c] Density measured at 100°C, 2·943 g ml^{-1}.

TABLE 10.101 HYDROGEN CHEMICAL SHIFTS (IN CYCLES SEC^{-1} AT 60 MC SEC^{-1}) OF 5 MOLE PER CENT CH_3CN IN VARIOUS SOLVENTS (RELATIVE TO EXTERNAL REFERENCE $CHCl_3$)(200)

Solvent	$-\chi_v(10^6)$	Chemical shift	
		Measured	Corrected
1. n-Hexane	0·586	358·7	340·5
2. Cyclohexene	0·576	353·7	334·3
3. *cis*-Butene-2	0·475[a]	367·3	335·3
4. *trans*-Butene-2	0·475[a]	371·3	339·3
5. Cyclohexene	0·576	353·7	334·3
6. Trimethylamine	0·610[a]	344·8	329·6
7. Ethyl ether	0·547	353·2	330·1
8. Ethyl formate	0·537	350·3	326·0
9. Cyclohexanone	0·614	338·3	323·7
10. Acetone	0·460	357·0	323·0
11. Acetaldehyde	0·393	369·1	326·8
12. Carbon tetrachloride	0·684	323·8	317·9
13. Chloroform	0·731	319·2	319·2
14. Methylene chloride	0·733	320·9	321·1
15. Ethyl chloride	0·664[a]	341·3	332·9
16. Acetonitrile	0·486[a]	344·8	314·1
17. Nitromethane	0·473[a]	366·6	334·2
18. Benzene	0·626	434·2	421·0
19. Mesitylene	0·652[a]	417·8	407·8
20. Nitrobenzene	0·598	364·8	348·1
21. Bromobenzene	0·771	376·2	381·2
22. Benzonitrile	0·658	361·4	352·3

[a] Estimated from Pascal's constants and interpolation of data of related compounds.

TABLE 10.102 HYDROGEN CHEMICAL SHIFTS (IN CYCLES SEC^{-1} AT 60 MC SEC^{-1}) OF CH_3CN AND CH_4 IN VARIOUS SOLVENTS (RELATIVE TO CHLOROFORM EXTERNAL REFERENCE)(414)

Solvent	Chemical shift		Ac-Me	$\Delta\nu(CH_3CN—CH_4)$
	Acetonitrile	Methane		
1. n-Hexane	358·7	452·9	−94·2	0
2. *trans*-Butene-2	371·3	469·4	−98·1	−3·9
3. *cis*-Butene-2	367·3	468·2	−100·9	−6·7
4. Acetone	357·0	469·9	−112·9	−18·7
5. Ethyl ether	353·2	458·1	−104·9	−10·7
6. Triethylamine	344·8	449·0	−104·2	−10·0
7. Acetonitrile	344·8	449·6	−104·8	−10·6
8. Benzene	434·2	470·5	−36·3	+57·9
9. Nitrobenzene	364·8	479·3	−114·5	−20·3
10. Nitromethane	366·6	476·8	−110·2	−16·0
11. CH_2Cl_2	320·9	425·5	−104·6	−10·4
12. $CHCl_3$	319·2	423·1	−103·9	−9·7
13. CCl_4	323·8	427·2	−103·4	−9·2

$\Delta\nu$ ($CH_3CN_{solution}$ − $CH_3CN_{n\text{-hexane}}$) was plotted against $(\varepsilon - 1)/(2\varepsilon + 2{\cdot}5)$ for certain selected solvents giving the linear graph shown in Fig. 10.58. Abraham[414] pointed out that the chemical shifts of CH_3CN and CH_4 both as 5 mole per cent solutions in the same solvent should include identical values of σ_a, σ_w and σ_b, hence any difference between the solvent shifts arises from σ_E or σ_H. Table 10.102 shows the chemical shifts, relative to the external reference $CHCl_3$, of 5 mole per cent solutions of CH_3CN and CH_4 in various solvents, including some solvents expected to produce large values of σ_a. The chemical shift difference $\Delta\nu$ (CH_3CN—CH_4)$_{solvent}$ for each solvent is found and then all the shifts are put on the scale with $\Delta\nu$ zero in n-hexane (the

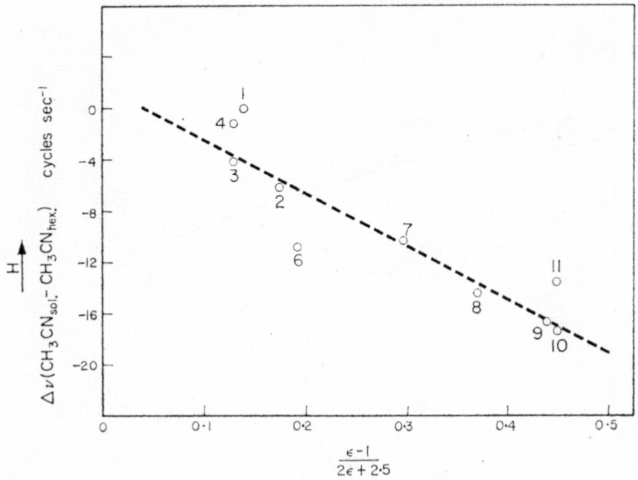

FIG. 10.58 Plot of the solvent shift of CH_3CN in a 5 mole per cent solution in various solvents (in cycles sec^{-1} at 60 Mc sec^{-1} relative to CH_3CN in a 5 mole per cent n-hexane solution) against $(\varepsilon - 1)/(2\,\varepsilon + 2{\cdot}5)$. The solvents are numbered as in Table 10.101. Buckingham, Schaefer and Schneider[200].

value in n-hexane is taken to arise solely from the different nature of the solutes). For acetonitrile ($\mu/\alpha = 1{\cdot}0 \times 10^6$, $n_D^\infty = 1{\cdot}34$),

$$\sigma_E = -11\,[(\varepsilon - 1)/(\varepsilon + 0{\cdot}9)] - 4{\cdot}3\,[(\varepsilon - 1)/(\varepsilon + 0{\cdot}9)]^2$$

and when $\Delta\nu$ (CH_3CN—CH_4) is plotted against $(\varepsilon - 1)/(\varepsilon + 0{\cdot}9)$ one obtains the graph shown in Fig. 10.59. The curve shown on the diagram was calculated from the above equation. The agreement between theory and experiment is very good except for benzene, and the anomalous high field shift in this case probably arises because of a large value of σ_H.

Diehl and Freeman[421] have modified the Buckingham theory of the σ_E shielding contribution to allow for the shape of the solute molecules (see Section 3.9).

Abraham[420] has shown that the solvent shifts of the polar solute methyl iodide in aliphatic solvents can be explained quantitatively in terms of σ_b, σ_a and σ_E (see equation (10.16)).

Hruska and co-workers[448] have measured the ^{1}H chemical shifts of *cis* and *trans* dichloro- and dibromoethylenes in solutions of dioxane/water. By varying the composition of the dioxane/water solvent, the dielectric constant of the system could be varied over the range 2 to 10 and by taking the $\Delta = \delta_{cis} - \delta_{trans}$ shifts as arising solely from the electric reaction field effect, the Buckingham reaction field equation could be tested: the equation was found to describe the solvent effects adequately.

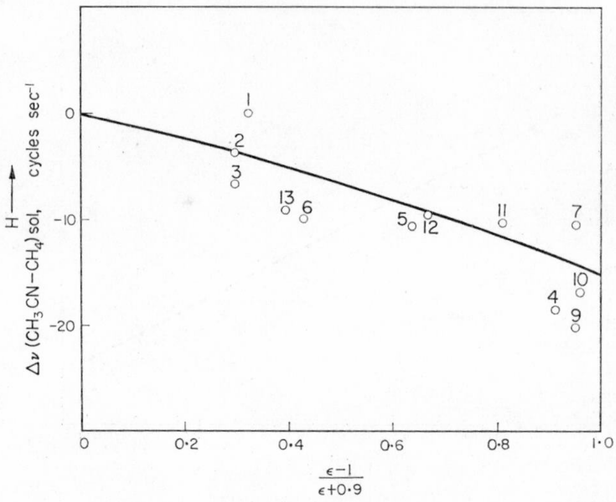

FIG. 10.59 The difference in the chemical shift values of acetonitrile and methane in various solvents (relative to the difference in n-hexane) against $(\varepsilon - 1)/(\varepsilon + 0{\cdot}9)$. Abraham[414].

Lumbroso and co-workers[446] have measured the reaction field shifts of some polar molecules and the van der Waals shifts in some non-polar gases. The observed van der Waals shifts are greater than the shifts predicted using a theoretical model proposed by Howard and co-workers[447] and the same is true of the polar shifts when they are compared with values calculated using Buckingham's reaction field theory[27, 200].

10.39.1 The Effects of Solvents on the Resonance Spectra of Acetylenic Molecules

Infrared measurements[196] have shown that acetylene is capable of self-association by the formation of weak hydrogen bonds involving the slightly acidic hydrogen atoms and the π-electrons of the triple bond. Monosubstituted acetylenes would also be expected to behave in this way and it is thought that in liquid acetylenes collisions of the type

R
|
C
|||
C
|
H
R—C≡C—H

allow the hydrogen nucleus to approach the triple bond more closely than collisions of the type

R—C≡C—H   H—C≡C—R

and, therefore, are more likely to occur. Because of the strong diamagnetic anisotropic effect associated with the triple bond of acetylenic systems, the proximity of the acetylenic hydrogen nuclei to the triple bonds will be reflected as a deshielding of the nuclei concerned. The addition of an inert solvent, such as cyclohexane, will cause self-association to decrease and the acetylenic hydrogen nuclei to experience increased shielding. Richards and Hatton[197] have found that both propargyl chloride ($ClCH_2C{\equiv}CH$) and phenyl acetylene show this behaviour on dilution with cyclohexane (a dilution shift ~0·4 ppm is observed). Other solvents have more marked effects on the shielding of acetylenic hydrogen nuclei due to the presence of specific interactions between solvent and solute. Table 10.103 summarises the chemical shifts of propargyl chloride, phenyl acetylene and benzoyl acetylene in a wide variety of solvents. For the purpose of comparing the chemical shifts in various solvents, the reference was taken as the acetylenic absorption signal of each compound measured

TABLE 10.103 THE ¹H CHEMICAL SHIFTS (τ VALUES) OF PROPARGYL CHLORIDE, PHENYL ACETYLENE AND BENZOYL ACETYLENE IN VARIOUS SOLVENTS[197]

Solvent	Propargyl chloride		Phenyl acetylene	Benzoyl acetylene
	≡CH	CH_2	≡CH	≡CH
Pure compound	7·41	5·87	6·91	6·42 †
Cyclohexane	7·81	6·13	7·26	6·90
N,N diMe acetamide	—	—	5·78	4·63
N,N diMe formamide	6·38	5·61	5·65	4·89
Pyridine	—	—	5·90	4·80
Acetone	6·94	5·77	6·39	5·49
Dioxane	7·07	5·87	6·50	5·87
Acetonitrile	7·20	5·83	6·65	5·75
Nitrobenzene	7·10	5·79	6·56	6·05
Nitromethane	7·27	5·82	6·74	6·18
Fluorobenzene	7·75	6·26	7·08	6·99
Thiophene	7·92	6·38	7·22	7·28
Benzene	8·12	6·58	7·29	7·42
Toluene	8·16	6·62	7·36	7·43

† Satd. soln. in CCl_4.

as a dilute solution in cyclohexane. Some solvents cause the acetylenic hydrogen nuclei to undergo decreased shielding; such solvents are all observed to contain strong electronegative centres which can act as proton acceptors and thus favour the formation of weak hydrogen bonds of the type

$$\rangle C{=}O \cdots\cdots H{-}C{\equiv}C{-}R$$

Diamagnetic circulations around the acetylenic hydrogen nuclei are influenced by the strong electric field of the carbonyl group in a manner which causes a deshielding of the nuclei. When acetonitrile is used as the solvent, the acetylenic hydrogen nuclei in propargyl chloride are deshielded but to a much lesser extent: this is attributed to the fact that the decreased shielding caused by the electronegative cyanide group is almost compensated for by the diamagnetic anisotropic effect of the cyanide group which causes an increased shielding as shown

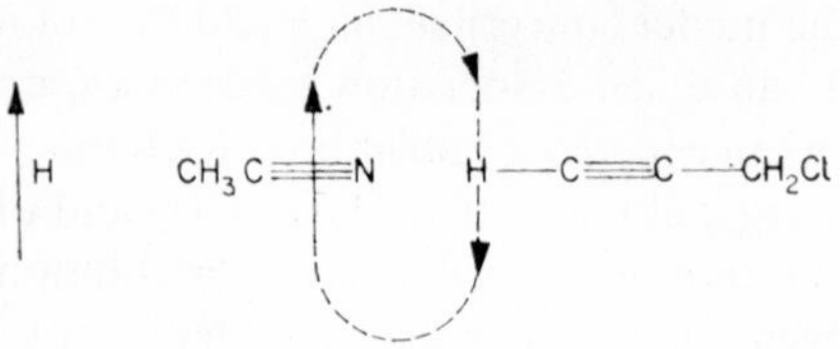

Solvents which cause the acetylenic hydrogen nuclei to experience an increased shielding include aromatic solvents containing strong polar substituents (examples are pyridine and nitrobenzene). If the aromatic molecule contains a strongly electron withdrawing group then decreased shielding accompanies the formation of a weak hydrogen bond as discussed above. The solvents benzene, toluene and thiophene all cause an increased shielding of the acetylenic hydrogen nuclei. It is worth noting that the —CH_2 group in propargyl chloride is influenced to about the same extent as the acetylenic hydrogen nuclei in benzene solutions. This appears to eliminate the possibility of a specific association of the type

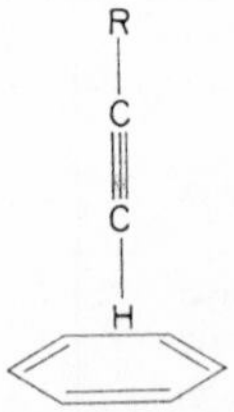

Kreevoy and co-workers[187] have measured the changes in acetylenic hydrogen shielding which accompany the dilution of monosubstituted acetylenes with pyridine: in all cases a decrease in shielding of ~ 1 ppm is observed on passing from an infinitely dilute solution in carbon tetrachloride to a similar solution in pyridine (see Table 10.104). This is thought to be due to aromatic ring current effects of the pyridine ring on the acetylenic hydrogen nucleus which is correctly positioned to experience the effect by the formation of a weak hydrogen bond between the nitrogen and acetylenic hydrogen atoms.

Medium effects on the acetylenic resonance absorption of propargyl bromide have also been studied[189]. The observed shifts are explained in terms of the formation of specific hydrogen bonded species.

TABLE 10.104 THE ^{1}H CHEMICAL SHIFTS AND SPIN COUPLING CONSTANTS OF SOME MONOSUBSTITUTED ACETYLENES IN (i) CARBON TETRACHLORIDE AND (ii) PYRIDINE SOLUTION[187]

R	τ CCl_4 ppm	τ pyridine ppm	$\Delta\tau$ ppm	J† cycles sec^{-1}
H	8·20			>0·5
n-C_3H_7	8·21			2·7
n-C_4H_9	8·27			2·4
n-C_5H_{11}	8·25	7·30	0·95	2·1
$ClCH_2$	7·60			2·7
$BrCH_2$	7·67			2·7
ICH_2	7·81			2·8
$HOCH_2$	7·67	6·82	0·85	2·7
$HOC(CH_3)_2$	7·72	6·80	0·92	>0·5
CH_3OCH_2	7·63	6·71	0·92	2·5
$CH_3OC(CH_3)_2$	7·67	6·75	0·92	>0·5
$C_6H_5OCH_2$	7·99	6·60	1·39	2·35
O=CH	8·11			>0·5
C_6H_5	7·07	6·03	1·04	>0·5
CH_2=CH	7·08			>0·5
$HOCH_2CH_2$	8·08			2·4

† Some J values were obtained from both pyridine solutions and carbon tetrachloride solutions of the compounds and there appears to be no solvent dependence.

10.39.2 The Effects of Solvents on the Resonance Spectra of Aromatic Molecules

When a sample of pure benzene is diluted with an inert solvent such as carbon tetrachloride, the single absorption band of the aromatic hydrogen nuclei is progressively displaced to lower field values (0·75 ppm displacement at infinite dilution)[198, 199]. Bothner-By and Glick[198] suggest that this decreased shielding is due to the break-down of weak intermolecular forces between the benzene rings. In the pure liquid these forces are thought to hold the planar rings parallel to each other (to some extent) in positions such that the hydrogen nuclei are shielded by the induced ring currents within an adjacent molecule: such an effect will act equally on all the aromatic nuclei[200, 201]. A similar though less well-pronounced solvent shift is observed in the ^{1}H resonance spectrum of toluene upon dilution. Schaefer and Schneider[201] have examined the solvent effects on the hydrogen resonance spectra of numerous substituted benzenes and their results are summarised in Table 10.105. The wide variation in chemical shifts of the aromatic hydrogen nuclei observed on changing solvents emphasises the necessity of reporting the solution conditions under which any particular measurement has been made. Without this information chemical shift data are often meaningless. Figure 10.60 shows the ^{1}H resonance spectrum

TABLE 10.105 THE ^{1}H CHEMICAL SHIFTS OF THE RING HYDROGEN NUCLEI IN *para*-DISUBSTITUTED BENZENES IN VARIOUS SOLVENTS(201)

Compound[a]	Pure liquid		5 mole % solution in					
			Hexane		Acetone		Benzene	
	ortho	*meta*	*ortho*	*meta*	*ortho*	*meta*	*ortho*	*meta*
NO_2–C_6H_4–CH_3			−34·4	14·6	−38·2	−2·6	−0·3	71·9
SO_2Cl–C_6H_4–CH_3			−23·8	7·2	−33·0	−8·8	8·7	69·3
CH_3CO–C_6H_4–CH_3	−4·9	35·3	−19·5	19·5	−25·4	9·2	3·1	53·1
CN–C_6H_4–CH_3	0	15·0	3·0	16·4	−10·9	4·7	42·2	58·4
F–C_6H_4–CH_3[b]	27·6	26·6	38·9	28·3	27·8	16·4	62·2	62·2
Cl–C_6H_4–CH_3	20·2	33·2	19·6	29·0	10·9	16·1	43·0	66·0
Br–C_6H_4–CH_3	20·4	44·8	9·8	31·6	1·8	18·0	34·9	70·3
I–C_6H_4–CH_3			−3·6	37·0	−10·7	25·1	21·8	76·8
NO_2–C_6H_4–F			−12·2	18·5	−26·2	4·0	42·5	70·9
SO_2Cl–C_6H_4–F			−35·3	16·5	−49·3	−9·1	20·7	88·7
Br–C_6H_4–F	18·7	47·3	5·1	36·3	−8·6	18·8	48·3	80·9

[a] Hydrogen atoms are designated *ortho* and *meta* with respect to the left-hand substituent.
[b] *Meta* hydrogen signal appears at lower field than the *ortho* signal.

$$``\tau" = 3{\cdot}5 + \frac{\nu_{CHCl_3 ext}}{60}$$

of *p*-methylnitrobenzene under various solution conditions(201) and the spectra serve to illustrate the general solvent effects experienced in such molecules(200). The spectrum of the ring hydrogen nuclei in *p*-methylnitrobenzene simply consists of a pair of AB doublets. A 5 mole per cent solution of the molecule in the inert solvent, hexane, is regarded as corresponding to the "isolated" molecule, free from all intermolecular interactions except van der Waals forces:

the ^{1}H resonance spectrum of the "isolated" molecule indicates the aromatic hydrogen nuclei to be less shielded than in the pure liquid state. If acetone is used as the solvent, a shift of all the ring hydrogen nuclei signals to lower fields is observed, while using benzene as the solvent causes them to be displaced to higher field values. It should also be noted that the solvent effects operate to different extents at the *ortho*- and *meta*-hydrogen nuclei and thus the internal

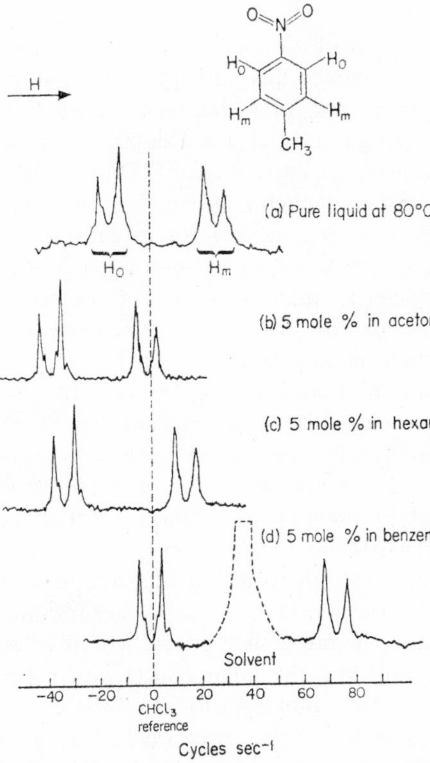

FIG. 10.60 The ^{1}H resonance spectrum of *p*-methylnitrobenzene at 60 Mc sec^{-1} under various solution conditions. Schaefer and Schneider[(201)].

chemical shift between the nuclei in the two positions varies with the solvent. In acetone and benzene solutions, the solvent interactions affect the shielding of the *meta*-hydrogen nuclei more than the *ortho*-hydrogen nuclei. The lone pair of electrons on the oxygen atom of the acetone causes it to be a strong *n*-type donor molecule, whilst the benzene molecule is a weak π-electron donor. Schaefer and Schneider have attempted to find the factor controlling the observed solvent effects on the shielding of aromatic hydrogen nuclei by considering all the possible ways in which the solvent shielding interaction could operate. The factors considered include:

(a) a purely magnetic contribution due to solvent–solute interaction in the magnetic field, (σ_a),
(b) the degree to which steric effects due to bulky substituent groups on the aromatic ring influence the solute–solvent interaction, (σ_w),
(c) polar interactions of solute and solvent molecules as influenced by changes in the dielectric constant of the medium, (σ_E),
(d) specific molecular interactions involving complex formation where the solvent and solute molecules have preferred orientations with respect to each other, (σ_H).

The behaviour of *para*-disubstituted aromatic compounds in hexane and benzene solutions can be explained qualitatively by assuming that in hexane solution, the weak intermolecular forces between the aromatic molecules cannot hold the molecules together and that the accompanying shielding is due to the absence of intermolecular ring current effects. Dilution of a substituted aromatic compound with benzene (which is of smaller molecular volume) would increase the possibility of intermolecular forces causing more of the aromatic systems to take up fixed positions with respect to each other and thus exposing the ring hydrogen nuclei to intermolecular ring current effects. However, if this were the complete picture the *ortho*- and *meta*-hydrogen nuclei would be affected equally by the ring current effect. Furthermore, the observed solvent shifts in dilute benzene solutions are much larger than would be expected from the differences in molecular volume between solute and solvent molecules. The influence of steric effects on the solvent chemical shifts cannot be very important since some disubstituted aromatic derivatives with substituents of very different size (such as *p*-tertbutyl toluene) have similar solvent effects at both *ortho*- and *meta*-positions. As regards the contribution to the shielding from the electric field of the polar molecules, this would be expected to show large variations if solvents of high dielectric constant are used: hexane and benzene have low dielectric constants and therefore such effects would be small. Acetone has a higher dielectric constant and the polar effects might well be appreciable. It was finally decided that the observed solvent effects can only be satisfactorily explained by postulating the formation of weak hydrogen-bond complexes of the type

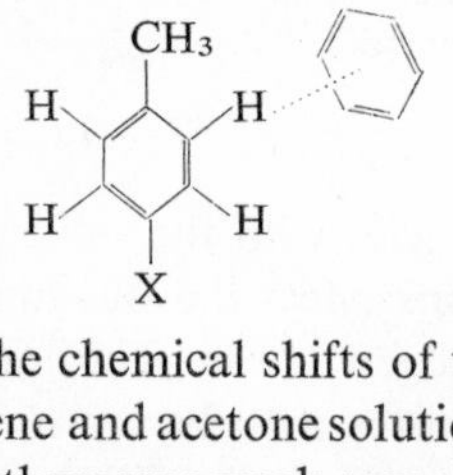

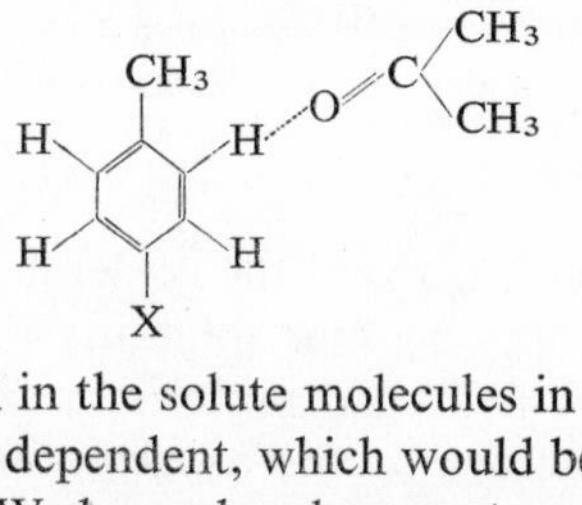

The chemical shifts of the aromatic nuclei in the solute molecules in both benzene and acetone solution are temperature dependent, which would be expected if there was weak association of this kind. We have already seen strong evidence that benzene can form weak complexes with molecules such as chloroform[(207)] where the CH bond of the latter is directed perpendicular to the plane of the benzene ring. In this position, the chemical shift of the chloroform hydrogen nucleus is displaced to high field values by the induced ring current effects.

10.39.3 The Effects of Solvents on the Resonance Spectra of Unsaturated Heterocyclic Ring Molecules

Schaefer and Schneider(275) have found that the shielding of ring hydrogen nuclei in unsaturated heterocyclic compounds depends to a large extent on solvent effects. When the molecules are examined as dilute solutions in the inert solvent hexane the measured chemical shifts can be regarded as free from contributions from intermolecular effects. By comparing the chemical shifts measured in solvents such as benzene and acetone, where specific solvent–solute interactions would be expected, with those in hexane solution, some information concerning the nature of the molecular interaction can be obtained. Table 10.106 gives the chemical shifts of the ring hydrogen nuclei in several heterocyclic molecules relative to chloroform external reference and corrected for differences in the bulk diamagnetic susceptibility(275). Figure 10.61 shows the drastic changes in the ^{1}H resonance spectrum of pyrrole when examined in various solvents and illustrates how solvents can be used to resolve overlapping multiplets. The low field quartet in Fig. 10.61 attributed to the α-hydrogen nuclei is influenced to the greatest extent by the change of solvent. Addition of acetone causes the α-hydrogen nuclei to be deshielded compared with their absorption signal in hexane solution. Benzene affects the α-hydrogen nuclei in the opposite manner producing an increased shielding. Both thiophene and furan behave like pyrrole in this respect, the α-hydrogen nuclei being more solvent dependent in acetone

TABLE 10.106 ^{1}H CHEMICAL SHIFTS OF THE RING HYDROGEN NUCLEI OF SEVERAL HETEROCYCLIC MOLECULES(275)

Compounds		5 mole per cent solution in					
		Hexane (ppm)		Acetone (ppm)		Benzene (ppm)	
		α	β	α	β	α	β
Pyrrole		0·935	1·307	0·673	1·358	1·403	1·455
N-n-Butyl pyrrole		0·997	1·452	0·757	1·433	1·275	1·418
Thiophene		0·263	0·450	−0·018	0·297	0·837	0·982
Furan		0·155	1·197	−0·102	1·027	0·730 ± 0·05	1·727
4-Methylpyridine		−0·093	0·533	−0·983	0·283	−0·683	1·183
	2:	−1·270		−1·612		−0·550	
	4:	0·232		−0·223		1·112	
	5:	−0·438		−0·537		0·052	
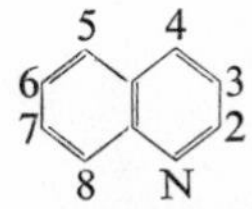	2:	−1·320		−1·422		−0·882	
	3:	0·325		0·022		1·102	
	4:	−0·443		−0·617		0·343	
	8:	−0·600		−0·807		−0·415	

Chemical shifts were measured in ppm from $CHCl_3$ external reference and corrected for differences in bulk diamagnetic susceptibility. "τ" = 3·5 + $\delta_{CHCl_3 ext}$ (very approximate conversion).

and benzene than the other ring hydrogen nuclei. However, in the case of 4-picoline it is the 3-hydrogen nuclei (*ortho* to the CH_3 group) which experience the largest solvent effects. This is similar in sign and magnitude to the solvent behaviour found for *para*-substituted toluenes (see Section 10.39.2) and may be

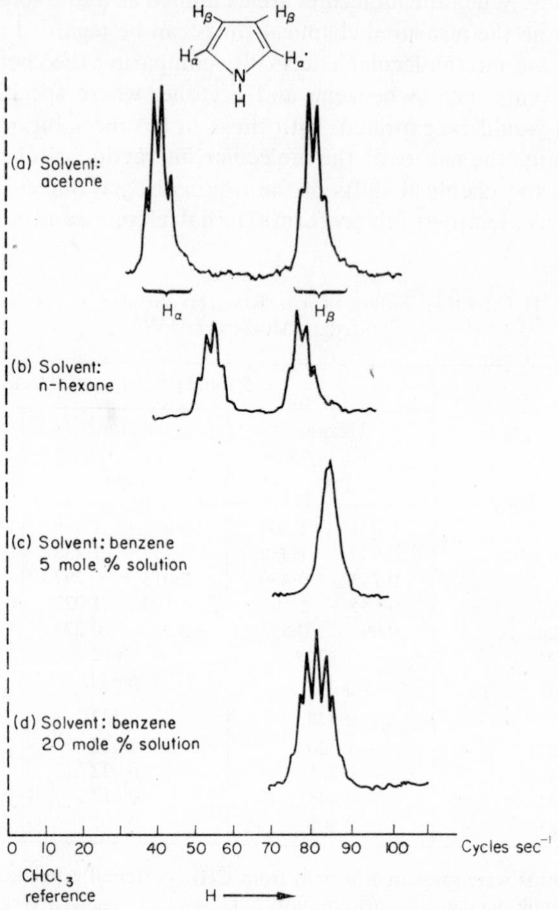

FIG. 10.61 The ^{1}H resonance spectra at 60 Mc sec^{-1} of the ring hydrogens in pyrrole: (a) 5 mole per cent solution in acetone, (b) 5 mole per cent solution in hexane, (c) 5 mole per cent solution in benzene and (d) 20 mole per cent solution in benzene. The spectra are shown on a common scale (corrected for bulk diamagnetic susceptibility differences) relative to a chloroform reference signal. Schaefer and Schneider[275].

attributed to preferential hydrogen bonding between the solvent and the β-hydrogen atoms of picoline. For quinoline, the most pronounced solvent effects are observed for the 3- and 4-hydrogen nuclei, while the hydrogen nuclei in the 8-position are affected least by benzene dilution. In thiazole, the hydrogen farthest from the nitrogen atom (position 5) exhibits the largest solvent effects.

Thus thiophene, furan and pyrrole all behave differently to *para*-disubstituted benzenes and 4-picolines in benzene or acetone solution. In the former, the hydrogen nuclei nearest to the electronegative atom are affected to the greatest extent. It is reasonable to assume that hydrogen bonding involving the NH group of pyrrole and the solvent molecule would influence the shielding of the α-hydrogen more than the β-hydrogen nuclei in the molecule. This, however, is not the major shielding factor since in the molecule *N*-n-butylpyrrole where NH hydrogen bonding effects are absent, similar solvent effects are observed. It must be concluded that there is preferential hydrogen bonding between the donor solvent molecules and the α-hydrogen atoms of the pyrrole.

10.40 Medium Effects in Gases

It has been assumed so far that the shielding constant of a gaseous sample is that of an isolated molecule. This is true of a gas at low pressures, but at high pressures the chemical shift of a gaseous sample can show appreciable medium effects(415, 416). In the case of an imperfect gas the shielding constant can be expanded as an inverse power series in the molar volume V_m(416) (see equation (3.142), σ is referred to as $\sum^{(i)}$)

$$\sigma = \sigma_0 + \left(\frac{\sigma_1}{V_m}\right) + \left(\frac{\sigma_2}{V_m}\right)^2 + \cdots \tag{10.18}$$

σ_0 is the shielding constant for an isolated molecule, σ_2 is small and can be neglected. σ_1 is determined by the collisions between two molecules and is given by

$$\sigma_1 = \frac{1}{2} N_0 \int \sigma_{\text{pair}} \exp\left(\frac{-\mu}{kT}\right) d\tau_2 \tag{10.19}$$

where N_0 is Avogadro's number, σ_{pair} is the shielding constant of species 1 due to the presence of species 2, μ is the intermolecular potential energy in the configuration τ_2, and $d\tau_2$ is an integral over all configurations of molecule 2 in the specimen tube. In a gas mixture containing a mole fraction x of solute molecules 1, which contains the nucleus whose shielding constant is under examination, and $(1 - x)$ of a solvent gas 2, then

$$\sigma = \sigma_0 + V_m^{-1}\ \{x\sigma_1{}^{(11)} + (1 - x)\sigma_1{}^{(12)} \cdots\} + \cdots$$

where the superscripts (11) and (12) refer to binary collisions between the species present. For small values of x, $\sigma_1{}^{(12)}$ can be equated to σ_1. σ_1 is made up of five contributions similar to those in equation (10.16)

$$\sigma_1 = (\sigma_1)_b + (\sigma_1)_a + (\sigma_1)_w + (\sigma_1)_E + (\sigma_1)_H$$

For a cylindrical sample, $(\sigma_1)_b$ is simply

$$(\sigma_1)_b = \frac{2}{3}\pi\,\chi_m$$

where $\chi_m = \chi_v/M$ is the molar diamagnetic susceptibility.

$(\sigma_{pair})_a$ for an axially symmetrical molecule 2 is given by equation (3.53) $(-\frac{1}{3}(\chi_{\parallel} - \chi_{\perp})(3\cos^2\theta_2 - 1)\,r^{-3})$ and with this equation and a Stockmayer potential for μ in equation (10.19) Buckingham *et al.*(200) obtained for $(\sigma_1)_a$

$$(\sigma_1)_a = -\left(\frac{N_0\,\pi}{1080}\right)(\chi_{\parallel} - \chi_{\perp})\left\{\tau^2 H_9(y) + y^4\left(\frac{\tau^4}{70}\right)H_{15}(y) + \cdots\right\}$$

where

$$\tau = \frac{\mu_1\,\mu_2}{\varepsilon\, r_0^3}$$

$$y = 2\left(\frac{\varepsilon}{\mathrm{kT}}\right)^{1/2}$$

μ_1 and μ_2 are the dipole moments of molecular species 1 and 2 respectively and the functions $H_n(y)$ are those tabulated by Buckingham and Pople(417).

$(\sigma_{pair})_E$ is given by $(\sigma_{pair})_E = -AE - BE^2$ (see Section 3.9), and Buckingham *et al.*(200) have shown that for the case of a polar solute in a non-polar solvent gas

$$(\sigma_1)_E = -\left(\frac{2}{3}\pi\right)N_0 A\left(\frac{\mu_1}{y^4}\right)\left[\left(\frac{\alpha_2}{r_0^3}\right)H_6(y) + \left(\frac{\theta_2^2}{2kTr_0^5}\right)H_8\,(y) + \cdots\right] \tag{10.20}$$

and for a non-polar solute in a polar solvent gas

$$(\sigma_1)_E = -\left(\frac{\pi\, N_0 B}{y^4}\right)\left[\frac{2}{3}\left(\frac{\mu_2^2}{r_0^3}\right)H_6\,(y) + \left(\frac{\theta_2^2}{r_0^5}\right)H_8(y)\right] \tag{10.21}$$

In equations (10.20) and (10.21), θ_2 is the molecular quadrupole moment and α_2 the polarisability of the solvent gas molecules.

$(\sigma_1)_w$ is found empirically to be negative and an approximate value may be obtained by assuming that the reduction in shielding is brought about by a fluctuating electric field in the solvent gas molecules whose mean square value $\langle F^2\rangle$ does not average to zero. Buckingham *et al.*(200) show that $\langle F^2\rangle$ is given approximately by

$$\langle F^2\rangle = \frac{3\alpha_2\, I_2}{r^6}$$

where I_2 is the ionisation potential of the solvent molecules and r is the distance between the two molecules. Hence

$$(\sigma_{pair})_w = -B\,\langle F^2\rangle$$

and substitution into equation (10.19) gives

$$(\sigma_1)_w = -\left(\frac{\pi\, N_0\, B}{y^4\, r_0^3}\right)\alpha^2\, I_2\left\{H_6(y) + \left(\frac{\tau^2}{48}\right)y^4\, H_{12}(y) + \cdots\right\} \tag{10.22}$$

σ_1 for a binary gas mixture can be obtained by measuring the chemical shift of the nucleus under consideration as a function of pressure; σ_1 is then given by

$$\sigma_1 = M\left(\frac{\delta\sigma}{\delta\varrho}\right) \tag{10.23}$$

where M is the molecular weight of the species 1 and ϱ is the density in g cm^{-3}; σ is in ppm. The value of σ_1 obtained from equation (10.23) will depend upon the mole fraction of the solute molecule in the gas mixture, hence it is necessary to determine σ_1 for several different mole fractions and then to extrapolate to zero concentration of the solute. Raynes, Buckingham and Bernstein[415] have measured infinite dilution values of $(\sigma_1)_{obs}$ for the non-polar hydrocarbon solutes CH_4 and C_2H_6 and for the polar solute HCl, and their results are shown in Table 10.107. The end column in Table 10.107 gives the quantity $[(\sigma_1)_{obs} - (\sigma_1)_b]$, which for the hydrocarbon solutes (where both $(\sigma_1)_a$ and $(\sigma_1)_E$ are negligible) may be equated to $(\sigma_1)_w$. A value of B can be obtained by finding the best fit of equation (10.22) to the data for CH_4, C_2H_4 and C_2H_6 and the value found in this way is $B = (1{\cdot}0 \pm 0{\cdot}3) \times 10^{-18}$ e.s.u.

For the polar solute HCl both $(\sigma_1)_w$ and $(\sigma_1)_E$ make contributions to $[(\sigma_1)_{obs} - (\sigma_1)_b]$ and the best fit of equations (10.20) and (10.22) to the observed data gives values of both A and B for this molecule. The values obtained by Bernstein *et al.*[415] are

$$A = (40{\cdot}4 \pm 2) \times 10^{-12} \quad \text{e.s.u.}$$

$$B = (0{\cdot}38 \pm 0{\cdot}1) \times 10^{-18} \quad \text{e.s.u.}$$

Bernstein and co-workers[418, 419] have determined $(\sigma_1)_{obs}$ and hence A and B for both hydrogen nuclei and fluorine nuclei in solute molecules, and their results are shown in Table 10.108. Petrakis and Bernstein[419] have discussed the physical significance of the A and B values. They suggest that the value of A measures the ease with which charge can be displaced in the direction of the XH or XF bond, thus A is positive in XH bonds and negative for XF. The value of B depends upon the atom polarisability of the H or F atom, that is, it measures the ease with which charge may be displaced perpendicular to the bond direction, and is therefore expected to increase as the double bond character of the X—F bond increases.

TABLE 10.107 VALUES OF $(\sigma_1)_{obs}$ FOR SOME BINARY GAS MIXTURES[415]

Solute	Solvent	$(\sigma_1)_{obs} \times 10^6$ (cm^3 mole^{-1})	$(\sigma_1)_b \times 10^6$ (cm^3 mole^{-1})	$\{(\sigma_1)_{obs} - (\sigma_1)_b\} \times 10^6$ (cm^3 mole^{-1})
CH_4	CH_4	−42	−36	−6
CH_4	HCl	−58	−47	−11
C_2H_4	C_2H_4	−50	−39	−11
C_2H_6	C_2H_6	−74	−56	−18
HCl	CH_4	−62	−36	−26
HCl	C_2H_6	−92	−56	−36
HCl	Kr	−94	−61	−33
HCl	CO_2	−98	−44	−54
HCl	SF_6	−114	−92	−22
HCl	Xe	−139	−95	−44
HCl	HCl	−150	−46	−104
HCl	H_2S	−176	−53	−123
HCl	OCS	−176	−68	−108

TABLE 10.108 VALUES OF THE BOND PARAMETERS *A* AND *B* FOR VARIOUS BOND SITUATIONS[419]

Bond	$A \times 10^{12}$ (e.s.u.)	$B \times 10^{18}$ (e.s.u.)
CH (in non-polar hydrocarbons)		1·0 ± 0·3
CH (in CHF_3)	2·92 ± 0·8	0·84 ± 0·3
HCl	40·4 ± 2·0	0·38 ± 0·1
H atom		0·74
CF in CF_4		16·4 ± 2·1
CF (in CHF_3)	−9·9 ± 3·6	15·1 ± 3·0
SF (in SF_6)		29·5 ± 2·4
SiF (in SiF_4)		43·5 ± 5·1

REFERENCES

1. J. N. SHOOLERY, *J. Chem. Phys.*, **21**, 1899 (1953).
2. L. H. MEYER, A. SAIKA and H. S. GUTOWSKY, *J. Amer. Chem. Soc.*, **75**, 4567 (1953).
3. L. H. MEYER and H. S. GUTOWSKY, *J. Phys. Chem.*, **57**, 481 (1953).
4. A. L. ALLRED and E. G. ROCHOW, *J. Amer. Chem. Soc.*, **79**, 5361 (1957).
5. M. L. HUGGINS, *J. Amer. Chem. Soc.*, **75**, 4123 (1953).
6. H. SPIESECKE and W. G. SCHNEIDER, *J. Chem. Phys.*, **35**, 722 (1961).
7. J. R. CAVANAUGH and B. P. DAILEY, *J. Chem. Phys.*, **34**, 1099 (1961).
8. A. A. BOTHNER-BY and C. NAAR-COLIN, *J. Amer. Chem. Soc.*, **80**, 1728 (1958).
9. B. P. DAILEY and J. N. SHOOLERY, *J. Amer. Chem. Soc.*, **77**, 3977 (1955).
10. N. F. RAMSEY, *Phys. Rev.*, **78**, 699 (1950).
11. J. R. CAVANAUGH and B. P. DAILEY, *J. Chem. Phys.*, **34**, 1094 (1961).
12. P. T. NARASIMHAN and M. T. ROGERS, *J. Amer. Chem. Soc.*, **82**, 5983 (1960).
13. J. N. SHOOLERY, Lecture Notes, Varian Associates Conference (1957).
14. S. BROWNSTEIN, B. C. SMITH, G. EHRLICH, and A. W. LAUBENGAYER, *J. Amer. Chem. Soc.*, **81**, 3826 (1959).
15. B. R. MCGARVEY and G. SLOMP, *J. Chem. Phys.*, **30**, 1586 (1959).
16. P. T. NARASIMHAN and M. T. ROGERS, *J. Chem. Phys.*, **31**, 1302 (1959).
17. J. I. MUSHER, *J. Chem. Phys.*, **35**, 1159 (1961).
18. J. TILLIEU, *Ann. Phys.*, **2**, 471, 631 (1957).
19. J. GUY and J. TILLIEU, *J. Chem. Phys.*, **24**, 1117 (1956).
20. D. R. WHITMAN, M. SAUNDERS, L. ONSAGER and H. E. DUBB, *J. Chem. Phys.*, **32**, 67 (1960).
21. G. S. REDDY and J. H. GOLDSTEIN, *J. Chem. Phys.*, **38**, 2736 (1963).
22. A. G. MORITZ and N. SHEPPARD, *Mol. Phys.*, **5**, 361 (1962).
23. J. I. MUSHER, *J. Amer. Chem. Soc.*, **83**, 1146 (1961).
24. J. I. MUSHER, *J. Chem. Phys.*, **37**, 34, 192 (1962).
25. R. F. ZÜRCHER, *Discuss. Faraday Soc.*, **34**, 66 (1962).
26. J. A. POPLE, *Discuss. Faraday Soc.*, **34**, 7 (1962).
27. A. D. BUCKINGHAM, *Can. J. Chem.*, **38**, 300 (1960).
28. M. KARPLUS, D. H. ANDERSON, T. C. FARRAR and H. S. GUTOWSKY, *J. Chem. Phys.*, **27**, 597 (1957).
29. M. KARPLUS and D. H. ANDERSON, *J. Chem. Phys.*, **30**, 6 (1959).
30. H. S. GUTOWSKY, M. KARPLUS and D. M. GRANT, *J. Chem. Phys.*, **31**, 1278 (1959).
31. H. S. GUTOWSKY, V. D. MOCHEL and B. G. SOMERS, *J. Chem. Phys.*, **36**, 1153 (1962).
32. P. C. LAUTERBUR and R. J. KURLAND, *J. Amer. Chem. Soc.*, **84**, 3405 (1962).
33. H. M. MCCONNELL, *J. Chem. Phys.*, **24**, 460 (1956).
34. C. N. BANWELL and N. SHEPPARD, *Discuss. Faraday Soc.*, **34**, 115 (1962).
35. H. M. MCCONNELL, *J. Chem. Phys.*, **23**, 2454 (1955).
36. M. BARFIELD and D. M. GRANT, *J. Amer. Chem. Soc.*, **83**, 4726 (1961).
37. H. J. BERNSTEIN and N. SHEPPARD, unpublished work quoted in reference 34.

38. A. D. Buckingham and K. A. McLauchlan, *Proc. Chem. Soc.*, 144 (1963).
39. M. Karplus, *J. Chem. Phys.*, **30**, 11 (1959).
40. R. E. Glick and A. A. Bothner-By, *J. Chem. Phys.*, **25**, 362 (1956).
41. R. U. Lemieux, R. K. Kullnig and R. Y. Moir, *J. Amer. Chem. Soc.*, **80**, 2237 (1958).
42. N. Sheppard and R. M. Lynden-Bell, *Proc. Roy. Soc.*, **A269**, 385 (1962).
43. J. C. Schug, P. E. McMahon and H. S. Gutowsky, *J. Chem. Phys.*, **33**, 843 (1960).
44. R. J. Abraham and K. A. McLauchlan, *Mol. Phys.*, **5**, 195 (1962).
45. R. J. Abraham, L. D. Hall, L. Hough and K. A. McLauchlan, *Chem. and Ind.*, 213 (1962).
46. R. J. Abraham, K. A. McLauchlan, L. D. Hall and L. Hough, *J. Chem. Soc.*, 3699 (1962).
47. J. I. Musher, *J. Chem. Phys.*, **34**, 594 (1961).
48. K. L. Williamson and W. S. Johnson, *J. Amer. Chem. Soc.*, **83**, 4623 (1961).
49. R. J. Abraham and J. S. E. Holker, *J. Chem. Soc.*, 806 (1963).
50. N. Sheppard and J. J. Turner, *Proc. Roy. Soc.*, **A252**, 506 (1959).
51. H. Conroy, *Advances in Organic Chemistry*. Vol. II, Interscience, N.Y. (1960).
52. P. T. Narasimhan and M. T. Rogers, *J. Chem. Phys.*, **34**, 1049 (1961).
53. R. J. Abraham and K. G. R. Pachler, *Mol. Phys.*, **7**, 165 (1964).
54. R. R. Fraser, R. U. Lemieux and J. D. Stevens, *J. Amer. Chem. Soc.*, **83**, 3901 (1961).
55. C. A. Reilly and J. D. Swalen, *J. Chem. Phys.*, **35**, 1522 (1961).
56. H. S. Gutowsky and C. Juan, *Discuss. Faraday Soc.*, **34**, 52 (1962).
57. F. Kaplan and J. D. Roberts, *J. Amer. Chem. Soc.*, **83**, 4666 (1961).
58. M. Karplus, *J. Amer. Chem. Soc.*, **84**, 2458 (1962).
59. J. D. Roberts, R. P. Lutz and D. R. Davis, *J. Amer. Chem. Soc.*, **83**, 246 (1961); D. R. Davis and J. D. Roberts, *J. Amer. Chem. Soc.*, **84**, 2252 (1962).
60. J. R. Holmes and D. Kivelson, *J. Amer. Chem. Soc.*, **83**, 2959 (1961).
61. M. Karplus, *J. Amer. Chem. Soc.*, **82**, 4431 (1960).
62. M. Karplus, *J. Chem. Phys.*, **33**, 1842 (1960).
63. H. M. McConnell, *J. Chem. Phys.*, **24**, 764 (1956).
64. G. Fraenkel, *J. Chem. Phys.*, **34**, 1466 (1961).
65. A. L. Allred and E. G. Rochow, *J. Inorg. Nuc. Chem.*, **5**, 264 (1958).
66. M. P. Brown and D. E. Webster, *J. Phys. Chem.*, **64**, 698 (1960).
67. E. B. Baker, *J. Chem. Phys.*, **26**, 960 (1957).
68. P. T. Narasimhan and M. T. Rogers, *J. Chem. Phys.*, **31**, 1430 (1959).
69. H. H. Jaffé, G. F. Reynolds, T. J. Flautt and R. E. Dessy, *J. Chem. Phys.*, **30**, 1422 (1959).
70. S. L. Stafford and J. D. Baldeschwieler, *J. Amer. Chem. Soc.*, **83**, 4473 (1961).
71. J. P. Maher and D. F. Evans, *Proc. Chem. Soc.*, 208 (1961).
72. G. Klose, *Ann. Phys.*, **8**, 220 (1961).
73. G. Klose, *Ann. Phys.*, **10**, 391 (1963).
74. J. Feeney and L. H. Sutcliffe, unpublished results.
75. J. E. Nordlander, W. G. Young and J. D. Roberts, *J. Amer. Chem. Soc.*, **83**, 494 (1961).
76. J. E. Nordlander and J. D. Roberts, *J. Amer. Chem. Soc.*, **81**, 1769 (1959).
77. G. M. Whitesides, J. E. Nordlander and J. D. Roberts, *J. Amer. Chem. Soc.*, **84**, 2010 (1962).
78. G. M. Whitesides, J. E. Nordlander and J. D. Roberts, *Discuss. Faraday Soc.*, **34**, 185 (1962).
79. F. A. L. Anet, *Proc. Chem. Soc.*, 327 (1959).
80. F. A. L. Anet, *J. Amer. Chem. Soc.*, **84**, 747 (1962).
81. A. A. Bothner-By and C. Naar-Colin, *J. Amer. Chem. Soc.*, **84**, 743 (1962).
82. A. D. Walsh, *Trans. Faraday Soc.*, **45**, 179 (1949).
83. B. P. Dailey, A. Gawer and W. C. Neikam, *Discuss. Faraday Soc.*, **34**, 18 (1962).
84. C. A. Reilly and J. D. Swalen, *J. Chem. Phys.*, **32**, 1378 (1960).
85. L. M. Jackman, *Nuclear Magnetic Resonance Spectroscopy*, Pergamon Press, London (1959).

86. H. S. Gutowsky and D. M. Grant, *J. Chem. Phys.*, **34**, 699 (1961).
87. J. D. Roberts, *An Introduction to the Analysis of Spin–Spin Splitting in High Resolution NMR Spectra*, W. A. Benjamin, N.Y. (1961).
88. G. L. Closs and L. E. Closs, *J. Amer. Chem. Soc.*, **82**, 5723 (1960).
89. J. Smidt and Th. J. de Boer, *Rec. Trav. Chim.*, **82**, 1235 (1960).
90. J. D. Graham and M. T. Rogers, *J. Amer. Chem. Soc.*, **84**, 2249 (1962).
91. H. M. Hutton and T. Schaefer, *Can. J. Chem.*, **41**, 684 (1963).
92. M. Karplus, *J. Phys. Chem.*, **64**, 1793 (1960).
93. R. R. Fraser, *Can. J. Chem.*, **40**, 1483 (1962).
94. R. K. Harris and N. Sheppard, *Proc. Chem. Soc.*, 418 (1961).
95. N. Muller and W. C. Tosch, *J. Chem. Phys.*, **37**, 1167 (1962).
96. F. R. Jensen, D. S. Noyce, C. H. Sederholm and A. J. Berlin, *J. Amer. Chem. Soc.*, **82**, 1256 (1960); **84**, 386 (1962).
97. R. U. Lemieux, R. K. Kullnig, H. J. Bernstein and W. G. Schneider, *J. Amer. Chem. Soc.*, **80**, 6098 (1958).
98. J. N. Shoolery and M. T. Rogers, *J. Amer. Chem. Soc.*, **80**, 5121 (1958).
99. T. Schaefer and W. G. Schneider, *Can. J. Chem.*, **41**, 966 (1963).
100. S. Brownstein, *J. Amer. Chem. Soc.*, **81**, 1606 (1959).
101. A. D. Cohen, N. Sheppard and J. J. Turner, *Proc. Chem. Soc.*, 118 (1958).
102. H. S. Gutowsky, L. H. Meyer and R. E. McClure, *Rev. Sci. Instruments*, **24**, 644 (1953).
103. R. U. Lemieux, R. K. Kullnig, H. J. Bernstein and W. G. Schneider, *J. Amer. Chem. Soc.*, **79**, 1005 (1957).
104. J. I. Musher and R. E. Richards, *Proc. Chem. Soc.*, 230 (1958).
105. J. I. Musher, *Spect. Acta*, **16**, 835 (1960).
106. S. Brownstein and R. Miller, *J. Org. Chem.*, **24**, 1886 (1959).
107. F. W. Lichtenthaler and H. O. L. Fischer, *J. Amer. Chem. Soc.*, **83**, 2005 (1961).
108. W. W. Lee, A. Benitez, C. D. Anderson, L. Goodman and B. R. Baker, *J. Amer. Chem. Soc.*, **83**, 1906 (1961).
109. K. L. Williamson and W. S. Johnson, *J. Amer. Chem. Soc.*, **83**, 4623 (1961).
110. L. W. Reeves and K. O. Strømme, *Can. J. Chem.*, **38**, 1241 (1960).
111. L. W. Reeves and K. O. Strømme, *Trans. Faraday Soc.*, **57**, 390 (1961).
112. F. A. L. Anet, *Can. J. Chem.*, **39**, 2262 (1961).
113. T. Schaefer and W. G. Schneider, *Can. J. Chem.*, **38**, 2066 (1960).
114. E. J. Corey, private communication.
115. J. Feeney, A. Ledwith and L. H. Sutcliffe, *J. Chem. Soc.*, 2021 (1962).
116. H. S. Gutowsky and A. L. Porte, *J. Chem. Phys.*, **35**, 839 (1961).
117. W. G. Schneider, H. J. Bernstein and J. A. Pople, *J. Amer. Chem. Soc.*, **80**, 3497 (1958).
118. C. N. Banwell and N. Sheppard, *Mol. Phys.*, **3**, 351 (1960).
119. T. Schaefer, *Can. J. Chem.*, **40**, 1 (1962).
120. N. Sheppard and C. N. Banwell, *Proc. Roy. Soc.*, **A 263**, 136 (1961).
121. J. M. Dowling and B. P. Stoicheff, *Can. J. Phys.*, **37**, 703 (1959).
122. B. Bak, D. Christensen, L. Hansen-Nygaard, J. Rostrup-Anderson, *Spect. Acta*, **13**, 120 (1958).
123. E. B. Whipple, W. E. Stewart, G. S. Reddy and J. H. Goldstein, *J. Chem. Phys.*, **34**, 2136 (1961).
124. A. A. Bothner-By and C. Naar-Colin, *J. Amer. Chem. Soc.*, **83**, 231 (1961).
125. S. Alexander, *J. Chem. Phys.*, **28**, 358 (1958).
126. S. Castellano and C. Caporiccio, *J. Chem. Phys.*, **36**, 566 (1962).
127. E. O. Bishop and R. E. Richards, *Mol. Phys.*, **3**, 114 (1960).
128. R. Freeman, *Mol. Phys.*, **4**, 385 (1961).
129. F. S. Mortimer, *J. Mol. Spect.*, **3**, 335, 340 (1959).
130. A. D. Cohen and N. Sheppard, *Proc. Roy. Soc.*, **A 252**, 488 (1959).
131. R. W. Fessenden and J. S. Waugh, *J. Chem. Phys.*, **30**, 944 (1959).
132. W. Brügel, Th. Ankel and F. Krückeberg, *Z. Elektrochem.*, **64**, 1121 (1960).

133. C. N. Banwell, N. Sheppard and J. J. Turner, *Spect. Acta*, **16**, 794 (1960).
134. S. Castellano and J. S. Waugh, *J. Chem. Phys.*, **34**, 295 (1961).
135. D. W. Moore and J. A. Happe, *J. Phys. Chem.*, **65**, 224 (1961).
136. C. S. Johnson, M. A. Weiner, J. S. Waugh and D. Seyferth, *J. Amer. Chem. Soc.*, **83**, 1306 (1961).
137. A. F. Clifford, *J. Phys. Chem.*, **63**, 1227 (1959).
138. S. Castellano and J. S. Waugh, *J. Chem. Phys.*, **35**, 1900 (1961).
139. G. S. Reddy and J. H. Goldstein, *J. Chem. Phys.*, **35**, 380 (1961).
140. R. W. Taft, *J. Amer. Chem. Soc.*, **79**, 1045 (1957).
141. J. A. Pople, W. G. Schneider and H. J. Bernstein, *High Resolution Nuclear Magnetic Resonance*, McGraw-Hill, N.Y. (1959).
142. C. P. Smyth, *Dielectric Behaviour and Structure*, McGraw-Hill, N.Y. (1955).
143. G. S. Reddy, L. Mandell and J. H. Goldstein, *J. Amer. Chem. Soc.*, **83**, 1300 (1961).
144. E. B. Whipple, W. E. Stewart, G. S. Reddy and J. H. Goldstein, *J. Chem. Phys.*, **34**, 2136 (1961).
145. E. B. Whipple, J. H. Goldstein and L. Mandell, *J. Amer. Chem. Soc.*, **82** ,3010 (1960).
146. J. A. Pople, *J. Chem. Phys.*, **24**, 1111 (1956).
147. C. E. Johnson and F. A. Bovey, *J. Chem. Phys.*, **29**, 1012 (1958).
148. R. R. Fraser, *Can. J. Chem.*, **38**, 549 (1960).
149. J. Feeney and L. H. Sutcliffe, unpublished results.
150. W. F. Beach and J. H. Richards, *J. Org. Chem.*, **26**, 3011 (1961).
151. D. R. Davis and J. D. Roberts, *J. Amer. Chem. Soc.*, **84**, 2252 (1962).
152. R. T. Hobgood, J. H. Goldstein and G. S. Reddy, *J. Chem. Phys.*, **35**, 2038 (1961).
153. R. T. Hobgood, G. S. Reddy and J. H. Goldstein, *J. Phys. Chem.*, **67**, 110 (1963).
154. A. A. Bothner-By and R. E. Glick, *J. Amer. Chem. Soc.*, **78**, 1071 (1956).
155. W. Gordy and W. J. O. Thomas, *J. Chem. Phys.*, **24**, 439 (1956).
156. P. L. Corio and B. P. Dailey, *J. Amer. Chem. Soc.*, **78**, 3043 (1956).
157. J. A. Pople, *Proc. Roy. Soc.*, **A239**, 550 (1957).
158. H. M. McConnell, *J. Chem. Phys.*, **27**, 226 (1957).
159. A. A. Bothner-By and C. Naar-Colin, *Ann. N.Y. Acad. Sci.*, **70**, 883 (1958).
160. P. T. Narasimhan and M. T. Rogers, *J. Phys. Chem.*, **63**, 1388 (1959).
161. W. G. Schneider, H. J. Bernstein and J. A. Pople, *J. Chem. Phys.*, **28**, 601 (1958).
162. A. A. Bothner-By, *J. Mol. Spect.*, **5**, 52 (1960).
163. J. W. Smith, *Electric Dipole Moments*, Butterworth, London (1955), p. 198.
164. E. B. Whipple, *J. Chem. Phys.*, **35**, 1039 (1961).
165. A. A. Bothner-By, C. Naar-Colin and H. Günther, *J. Amer. Chem. Soc.*, **84**, 2748 (1962).
166. L. M. Jackman and R. H. Wiley, *J. Chem. Soc.*, 2881 (1960).
167. E. B. Whipple, J. H. Goldstein and G. R. McClure, *J. Amer. Chem. Soc.*, **82**, 3811 (1960).
168. G. S. Reddy and J. H. Goldstein, *J. Amer. Chem. Soc.*, **83**, 2045 (1961).
169. L. M. Jackman and R. H. Wiley, *J. Chem. Soc.*, 2886 (1960).
170. R. R. Fraser and D. E. McGreer, *Can. J. Chem.*, **39**, 505 (1961).
171. Reference 141, p. 194.
172. J. A. Elvidge and L. M. Jackman, *Proc. Chem. Soc.*, 89 (1959).
173. C. N. Banwell, A. D. Cohen, N. Sheppard and J. J. Turner, *Proc. Chem. Soc.*, 266 (1959).
174. R. A. Hoffman, *Mol. Phys.*, **1**, 326 (1958).
175. R. A. Hoffman and S. Gronowitz, *Acta Chem. Scand.*, **13**, 1477 (1959).
176. E. I. Snyder and J. D. Roberts, *J. Amer. Chem. Soc.*, **84**, 1582 (1962).
177. S. L. Manatt and D. D. Elleman, *J. Amer. Chem. Soc.*, **84**, 1579 (1962).
178. B. Bak, J. N. Shoolery and G. A. Williams, *J. Mol. Spect.*, **2**, 525 (1958).
179. H. M. McConnell, *J. Chem. Phys.*, **30**, 126 (1959).
180. R. T. Hobgood, J. H. Goldstein and G. S. Reddy, *J. Chem. Phys.*, **35**, 2038 (1961).
181. T. S. Piper and G. Wilkinson, *J. Inorg. Nuc. Chem.*, **3**, 104 (1956).
182. L. D. Dave, D. F. Evans and G. Wilkinson, *J. Chem. Soc.*, 3684 (1959).

183. W. Strohmeier and R. M. Lemon, *Z. Natur.*, **14**a, 109 (1959).
184. M. L. H. Green and G. Wilkinson, *J. Chem. Soc.*, 4314 (1958).
185. M. L. H. Green, L. Pratt and G. Wilkinson, *J. Chem. Soc.*, 3753 (1959).
186. M. S. Barber, J. B. Davis, L. M. Jackman and B. C. L. Weedon, *J. Chem. Soc.*, 2870 (1960).
187. M. M. Kreevoy, H. B. Charman and D. R. Vinard, *J. Amer. Chem. Soc.*, **83**, 1978 (1961).
188. J. V. Hatton and R. E. Richards, *Trans. Faraday Soc.*, **56**, 315 (1960).
189. E. B. Whipple, J. H. Goldstein, L. Mandell, G. S. Reddy and G. R. McClure, *J. Amer. Chem. Soc.*, **81**, 1321 (1959).
190. P. T. Narasimhan and M. T. Rogers, *J. Chem. Phys.*, **33**, 727 (1960).
191. H. M. McConnell, *J. Mol. Spect.*, **1**, 11 (1957).
192. J. N. Shoolery, *J. Mol. Spect.*, **63**, 110 (1960).
193. E. I. Snyder and J. D. Roberts, *J. Amer. Chem. Soc.*, **84**, 1582 (1962).
194. E. I. Snyder, L. J. Altman and J. D. Roberts, *J. Amer. Chem. Soc.*, **84**, 2004 (1962).
195. R. C. Hirst and D. M. Grant, *J. Amer. Chem. Soc.*, **84**, 2009 (1962).
196. J. C. D. Brand, G. Eglinton and J. F. Morman, *J. Chem. Soc.*, 2526 (1960).
197. R. E. Richards and J. V. Hatton, *Trans. Faraday Soc.*, **57**, 28 (1961).
198. A. A. Bothner-By and R. E. Glick, *J. Chem. Phys.*, **26**, 1651 (1957).
199. J. R. Zimmerman and M. R. Foster, *J. Phys. Chem.*, **61**, 282 (1957).
200. A. D. Buckingham, T. Schaefer and W. G. Schneider, *J. Chem. Phys.*, **32**, 1227 (1960).
201. T. Schaefer and W. G. Schneider, *J. Chem. Phys.*, **32**, 1218 (1960).
202. L. P. Hammett, *Trans. Faraday Soc.*, **34**, 156 (1938).
203. R. W. Taft, S. Ehrenson, I. C. Lewis and R. E. Glick, *J. Amer. Chem. Soc.*, **81**, 5352 (1959).
204. M. Charton-Koechlin and M. A. Leroy, *J. chim. Phys.*, **56**, 850 (1959).
205. P. C. Lauterbur, *Ann. N.Y. Acad. Sci.*, **70**, 841 (1958).
206. H. S. Gutowsky, D. W. McCall, B. R. McGarvey and L. H. Meyer, *J. Amer. Chem. Soc.*, **74**, 4809 (1952).
207. G. J. Korinek and W. G. Schneider, *Can. J. Chem.*, **35**, 1157 (1957).
208. H. Spiesecke and W. G. Schneider, *J. Chem. Phys.*, **35**, 731 (1961).
209. I. Yamaguchi and N. Hayakawa, *Bull. Chem. Soc. Japan* **33**, 1128 (1960).
210. R. R. Fraser, *Can. J. Chem.*, **38**, 2226 (1960).
211. P. Diehl, *Helv. Chim. Acta*, **44**, 829 (1961).
212. A. C. Farthing and B. Nam, *Steric Effects in Conjugated Systems*, Butterworth, London (1958), p. 131.
213. W. S. Brey and K. D. Lawson, private communication.
214. G. W. Smith, private communication.
215. J. S. Martin and B. P. Dailey, *J. Chem. Phys.*, **39**, 1722 (1963).
216. F. C. Stehling, *Anal. Chem.*, **35**, 773 (1963).
217. N. F. Chamberlain, *Anal. Chem.*, **31**, 56 (1959).
218. C. Heathcock, *Can. J. Chem.*, **40**, 1865 (1962).
219. K. A. Kun and H. G. Cassidy, *J. Org. Chem.*, **26**, 3223 (1961).
220. R. E. Klinck and J. B. Stothers, *Can. J. Chem.*, **40**, 1071 (1962).
221. J. B. Leane and R. E. Richards, *Trans. Faraday Soc.*, **55**, 707 (1959).
222. S. Brownstein, *J. Amer. Chem. Soc.*, **80**, 2300 (1958).
223. R. A. Hoffman, P. O. Kinell and G. Bergstrom, *Arkiv. Kemi*, **15**, 533 (1960).
224. D. D. Elleman and S. L. Manatt, *J. Chem. Phys.*, **36**, 2346 (1962).
225. C. E. Johnson and F. A. Bovey, *J. Chem. Phys.*, **29**, 1012 (1958).
226. J. S. Waugh and R. W. Fessenden, *J. Amer. Chem. Soc.*, **79**, 846 (1957).
227. J. A. Pople, *J. Chem. Phys.*, **24**, 1111 (1956).
228. H. J. Bernstein, W. G. Schneider and J. A. Pople, *Proc. Roy. Soc.*, **A236**, 515 (1956).
229. N. Jonathan, S. Gordon and B. P. Dailey, *J. Chem. Phys.*, **36**, 2443 (1962).
230. T. P. Schaefer and R. E. Richards, *Trans. Faraday Soc.*, **54**, 1280 (1958).
231. B. D. Nageswara Rao and P. Venkateswarlu, *Proc. Indian. Acad. Sci.*, **54**, 1 (1961).

232. R. E. Richards and T. Schaefer, *Mol. Phys.*, **1**, 331 (1958).
233. B. Dischler and G. Englert, *Z. Natur.*, **16**a, 1180 (1961).
234. J. Martin and B. P. Dailey, *J. Chem. Phys.*, **37**, 2594 (1962).
235. D. W. A. Sharp and N. Sheppard, *J. Chem. Soc.*, 674 (1957).
236. R. B. Moodie, T. M. Connor and R. Stewart, *Can. J. Chem.*, **37**, 1402 (1959).
237. D. E. O'Reilly and H. P. Leftin, *J. Phys. Chem.*, **64**, 1555 (1960).
238. R. Dehl, W. R. Vaughan and R. S. Berry, *J. Org. Chem.*, **24**, 1616 (1959).
239. C. MacLean, J. H. van der Waals and E. L. Mackor, *Mol. Phys.*, **1**, 247 (1958).
240. S. S. Danyluk and W. G. Schneider, *J. Amer. Chem. Soc.*, **82**, 997 (1960).
241. S. S. Danyluk and W. G. Schneider, *Can. J. Chem.*, **40**, 1777 (1962).
242. P. C. Lauterbur, private communication.
243. H. Spiesecke and W. G. Schneider, *Tetrahedron Letters*, 468 (1961).
244. C. MacLean and E. L. Mackor, *J. Chem. Phys.*, **34**, 2208 (1961).
245. A. Julg, *J. chim. Phys.*, **52**, 377 (1955).
246. R. Pariser, *J. Chem. Phys.*, **25**, 1112 (1956).
247. G. G. Hall, A. Hardisson and L. M. Jackman, *Discuss. Faraday Soc.*, **34**, 15 (1962).
248. G. Fraenkel, R. E. Carter, A. McLachlan and J. H. Richards, *J. Amer. Chem. Soc.*, **82**, 5846 (1960).
249. G. S. Reddy and J. H. Goldstein, *J. Amer. Chem. Soc.*, **84**, 583 (1962).
250. C. MacLean and E. L. Mackor, *Mol. Phys.*, **4**, 241 (1961).
251. J. R. Leto, F. A. Cotton and J. S. Waugh, *Nature*, **180**, 978 (1957).
252. G. S. Reddy and J. H. Goldstein, *J. Phys. Chem.*, **65**, 1539 (1961).
253. J. B. Leane and R. E. Richards, *Trans. Faraday Soc.*, **55**, 518 (1959).
254. E. J. Corey, G. Slomp, S. Dev, S. Tobinaga and E. R. Glazier, *J. Amer. Chem. Soc.*, **80**, 1204 (1958).
255. R. J. Abraham and H. J. Bernstein, *Can. J. Chem.*, **37**, 1056 (1959).
256. R. J. Abraham and H. J. Bernstein, *Can. J. Chem.*, **39**, 905 (1961).
257. Varian Technical Information Bulletin No. 50.
258. S. Gronowitz, A. Hornfeldt, B. Gestblom and R. A. Hoffman, *Arkiv. Kemi.*, **18**, 133 (1961).
259. S. Gronowitz, A. Hornfeldt, B. Gestblom and R. A. Hoffman, *Arkiv. Kemi.*, **18**, 151 (1961).
260. R. J. Tuite, A. D. Josey and H. R. Snyder, *J. Amer. Chem. Soc.*, **82**, 4360 (1960).
261. A. D. Cohen and K. A. McLauchlan, *Discuss. Faraday Soc.*, **34**, 132 (1962).
262. R. A. Hoffman and S. Gronowitz, *Arkiv. Kemi.*, **16**, 563 (1960).
263. R. J. Abraham, E. Bullock and S. S. Mitra, *Can. J. Chem.*, **37**, 1859 (1959).
264. G. S. Reddy and J. H. Goldstein, *J. Amer. Chem. Soc.*, **83**, 5020 (1961).
265. G. S. Reddy and J. H. Goldstein, *J. Amer. Chem. Soc.*, **83**, 2045 (1961).
266. A. Taurins and W. G. Schneider, *Can. J. Chem.*, **38**, 1237 (1960).
267. J. Ellis, A. H. Jackson, G. W. Kenner and J. Lee, *Tetrahedron Letters*, No. 2, 23 (1960).
268. R. J. Abraham, *Mol. Phys.*, **4**, 145 (1961).
269. E. D. Becker, R. B. Bradley and C. J. Watson, *J. Amer. Chem. Soc.*, **83**, 3743 (1961).
270. R. J. Abraham, A. H. Jackson and G. W. Kenner, *J. Chem. Soc.*, 3468 (1961).
271. E. D. Becker and R. B. Bradley, *J. Chem. Phys.*, **31**, 1413 (1959).
272. L. A. Cohen, J. W. Daly, H. Kny and B. Witkop, *J. Amer. Chem. Soc.*, **82**, 2184 (1960).
273. H. J. Bernstein, J. A. Pople and W. G. Schneider, *Can. J. Chem.*, **35**, 1487 (1957).
274. W. Brügel, *Z. Elektrochem.*, **66**, 159 (1962).
275. T. Schaefer and W. G. Schneider, *J. Chem. Phys.*, **32**, 1224 (1960).
276. M. Freymann, R. Freymann and D. Libermann, *Compt. Rend.*, **250**, 2185 (1960).
277. M. Freymann and R. Freymann, *Compt. Rend.*, **248**, 677 (1959).
278. M. Freymann and R. Freymann, *Arch. des Sci.*, **12**, 207 (1959).
279. V. J. Kowalewski and D. G. de Kowalewski, *J. Chem. Phys.*, **36**, 266 (1962).
280. E. B. Baker, *J. Chem. Phys.*, **23**, 1981 (1955).
281. B. D. Nageswara Rao and P. Venkateswarlu, *Proc. Indian Acad. Sci.*, **54**, 305 (1961).
282. J. N. Shoolery, *Discuss. Faraday Soc.*, **34**, 104 (1962).

283. T. Schaefer, *Can. J. Chem.*, **39**, 1864 (1961).
284. F. A. L. Anet, *J. Chem. Phys.*, **32**, 1274 (1960).
285. A. R. Katritzky and J. M. Lagowski, *J. Chem. Soc.*, 43 (1961).
286. R. Bonnett and D. E. McGreer, *Can. J. Chem.*, **40**, 177 (1962).
287. J. A. Elvidge and L. M. Jackman, *J. Chem. Soc.*, 859 (1961).
288. S. Gronowitz and R. A. Hoffman, *Arkiv. Kemi.*, **13**, 279 (1958).
289. S. Gronowitz and R. A. Hoffman, *Arkiv. Kemi.*, **15**, 45 (1959).
290. S. Gronowitz and R. A. Hoffman, *Acta Chem. Scand.*, **13**, 1687 (1959).
291. S. Gronowitz and R. A. Hoffman, *Arkiv. Kemi.*, **16**, 501 (1960).
292. S. Gronowitz and R. A. Hoffman, *Arkiv. Kemi.*, **16**, 515 (1960).
293. S. Gronowitz and R. A. Hoffman, *Arkiv. Kemi.*, **16**, 539 (1960).
294. K. Takahashi, Y. Matsuki, T. Mashiko and G. Hazato, Lecture to the Annual Meeting of the Chemical Society of Japan, Tokyo, April (1958).
295. S. Fujiwara, M. Katayama, S. Hayashi, H. Shimizu and S. Nishimura, *Bull. Chem. Soc. Japan*, **32**, 201 (1959).
296. P. L. Corio and I. Weinberg, *J. Chem. Phys.*, **31**, 569 (1959).
297. R. A. Hoffman and S. Gronowitz, *Arkiv. Kemi.*, **16**, 471 (1960).
298. R. A. Hoffman, *Arkiv. Kemi.*, **17**, 1 (1961).
299. S. Goodwin, J. N. Shoolery and L. F. Johnson, *J. Amer. Chem. Soc.*, **81**, 3065 (1959).
300. P. C. Lauterbur, *Determination of Organic Structures by Physical Methods*, Vol. 2, Chapt. 7, Editors F. C. Nachod and W. D. Phillips, Academic Press, New York (1962).
301. G. Slomp, private communication.
302. G. Slomp and F. A. MacKellar, *J. Amer. Chem. Soc.*, **84**, 204 (1962).
303. G. Slomp and B. R. McGarvey, *J. Amer. Chem. Soc.*, **81**, 2200 (1959).
304. R. F. Zürcher, *Helv. Chim. Acta*, **44**, 1380 (1961).
305. C. Y. Hopkins and H. J. Bernstein, *Can. J. Chem.*, **37**, 775 (1959).
306. M. Takeda and O. Jardetzky, *J. Chem. Phys.*, **26**, 1346 (1957).
307. O. Jardetzky and C. D. Jardetzky, *J. Biol. Chem.*, **233**, 383 (1958).
308. F. A. Bovey and G. V. D. Tiers, *J. Amer. Chem. Soc.*, **81**, 2870 (1959).
309. D. Y. Curtin, J. A. Gourse, W. H. Richardson and K. L. Rinehart, *J. Org. Chem.*, **24**, 93 (1959).
310. G. J. Karabatsos, J. D. Graham and F. M. Vane, *J. Amer. Chem. Soc.*, **84**, 753 (1962).
311. C. D. Jardetzky, *J. Amer. Chem. Soc.*, **82**, 229 (1960).
312. C. D. Jardetzky, and O. Jardetzky, *J. Amer. Chem. Soc.*, **82**, 222 (1960).
313. L. Crombie and J. W. Lown, *J. Chem. Soc.*, 775 (1962).
314. J. I. Musher and E. J. Corey, *Tetrahedron*, **18**, 791 (1962).
315. C. M. Huggins, G. C. Pimentel and J. N. Shoolery, *J. Phys. Chem.*, **60**, 1311 (1956).
316. A. D. Cohen and C. Reid, *J. Chem. Phys.*, **25**, 790 (1956).
317. L. W. Reeves, *Trans. Faraday Soc.*, **55**, 1684 (1959).
318. A. L. Porte, H. S. Gutowsky and I. M. Hunsberger, *J. Amer. Chem. Soc.*, **82**, 5057 (1960).
319. L. W. Reeves, *Trans. Faraday Soc.*, **55**, 1684 (1959).
320. R. A. Ogg and J. D. Ray, *J. Chem. Phys.*, **26**, 1339 (1957).
321. J. Feeney and L. H. Sutcliffe, *Proc. Chem. Soc.*, 118 (1961).
322. J. Feeney and L. H. Sutcliffe, *J. Chem. Soc.*, 1123 (1962).
323. C. W. Kern and W. N. Lipscomb, *J. Chem. Phys.*, **37**, 260 (1962).
324. R. A. Ogg, *J. Chem. Phys.*, **22**, 560 (1954).
325. H. S. Gutowsky and A. Saika, *J. Chem. Phys.*, **21**, 1688 (1953).
326. J. D. Roberts, *J. Amer. Chem. Soc.*, **78**, 4495 (1956).
327. H. Watanabe, K. Ito and M. Kubo, *J. Chem. Phys.*, **34**, 1043 (1961).
328. C. W. Kern and W. N. Lipscomb, *J. Chem. Phys.*, **37**, 275 (1962).
329. S. Forsen, *Acta Chem. Scand.*, **13**, 1472 (1959).
330. L. H. Meyer, A. Saika and H. S. Gutowsky, *J. Amer. Chem. Soc.*, **75**, 4567 (1953).
331. R. J. Abraham, J. A. Pople and H. J. Bernstein, *Can. J. Chem.*, **36**, 1302 (1958).

332. D. E. Webster, *J. Chem. Soc.*, 5132 (1960).
333. J. F. J. Dippy, *Chem. Rev.*, **25**, 151 (1939).
334. M. L. H. Green, L. Pratt and G. Wilkinson, *J. Chem. Soc.*, 3916 (1958).
335. R. A. Friedel, I. Wender, S. L. Shufler and H. W. Sternberg, *J. Amer. Chem. Soc.*, **77**, 3951 (1955).
336. R. M. Stevens, C. W. Kern and W. N. Lipscomb, *J. Chem. Phys.*, **37**, 279 (1962).
337. F. A. Cotton and G. Wilkinson, *Chem. and Ind.*, 1305 (1956).
338. T. S. Piper and G. Wilkinson, *J. Inorg. Nuc. Chem.*, **3**, 104 (1956).
339. J. Chatt, L. A. Duncanson and B. L. Shaw, *Proc. Chem. Soc.*, 343 (1957).
340. W. P. Griffith and G. Wilkinson, *J. Chem. Soc.*, 2757 (1959).
341. F. A. Cotton, J. L. Down and G. Wilkinson, *J. Chem. Soc.*, 833 (1959).
342. J. Feeney, J. Lee and L. H. Sutcliffe, unpublished results.
343. R. S. Milner and L. Pratt, *Discuss. Faraday Soc.*, **34**, 88 (1962).
344. D. R. Eaton, A. D. Josey, W. D. Phillips and R. E. Benson, *Discuss. Faraday Soc.*, **34**, 77 (1962).
345. D. R. Eaton, A. D. Josey, W. D. Phillips and R. E. Benson, *J. Chem. Phys.*, **37**, 347 (1962).
346. D. R. Eaton, W. D. Phillips and D. J. Caldwell, *J. Amer. Chem. Soc.*, **85**, 397 (1963).
347. H. Primas, R. Ernst and R. Arndt. Paper presented at the International Meeting of Molecular Spectroscopy, Bologna, Sept. (1959).
348. K. B. Wiberg and B. J. Nist, *J. Amer. Chem. Soc.*, **83**, 1226 (1961).
349. T. L. Brown, D. W. Dickerhoof and D. A. Bafus, *J. Amer. Chem. Soc.*, **84**, 1371 (1962).
350. H. M. Hutton and T. Schaefer, *Can. J. Chem.*, **40**, 875 (1962).
351. J. S. G. Cox, E. O. Bishop and R. E. Richards, *J. Chem. Soc.*, 5118 (1960).
352. N. Muller and W. C. Tosch, *J. Chem. Phys.*, **37**, 1167 (1962).
353. J. B. Bredenberg and J. N. Shoolery, *Tetrahedron Letters*, 285 (1961).
354. D. D. Perrin and D. R. Perrin, *J. Amer. Chem. Soc.*, **84**, 1922 (1962).
355. A. Davison, W. McFarlane, L. Pratt and G. Wilkinson, *J. Chem. Soc.*, 3653 (1962).
356. W. Seiffert, *Ang. Chem. Int. Ed.*, **1**, 215 (1962).
357. D. R. Eaton, A. D. Josey, W. D. Phillips and R. E. Benson, *Mol. Phys.*, **5**, 407 (1962).
358. E. A. La Lancette, D. R. Eaton, R. E. Benson, W. D. Phillips, *J. Amer. Chem. Soc.*, **84**, 3968 (1962).
359. R. H. Holm, *J. Amer. Chem. Soc.*, **83**, 4683 (1961).
360. J. E. Drake and W. L. Jolly, *J. Chem. Soc.*, 2807 (1962).
361. W. G. Paterson and N. R. Tipman, *Can. J. Chem.*, **40**, 2122 (1962).
362. E. A. V. Ebsworth and J. J. Turner, *J. Chem. Phys.*, **36**, 2628 (1962).
363. V. J. Kowalewski and D. G. de Kowalewski, *J. Chem. Phys.*, **37**, 2603 (1962).
364. R. Freymann, M. Dvolaitzky and J. Jacques, *Compt. Rend.*, **253**, 1436 (1961).
365. C. MacLean and E. L. Mackor, *Discuss. Faraday Soc.*, **34**, 165 (1962).
366. L. M. Jackman, F. Sondheimer, Y. Amiel, D. A. Ben-Efraim, Y. Gaoni, R. Wolovsky and A. A. Bothner-By, *J. Amer. Chem. Soc.*, **84**, 4307 (1962).
367. G. G. Hall and A. Hardisson, *Proc. Roy. Soc.*, **A 268**, 328 (1962).
368. R. Freeman and D. H. Whiffen, *Mol. Phys.*, **4**, 321 (1961).
369. K. B. Wiberg, B. R. Lowry and B. J. Nist, *J. Amer. Chem. Soc.*, **84**, 1594 (1962).
370. F. A. L. Anet, *Can. J. Chem.*, **39**, 789 (1961).
371. T. Schaefer, *J. Chem. Phys.*, **36**, 2235 (1962).
372. D. D. Elleman and S. L. Manatt, *J. Amer. Chem. Soc.*, **83**, 4095 (1961).
373. V. J. Kowalewski and D. G. de Kowalewski, *J. Chem. Phys.*, **37**, 1009 (1962).
374. J. C. Schug and J. C. Deck, *J. Chem. Phys.*, **37**, 2618 (1962).
375. H. D. Kaesz and N. Flitcroft, *J. Amer. Chem. Soc.*, **85**, 1377 (1963).
376. J. M. Anderson, J. D. Baldeschwieler, D. C. Dittmer and W. D. Phillips, *J. Chem. Phys.*, **38**, 1260 (1963).
377. J. C. W. Chien and J. F. Walker, *J. Poly. Sci.*, **45**, 239 (1960).

378. J. I. Musher, *J. Chem. Phys.*, **34**, 594 (1961).
379. F. C. Stehling, private communication.
380. W. C. Neikam and B. P. Dailey, *J. Chem. Phys.*, **38**, 445 (1963).
381. J. G. Powles, *Polymer*, **1**, 219 (1960).
382. W. P. Slichter, *Advances in Polymer Science*, **1**, 35 (1958).
383. J. A. Sauer and A. E. Woodward, *Rev. Mod. Phys.*, **32**, 88 (1960).
384. F. A. Bovey, G. V. D. Tiers and G. Filipovich, *J. Poly. Sci.*, **38**, 73 (1959).
385. A. Odiyama, *J. Phys. Soc. Japan*, **14**, 777 (1959).
386. M. Saunders, A. Wishnia and J. G. Kirkwood, *J. Amer. Chem. Soc.*, **79**, 3289 (1957).
387. O. Jardetzky and C. D. Jardetzky, *J. Amer. Chem. Soc.*, **79**, 5322 (1957).
388. F. A. Bovey and G. V. D. Tiers, *J. Poly. Sci.*, **A1**, 849 (1963).
389. Hung Yu Chen, *Anal. Chem.*, **34**, 1134 (1962).
390. W. R. Edwards and N. F. Chamberlain, *J. Poly. Sci.*, **A1**, 2299 (1963).
391. F. A. Bovey and G. V. D. Tiers, *Advances in Polymer Science*, **3**, 139 (1963).
392. F. A. Bovey and G. V. D. Tiers, *J. Poly. Sci.*, **44**, 173 (1960).
393. T. G. Fox, W. E. Goode, S. Gratch, C. M. Huggett, J. F. Kincaid, A. Spell and J. D. Stroupe, *J. Poly. Sci.*, **31**, 173 (1958).
394. U. Johnsen and K. Tessmar, *Kolloid Zeitschrift*, **168**, 160 (1960).
395. F. A. Bovey, E. W. Anderson, D. C. Douglass and J. A. Manson, *J. Chem. Phys.*, **39**, 1199 (1963).
396. U. Johnsen, *J. Poly. Sci.*, **54**, S 6 (1961).
397. F. A. Bovey and G. V. D. Tiers, *Chem. and Ind.*, 1826 (1962).
398. W. C. Tincher, *J. Poly. Sci.*, **62**, S 148 (1962).
399. F. C. Stehling, Paper No. 45, Division of Polymer Chemistry, American Chem. Soc. National Meeting, Washington, March (1962); *J. Poly. Sci.*, **A2**, 1815 (1964).
400. S. Satoh, R. Chujo, T. Ozeki and E. Nagai, *J. Poly. Sci.*, **62**, S 101 (1962).
401. S. Brownstein, S. Bywater and D. J. Worsfold, *J. Phys. Chem.*, **66**, 2067 (1962).
402. T. Yoshino, H. Kyogoku, J. Komiyama and Y. Manabe, *J. Chem. Phys.*, **38**, 1026 (1963).
403. R. J. Kern and J. V. Pustinger, *Nature*, **185**, 236 (1960).
404. A. Nishioka, H. Watanabe, I. Yamaguchi and H. Shimizu, *J. Poly. Sci.*, **45**, 232 (1960).
405. C. E. H. Bawn and A. Ledwith, *Quart. Rev.*, **16**, 361 (1962).
406. S. Gronowitz, B. Gestblom and R. A. Hoffman, *Acta Chem. Scand.*, **15**, 1201 (1961).
407. P. F. Cox, *J. Amer. Chem. Soc.*, **85**, 380 (1963).
408. D. Chapman, *J. Chem. Soc.*, 131 (1963).
409. P. R. Wells, *J. Chem. Soc.*, 1967 (1963).
410. D. J. Cram and L. A. Singer, *J. Amer. Chem. Soc.*, **85**, 1084 (1963).
411. E. A. V. Ebsworth and J. J. Turner, *J. Phys. Chem.*, **67**, 805 (1963).
412. J. E. Drake and W. L. Jolly, *J. Chem. Phys.*, **38**, 1033 (1963).
413. J. H. Hildebrand and R. L. Scott, *Solubility of Non-electrolytes*, Reinhold, New York (1950), p. 427.
414. R. J. Abraham, *J. Chem. Phys.*, **34**, 1062 (1961).
415. W. T. Raynes, A. D. Buckingham and H. J. Bernstein, *J. Chem. Phys.*, **36**, 3481 (1962).
416. S. Gordon and B. P. Dailey, *J. Chem. Phys.*, **34**, 1084 (1961).
417. A. D. Buckingham and J. A. Pople, *Trans. Faraday Soc.*, **51**, 1173 (1955).
418. L. Petrakis and H. J. Bernstein, *J. Chem. Phys.*, **37**, 2731 (1962).
419. L. Petrakis and H. J. Bernstein, *J. Chem. Phys.*, **38**, 1562 (1963).
420. R. J. Abraham, *Mol. Phys.*, **4**, 369 (1961).
421. P. Diehl and R. Freeman, *Mol. Phys.*, **4**, 39 (1961).
422. A. A. Bothner-By, *J. Mol. Spect.*, **5**, 52 (1960).
423. J. P. Maher and D. F. Evans, *Proc. Chem. Soc.*, 176 (1963).
424. N. van Meurs, *Spect. Acta*, **19**, 1695 (1963).
425. J. V. Hatton, W. G. Schneider and W. Siebrand, *J. Chem. Phys.*, **39**, 1330 (1963).
426. O. Jardetzky, *J. Amer. Chem. Soc.*, **85**, 1823 (1963).

427. W. G. PATERSON and G. BIGAM, *Can. J. Chem.*, **41**, 1841 (1963).
428. S. CAWLEY and S. S. DANYLUK, *Can. J. Chem.*, **41**, 1850 (1963).
429. H. KASIWAGA and J. NIVA, *Bull. Chem. Soc. Japan*, **36**, 405 (1963).
430. H. KASIWAGA, N. NAKAGAWA and J. NIVA, *Bull. Chem. Soc. Japan*, **36**, 410 (1963).
431. D. M. GRAHAM and C. E. HOLLOWAY, *Can. J. Chem.*, **41**, 2114 (1963).
432. D. R. EATON, A. D. JOSEY and W. A. SHEPPARD, *J. Amer. Chem. Soc.*, **85**, 2689 (1963).
433. M. J. S. DEWAR and R. C. FAHEY, *J. Amer. Chem. Soc.*, **85**, 2704 (1963).
434. K. B. WIBERG and B. J. NIST, *J. Amer. Chem. Soc.*, **85**, 2788 (1963).
435. F. A. L. ANET, R. A. B. BANNARD and L. D. HALL, *Can. J. Chem.*, **41**, 2331 (1963).
436. C. R. MCCOY and A. L. ALLRED, *J. Inorg. Nuc. Chem.*, **25**, 1219 (1963).
437. D. F. GAINES, R. SCHAEFFER and F. TEBBE, *J. Phys. Chem.*, **67**, 1937 (1963).
438. J. D. MEMORY and T. B. COBB, *J. Chem. Phys.*, **39**, 2386 (1963).
439. W. D. HORROCKS and G. N. LA MAR, *J. Amer. Chem. Soc.*, **85**, 3512 (1963).
440. E. A. V. EBSWORTH and S. G. FRANKISS, *J. Amer. Chem. Soc.*, **85**, 3516 (1963).
441. Z. K. CHEEMA, G. W. GIBSON and J. F. EASTHAM, *J. Amer. Chem. Soc.*, **85**, 3517 (1963).
442. D. J. PATEL, M. E. H. HOWDEN and J. D. ROBERTS, *J. Amer. Chem. Soc.*, **85**, 3218 (1963).
443. R. SUMMITT, J. J. EISIH, J. T. TRAINOR and M. T. ROGERS, *J. Phys. Chem.*, **67**, 2362 (1963).
444. R. S. PORTER, S. W. NICKSIC and J. F. JOHNSON, *Anal. Chem.*, **35**, 1948 (1963).
445. E. O. BISHOP and J. I. MUSHER, *Mol. Phys.*, **6**, 621 (1963).
446. N. LUMBROSO, T. K. WU and B. P. DAILEY, *J. Phys. Chem.*, **67**, 2469 (1963).
447. B. B. HOWARD, B. LINDER and M. J. EMERSON, *J. Chem. Phys.*, **36**, 485 (1962).
448. F. HRUSKA, E. BOCK and T. SCHAEFER, *Can. J. Chem.*, **41**, 3034 (1963).
449. T. SCHAEFER, W. F. REYNOLDS and T. YONEMOTO, *Can. J. Chem.*, **41**, 2969 (1963).
450. L. W. REEVES and E. J. WELLS, *Can. J. Chem.*, **41**, 2698 (1963).
451. J. A. ELVIDGE and R. G. FOSTER, *J. Chem. Soc.*, 590 (1963).
452. M. FRANCK-NEUMANN and J. M. LEHN, *Mol. Phys.*, **7**, 197 (1964).
453. S. BROWNSTEIN, *Can. J. Chem.*, **40**, 870 (1962).
454. A. ZWEIG, J. E. LEHNSEN, J. E. LANCASTER and M. J. NEGLIA, *J. Amer. Chem. Soc.*, **85**, 3940 (1963).
455. B. L. SHAPIRO, S. J. EBERSOLE, G. J. KARABATSOS, F. M. VANE and S. L. MANATT, *J. Amer. Chem. Soc.*, **85**, 4041 (1963).
456. L. L. LOHR and W. N. LIPSCOMB, *Inorg. Chem.*, **3**, 22 (1964).
457. M. W. DIETRICH and R. E. KELLER, *Anal. Chem.*, **36**, 258 (1964).
458. R. H. HOLM, A. CHAKRAVORTY and G. O. DUDEK, *J. Amer. Chem. Soc.*, **86**, 379 (1964).
459. R. CHUJO, S. SATOH and E. NAGAI, *J. Poly. Sci.*, **A2**, 895 (1964).
460. R. T. HOBGOOD and J. H. GOLDSTEIN, *J. Mol. Spect.*, **12**, 76 (1964).
461. M. D. RAUSCH and V. MARK, *J. Org. Chem.*, **28**, 3225 (1963).
462. E. A. V. EBSWORTH and J. J. TURNER, *Trans. Faraday Soc.*, **60**, 256 (1964).
463. S. H. MARCUS and S. I. MILLER, *J. Phys. Chem.*, **68**, 331 (1964).
464. F. HRUSKA, T. SCHAEFER and C. A. REILLY, *Can. J. Chem.*, **42**, 697 (1964).
465. D. R. EATON, A. D. JOSEY, W. D. PHILLIPS and R. E. BENSON, *J. Chem. Phys.*, **39**, 3513 (1963).
466. V. M. S. GIL and J. N. MURRELL, *Trans. Faraday Soc.*, **60**, 248 (1964).
467. W. HOFMAN, L. STEFANIAK, T. URBANSKI and M. WITANOWSKI, *J. Amer. Chem. Soc.*, **86**, 554 (1964).
468. K. L. WILLIAMSON, C. A. LANFORD and C. R. NICHOLSON, *J. Amer. Chem. Soc.*, **86**, 762 (1964).
469. C. T. MATHIS and J. H. GOLDSTEIN, *J. Phys. Chem.*, **68**, 571 (1964).
470. G. W. SMITH, *J. Mol. Spect.*, **12**, 146 (1964).
471. J. A. ELVIDGE and R. G. FOSTER, *J. Chem. Soc.*, 981 (1964).
472. A. G. MASSEY, E. W. RANDALL and D. SHAW, *Spectrochim. Acta*, **20**, 379 (1964).
473. F. C. STEHLING, *J. Poly. Sci.*, **A2**, 1815 (1964).
474. S. BROWNSTEIN and D. M. WILES, *J. Poly. Sci.*, **A2**, 1901 (1964).
475. P. BATES, S. CAWLEY and S. S. DANYLUK, *J. Chem. Phys.*, **40**, 2415 (1964).

476. V. S. Watts, G. S. Reddy and J. H. Goldstein, *J. Mol. Spect.*, **11**, 325 (1963).
477. B. L. Shapiro, R. M. Kopchick and S. J. Ebersole, *J. Chem. Phys.*, **39**, 3154 (1963).
478. B. L. Shapiro, S. J. Ebersole and R. M. Kopchick, *J. Mol. Spect.*, **11**, 326 (1963).
479. A. C. Huitric, J. B. Carr, W. F. Trager and B. J. Nist, *Tetrahedron*, **19**, 2145 (1963).
480. P. Laszlo and R. von Ragné Schleyer, *J. Amer. Chem. Soc.*, **86**, 1171 (1964).
481. A. D. Buckingham, *Can. J. Chem.*, **38**, 300 (1960).
482. H. C. Clark, J. T. Kwon, L. W. Reeves and E. J. Wells, *Inorg. Chem.*, **3**, 907 (1964).
483. V. Mark and M. D. Rausch, *Inorg. Chem.*, **3**, 1067 (1964).
484. M. I. Levenberg and J. H. Richards, *J. Amer. Chem. Soc.*, **86**, 2634 (1964).
485. J. Lehn and J. Riehl, *Mol. Phys.*, **8**, 33 (1964).
486. B. P. Dailey, *J. Chem. Phys.*, **41**, 2304 (1964).
487. S. Ebersole, S. Castellano and A. A. Bothner-By, *J. Phys. Chem.*, **68**, 3430 (1964).
488. T. K. Wu and B. P. Dailey, *J. Chem. Phys.*, **41**, 2796 (1964).
489. C. H. van Dyke and A. G. MacDiarmid, *Inorg. Chem.*, **3**, 1071 (1964).
490. P. J. Black and M. L. Heffernan, *Austral. J. Chem.*, **17**, 558 (1964).
491. G. E. McCasland, S. Furuta, L. F. Johnson and J. N. Shoolery, *J. Org. Chem.*, **29**, 2354 (1964).
492. N. S. Bhacca and D. H. Williams, *Applications of NMR Spectroscopy in Organic Chemistry*, Holden-Day, Inc., San Francisco (1964).
493. P. Laszlo and J. I. Musher, *J. Chem. Phys.*, **41**, 3906 (1964).

CHAPTER 11

^{19}F NUCLEAR MAGNETIC RESONANCE STUDIES

11.1 Introduction

THE rapid outflow of scientific publications dealing with every aspect of ^{19}F nuclear magnetic resonance during the last few years is a reflection of the widespread interest which has grown in this field. By virtue of the large values of ^{19}F chemical shifts and spin coupling constants it is often possible to obtain more information about molecular structures and molecular dynamic processes for fluorine-containing molecules than for the analogous hydrogen-containing molecules (see Sections 9.5.5 and 11.13.3). Theoretically, our understanding of the origin of ^{19}F chemical shifts and coupling constants is not as well-developed as that for ^{1}H nuclei due mainly to the greater complexity of the fluorine electronic configuration.

Fluorine-19 is the only naturally occurring isotope of this element and it is an ideal nucleus for NMR investigation. Although it is both less sensitive to NMR detection and is usually easier to saturate than the hydrogen nucleus, fluorine resonance spectra can be obtained with ease using standard commercial spectrometers. ^{19}F has a spin number of one half ($I = \frac{1}{2}$) and thus does not possess a quadrupole moment. Its univalency and reactivity are together reponsible for the large number of fluorine-containing compounds which are available for examination, and furthermore many of these compounds are liquids at 25°C. The ranges of observed coupling constants and chemical shifts in ^{19}F resonance studies are large compared with those found in ^{1}H spectra because each effect is controlled by a different factor for each nucleus. The sensitivity requirements demanded by pure fluorine-containing liquid compounds are not sufficiently stringent to interfere seriously with the resolution (e.g. splittings of 0·3 cycles sec^{-1} can be readily resolved at 56·4 Mc sec^{-1} in ^{19}F resonance spectra). Compounds containing several differently shielded fluorine nuclei coupled by indirect spin–spin interactions often show simple first order type spectra (see Fig. 11.1) because the chemical shift differences are large compared with the coupling constants involved. The difference in magnitude between the chemical shifts and the coupling constants found in most ^{19}F spectra may necessitate the use of two different sweep rates to obtain the chemical shifts of the absorption bands (fast sweep rates $\sim$30 cycles sec^{-2} and the fine-structure on the bands $\sim$0·2 cycles sec^{-2} as in ^{1}H resonance spectra).

Both internal and external referencing procedures have been used in the measurement of ^{19}F resonance spectra. Trifluoroacetic acid is the compound most commonly used as an external reference and most of the chemical shifts quoted with respect to this reference in the literature have not been corrected for bulk diamagnetic susceptibility effects (which although small are not always negligible)(1). Filipovich and Tiers(2) have suggested that ^{19}F chemical shifts should be reported at infinite dilution in trichlorofluoromethane, $CFCl_3$, using this substance as an internal reference (see Section 7.2.2). Solutions of less than 10% in $CFCl_3$ can be regarded as infinitely dilute and when it is impractical to examine dilute solutions, extrapolation to infinite dilution can be conducted. Table 11.1 indicates the large discrepancies between ^{19}F chemical shifts when measured from an external and an internal reference and points to the need for some standardisation in the referencing of ^{19}F resonance spectra using an internal reference.

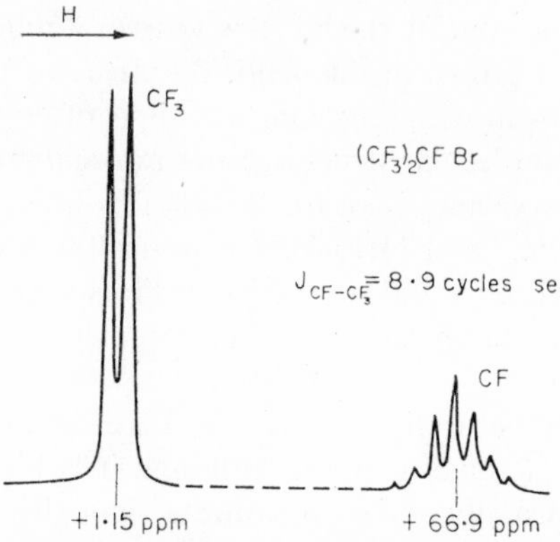

FIG. 11.1 The ^{19}F resonance spectrum of $(CF_3)_2CFBr$ at 56·4 Mc sec^{-1}. Chemical shifts are to high fields of the external reference CF_3COOH.

Evans(1) has studied the effects of solvents on the shielding of ^{19}F nuclei and in some cases observed effects too large to be explained in terms of changes in bulk diamagnetic susceptibility (for which he corrected): he suggested that the origin of such shielding might be due to an increase in the paramagnetic shielding term caused by the presence of polarised solvent molecules, and he advocated caution in the use of $CFCl_3$ as an internal reference as suggested by Tiers. Other workers(3) have recommended extrapolation of chemical shifts to infinite dilution in several different solvents to overcome this difficulty when very accurate ^{19}F chemical shifts are required. The increase in the paramagnetic term which accompanies dilution is thought to be due to a change in the value of ΔE, the mean electronic excitation energy, resulting from the increased dispersion forces between the solute and solvent molecules(1). The solvent dependence of ^{19}F chemical shifts in several different systems is found to be roughly similar, the ^{19}F nuclei being progressively deshielded by increasing the dilution with the solvent(1). Table 11.2 gives the observed solvent shifts for various fluoro-organic compounds in the solvents $CHBr_3$ and CCl_4. Quite large ^{19}F chemical shift differences have been measured when benzotrifluoride is examined over the temperature range $-29°C$ to $159°C$ ($1{\cdot}06 \times 10^{-2}$ ppm $°C^{-1}$ linear increase of shielding with temperature)[1]. Change in pressure of gaseous carbon tetrafluoride is also accompanied by a variation in chemical shift ($1{\cdot}15 \pm 0{\cdot}15 \times 10^{-2}$ ppm atmosphere^{-1} decrease in shielding with increased pressure). Hence in both cases, separation of the molecules either by heating the sample or decreasing its pressure results in an increased shielding of the ^{19}F nuclei involved: this is consistent with the decrease in the effects of the dispersion forces as one separates the molecules in the system[1]. Intramolecular interactions, similar to the above intermolecular interactions, have been observed in molecules which contain fluorine atoms in close proximity to other groups. If internal van der Waals forces between the atoms are large then the fluorine

TABLE 11.1 ^{19}F CHEMICAL SHIFTS MEASURED FROM CCl_3F USED AS AN INTERNAL AND AN EXTERNAL REFERENCE COMPOUND[2]

Pure compound	φ_{ext}	φ_{int}	Difference $\Delta\varphi$
$C_6H_5SO_2F$	−65·38	−65·497	+0·12
$CFBr_3$	− 8·85	− 7·397	−1·45
$BrCF_2CF_2Br$	+63·32	+63·403	+0·08
$C_6H_5CF_3$	+63·95	+63·747	+0·20
$CFCl_2CFCl_2$	+67·27	+67·750	−0·48
CF_3CO_2H	+78·45	+76·539	+1·91
C_6H_5F	+113·68	+113·123	+0·56
$(CF_2)_4$	+138·03		
$(C_2H_5)_3SiF$	+176·78	+176·24	+0·54
n-$C_6H_{13}F$	+219·42	+219·022	+0·40
CF_2Br_2		− 6·768	
CF_3CCl_3		+82·204	

φ_{ext} = chemical shift of pure liquids measured in ppm from CCl_3F external reference.
φ_{int} = chemical shift measured in ppm from CCl_3F internal reference and extrapolated to infinite dilution in CCl_3F.

TABLE 11.2 SOLVENT SHIFTS (MEASURED RELATIVE TO HEPTANE SOLUTIONS) IN THE ^{19}F RESONANCE SPECTRA OF SOME FLUORO-ORGANIC COMPOUNDS AT INFINITE DILUTION IN BROMOFORM AND CARBON TETRACHLORIDE[1]

Compound	$CHBr_3$		CCl_4		Compound	$CHBr_3$		CCl_4	
	δ	δ (corr.)	δ	δ (corr.)		δ	δ (corr.)	δ	δ (corr.)
$(CH_3)_3CF$	5·95	5·18	2·55	2·32	$C_6H_5CF_3$	4·03	3·26	1·70	1·47
$CF_2{=}CCl_2$	4·87	4·10	2·01	1·78	CCl_3F	2·83	2·06	1·30	1·07
CF_4	4·55	3·82	1·95	1·72	$(CCl_2F)_2$	2·71	1·94	1·05	0·82
$C_5H_{11}F$	4·53	3·76	1·88	1·64	CBr_3F	1·57	0·80	0·81	0·58
$(C_6H_5)_3CF$	4·03	3·26	1·70	1·47					

δ is measured in ppm from the corresponding ^{19}F resonance band in the spectrum of a dilute solution of the sample in heptane.
δ_{corr} is the solvent shift corrected for differences in bulk susceptibility.

nuclei are deshielded. Howard and co-workers[4] have estimated the effect of intermolecular dispersion forces on ^{19}F chemical shifts and their calculated chemical shift contributions are in semi-quantitative agreement with experimental values.

Glick and Ehrenson[3] have correlated "corrected" solvent shifts with molar polarisabilities of the solvent molecules for several halomethanes. However, Evans[1] has pointed out that the size of the solvent molecule will also play an important role in determining the solvent shifts and that the correlation observed by Glick and Ehrenson is due to the polarisabilities of the halomethanes being related in an approximate manner to their molar volumes. This is supported by the fact that many solvent shifts are temperature dependent whereas molar polarisabilities are independent of temperature. Howard *et al.*[4] have reached a similar conclusion from their theoretical study of intermolecular dispersion effects on ^{19}F chemical shifts.

All the ^{19}F chemical shifts quoted in this chapter have positive values when the absorption band is to high field of the reference signal.

11.2 Fluorine Chemical Shifts

It has been seen already that the dominant contribution to the shielding of fluorine nuclei arises in the second order paramagnetic term of Ramsey's expression for nuclear shielding (see Section 4.6). The diamagnetic contribution to ^{19}F shielding can account only for 1 per cent of the observed chemical shift in most fluorine-containing compounds, whilst the paramagnetic term has been shown by Saika and Slichter to be appreciable in all but the completely ionic fluoride ions[5]. The magnitude of this effect is dependent on the degree of ionic character in the bond and this has been shown to be consistent with observations of the ^{19}F chemical shifts found in an extensive series of binary fluorides[6] where the shielding of the fluorine atoms generally decreases with increase in the electronegativity of the attached atom[6]. An increase in the electronegativity of the attached atom decreases the ionic character of the bond between the fluorine atom and the atom concerned and thus increases the paramagnetic contribution to the shielding. However, it is possible to have a compound containing an ionic type fluorine atom (see nitrosyl fluoride, Section 11.20) which experiences a large paramagnetic deshielding effect due to the presence of a low-lying electronic energy level of suitable symmetry in the molecule[7]. Thus, other factors besides electronegativity of the substituents can influence the shielding of fluorine nuclei. Evans has suggested that intramolecular dispersion type forces of adjacent groups on neighbouring fluorine atoms can influence the shielding by increasing the paramagnetic contribution. The dispersion forces are largest when the groups concerned are in close proximity to the fluorine atom and consequently the effect will be most pronounced for bulky groups. It has been observed that the presence of bulky groups does indeed influence the shielding of a fluorine atom in a manner opposite to that expected on normal electronegativity grounds[8]. A further contribution to the shielding of fluorine nuclei is the occurrence of partial double bonded and ionic species in saturated halofluorocarbon derivatives[9,10]. These effects also give rise to chemical shifts for fluorine nuclei in the opposite direction to that expected from electronegativity considerations. However, it is possible to account for ^{19}F chemical shift contributions attributed to both bulky group dispersion forces and to the presence of double bond character in terms of the presence of low-lying electronic energy levels in the molecules. If these have the correct symmetry for mixing with the ground state they can introduce a large paramagnetic shielding effect. Gutowsky and Hoffman have also suggested that the use of higher energy orbitals in the hybridised orbitals of atoms attached to fluorine atoms results in increased shielding of the fluorine atom[6].

In fluorine-containing conjugated molecules, differences in ^{19}F nuclear shielding are determined largely by the π electron charge densities and the C—F bond orders[172, 173]. This is not the case for fluorine nuclei in the *ortho* position to substituents in aromatic rings, where van der Waals' dispersion effects appear to make appreciable shielding contributions[189].

Tiers has reported a deuterium isotopic effect on ^{19}F chemical shifts: the —CF_2D group in n-C_3F_7D is found to be shifted 0·60 ppm to higher fields of the resonance band of the group in the hydrogen-containing analogue, n-C_3F_7H. Gutowsky[12] attributes this increased shielding to the difference in the vibrational amplitude of the hydrogen and deuterium atoms in the molecule. Isotope effects have also been observed in the systems F—C—D (H)[179], F—^{13}C(^{12}C)[13, 80, 81], F—C—^{13}C(^{12}C)[13, 80, 81], F—^{29}Si(^{28}Si)[14], F—^{33}S(^{32}S)[180] and F—^{34}S(^{32}S)[180]. In every case the fluorine attached to the heavier nucleus is the more shielded. This is consistent with the predicted differences in zero point vibrational amplitudes: the heavier isotope has a smaller vibrational amplitude, which causes the electrons of the fluorine atom to be less polarised and results in increased ^{19}F shielding[180].

11.3 ^{19}F Spin–Spin Coupling Constants

In Chapter 5 it is shown that F—F indirect spin coupling is not controlled solely by the Fermi contact term but that the dipole effect can also make a significant contribution to the coupling. Consequently, theoretical predictions of coupling constants involving fluorine nuclei are difficult to make but in some simple cases a limited success has been achieved in this direction (see Section 5.8). Pople[164] has calculated F—F and H—F coupling constants in several fluorine-containing compounds and he has shown that although the electron–orbital interaction is appreciable it does not constitute the dominant part of the coupling constants. This is seen in Table 5.13 where the experimentally observed values[9, 19, 32–34] of J_{FF} and J_{HF} are compared with the estimated contribution from electron–orbital interaction (see Section 5.8.2).

Coupling constants involving a fluorine nucleus do not always decrease monotonically with the number of bonds separating the interacting nuclei. An example of this phenomenon is found in the ^{19}F resonance spectrum of $(CF_3)_2NCF_2CF_3$ where the fluorine nuclei of the CF_2 group are coupled very weakly with the adjacent CF_3 group ($J_{CF_2\text{-}CF_3} < 1$ cycle sec^{-1}) but strongly coupled to the more remote $(CF_3)_2N$ group ($J = 16$ cycles sec^{-1})[15]. A similar state of affairs has been observed in the ^{19}F spectrum of the CF_3 group in perfluoromethyl cyclohexane $C_6F_{11}CF_3$: the CF_3 group couples more strongly with the two neighbouring ring CF_2 groups than with the single fluorine nucleus on the substituted carbon atom as can be seen from the spectrum comprising a quintet of doublets shown in Fig. 11.2 ($J_{CF_3-CF_2} = 14{\cdot}2$ cycles sec^{-1} and $J_{CF_3CF} = 6{\cdot}1$ cycles sec^{-1})[16]. This apparent anomaly is also commonly found in fluoroalkanes[17], difluorobenzenes[19] and in cyclic butanes[18]. In the fluoroalkanes, this behaviour is a consequence of the small coupling which is usually observed between fluorine nuclei on adjacent carbon atoms in such molecules[17, 20]. Several examples of these very small F—F coupling constants are given in Table 11.3. It has been suggested that the magnitudes of F—F coupling constants depend

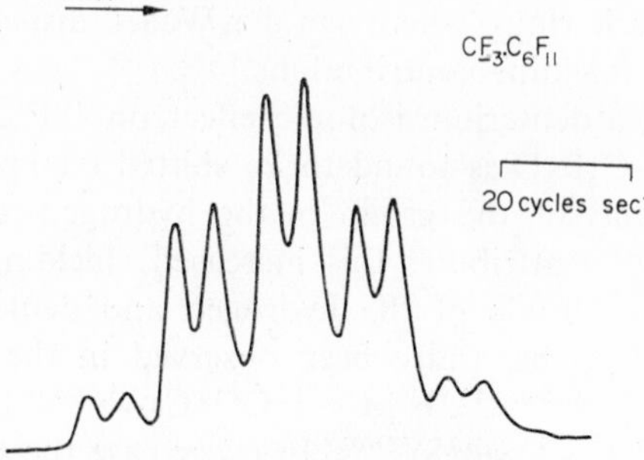

FIG. 11.2 The ^{19}F resonance spectrum at 56·4 Mc sec^{-1} of the CF_3 group of neat perfluoromethyl cyclohexane.

to a large extent on the spatial proximity of the interacting fluorine atoms[17] and that the small *vicinal* J values observed in perfluoroethyl groups reflect the large spatial separation of the methyl and methylene fluorine nuclei in this group (2·73 Å). Spin–spin coupling constants between fluorine nuclei in the 1,3-positions of a free carbon chain, where the fluorine nuclei are closer together in some conformations, have values between 7 and 10 cycles sec^{-1}: replacement of the intervening carbon atom with a nitrogen atom in the chain increases the coupling constant (10–17 cycles sec^{-1}). Fluorine nuclei in similar positions in ring compounds generally have smaller coupling constants. In substituted ethanes the coupling constants between fluorine nuclei on adjacent carbon atoms are much larger than those found in perfluoroethyl derivatives (for example, in CF_2Br CFBrCl, $J_{CF_2-CF} = 18$ cycles sec^{-1}). The steric interactions in such molecules were thought to force the fluorine atoms into closer proximity with each other, thereby increasing the F—F spin–spin coupling[17]. Evans[22] has determined the relative signs of F—F spin coupling constants in substituted fluoroethanes and he has found that in all cases the J_{FF}^{vic} coupling constant is of opposite sign to both J_{FF}^{gem} and $J_{FF}^{1,3}$. The evidence that F—F spin coupling operates via a spatial mechanism is based mainly on the observed relationship between the numerical values of the J_{FF} constants and the distance between the coupled fluorine nuclei. If account is taken of the different relative signs of the various

TABLE 11.3 ^{19}F SPIN–SPIN COUPLING CONSTANTS IN FLUOROALKANES[17]

Serial number	Compound	Coupling constants (cycles sec^{-1})
1†	$\begin{array}{l}CF_3-CF_2 \\ \qquad\qquad\searrow N-CF_3 \\ CF_3-CF_2 \nearrow \\ \ \ a \qquad\ b \qquad\qquad c\end{array}$	$J_{ab'} + J_{ab} = 10.2$ $J_{ac} = 6.8$ $J_{bc} = 15.8$
2†	$\begin{array}{l}CF_3-CF_2 \\ \qquad\qquad\searrow N-CF_2-CF_3 \\ CF_3-CF_2 \nearrow \\ \ \ a \qquad\ b \qquad\quad b \qquad a\end{array}$	$J_{ab} + J_{ab'} = 13.6$
3†	$CF_3-CF_2-O-CF_2-CF_3$ $\ \ a \qquad\ b \qquad\quad b \qquad\ a$	$J_{ab} + J_{ab'} = 3.4$
4[162]	CF_3-CF_2-COOH $\ \ a \qquad\ b$	$J_{ab} = 1.38$
5[15]	$\begin{array}{l}\qquad\qquad\qquad CF_3 \\ \qquad\qquad\quad \nearrow \\ CF_3-CF_2N \\ \qquad\qquad\quad \searrow \\ \qquad\qquad\qquad CF_3 \\ \ \ a \qquad\ b \qquad\ c\end{array}$	$J_{ab} \leqq 1$ $J_{ac} = 6$ $J_{bc} = 16$
6	$CF_3-CF_2-CF_2-NF_2$ $\ \ a \qquad\ b \qquad\ c \qquad\ d$	$J_{ab} \leqq 1$ $J_{ac} = 8.6$ $J_{ad} = 2.2$ $J_{bc} = 1$ $J_{bd} = 10.5$ $J_{cd} \leqq 1$
7	$CF_3-CF_2-CF_2-COOH$ $\ \ a \qquad\ b \qquad\ c$	$J_{ab} \leqq 1$ $J_{ac} = 9.9$ $J_{bc} \leqq 1$
8	$CF_3-CF_2-CF_2-COOCH_3$ $\ \ a \qquad\ b \qquad\ c$	$J_{ab} \leqq 1$ $J_{ac} = 9.0$ $J_{bc} \leqq 1$
9	$CF_3-CF_2-CFCH_3$ $\ \ a \qquad\ b \qquad\ c$	$J_{ab} \leqq 1$ $J_{ac} = 10.8$ $J_{bb'} = 270.4$ $J_{bc} = 14.6$ $J_{b'c} = 14.6$
10	$(CF_3)_3CF$ $\qquad a \quad\ b$	$J_{ab} = 4.0$
11	$CF_3-CF_2-CF_2H(D)$ $\ \ a \qquad\ b \qquad\ c$	$J_{ab} \leqq 1$ $J_{ac} \leqq 1$ $J_{bc} = 4.0\ \ 4.5$
12	$\begin{array}{l}\qquad\qquad CF_2-CF_2 \\ \qquad\quad \nearrow \qquad\qquad\ \searrow \\ CF_3-N \qquad\qquad\qquad\ O \\ \qquad\quad \searrow \qquad\qquad\ \nearrow \\ \qquad\qquad CF_2-CF_2 \\ \ \ a \qquad\qquad b \qquad\ c\end{array}$	$J_{ab} = 13.6$

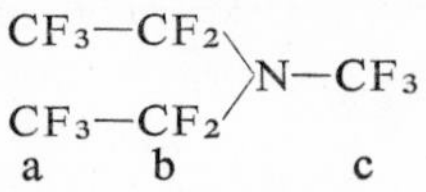

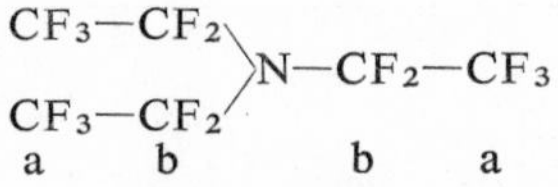

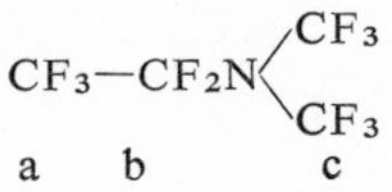

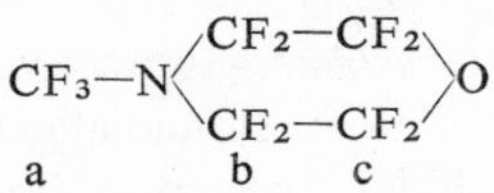

(continued)

Serial number	Compound	Coupling constants (cycles sec^{-1})
13	CF$_3$—N$\genfrac{}{}{0pt}{}{\diagup \text{CF}_2\text{—CF}_2 \diagdown}{\diagdown \text{CF}_2\text{—CF}_2 \diagup}CF_2$ a b c d	$J_{ab} = 16 \cdot 4$
14	CF$_3$—CF$_2$—N$\genfrac{}{}{0pt}{}{\diagup \text{CF}_2\text{—CF}_2}{\diagdown \text{CF}_2\text{—O}}$ a b c e d	$J_{ab} \leqq 1$ $J_{ac} = 6 \cdot 5$ $J_{ad} = 6 \cdot 5$ $J_{ae} \leqq 1$ $J_{bc} = 9 \cdot 9$ $J_{bd} = 9 \cdot 9$ $J_{be} \leqq 1$ $J_{cd} \leqq 1$ $J_{ce} \leqq 1$ $J_{de} = 3 \cdot 5$
15[163]	C$_6$H$_5$—CH—CH$_2$ \| \| CF$_2$—CF$_2$ a b	$J_{ab} \leqq 1$ $J_{ab'} \leqq 1$
16[34]	CF$_2$Br—CFBrCl a c b	$J_{ab} = 159$ $J_{ac} = 13$ $J_{bc} = 14$
17[46, 48]	CF$_2$Br—CFHCl a c b	$J_{ab} = 177$ $J_{ac} = 18$ $J_{bc} = 18$

† Because the CF$_2$ groups are strongly coupled, the CF$_3$ groups will only "see" the combined spin states of the CF$_2$ groups and it is possible only to obtain the sum of the two coupling constants ($J_{ab} + J_{ab'}$) from the multiplet splittings[21].

F—F coupling constants, one cannot correlate the coupling behaviour with internuclear distance in this simple manner. This suggests that the major F—F spin coupling mechanism proceeds through the bonds and not through space. Ng and Sederholm[198] have suggested that F—F coupling operates by both "through bonds" and "through space" mechanisms. For *geminal* coupling constants both mechanisms are thought to be important; for *vicinal* coupling the "through bond" term is considered to be dominant and for coupling between nuclei separated by more than three bonds the spatial mechanism is invoked to explain the coupling. The "through bond" contribution would be expected to decrease with increasing electronegativity of the substituents and this is found to be the case for J_{FF}^{vic} values in an extensive series of fluoroethanes.

Effect of Temperature on Coupling Constants. Gutowsky and co-workers[192] have shown that vibrational motions of atoms should affect coupling constants and therefore coupling constants would be expected to show an intrinsic varia-

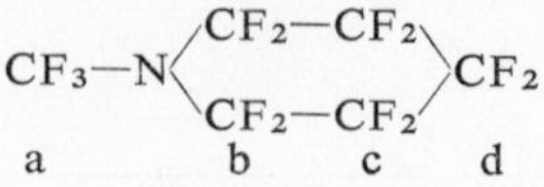

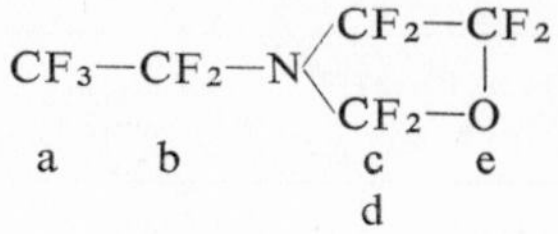

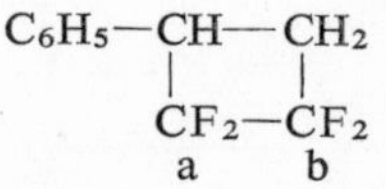

tion with temperature. For F—F and H—F coupling constants such variations have been observed[191]: in CF_3CFCl_2, where conformational effects will not influence the coupling constants, the J_{F-F} value decreases from 6·1 cycles sec^{-1} at -65°C to 5·6 cycles sec^{-1} at $+90$°C; likewise in CF_3CF_2COOH, J_{F-F} is 1·7 cycles sec^{-1} at -29°C and 1·3 at $+85$°C. Conformational studies based on the measurement of variations of coupling constants with temperature invariably assume that the coupling constants in the various isomers are temperature independent and the results obtained from such studies may be subject to appreciable errors from this source. Similar effects have been observed in the case of fluoroalkenes[191] such as $CF_2{=}CFCOF$ where two NMR-distinguishable isomers (I and II) can be frozen out at -105°C

(I) 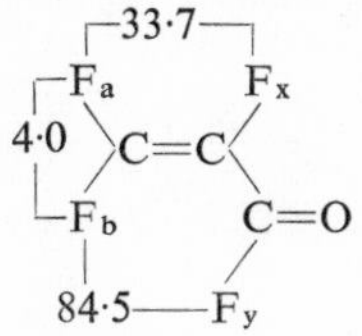

cycles sec^{-1}

(II) 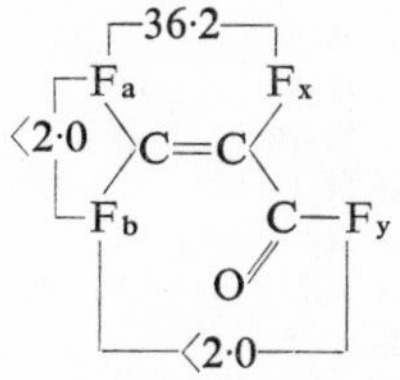

cycles sec^{-1}

The J_{ab} and J_{ax} values observed at -105°C for each isomer are smaller than their averaged values at room temperature ($J_{ab} = 6·0$ and $J_{ax} = 36·8$ cycles sec^{-1}) which can only be explained by assuming that the coupling constants in the individual isomers show an intrinsic variation with temperature[191]. Solvent variations can also affect F—F coupling constants[201].

Long Range ^{19}F *Coupling Constants.* Many long range coupling constants involving ^{19}F nuclei have been reported [190]: several are given in Table 11.4.

A long range H—F spin coupling constant between nuclei separated by five saturated bonds has been observed in the spectra of 1,1-difluoro-2,2-dichloro-3-phenyl-3-methylcyclobutane (I)[37]

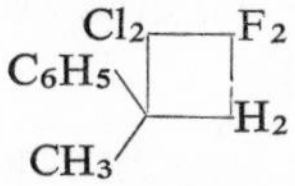

(I)

The two fluorine atoms are non-equivalent and one of them couples with the hydrogen nuclei of the CH_3 group at the 3-position ($J_{HF} = 2$ cycles sec^{-1}). By examining the spectra of the molecule labelled stereospecifically with deuterium at the 4-position, one can suggest that the interacting fluorine nucleus is probably *cis* to the methyl group. Other workers[38] have measured long range H—F coupling constants across 5 and 6 saturated bonds in steroids of the type

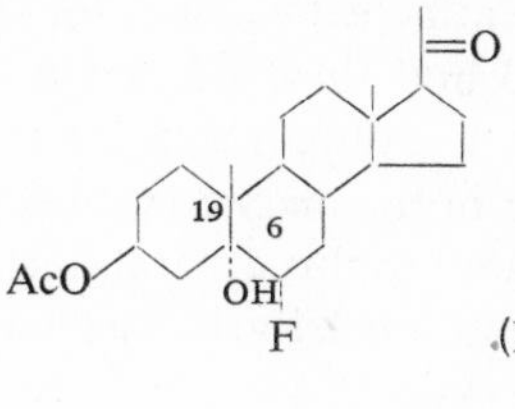

(II)

In the 6-β-fluoro steroid (II), a J_{HF} coupling constant of 4·3 cycles sec^{-1} is observed between the fluorine nucleus and the angular methyl group at C_{19}: again the interacting groups have a *cis* relationship to each other. Hence, the H—F long range coupling mechanism in saturated systems might well involve stereospecific interactions.

TABLE 11.4 LONG RANGE ^{19}F COUPLING CONSTANTS[190]

Compound	Coupling constants (cycles sec^{-1})		
	H—C—C—F	H—C—C—C—F	F—F
$CH_3C(O)F$	6·9		
CF_3CH_2Cl	8·5		
CF_3CH_2Br	9·0		
CF_3CH_2OH	8·9		
CF_3CH_3	12·8		
CF_2ClCH_3	14·8		
$(CH_3)_3CF$	20·4		
p-$CH_3C(O)C_6H_4F$	8·7	5·5	
p-$NO_2C_6H_4F$	8·2	4·8	
p-$CH_3OC_6H_4F$	7·8	4·8	
p-$CF_3C_6H_4F$	8·5	5·1	
p-BrC_6H_4F	8·1	4·9	
CF_3—C≡C—CF_3			2·2
$(CF_3)_2O$			8·0
$(CF_3)_3N$			10·8
CF_3=SF_2			10·7

Many F—F long range coupling constants have been detected between nuclei separated by five saturated bonds: a F—F coupling constant between nuclei separated by six bonds has been found in the ^{19}F spectrum of $(CF_3)_2NCF_2CFBrCF_3$ ($J_{F-C-N-C-C-CF}$ = 1·7 cycles sec^{-1})[174].

11.4 BINARY FLUORIDES

As we have already seen, an increase in the electronegativity of an atom attached directly to the fluorine atom in binary fluorides causes a decrease in the ^{19}F nuclear shielding if we consider a series of elements which are in the same oxidation state and which belong to the same group of the Periodic Table. Examination of the list of ^{19}F chemical shifts for several binary fluorides given in Table 11.5 supports this statement. Plots of the ^{19}F chemical shifts against the electronegativities of the attached element for several series of binary fluorides are shown in Fig. 11.3 and they indicate a fairly linear relationship in nearly all cases[6]. Within each group, increasing the nuclear charge of the element M results in a decrease in the magnetic shielding of the attached fluorine atom. There are a few exceptions to this general rule, an example being the molecule SF_6 in which the fluorine nuclei are shielded more than those in SeF_6.

In some cases it is possible to confirm the molecular structure of a binary fluoride from its ^{19}F resonance spectrum. Iodine pentafluoride was shown to have a tetragonal pyramid structure, its ^{19}F resonance spectrum consisting of two absorption bands in the intensity ratio 4 : 1. This supports the structure found by other methods(40). BrF_5 gave a similar ^{19}F spectrum to IF_5 thus indicating these molecules to have similar structures: in both cases fine structure due to spin–spin coupling is observed on the absorption bands and the weaker of the two components occurs at the lower value of the applied magnetic field.

TABLE 11.5 ^{19}F CHEMICAL SHIFTS IN BINARY FLUORIDES(6, 41)

Compound	$\delta_{CF_3COOH\,ext}$(41) ppm	$\delta_{F_2\,ext}$(6) ppm	M—F coupling	
			M	J_{MF} cycles sec^{-1}
NF_3	−219	+285·0	^{14}N	160
ClF_3	−193, −81	+343·4		
BrF_3	−54·3	+461·1		
PF_3	−42·3	+463·7	^{31}P	1441
AsF_3	−35·0	+469·1		
SbF_3	−23·9	+507·9		
BF_3	+54·2	+555·5	^{11}B	10
SF_4	−195, −148			
SeF_4	−141			
TeF_4	−51·4			
CF_4	−11·9	+491·0		
BF_4^-	+71·0			
SiF_4	+833	+598·9	^{29}Si	178
GeF_4	+99·0	+608·8		
BrF_5	−349, −219	+290·5, +152·9		
IF_5	−138, −95·8	+418·2, +368·9		
PF_5	−0·7	+502·1	^{31}P	916
AsF_5	−11·3			
SbF_5	+6·8, +26·2, +52	+537·3		
MoF_6	−355		^{95}Mo, ^{97}Mo	44
WF_6	−242		^{183}W	48
SeF_6	−128	+372·7	^{77}Se	1400
SF_6	−127	+375·6		
TeF_6	−20·6	+485·9	^{125}Te	3688
			^{123}Te	3052
PF_6^-	−11·6		^{31}P	710
SiF_6^{2-}	+49·8		^{29}Si	110
AsF_6^-	−18·1		^{75}As	930
SbF_6^-	+32·3		^{121}Sb	1843
BeF_2		+599·1		
F^-		+548·2		
F_2		0·0		
HF		+625·0		
IF_7		+261·5		

From consideration of the above results an approximate conversion between the two reference scales is obtained $\delta_{CF_3COOH\,ext} = \delta_{F_2\,ext} - 504$ ppm.

The pentagonal bipyramidal structure of iodine heptafluoride[40] could not be confirmed unequivocally due to overlap of the different fluorine absorption multiplets (J_{IF} = 2100 cycles sec^{-1} [200]).

By changing the oxidation state of the element attached to the fluorine in binary fluorides, changes in the shielding of the fluorine atoms are observed (see the chemical shifts of the trihalides and pentahalides of phosphorus and antimony given in Table 11.5). The increase in shielding of fluorine nuclei attached to the atom in the higher valency state has been attributed to the need for the use of higher energy *s* and *d* orbitals in addition to *p* orbitals in the hybridised states of the phosphorus and antimony atoms in the higher valency state.

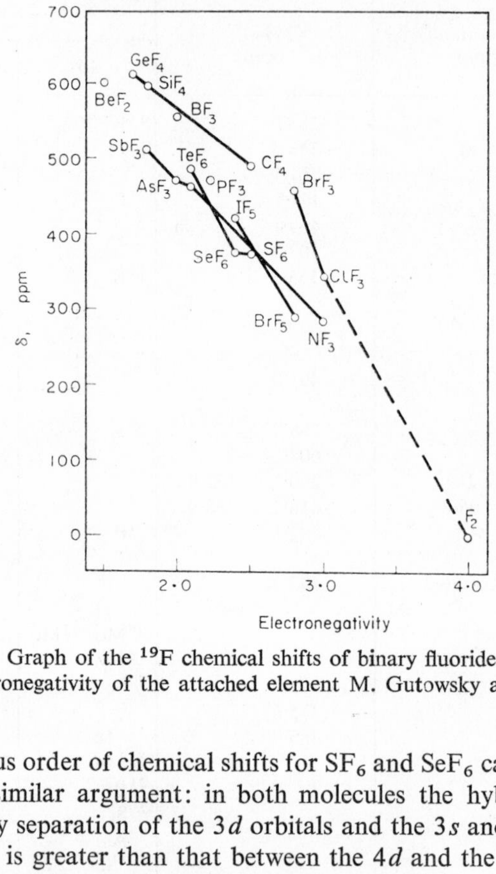

FIG. 11.3 Graph of the ^{19}F chemical shifts of binary fluorides, MF_x, against the electronegativity of the attached element M. Gutowsky and Hoffman[6].

The anomalous order of chemical shifts for SF_6 and SeF_6 can also be explained by use of a similar argument: in both molecules the hybridisation is d^2sp^3 but the energy separation of the $3d$ orbitals and the $3s$ and $3p$ orbitals of the sulphur atom is greater than that between the $4d$ and the $4s$ and $4p$ orbitals of the selenium, which results in the fluorine atoms in SF_6 being more shielded than those in SeF_6. It should be mentioned that halogen fluorides do not conform to these ideas since they have lower ^{19}F shielding in the higher oxidation states[6].

The lower shielding of the apex fluorine atom in BrF_5 and IF_5 is attributed to the fact that the apex bond is almost completely *p* in character whilst the other bonds are d^2p^2 hybridised.

Muetterties and Phillips[41], in their NMR investigation of a series of MF_x compounds, have repeated much of the early work on binary fluorides and a summary of their results is given in Table 11.5. Where their studies overlap those of previous workers[6, 9, 42] excellent agreement is observed. By examining the ^{19}F resonance spectra of SF_4, SeF_4 and TeF_4 over a range of temperature it was established that exchange of fluorine atoms was taking place in each compound at room temperature, with the rates of fluorine exchange being in the order $SF_4 < SeF_4 < TeF_4$. The proposed mechanism for the exchange of fluorine atoms involves the formation of dimers as intermediates.

Shoolery[43] has examined UF_6 and found the fluorine nuclei to be much less shielded than those in F_2 (330 ppm to low fields of the F_2 absorption band): this is attributed to the large value of the paramagnetic contribution which results from the small electronic excitation energy ΔE for uranium hexafluoride[44].

11.5 Halofluorohydrocarbons

Several workers have examined such hydrocarbons and in all cases anomalous ^{19}F chemical shifts have been obtained[9, 10]. Successive fluorination of methane would be expected to result in a decrease in the ionic character of the C—F bonds and a corresponding decrease in the shielding of the ^{19}F nuclei. Examination of the ^{19}F chemical shifts of the fluoromethanes given in Table 11.6 shows that such a state of affairs prevails. Measurements of the ^1H spectra of these

Table 11.6 ^{19}F Chemical Shifts and Spin Coupling Constants in Fluoromethanes[9, 158]

Compound	^{19}F Chemical shifts (ppm)		Coupling constants (cycles sec^{-1})		
	$\delta^{(9)}_{CF_4\,ext}$	$\varphi^{(158)}_{CCl_3F\,int}$	$J^{(158)}_{HF}$	$J^{(158)}_{^{13}CF}$	$J^{(158)}_{^{13}CH}$
CH_3F	+210·0	+271·9	46·4	157·5	149·1
CH_2F_2	+80·9	+143·4	50·2	235	184·5
CHF_3	+18·2	+78·6	79·7	274·3	239·1
CF_4	0·0	+63·3	—	259·2	—

$\delta_{CF_3COOH\,ext} = \delta_{CF_4\,ext} - 11{\cdot}9$ ppm.

Table 11.7 ^{19}F Chemical Shifts in Fluorochloromethanes[9]

Compound	Chemical shift $\delta_{CF_4\,ext}$ ppm
$CFCl_3$	−76·7
CF_2Cl_2	−60·4
CF_3Cl	−36·8
CF_4	0·0

$\delta_{CF_3COOH\,ext} = \delta_{CF_4\,ext} - 11{\cdot}9$ (very approximate conversion).

compounds indicates that the ionic character of the C—H bond decreases as that of the C—F bond increases[9].

Successive fluorination of tetrachloromethane would be expected to be accompanied by similar changes in ^{19}F chemical shifts since chlorine, like hydrogen, is less electronegative than fluorine. It can be seen from the data in Table 11.7 that the fluorine nuclei in this series of fluorochloromethanes are shielded in the opposite manner to that predicted by electronegativity considerations. Furthermore, $CFCl_3$ would be expected to have a ^{19}F chemical shift intermediate between CFH_3 and CF_4 (i.e. CFF_3) on simple inductive grounds. To explain these anomalous chemical shifts it was thought necessary to postulate the presence of contributions to the molecular structures of the halomethanes of double bonded structures and ionic species of the type

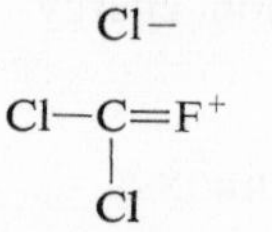

$$
\begin{array}{cc}
\overset{\displaystyle Cl-}{\underset{\displaystyle Cl}{\overset{|}{Cl-C=F^{+}}}} \ (I) & \qquad \text{and} \qquad \overset{\displaystyle Cl+}{\underset{\displaystyle Cl}{\overset{\|}{Cl-C \quad F^{-}}}} \ (II)
\end{array}
$$

It was assumed that fluorine atoms are more able to form double bonds than chlorine atoms, thus type I structures would play a more important part than other types of structure in the overall structure of the molecule. In ordinary fluoromethanes, the inductive effects are large and dominate the shielding of the ^{19}F nuclei in these molecules. Inductive effects are much smaller in fluorohalomethanes and consequently the contribution of double bonded structures to the overall molecular structure could become the dominant shielding factor for the fluorine nuclei. This would result in the C—F bonds decreasing in

TABLE 11.8 ^{19}F CHEMICAL SHIFTS IN
FLUOROCHLOROALKANES[10]

Compound	$\delta_{CF_3COOH\ ext}$ ppm
CCl_3F	−78·6
CF_3COOH	0·0
$F_3C\diagdown$	+7·33
$\quad CCl_2F$	−0·33
$CClF_2—CClF_2$	−6·00
$Cl_2FC\diagdown$	−6·00
$\quad CClF_2$	−10·1
$CF_3\diagdown$	−5·33
$\quad CCl_2$	
$\qquad \diagdown CClF$	+42·4
$\qquad\qquad \diagdown CF_3$	−3·73
CF_3	−6·00
\mid	+109·6
CF	+47·9
$F_2C\ \ CF_2$	
$\mid \quad \mid$	
$F_2C\ \ CF$	
$\diagdown C \diagup CF_3$	
F_2

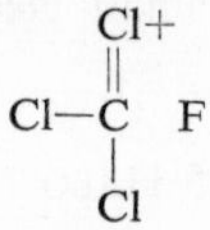

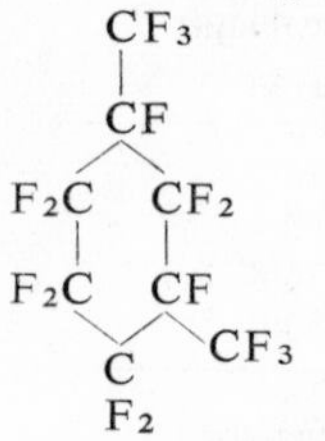

ionicity as the fluorine substitution decreases. However, it is more likely that the increased availability of low-lying excited states in CH_3X molecules upon substitution of a F or a Cl atom for a H atom causes the deshielding of the fluorine nuclei (see Section 11.8)[56].

Smith and Smith[10] have examined a more general series of fluorocarbons and observed similar results for the fluorochloromethanes (see Table 11.8 in which the ^{19}F chemical shifts are measured from trifluoroacetic acid external reference). The ^{19}F shielding constants increase with increase of the total electronegativity of the atoms on the nearest carbon atom, which indicates that simple inductive effects are not controlling the shielding of the fluorine nuclei in these molecules.

11.6 Substituted Fluoroalkanes

Many substituted fluoroethanes have been examined by NMR in connection with investigations of hindered rotation about the C—C bond (see Section 9.5.5). Table 11.9 contains typical ^{19}F chemical shifts found in molecules of this type[20, 45-49]. The presence of a hydrogen atom on the same carbon

Table 11.9 ^{19}F Chemical Shifts in Fluoroethanes[49]

Compound	Chemical shifts (ppm)†					
	CF_3		CF_2		CF	
	$\delta^{ext}_{CFCl_3}$	$\delta^{ext}_{CF_3COOH}$	$\delta^{ext}_{CFCl_3}$	$\delta^{ext}_{CF_3COOH}$	$\delta^{ext}_{CFCl_3}$	$\delta^{ext}_{CF_3COOH}$
CF_3CFCl_2	85·8	5·9			77·8	−2·1
$CF_3CFClBr$	84·3	4·4			77·0	−2·9
$CF_2ClCFCl_2$			68·5	−11·4	72·5	−7·4
$CF_2BrCHFCl$			63·5	−16·4	146·0	66·1
$CF_2BrCHFBr$			61·0	−18·9	148·0	68·1
$CF_2ClCHFBr$			67·0	−12·9	152·0	72·1
CF_2BrCH_2Cl			54·5	−25·4		
CF_2ClCF_2Cl			72·5	− 7·4		
$CF_2BrCHBrC_6H_5$				−26·5‡		
$CF_2ClCHClC_6H_5$				−17·6‡		

† The chemical shifts were measured in ppm from $CFCl_3$ external reference and extrapolated to the CF_3COOH external reference scale using the conversion.

$$\delta_{CF_3COOH\,ext} = \delta_{CFCl_3\,ext} - 79{\cdot}9 \text{ ppm}.$$

‡ Obtained from reference 34 and extrapolated to the CF_3COOH external reference scale from CF_2BrCF_2Br reference.

atom as the fluorine atom causes the latter to be well shielded. In Table 11.10, the J_{HF} and J_{FF} coupling constants observed in several fluorinated ethanes are given. Coupling between *geminal* fluorine atoms varies over a wide range of values (152 to 343 cycles sec^{-1}) in the molecules considered and these coupling constants do not depend in a regular manner on the electronegativity of the *geminal* substituent[171]. It is known, however, that the Fermi contact term does not dominate such fluorine–fluorine spin–spin interactions. Elleman and co-workers[50, 51] have examined the NMR spectra of several liquid fluorocarbons and their results, obtained from a first order analysis of the spectra, are summarised in Tables 11.11 and 11.12. Spin coupling constants between hydrogen

TABLES 11.10 F–F AND H–F COUPLING CONSTANTS IN SUBSTITUTED ETHANES

Compound	*Geminal* coupling constants (cycles sec^{-1})			*Vicinal* coupling constants (cycles sec^{-1})			
	F–F	H–F		F–F	F–F′	F–H	F′–H
CH_2BrCF_2Br[48]						22†	4†
CH_2ClCF_2Br[49]						21†	3†
CH_2ClCF_2Cl[48]						16†	6†
$CH_2ICF_2[C_2F_5]$[48]						29†	6†
$CF_2ClCFCl_2$[49]				9·5			
$CF_2BrCFBr_2$[47]				19			
$CF_2BrCHFBr$[49]	174	48		24	21	3·2	9·1
$CF_2BrCHFCl$[46, 48]	177	48		18	18	3·5	6·3
$CF_2BrCFClBr$[34]	159			13	14		
$CF_2ClCHFBr$[49]	173	48		20	19	3·9	7·1
$CF_2CCHClC_6H_5$[34]	158					6	9
$CF_2BrCHClBr$[34]	154				10	7	
$CF_2BrCHBrC_6H_5$[34]	152					6	15
$CF_2BrCBr(CN)Me$[45]	155						
$CF_2(SiCl_3)CFClH$[171]	343	48·1		16·8	16·8	6·6	10·1
$CF_2(CF_3)CFICl$[20]	270·4						

† These values have been calculated by assuming $J_{FF} = 175$ and $J_{HH} < 20$ cycles sec^{-1}.

TABLE 11.11 ^{19}F CHEMICAL SHIFTS AND SPIN COUPLING CONSTANTS FOR A SERIES OF HALOGENATED ETHANES[50]

Compound	Chemical shifts (ppm)†		Coupling constants (cycles sec^{-1})				
	δ_{F_1}	δ_{F_2}	$J_{F_1F_2}$	$J_{H_1F_1}$	$J_{H_1F_2}$	$J_{H_2F_1}$	$J_{H_2F_2}$
CH_3CH_2F		+76·95			25·7		47·5
CHF_2CH_3	−25·91			57·2		20·8	
CF_3CH_3	−73·47					12·8	
CF_2ClCH_3	−90·82					15·0	
CF_2BrCH_3	−98·86					15·9	
CF_3CH_2Cl	−63·98					8·4	
CF_3CH_2Br	−67·47					8·9	
CF_3CF_2H	−47·76	+3·88	2·8			2·6	52·6
CF_3CFH_2	−56·61	+105·4	15·5			8·0	45·5
CF_2HCF_2H	+2·21	+2·21		52·1		4·8	

All samples examined as pure liquids.

† Chemical shifts measured in ppm from octafluorocyclobutane external reference.

$$\delta_{CF_3COOH\,ext} = \delta_{C_4F_8\,ext} + 59 \text{ (approximate conversion).}$$

TABLE 11.12 ^{19}F CHEMICAL SHIFTS AND SPIN COUPLING CONSTANTS OF HALOGENATED PROPANES[51]

Compound	Chemical shifts (ppm)†			Coupling constants (cycles sec^{-1})										
	δ_{F_1}	δ_{F_2}	δ_{F_3}	$J_{F_1H_2}$	$J_{H_1F_1}$	$J_{H_1F_2}$	$J_{H_1F_3}$	$J_{F_1H_3}$	$J_{F_2H_3}$	$J_{F_1F_3}$	$J_{F_1F_2}$	$J_{F_2F_3}$	$J_{H_3F_3}$	$J_{H_3F_2}$
$CHF_2CF_2CHF_2$	+3·27	−0·20	+3·27		52·7	8·5					4·2			
$CF_3CH_2CF_3$	−71·69		−71·69	9·2										
$CF_3CHClCF_3$	−65·22		−65·22		5·9									
$CF_3CH_2CH_3$	−66·21			10·6				0·4						
$CHF_2CF_2CH_2F$	+3·24	−7·54	+109·01		52·6	4·2	1·5	1·4				13·9	45·9	12·0
$CF_3CF_2CH_2F$	−51·00	−7·97	+108·17							7·9		15·2	46·0	11·7
$CF_3CF_2CHF_2$	−52·22	−1·98	+2·86							7·3		4·5	52·1	4·5
$CF_2ClCF_2CH_2F$	−65·64	−13·76	+103·57					1·0		7·7	2·8	15·1	45·9	11·8
$CF_2BrCF_2CH_2F$	−71·25	−16·60	+105·15					0·9		7·7	3·9	15·5	46·0	11·7
CHF_2CF_2CHFBr	{ +0·66	−9·23	+24·22		52·9	4·6			7·4			16·7	48·7	
	{ +1·17													
CHF_2CF_2CHFCl	{ +1·66	−5·89	+20·77		52·3	4·6			7·2				47·5	
	{ +1·97													

† Chemical shifts measured in ppm from octafluorocyclobutane external reference. $\delta_{CF_3COOH\,ext} = \delta_{C_4F_8\,ext} + 59$ (approximate conversion).

and fluorine nuclei within the same substituted methyl group are approximately 50 cycles sec^{-1}. $J_{F_1H_2}$ values for the series of molecules CF_3CH_2X increase progressively from 8·0 to 12·8 cycles sec^{-1} for the series of substituents X = F, Cl, Br, H. In the series $CF_2X\,CH_3$ the $J_{F_1H_2}$ values increase progressively from 12·8 to 20·8 cycles sec^{-1} for the substituents X = F, Cl, Br, H. Use has been made of the spin coupling constants found in the simple ethanes to assist in assigning the more complex spectra of fluorinated propanes (see Table 11.12), butanes, pentanes, hexanes and octanes[51].

An investigation of the NMR spectra of difluoromethyl (CHF_2X) groups in a wide variety of molecules has revealed that the J^{gem}_{HF} coupling constants in such species increase markedly with increase in the electronegativity of the substituent X (J^{gem}_{HF} values in the range 53·4–75·6 cycles sec^{-1} were observed)[25]. The electronegativity of the first atom of the substituent appears to be mainly responsible for the variations in the magnitude of H—F *geminal* coupling constants.

11.6.1 Relative Signs of ^{19}F *Spin Coupling Constants in Fluoroalkanes*

In order to further the theoretical understanding of H—F and F—F spin coupling constants it is necessary to know the relative signs of such coupling constants in various molecules. The advent of double irradiation techniques has enabled this information to be elucidated for the coupling constants in

TABLE 11.13 RELATIVE SIGNS OF ^{19}F SPIN COUPLING CONSTANTS IN FLUOROALKANES AND FLUOROALKENES[22–24, 167]

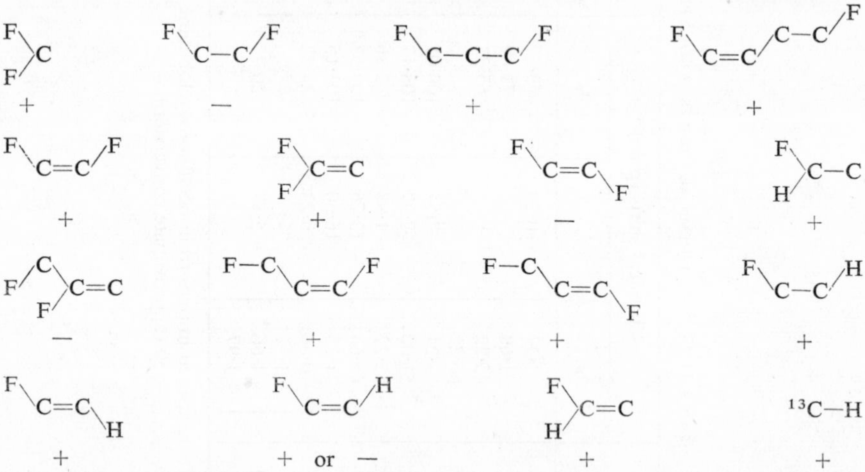

The signs given in this table are absolute providing $J_{^{13}C-H}$ is positive. If $J_{^{13}C-F}$ is opposite in sign[168] to $J_{^{13}C-H}$, then the following assignments can be made[80, 169],

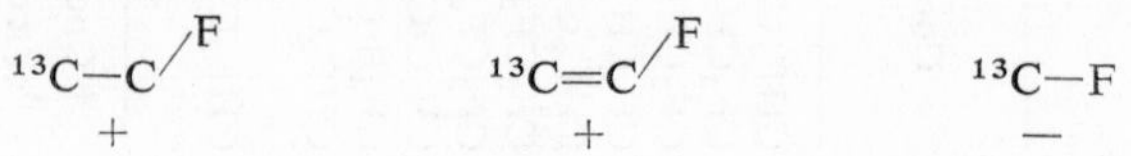

many common molecules, and a summary of the relative signs of ^{19}F coupling constants measured by several workers is given in Table 11.13[22, 23, 24, 167]. The double irradiation spin decoupling experiments have shown that the two H—F coupling constants in 1,1,1,2-tetrafluoroethane, CF_3CFH_2, have the same sign. Similar results are found for $CHFBrCF_2Br$ and $CF_3CF_2CHF_2$[22]. This result is opposite to that found for H—H and F—F coupling where the *geminal* and *vicinal* coupling constants are opposite in sign. Elleman and Manatt[23] have confirmed that J_{FF}^{gem} has the opposite sign to both J_{FF}^{gauche} and J_{FF}^{trans} in the ^{19}F spectrum of $CFBr_2CF_2Br$ measured at -110°C. In $CF_3CF_2CF_2Br$ and $CF_3CF_2CF_2I$ they find that $J_{F_1F_3}$ has an opposite sign to both $J_{F_1F_2}$ and $J_{F_2F_3}$[160].

11.6.2 NMR Parameters Obtained from Conformational Studies of Substituted Ethanes

From a study of the variation in coupling constants with change of temperature for several substituted ethanes, Gutowsky and co-workers[26] have been able to obtain a good deal of information associated with the conformations of such molecules. Table 5.19 gives a list of H—F and F—F spin coupling constants for nuclei in various configurations in the ethanes examined. It is seen that for the *vicinal* HF and FF coupling constants, $J_{trans} > J_{gauche}$. Some of the *trans* and *gauche* FF coupling constants have opposite signs, which supports the "cancellation" theory for the observation of small F—F coupling constants in perfluoroethyl groups[15, 27].

Sederholm and co-workers[28] have examined the ^{19}F resonance spectra of the substituted ethane CFClBrCFClBr at a series of temperatures in the range 177 to 300°K. From the spectral changes, the room temperature spectrum is shown to be a superposition of the rapidly rotating *dl* and *meso* isomers of the compound and the low temperature spectra to be a superposition of spectra from the various rotamers of the two isomers. They observed that the fluorine nucleus *gauche* to a Br and a F atom is least shielded (0·00 ppm), while the shielding of a fluorine nucleus *gauche* to a F and a Cl atom (6·5 ppm) is greater than one *gauche* to a Br and a Cl atom (3·8 ppm). These results might be significant in that the variations in shielding are probably spatial in origin since the fluorine in all the molecules will experience similar inductive effects.

11.7 Fluorocarbon Compounds Containing Nitrogen

Tables 11.14 and 11.15 summarise the ^{19}F resonance data obtained for a series of fluorocarbon nitrogen compounds[52, 53, 58]. Included in Table 11.14 are the ^{19}F chemical shifts of two fluoropyrimidines[53]: it is often possible to characterise substituted fluoropyrimidines from their ^{19}F resonance spectra.

11.8 Other Fluorocarbon Derivatives

Muller, Lauterbur and Svatos[54] have examined the ^{19}F resonance spectra of a large number of fluorocarbon derivatives and their results along with those of other workers[159] are summarised in Tables 11.16 and 11.17, the

Table 11.14 ^{19}F Chemical Shifts of Fluorocarbon Nitrogen Compounds[52, 53]

Compound		Intensity	Chemical shift	Fine structure
$(CF_3CO)_2NCH_3$			5·57	2 non-equiv. quartets
$CH_3CON(CF_3)_2$			−21·3	Singlet
$C_6H_5CON(CF_3)_2$			−21·5	Singlet
$CO(CF_2)_3CONC_6H_5$ (a b)	a	1	42·1	Triplet
	b	2	57·1	Quintet
$CO(CF_2)_3CONCO(CF_2)_3CONCO(CF_2)_3CO$ (c d, a b)	a	2	41·7	Singlet
	b	1	46·7	Singlet
	c	2	49·0	Triplet
	d	4	55·6	Quintet
$(CF_3CO)_4N_2$		1	−2·1	Singlet
		1	2·0	Singlet
		1	4·1	Singlet
		1	10·6	Singlet
$BrCF_2CF_2CF_2CONCO$ (a b c)	a	1	−14·2	Triple triplet
	b	1	40·1	Triplet
	c	1	38·7	Triplet
$BrCF_2CF_2CF_2CONH_2$ (a b c)	a	1	−15·1	Triple triplet
	b	1	42·1	Triplet
	c	1	42·2	Triplet
2,4,6-trifluoropyrimidine[53] 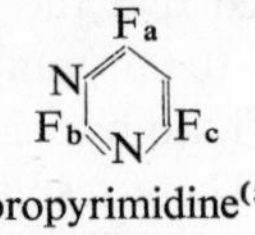	a, c	2	−22·9	
	b	1	−35·6	
Tetrafluoropyrimidine[53] 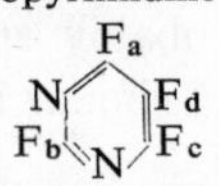	a, c	2	−6·3	
	b	1	−31·3	
	d	1	95·2	

Chemical shifts were measured in ppm from CF_3COOH external reference.

^{19}F chemical shifts having been measured from trifluoroacetic acid external reference.

The groups $—CF_3$, $>CF_2$ and $\rangle CF$ are found to have absorption bands which are separated by large chemical shifts, the characteristic regions over

TABLE 11.15 ^{19}F CHEMICAL SHIFTS OF CYCLIC AND NON-CYCLIC NITROGEN COMPOUNDS[58]

Nitrogen-containing compounds	Group	Chemical shift	Fine structure
A. Cyclic			
$\begin{array}{c} \text{b} \quad \text{c} \\ \text{a} \quad /\text{CF}_2\text{CF}_2\backslash \\ \text{CF}_2\!\!\!\big\langle \qquad \big\rangle\!\text{NF} \\ \backslash\text{CF}_2\text{CF}_2/ \end{array}$	$CF_2(a)$	56·7	a
	$CF_2(b)$	54·5	a
	$CF_2(c)$	32·7	a
	NF	36·6	a
$\begin{array}{c} \text{b} \quad \text{c} \\ \text{a} /\text{CF}_2\text{CF}_2\backslash \qquad /\text{CF}_2\text{CF}_2\backslash \\ \text{CF}_2\!\big\langle \quad \big\rangle\!\text{N}\!-\!\text{N}\!\big\langle \quad \big\rangle\!\text{CF}_2 \\ \backslash\text{CF}_2\text{CF}_2/ \qquad \backslash\text{CF}_2\text{CF}_2/ \end{array}$	$CF_2(a)$	56·2	a
	$CF_2(b)$	55·3	a
	$CF_2(c)$	19·1	a
$\begin{array}{c} \text{b} \quad \text{c} \\ \text{a} /\text{CF}_2\text{CF}_2\backslash \\ \text{CF}_2\!\big\langle \qquad \big\rangle\!\text{NCF}_3 \\ \backslash\text{CF}_2\text{CF}_2/ \end{array}$	$CF_2(a)$	57·8	a
	$CF_2(b)$	55·2	a
	$CF_2(c)$	16·8	Quartet
	CF_3	−25·3	Quintet
$\begin{array}{c} \text{a} \quad \text{b} \\ /\text{CF}_2\text{CF}_2\backslash \\ \text{O}\!\big\langle \qquad \big\rangle\!\text{NCF}_3 \\ \backslash\text{CF}_2\text{CF}_2/ \end{array}$	$CF_2(a)$	9·6	a
	$CF_2(b)$	17·0	Quartet
	CF_3	−24·0	Quintet
$\begin{array}{c} \text{a} \quad \text{b} \\ /\text{CF}_2\text{CF}_2\backslash \\ \text{O}\!\big\langle \qquad \big\rangle\!\text{NF} \\ \backslash\text{CF}_2\text{CF}_2/ \end{array}$	$CF_2(a)$	4·8	a
	$CF_2(b)$	33·7	a
	NF	36·0	a
$\begin{array}{c} \text{a} \ \text{CF}_2\!-\!\text{O} \\ \quad\ \mid \qquad \mid \\ \text{b} \ \text{CF}_2 \ \text{CF}_2 \ \text{c} \\ \qquad \backslash \quad / \\ \qquad \text{NCF}_2\text{CF}_3 \\ \qquad\quad \text{d} \end{array}$	$CF_2(a)$	14·9	a
	$CF_2(b)$	22·2	Quintet
	$CF_2(c)$	−20·6	a
	$CF_2(d)$	8·6	Quintet
	CF_3	10·6	Triplet
B. Non-cyclic			
$\begin{array}{c} \text{a} \quad \text{b} \quad \text{c} \quad \text{d} \qquad\quad \text{e} \\ (\text{CF}_3\text{CF}_2\text{CF}_2\text{CF}_2)_2\text{NCF}_3 \end{array}$	$CF_3(a)$	5·0	Triplet
	$CF_3(e)$	−26·5	a
	$CF_2(b)$	25·0	a
	$CF_2(c)$	21·9	a
	$CF_2(d)$	10·0	a
$\begin{array}{c} \text{a} \qquad\ \text{b} \\ (\text{CF}_3\text{CF}_2)_2\text{NCF}_2 \end{array}$	$CF_3(a)$	7·7	a
	$CF_3(b)$	−25·3	a
	CF_2	16·8	a
$\begin{array}{c} \text{a} \quad \text{b} \\ \text{CF}_3\text{CF}_2\text{CF}_2\text{NF}_2 \end{array}$	CF_3	6·4	Triplet
	$CF_2(a)$	27·1	Quartet
	$CF_2(b)$	51·1	Triplet
	NF_2	−92·0	a
$(CF_3)_2NC(O)F$	CF_3	−20·0	Doublet
	CF	−81·0	Septet
$(CF_3)_2NC(O)N(CF_3)_2$	CF_3	−20·4	None
$(CF_3)_2CHC\!\equiv\!N$	CF_3	−10·6	Doublet
$\begin{array}{c} \text{a} \quad \text{b} \quad \text{c} \qquad \text{d} \\ \text{CF}_3\text{CF}_2\text{CF}_2\text{CF}\!=\!\text{NCF}_3 \end{array}$	$CF_3(a)$	5·2	Triplet
	$CF_3(d)$	−36·2	Doublet
	$CF_2(b)$	42·4	Quintet
	$CF_2(c)$	51·4	Doublet
	CF	−52·7	a
$CF_2\!=\!NCF_3$	CF_3	−18·8	a
	CF	−44·6	Doublet
	CF	−25·2	Doublet
$HN(CH_3CH_2F)_2$	CF	145·5	a

a—Broad unresolved multiplet.
Chemical shifts were measured in ppm from CF_3COOH external reference.

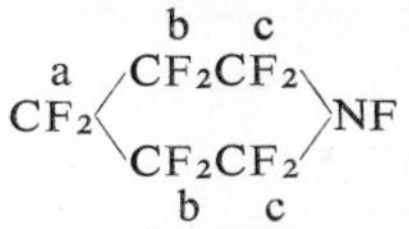

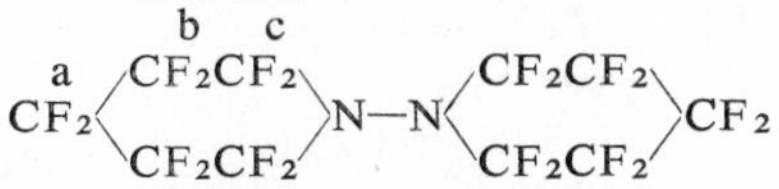

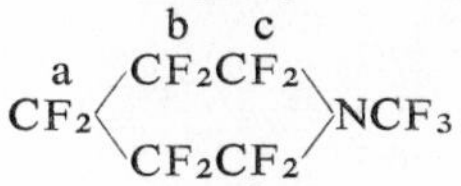

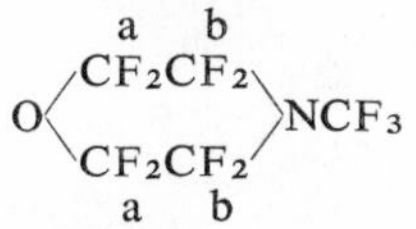

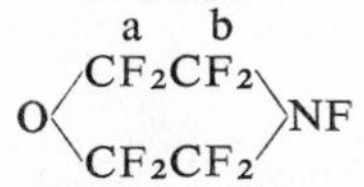

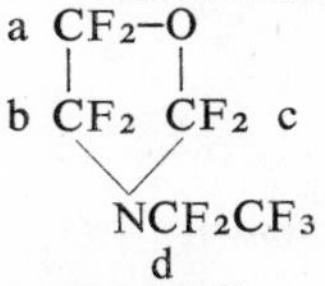

TABLE 11.16 RANGE OF ^{19}F CHEMICAL SHIFTS IN A SERIES OF FLUOROCARBONS(58)

Group	No. obsd.	Range of δ's found
CH_2CH_2F	3	149·5 to 145·5
C_3CF	2	112·5, 107·0
C—CF_2—C	17	57·8 to 21·9
C—CF_2—N	10	51·1 to 8·6
C—NF—C	2	36·6, 36·0
C—CF_2—O	6	14·9 to −6·2
CF_3—CF_2—	10	11·9 to 3·2
All other CF_3—C	10	0·0 to −19·7
C=CF—O	3	−9·4 to −11·8
CF_3—N	9	−18·8 to −36·2
O—CF_2—N	1	−20·6
CF_2=N	1	−25·2 and −44·6
C—CF=N	1	−52·7
N—C(O)F	1	−81·0
C—NF_2	1	−92·0

Chemical shifts were measured in ppm from CF_3COOH external reference.

TABLE 11.17 ^{19}F CHEMICAL SHIFTS OF PERFLUOROALKYL GROUPS IN SUBSTITUTED FLUOROPROPANES(159)

$CF_3CF_2CF_2X$				
	Chemical shifts (ppm)[a]			
Substituent (X)	—CF_3	—CF_2—	—CF_2X	Reference
—I	1·97	40·7	−17·5	[b]
—Cl	4·62	48·7	−6·7	[b]
—S—S—	4·00	47·0	13·6	[b]
—SF_4—	5·0	50·0	16·5	101
—SF_5	5·0	50·7	18·8	101
—CN	5·03	51·3	30·6	[b]
—$(CF_2)_n$—	4·8	46·6	34·4	54
—	3·60	49·1	35·0	[b]
—COCl	4·67	49·2	37·2	[b]
—$COOC_2H_5$	4·67	50·5	42·7	[b]
—COOH	4·87	50·5	43·5	[b]
—COF	5·35	51·3	43·5	[b]
—NF_2	6·4	27·1	51·1	54
—CF=	5·2	42·4	51·4	54
—H	7·48	57·0	61·2	[b]

[a] The chemical shifts are in parts per million from CF_3COOH external reference.
[b] Private communication from H. Foster quoted in reference 159.

which the chemical shifts of such absorption bands extend in fluorocarbons being (referred to external CF_3COOH)

$$CF_3 = -14 \text{ to } +8 \text{ ppm}$$

$$C{-}CF_2{-}C = +27{\cdot}1 \text{ to } +57 \text{ ppm}$$

$$\left.\begin{matrix} C \\ C \end{matrix}\right\rangle CF{-}C = +107 \text{ to } +113 \text{ ppm}$$

Hydrogen chemical shifts for the analogous hydrogen-containing alkyl groups are in the opposite order to the fluorine chemical shifts. The amount of charge which a fluorine atom can withdraw from the carbon atom to which it is attached decreases as the fluorine substitution increases. This results in the ionic character of the C—F bond decreasing and an appropriate decrease in the shielding of the fluorine nucleus is observed. By varying the substituents to which these alkyl groups are attached, variations in ^{19}F chemical shifts are obtained and such variations are not always easy to interpret since bulky groups in close proximity to a fluorine atom can cause it to be "repulsively deshielded". Repulsive deshielding could be a consequence of dispersion forces

TABLE 11.18 ^{19}F CHEMICAL SHIFTS IN A SERIES OF FLUOROALKANES[8]

CF_3—CF_2—CF_2—CF_3	CF_3—CF_2—CF_2—CH_2I
6·5 51·5	7·5 51·5 33·5
CF_3—CF_2—CF_2—CF_2—CF_2—CF_2—CF_3	CF_3—CF_2—CF_2—COCl
7·5 51·5 47·5 47·5	6·5 51·5 39·5
CF_3—CF_2—CF_2—CF_2—CF_2H	CF_3—CF_2—CF_2—CCl_3
7·5 51·5 48·5 54·5 (61·5, 63·5)	6·5 42·5 32·5
HCF_2—CF_2—CF_2—CF_2H	CF_3—CF_2—CF_2—CF_2—CF_2—CCl_3
54·5 (62·5, 63·5)	6·5 51·5 47·5 41·5 34·5
CF_3—CF_2—CF_2—CH_2Cl	CCl_3—CF_2—CF_2—COCl
7·5 51·5 42·5	(28·5, 30·5)
CF_3—CF_2—CF_2—CH_2Br	CCl_3—CF_2—CF_2—CF_2—COCl
7·5 51·5 39·5	31·5 (35·5, 37·5)

The ^{19}F chemical shifts are given in ppm from CF_3COOH external reference: the original shifts from which these were calculated were measured from octafluorocyclobutane internal reference

$$\delta_{CF_3COOH\,ext} = \delta_{C_4F_8\,int} + 61{\cdot}5 \text{ ppm}.$$

between the bulky group and a particular fluorine atom, which cause the shielding to be different from that expected from electronegativity considerations. An example of this is the greater shielding of CF_3 groups in $(CF_3)_3CF$ than in $(CF_3)_4C$: a fluorine atom, being more electronegative than the CF_3 group[55], would be expected with decrease the electron density of the CF_3 groups within $(CF_3)_3CF$ as compared with those in $(CF_3)_4C$ and thus decrease the ^{19}F shielding in the CF_3 groups of the former compared with the latter. This repulsive deshielding effect has been characterised by Tiers[8] who has examined a series of fluorocarbons containing many bulky substituents. He found that repulsive steric interactions caused a deshielding effect which was equivalent to a net displacement of electrons away from the fluorine atom concerned. Evans[1] has interpreted this effect in terms of changes in the paramagnetic contribution to the shielding due to intramolecular dispersion forces between the bulky groups and the fluorine atoms. Table 11.18 lists the ^{19}F chemical shifts, from trifluoroacetic acid reference, of the fluorocarbon series examined by Tiers. Observations of the ^{19}F chemical shifts in the perfluoroalkyl chlorides, bromides and iodides indicate the apparent electron withdrawing power of the substituents to be $I > Br > Cl > F \gg CF_2I > CF_2Br > CF_2Cl > CF_3$. The

TABLE 11.18 A ^{19}F CHEMICAL SHIFTS (φ^* VALUES) OF FLUOROCARBON SULPHIDES[94]

Compound	Conc.[a]	φ^*-values[b] and multiplicities[c] for				
		CF_3	$—CF_2—$	$—(CF_2)_3—$	$—CF_2—$	$(CF_2)_2S_x$
$(n\text{-}C_3F_7)_2S$	10·0	80·58 t[d]	124·22 b; 8·2			83·81 b; 17
$(n\text{-}C_3F_7)_2S_2$	12·7	80·88 t[e]	124·21 b; 4·5			90·80 m(q?)
$(n\text{-}C_3F_7)_2S_3$	10·0	80·80 t[f]	124·22 b; 5·3			91·82 q[f]
$(n\text{-}C_7F_{15})_2S_2$	16·0	81·54 t[g]	126·5	122·5	119·7	89·79 b; 26
$(CF_2)_4S$	6·0				131·91 t[h]	87·04 t[h]
$1,4\text{-}(CF_2)_4S_2$	20·0					91·08[i] b[i]

[a] Volume per cent in CCl_3F (wt/vol. for perfluoroheptyl disulphide).

[b] Standard deviation less than $\pm 0{\cdot}01$ for all values given to two decimals, and $\pm 0{\cdot}15$ for others.

[c] Symbols for multiplicity: s, singlet; t, triplet; q, quartet; m, multiplet resolved but not analysed; b, broad and unresolved peak, width at half-height, $W\frac{1}{2}$, being given in cycles sec^{-1}.

[d] $J(CF_3—C—CF_2) = 9{\cdot}5 \pm 0{\cdot}2$ cycles sec^{-1}.

[e] $J(CF_3—C—CF_2) = 9{\cdot}2 \pm 0{\cdot}1$ cycles sec^{-1}.

[f] $J(CF_3—C—CF_2) = 9{\cdot}10 \pm 0{\cdot}05$ cycles sec^{-1}.

[g] $J(CF_3—C—CF_2) = 9{\cdot}40 \pm 0{\cdot}05$ cycles sec^{-1}; each component is an indistinct triplet having $J - 2{\cdot}5$ cycles sec^{-1}.

[h] $J = 4{\cdot}4 \pm 0{\cdot}1$ cycles sec^{-1} each component appears to be a triplet having $J = 2{\cdot}9 \pm 0{\cdot}5$ cycles sec^{-1}.

[i] Line width is temp. dependent. At 0% concn., $\varphi = 91{\cdot}05$.

bulkiness of some of the groups appears to offset their lower electronegativity in influencing their ability to withdraw electrons from adjacent fluorine containing alkyl groups. Such "steric" effects also operate when a $—CH_2$ or a $—CF_2$ group is interposed between the bulky group and the fluorine atom being examined.

However, it is now thought that when a CF_2 group is directly bonded to a chlorine, bromine or iodine atom, the presence of low-lying excited states is the dominant molecular feature controlling the fluorine shielding[56]. The increasingly higher energy orbitals used in progressing along the series X = F, Cl, Br, I, leads to a corresponding increase in the availability of low-lying excited states in the —CF_2X groups. If the low-lying states have the correct symmetry to be "mixed" with the ground state by the magnetic field then one would expect the large paramagnetic shifts to low fields as observed. These ideas can also explain the ^{19}F shielding in fluoromethanes and chlorofluoromethanes: substitution of a F or Cl atom for a hydrogen atom increases the number of accessible excited states and thus causes deshielding of the fluorine nuclei.

Proximity of fluorine atoms to nitrogen and oxygen atoms in a molecule produces deshielding of the fluorine nuclei as would be expected from simple inductive considerations (for example, the ^{19}F chemical shifts for the C—NF—C groups are ~ 70 ppm to low fields of that for the $\genfrac{}{}{0pt}{}{\text{C}}{\text{C}}\!\!>$CF—C group).

Table 11.18 A presents the shielding values for a series of fluorocarbon sulphides and it is seen that the ^{19}F resonances of —CF_2—S— groups fall generally in the range 80–95φ^*, midway between the values observed for analogous CF_2 groups in the isoelectronic P and Cl compounds[94]. Although the concept of the mixing of low-lying excited states with the ground state predicts the gross shielding observed for the —CF_2S— group, the U.V. absorption maxima for the molecules predict a reverse order of the φ^* values. Thus, if the shielding is controlled by this energy "mixing" effect, then the "low-lying electronic states" associated with the U.V. absorption maxima probably have the wrong symmetry properties to influence the shielding.

11.9 Perfluoroalkyl and Perfluoroacyl Metal Compounds

The ^{19}F chemical shifts and spin coupling constants of several molecules of this type are given in Table 11.19[56]. When a —CF_2 group is bonded directly to a transition metal atom, the fluorine nuclei experience a deshielding effect which is thought to be related to the presence of low-lying excited electronic states in the carbon–metal bonds. In these molecules, the large down-field shift of the fluorine nuclei is similar in magnitude to the corresponding shifts in perfluoroalkyl halides (see Table 11.19). Neither the diamagnetic shielding contribution nor the neighbour anisotropic contribution is sufficiently large to explain the observed paramagnetic ^{19}F chemical shifts. This paramagnetic contribution will be large if the molecule has several low-lying excited states with the correct symmetry to allow them to be "mixed" with the ground state by the magnetic field. In this case the mixing involves the partly filled *d* electronic orbitals and causes a paramagnetic shielding contribution of ~ 50 ppm in the α-CF_2 group. The introduction of a carbonyl group between the transition metal atom and the —CF_2 group removes the deshielding effect. Similarly the deshielding is absent when the —CF_2 group is attached to a tin or phosphorus atom. While the electronegativity of the atom bonded directly to the —CF_2 group will undoubtedly have some shielding influence on the fluorine nuclei, other factors must also be considered. This is illustrated by the observed similar fluorine shielding in the α-CF_2 group of the tin and phosphorus compounds where electronegativity differences are considerable. However, because there are no partially filled d orbitals in these molecules the paramagnetic shielding contribution is not large[56].

TABLE 11.19 ^{19}F CHEMICAL SHIFTS AND SPIN COUPLING CONSTANTS FOR SEVERAL PERFLUOROALKYL AND PERFLUOROACYL METAL COMPOUNDS[56]

Compound	CF_3	β CF_2	α CF_2	$J_{\alpha\beta}{}^c$	$J_{\alpha\gamma}{}^c$
$C_2F_5Mn(CO)_5$	84·0		68·8	1·5	
$C_2F_5COMn(CO)_5$	80·3		114·5	0·7	
$C_2F_5Re(CO)_5$	84·2		74·9	1·9	
$C_2F_5CORe(CO)_5{}^a$	80·5		116·7	0·7	
$(C_2F_5)_2Fe(CO)_4{}^a$	83·7		74·0	2·0	
$C_2F_5Fe(CO)_4I$	83·5		59·0	1·8	
$(C_2F_5)_2Sn(CH_3)_2$	83·7		118·9		
$C_2F_5Sn(C_2H_5)_3$	84·4		120·3		
$C_2F_5Sn(C_4H_9)_3$	83·9		120·4	1·4	
C_2F_5I	85·4		65·2	4·6	
$C_3F_7Mn(CO)_5$	78·8	115·3	65·6	~0	12·4
$C_3F_7Re(CO)_5$	78·5	115·1	72·7	~0	12·3
$C_3F_7CORe(CO)_5{}^a$	81·0	126·7	113·7	~0	9·3
$C_3F_7COC_5H_5(CO)I^a$	79·1	114·1	56·3	~0	
$(C_3F_7)_2Fe(CO)_4{}^a$	78·6	115·3	69·1	~0	11·1
$C_3F_7Fe(CO)_4I^b$	78·2	114·4	54·9	~0	11·4
$C_3F_7Sn(C_4H_9)_3$	80·3	122·7	118·2	~0	9·5
$(C_3F_7)_2PI^d$	81·2	119·7	102·9	3·2	9·2
$(C_3F_7)_2PCl^e$	81·2	122·7	120·1		9·6
C_3F_7I	79·6	118·2	60·5	4·6	9·3
C_3F_7Cl	80·7	125·2	69·5	1·6	9·0

Chemical shifts are in ppm relative to CCl_3F, increasing to high field. Unless otherwise stated, they were obtained with trichlorofluoromethane as solvent and solution concentrations 15% or less.

[a] Tetrahydrofuran solution, CCl_3F external standard.

[b] Dichloromethane solution, CCl_3F external standard.

[c] Coupling constants in cycles sec^{-1}, $J_{\beta\gamma}$ not observed in perfluoropropyl compounds.

[d] $J_{PF\alpha} = 23{\cdot}6$, $J_{PF\beta} = 36{\cdot}2$, $J_{PF\gamma} = 9{\cdot}2$.

[e] $J_{PF\alpha} = 58{\cdot}4$, $J_{PF\beta} = 36{\cdot}5$, $J_{PF\gamma} = 9{\cdot}6$.

McClellan[57] has examined the ^{19}F resonance spectra of several perfluoroalkyl and perfluoroacyl derivatives of manganese and cobalt carbonyls: their ^{19}F chemical shifts are given in Table 11.20.

Table 11.21 lists the ^{19}F chemical shifts and the coupling constants involving fluorine nuclei for three mercury fluoroalkyls[152]. It is interesting to note that the fluorine atoms in the CF_3 group of a perfluoroethyl group are coupled less strongly with the mercury atom than are those in the CF_2 group: this is a reversal of the Hg—H coupling behaviour found in non-fluorinated mercury alkyls (see Section 10.3.2).

TABLE 11.20 ^{19}F CHEMICAL SHIFTS OF SOME PERFLUOROALKYL METAL CARBONYLS(57)

Compound	Chemical shifts (ppm from external CF_3COOH)	Intensity ratios
$CF_3Mn(CO)_5$	$-85{\cdot}8$ (s)[a]	
i-$C_3F_7Mn(CO)_5$	$-8{\cdot}9$ (s),[b] $+87{\cdot}1$ (s)[b]	6:1
n-$C_3F_7Mn(CO)_5$[c]	$+0{\cdot}45$ (t), $-11{\cdot}3$ (q), $+37{\cdot}6$ (s)	3:2:2
$H(CF_2)_4COMn(CO)_5$[d]	$+60{\cdot}8$ (d), $+33{\cdot}6$ (s) $+ 46{\cdot}2$ (s) $+ 51{\cdot}8$ (s)	1:1:1:1
$CF_3Co(CO)_4$	-87 (s)	
$C_2F_5Co(CO)_4$	$+6{\cdot}0$ (s),[b] $-19{\cdot}3$ (s)[b]	3:2
n-$C_3F_7Co(CO)_4$[e]	$+2{\cdot}0$ (t), $-25{\cdot}5$ (q), $+18{\cdot}4$ (s)	3:2:2

The letters s, d, t and q refer to singlet, doublet, triplet and quartet respectively. The first entry in the chemical shift column is for the F nuclei attached to the terminal carbon atom and the last entry is for the F nuclei attached to the carbon atom adjacent to the metal.

[a] 50 per cent solution in tetrahydrofuran was used.

[b] Fine structure was not resolved.

[c] $J_{FF} = 8$ cycles sec^{-1}.

[d] $J_{FH} = 50$ cycles sec^{-1}.

[e] $J_{FF} = 10$ cycles sec^{-1}.

TABLE 11.21 ^{19}F CHEMICAL SHIFTS AND SPIN–SPIN COUPLING CONSTANTS IN MERCURY FLUOROALKYLS(152)

Compound	Coupling constants (cycles sec^{-1})				Chemical shift† (ppm)		
	J_{Hg-CF_3}	J_{Hg-CF_2}	J_{Hg-CH_2}	J_{Hg-CF}	δ_{CF_3}	δ_{CF_2}	δ_{CF}
$(C_2F_5)_2Hg$	71	770			$+6{\cdot}0$	$+31{\cdot}9$	
$(CF_3CH_2)_2Hg$	224		130		$+28{\cdot}9$		
$(CF_3CHF)_2Hg$	161			480	$-0{\cdot}6$		$+146{\cdot}3$

† δ measured in ppm from CF_3COOH external reference.

11.10 FLUORINATED AROMATIC COMPOUNDS

11.10.1 ^{19}F *Chemical Shifts of Benzene Derivatives*

Substitution of a benzene molecule influences the *ortho*, *meta* and *para* positions to the substituent in different ways: the *ortho* position is influenced by a combination of inductive, resonance and steric effects, the *meta* position mainly by inductive effects and the *para* position mainly by resonance effects. Several workers have attempted to obtain information about the electron distribution in aromatic systems by examining the ^{19}F resonance spectra of fluorobenzene derivatives. A series of *meta*- and *para*-substituted fluorobenzenes has been examined by Gutowsky and co-workers(59) and the ^{19}F chemical shifts for the two types of compound have been correlated with the Hammett substituent constants(58) for the molecules (see Table 11.22). In both cases a

TABLE 11.22 ^{19}F CHEMICAL SHIFTS AND HAMMETT CONSTANTS FOR A SERIES OF MONOSUBSTITUTED BENZENES[59]

Substituent	*Ortho*† δ ppm	*Meta*† δ ppm	Hammett σ constant	*Para*† δ ppm	Hammett σ constant	Taft σ_I constant[60]	Taft σ_R constant[60]
NO_2	+5·6	−3·3	+0·710	−10·8	+0·778	+0·63	+0·15
CN	−5·2	−3·0	+0·608	−9·6	+0·656	+0·59	+0·07
COOH	−3·5	−0·5	+0·355	−6·9	+0·728		
I	−19·3	−2·6	+0·352	+1·2	+0·276	+0·38	−0·10
Br	−5·5	−2·4	+0·391	+2·3	+0·232	+0·45	−0·22
Cl	+2·7	−2·1	+0·373	+2·4	+0·227	+0·47	−0·24
F	+25·9	−3·1	+0·337	+6·4	+0·062	+0·50	−0·44
CH_3	+5·0	+0·9	−0·069	+5·5	−0·170	−0·05	−0·13
CH_3CONH	+12·8	−1·0		+5·7			
OH	+25·0	−0·9	+0·10	+10·6	−0·36	+0·25	−0·61
CH_3O	+22·4			+11·4	−0·268	+0·23	−0·50
C_2H_5O	+21·7	−1·3	+0·15	+11·5	−0·25		
NH_2	+23·1	+0·2	−0·161	+14·6	−0·660	+0·10	−0·76

† Chemical shifts measured in ppm from C_6H_5F internal reference:
$$\delta_{CF_3COOH\,ext} = \delta_{C_6H_5F\,int} + 35{\cdot}6 \text{ ppm.}$$

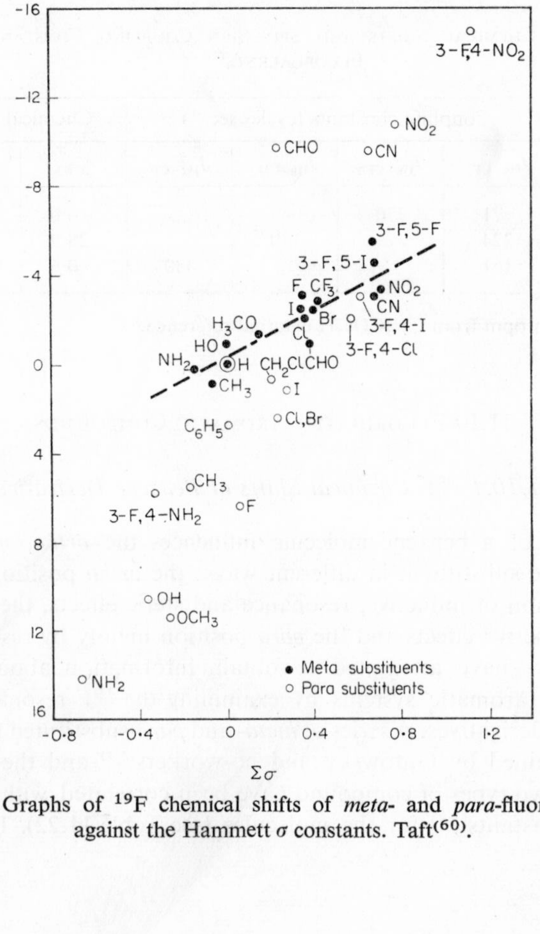

FIG. 11.4 Graphs of ^{19}F chemical shifts of *meta*- and *para*-fluorobenzenes against the Hammett σ constants. Taft[60].

roughly linear correlation between the two parameters is observed and the linear plots can be represented by the equations:

$$\sigma_m = -0{\cdot}169\,\delta_m$$

$$\sigma_p = -0{\cdot}0560\,\delta_p + 0{\cdot}271$$

where σ_m and σ_p are the Hammett substituent parameters and δ_m and δ_p are the ^{19}F chemical shifts, for the *meta*- and *para*-substituted fluorobenzenes respectively. Figure 11.4 shows the linear graphs obtained when the ^{19}F chemical

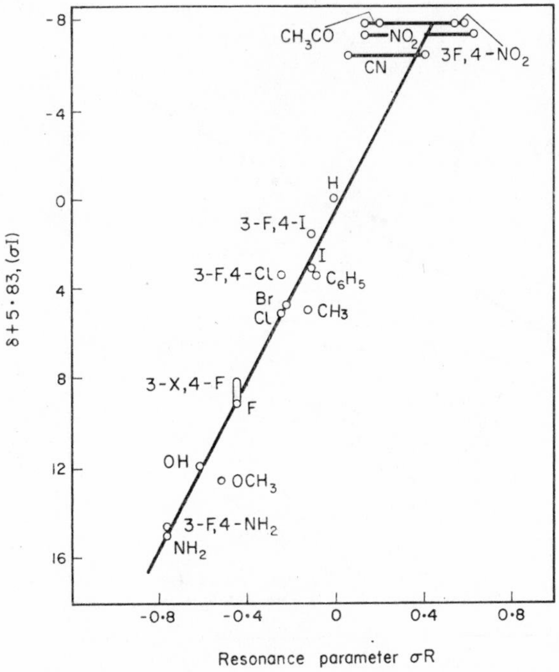

FIG. 11.5 Graph showing the correlation of the ^{19}F chemical shifts in *para*-fluorobenzenes with the Taft σ_I and σ_R contributions to the Hammett constants. Taft[(60)].

shifts are plotted against the Hammett σ constants for the *meta* and *para* substituted fluorobenzenes[(60)].

Values of δ_p, δ_m and δ_o were found to show a roughly linear relationship with each other when any pair of the above parameters are compared within a series of compounds, which suggests that resonance effects are proportional to inductive effects.

Taft[(60)] has separated quantitatively Hammett σ parameters into their component inductive (σ_I) and resonance (σ_R) contributions. He defines the inductive contribution (σ_I) as a measure of the free energy effect of the substituent (relative to the hydrogen atom) resulting from its power to attract or repel electrons either through space or through sigma bonds. The resonance contribution (σ_R) is taken as a measure of the free energy effect resulting from the power of the substituent to attract or repel electrons through resonance with the π orbitals of the benzene system[60]. Using the ^{19}F chemical shift data of Gutowsky *et al.*[59] a very close correlation is obtained between the

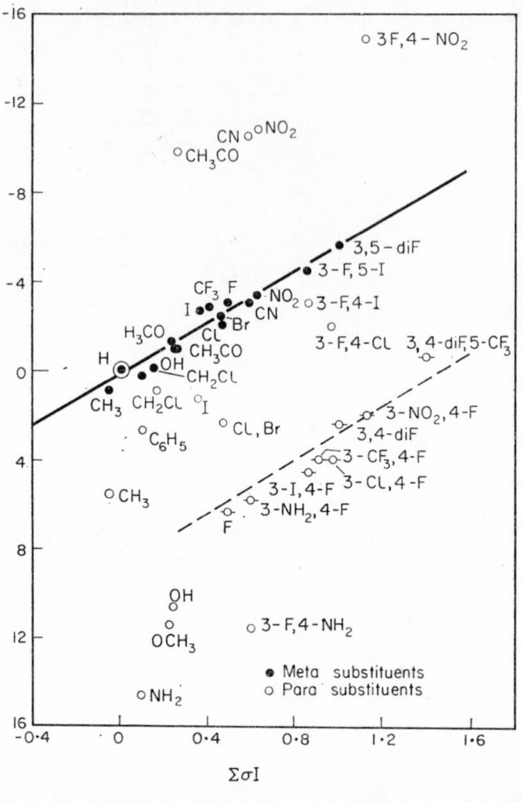

FIG. 11.6 Graphs of ^{19}F chemical shifts of *para*- and *meta*-fluorobenzenes plotted against the Taft σ_I contributions to the Hammett constants. Taft[60].

^{19}F chemical shifts in *meta*-substituted fluorobenzenes and the Taft σ_I constants which can be represented by the linear equation:

$$\delta_m = -(5{\cdot}83 \pm 0{\cdot}26)(\textstyle\sum \sigma_I) + 0{\cdot}2$$

where the summation $\sum \sigma_I$ is adopted to include 3,5-disubstituted benzene derivatives. A similar exact relationship can be found for the ^{19}F chemical shifts in *para*-substituted fluorobenzenes involving both the inductive and resonance components of the Hammett constant.

$$\delta_p = -(5{\cdot}83)(\textstyle\sum \sigma_I) - (18{\cdot}80 \pm 0{\cdot}81)(\sigma_R) + 0{\cdot}8$$

These results are presented graphically in Figs. 11.5 and 11.6. Comparison of Fig. 11.4 with Figs. 11.5 and 11.6 clearly demonstrates that the correlation of ^{19}F chemical shifts with Taft's σ_I and σ_R contributions is much better than that with Hammett's σ values.

The shielding of the ^{19}F nucleus in the halogen *ortho*-substituted fluorobenzenes decreases with decrease in the electronegativity of the halogen substituent in the series F, Cl, Br and I. Deshielding due to intramolecular electric fields arising mainly from van der Waals interactions of the more bulky halogen atom with the adjacent fluorine atom could account for the anomalous chemical shift behaviour(189).

Karplus and Das(61) have explained the ^{19}F chemical shifts found in a series of polyfluorobenzenes by calculating a magnetic shielding tensor expression in terms of localised bond properties such as ionicity, hybridisation and multiple bond character. Prosser and Goodman(172) have extended these ideas and they have given an equation (equation (4.32)) relating the fluorine chemical shifts in conjugated compounds with π-electron charge densities on the fluorine atom and the bonded carbon atom and with the C—F bond order. This equation gives good agreement with experimental values for *para*-X-C_6H_4F compounds(173, 193).

11.10.2 Spin–Spin Interaction in Fluorinated Aromatic Compounds

By examining the NMR spectra of various deuterofluorobenzenes, Bak, Shoolery and Williams(29) obtained the J_{H-F} coupling constants between the nuclei in the *ortho*, *meta* and *para* positions. The values they measured were $J_{FH}^{ortho} = 9{\cdot}4$ cycles sec^{-1}, $J_{FH}^{meta} = 5{\cdot}8$ cycles sec^{-1} and $J_{FH}^{para} = 0{\cdot}0 \pm 0{\cdot}5$ cycles sec^{-1}. These values have been used by Fujiwara and Shimizu(30) to enable them to analyse fully the ^{1}H resonance spectrum of monofluorobenzene in terms of an ABB′CC′X system.

A large number of substituted fluoroaromatic compounds have been investigated by Gutowsky and co-workers(19) and the J_{HF} and J_{FF} values obtained from these compounds are included in Table 11.23. In some cases the relative signs of the J_{HF} coupling constants within a molecule are found to be different. The factors controlling the magnitude of the *ortho* coupling constants are the positions of the interacting nuclei with respect to each other in the ring and the nature of the interacting nuclei(19, 183). Variation of the substituents in an aromatic ring proves to be of lesser importance. The range of values for the various coupling constants are indicated in Table 11.24. The coupling constants involving fluorine nuclei in aromatic molecules cannot be explained by attributing the dominant role in any coupling mechanism to either the π or the σ electron systems. Williams and Gutowsky have considered the various interactions controlling the F—F and H—F coupling in aromatic compounds. They found that the major contribution to the coupling is through a Fermi contact term, involving 5 electrons (the observed coupling constants indicate there to be about 5 per cent fluorine 2s character in the CF bond)(31). Pople(164)

TABLE 11.23 SPIN–SPIN COUPLING

Compound [a]	J_{HH}^{ortho}	J_{HH}^{meta}	J_{HH}^{para}
2,3,5,6-Tetrachlorofluorobenzene			
2-Nitro-3-fluoro-5,6-dichlorobenzotrifluoride			
2,6-Dinitro-3,5-dichlorobenzene			<1·0
2,4-Dimethyl-6-nitroaniline		1·2 ± 0·3	
2,4-Difluoromesitylene			
2-Fluoromesitylene			
2,6-Dichloro-3,5-difluorobenzotrifluoride			
1,3,5-Trifluoro-2,6-dichlorobenzene			
2,4-Dinitro-6-chlorophenol		2·7 ± 0·1	
2,6-Dibromophenol	7·9 ± 0·2		
1,4-Difluoro-2,3,5-trichlorobenzene			
2-Fluoro-4,6-dichlorophenol		2·3 ± 0·1	
2-Amino-3,5-difluoro-4-chloronitrobenzene			
2-Fluoro-4,5-dichlorophenol			0·4 ± 0·2
2,6-Dichloro-3-fluorobenzotrifluoride			
2,3-Difluoro-5,6-dibromonitrobenzene			
2,4-Dichloro-3,5-difluoronitrobenzene			
2,4-Dichloro-3,6-difluoronitrobenzene			
2-Chloro-4,5-difluoronitrobenzene			<1·0

[a] The signs given for some of the constants indicate relative signs only; absolute signs were not determined for any of the constants.

has shown that the electron-orbital contribution to F—F and H—F coupling constants in fluorobenzenes is appreciable (see Table 5.13).

In *p*-fluorotoluene the J_{H-F} coupling is much larger than the chemical shifts between the non-equivalent hydrogen atoms and this results in an average value of J_{HF}^{ortho} and J_{HF}^{meta} being observed: $\frac{1}{2}(J_{HF}^{ortho} + J_{HF}^{meta}) = \pm 7{\cdot}4$ cycles sec^{-1}[35]. However, the ^{1}H resonance spectrum can equally well be shown to be consistent with the normal aromatic HF coupling constants of $J_{HF}^{ortho} = 8{\cdot}6$ and $J_{HF}^{meta} = 7{\cdot}0$ cycles sec^{-1}. When *p*-fluorotoluene is dissolved in various solvents the chemical shift between the chemically non-equivalent types of hydrogen atom can be increased: from the resulting complex spectrum there is some evidence that $J_{HF}^{ortho} \neq J_{HF}^{meta}$[35].

Relative Signs of ^{19}F *Spin Coupling Constants in Aromatic Compounds.* Evans[165] has conducted spin decoupling experiments on 2,3-dichloro-1,4,5-trifluorobenzene and 2-chloro-1,4,5-trifluoro-3-nitrobenzene and found that the relative signs of the F—F and H—F spin coupling constants between ring hydrogen nuclei are:

$$\text{(i)} \quad \pm J_{FF}^{ortho} \mp J_{FF}^{meta} \mp J_{FF}^{para}$$

$$\text{(ii)} \quad \pm J_{HF}^{ortho} \pm J_{HF}^{meta} \pm J_{HF}^{para}$$

The results for the F—F coupling constants are in disagreement with the molecular orbital calculation of Williams and Gutowsky[31] who suggested that the signs of all three F—F coupling constants are positive. The observed

CONSTANTS IN SUBSTITUTED BENZENES[(19)]

J_{HF}^{ortho}	J_{HF}^{meta}	J_{HF}^{para}	J_{FF}^{ortho}	J_{FF}^{meta}	J_{FF}^{para}
		2·1 ± 0·1			
8·4 ± 0·3					
	7·7 ± 0·3				
	7·0 ± 0·4				
7·8 ± 0·3					
8·6 ± 0·2		2·2 ± 0·2		1·9 ± 0·2	
+8·4 ± 0·2	+6·3 ± 0·2				12·0 ± 0·2
+9·6 ± 0·3 [b]		−2·1 ± 0·2 [b]			
+9·4 ± 0·3 [b]		−2·2 ± 0·3 [b]		3·1 ± 0·1	
+10·1 ± 0·2 [b]	+8·3 ± 0·2 [b]				
≧ +6·2 ± 0·2 [b]	≦ +6·2 ± 0·2 [b]				
8·7 ± 0·3	6·8 ± 0·3		20·2 ± 0·3		
8·0 ± 0·1 [b]		2·3 ± 0·1 [b]		4·2 ± 0·2	
8·2 ± 0·4 [b]	6·3 ± 0·4 [b]				14·4 ± 0·4
9·5 ± 0·2	7·1 ± 0·2		20·8 ± 0·3		

[b] The assignment of the numerical values to particular coupling constants is based on relative magnitudes found unambiguously in other compounds.

relative signs of the H—F coupling constants are in accord with earlier results based on the detailed analysis of the ^{19}F NMR spectra of fluoroaromatic compounds[(19, 29)].

TABLE 11.24 ^{19}F SPIN–SPIN COUPLING CONSTANTS IN CYCLES SEC^{-1} FOR SUBSTITUTED BENZENES[(19, 189)]

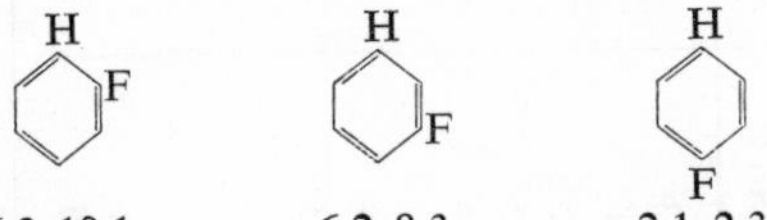

6·2–10·1   6·2–8·3   2·1–2·3

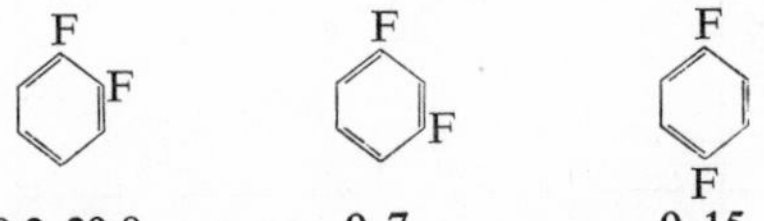

20·2–20·8   0–7   0–15

11.10.3 Substituted Benzotrifluorides

The ^{19}F chemical shifts of a series of monosubstituted benzotrifluorides have been measured[(59, 63)]. Substituent effects on the ^{19}F chemical shifts are about ten times smaller than those observed in fluorobenzenes and furthermore, they are in the opposite direction. No explanation of this latter effect has been suggested.

TABLE 11.25 ^{19}F CHEMICAL SHIFTS IN A SERIES OF POLYSUBSTITUTED FLUOROBENZENES[59]

Substituents	Chemical shift δ ppm †	Substituents	Chemical shift δ ppm †	Substituents	Chemical shift δ ppm †
3-NO_2, 4-NH_2	+14·3	2,4-di F	+30·4	2-CF_3, 4-F	+7·4
2-NO_2, 4-NH_2	+21·6	3,4-di F	+2·4	3-CF_3, 4-F	+4·0
3,5-di F	−5·5	2,5-di F	+20·9	2,4,6-tri CH_3	+15·0
3-F, 5-I	−4·5	2-Cl, 4-F	+8·6	2,5-di Cl, 4-F	+5·5
2,4-di NO_2	−5·4	3-Cl, 4-F	+3·9	2,5-di Br, 4-F	−2·2
2-NH_2, 4-F	+28·7	2-Cl, 5-F	−2·0	2,4,5-tri F	+26·7
3-NH_2, 4-F	+5·8	3-F, 4-Cl	−2·0	2-Br, 4,5-di F	−4·3
2-NH_2, 5-F	+18·3	2-Br, 4-F	+0·8	2,4-di F, 5-Br	+27·5
3-F, 4-NH_2	+11·5	3-Br, 4-F	+4·0	2,5-di F, 4-Br	+20·6
2-NO_2, 4-F	+10·3	2-I, 4-F	−12·3	2,5-di F, 3-CF_3	+17·7
3-NO_2, 4-F	+2·0	3-I, 4-F	+4·5	2,4-di F, 6-CF_3	+32·0
2-NO_2, 5-F	−1·1	2-I, 5-F	−23·6	3,4-di F, 5-CF_3	−0·7
3-F, 4-NO_2	−14·9	3-F, 4-I	−3·0	2,4,6-tri CH_3, 3-F	+9·6

† Chemical shifts measured in ppm from C_6H_5F internal reference.
The observed fluorine nucleus is at the 1-position.

F—F coupling constants in several 2-F,6-X-benzotrifluorides have been measured and the values depend markedly on the nature of the substituent X(J_{F-CF_3} = 13 to 34 cycles sec^{-1})[184]. The coupling constants are roughly proportional to the ^{19}F chemical shifts of the CF_3 group and to the size of the substituent X.

11.10.4 Polysubstituted Fluorobenzene Derivatives

Several polysubstituted benzene derivatives have been studied and typical observed ^{19}F chemical shifts are given in Table 11.25. In several cases, the chemical shifts are found to be additive and it is possible to predict chemical shift values by the summation of known chemical shift contributions from the substituents[59]. The ^{19}F chemical shifts of a group of aromatic polyfluoro amino derivatives have been measured by Tatlow and co-workers with a view to confirming the structures of the molecules[65].

TABLE 11.26 ^{19}F CHEMICAL SHIFTS IN MONOSUBSTITUTED PERFLUOROBENZENES[189]

C_6F_5X Substituent X	$\delta_{(ortho)}$ ppm	$\delta_{(para)}$ ppm	$\delta_{(meta)}$ ppm
F	162·28	162·28	162·28
Cl	140·61	156·11	161·48
Br	132·54	154·65	160·60
I	119·18	152·53	159·65
$SnMe_3$	122·30	152·75	160·67
HgMe	121·91	153·52	160·05
C_6F_5	138·25	150·27	160·76
$NHCH_3$	161·89	173·07	165·21
H	138·89	153·50	162·06

Precision ±0·08 ppm.
Chemical shifts were measured from $CFCl_3$ internal reference present at 5 mole per cent in a 5 mole per cent solution of the compounds in CCl_4.

Several monosubstituted perfluorobenzene compounds, C_6F_5X, have been examined by NMR and Table 11.26 lists typical ^{19}F chemical shifts[64,189,196,197]. The ^{19}F chemical shifts for the nuclei in the *ortho* positions are not consistent with predictions based on π-electron densities alone: such anomalies are also observed in chlorofluorobenzenes and they have been attributed to van der Waals interactions[189].

11.10.5 Fluoronaphthalenes

By measuring the ^{19}F chemical shifts in α- and β-fluoronaphthalene, Isobe and co-workers[62] have shown the fluorine nuclei in these molecules to be more shielded than that of monofluorobenzene. Since this behaviour is the exact opposite to that observed for ^{1}H resonance shifts in aromatic molecules it was interpreted as indicating the absence of large ring current effects on the shielding of aromatic ring fluorine nuclei. Although the ring current effects will be of the same order of magnitude for both ^1H and ^{19}F shielding, in view of the large variations in ^{19}F shielding from other sources the ring current effects are negligible.

11.11 Fluoroalkenes

11.11.1 Perfluorovinyl Derivatives

The ^{19}F chemical shifts and spin coupling constants for several perfluorovinyl derivatives of metals and metalloids are given in Tables 11.27, 11.28 and 11.29[66]. In all the molecules examined, the fluorine shielding is in the order $\sigma_{F_1} < \sigma_{F_2} < \sigma_{F_3}$ and there appears to be very little correlation between

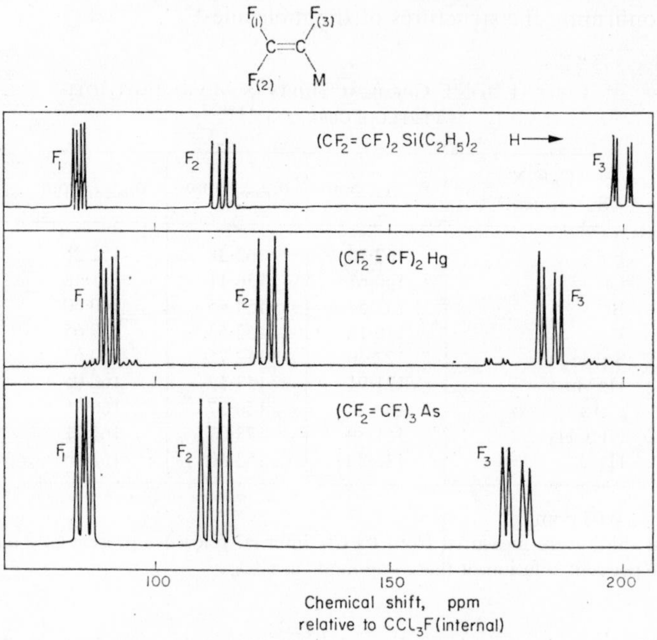

FIG. 11.7 ^{19}F resonance spectra of some perfluorovinyl metal compounds. Coyle, Stafford and Stone[66].

the observed ^{19}F chemical shifts and the nature of the substituent atoms. A boron substituent causes the terminal $=CF_2$ fluorine nuclei to be significantly deshielded, a fact which might be due to mesomeric electron withdrawal by the boron atom[66]. Figure 11.7 shows the ^{19}F resonance spectra of three typical perfluorovinyl metallic compounds, each featuring the three quartets characteristic of the weakly coupled three spin APX system. The high field quartet of tris (perfluorovinyl) arsine shows additional fine structure due to long range F–F spin coupling between magnetically non-equivalent fluorine nuclei in the different perfluorovinyl groups (the molecule is an AA′A″PP′P″XX′X″

TABLE 11.27 ^{19}F CHEMICAL SHIFTS OF SOME PERFLUOROVINYL COMPOUNDS[66]

$$\begin{array}{c} F_{(1)} \\ \diagdown \\ F_{(2)} \diagup \end{array} C = C \begin{array}{c} \diagup F_{(3)} \\ \diagdown M \end{array}$$

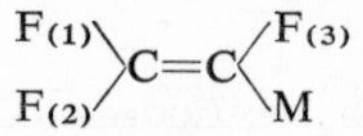

Compound	Chemical shift †		
	$F_{(1)}$	$F_{(2)}$	$F_{(3)}$
$CF_2{=}CFBCl_2$	71·6	87·9	184·5
$CF_2{=}CFBF_2$ ‡	72·8	99·8	206·6
$(CF_2{=}CF)_3B$	72·7	91·1	185·9
$(CF_2{=}CF)_2Hg$	89·9	124·5	185·0
$(CF_2{=}CF)_3As$	84·8	112·7	177·0
$(CF_2{=}CF)_2Si(C_2H_5)_2$	83·5	114·3	199·7
$(CF_2{=}CF)_2Ge(CH_3)_2$	86·6	118·6	195·5
$(CF_2{=}CF)_4Ge$	80·1	112·7	196·5
$(CF_2{=}CF)_2Sn(CH_3)_2$	85·9	121·2	194·6
$(CF_2{=}CF)Sn(C_4H_9)_3$	88·1	123·3	192·7
$(CF_2{=}CF)_2Sn(C_6H_5)_2$	84·3	118·6	193·2
$CF_2{=}CFCl$ †† (reference 68)	105	121	145
$CF_2{=}CFH$ ††	103	127	185
$CF_2{=}CFC_6H_5$ ††	102	133	193

† In parts per million, relative to CCl_3F internal reference. All compounds measured in 10 mole per cent solution in CCl_3F.

‡ BF_2 fluorines at 86·7 ppm. Concentration 25 per cent; chemical shifts in 10 per cent solution will differ by less than 1 ppm.

†† Approximate values.

TABLE 11.28 APPROXIMATE F–F COUPLING CONSTANTS IN PERFLUOROVINYL METAL COMPOUNDS[66]

$$\begin{array}{c} F_{(1)} \\ \diagdown \\ F_{(2)} \diagup \end{array} C = C \begin{array}{c} \diagup F_{(3)} \\ \diagdown M \end{array}$$

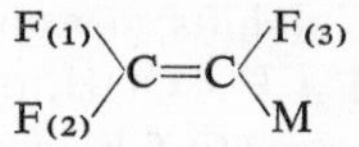

Compound	F—F coupling constants (cycles sec^{-1})		
	J_{gem}	J_{cis}	J_{trans}
$CF_2{=}CFBCl_2$	7	19	114
$CF_2{=}CFBF_2$	18	—	117
$(CF_2{=}CF)_3B$	< 5	24	110
$(CF_2{=}CF)_2Hg$	75	37	109
$(CF_2{=}CF)_2Si(C_2H_5)_2$	62	26	117
$(CF_2{=}CF)_2Ge(CH_3)_2$	72	32	118
$(CF_2{=}CF)_4Ge$	71	32	118
$(CF_2{=}CF)_2Sn(CH_3)_2$	75	34	116
$(CF_2{=}CF)Sn(C_4H_9)_3$	79	34	115
$(CF_2{=}CF)_2Sn(C_6H_5)_2$	68	34	118

$J^{199}_{Hg-^{19}F}$ coupling constants in $(CF_2{=}CF)_2Hg$ are $J_{HgF1} = 223$, $J_{HgF2} = 17$ and $J_{HgF3} = 820$ cycles sec^{-1}.

J_{Sn-F} coupling constants in $(CF_2{=}CF)_2Sn(CH_3)_2$ are $J_{SnF1} = 29$, $J_{SnF2} = 25$ and $J_{SnF3} = 208$ cycles sec^{-1}.

system). Similar behaviour is found in the ^{19}F spectra of other perfluorovinyl metallic compounds[66].

TABLE 11.29 ^{19}F CHEMICAL SHIFTS AND SPIN COUPLING CONSTANTS OF SOME FLUOROALKENES[79]

Fluorine chemical shifts

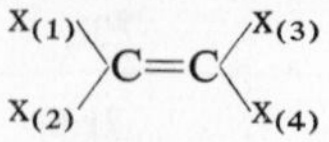

$$\begin{array}{c} X_{(1)} \\ \diagdown \\ X_{(2)} \end{array} C{=}C \begin{array}{c} X_{(3)} \\ \diagup \\ X_{(4)} \end{array}$$

Compound	$X_{(1)}$	$X_{(2)}$	$X_{(3)}$	$X_{(4)}$	$\delta_{(1)}$	$\delta_{(2)}$	$\delta_{(3)}$	$\delta_{(4)}$
CF$_3$CF:CF$_2$	CF$_3$	F	F	F	72	192	107	93
CF$_2$ClCF:CF$_2$	CF$_2$Cl	F	F	F	58	185	106	95
CF$_3$CF:CFMn(CO)$_5$	CF$_3$	F	F	Mn	67	165	95	
CF$_3$CF:CFFe(CO)$_2$C$_5$H$_5$	CF$_3$	F	F	Fe	66	166	86	

Chemical shifts are in ppm relative to internal CCl$_3$F (0·0 ppm) increasing to high field.

Fluorine coupling constants (cycles sec^{-1})‡

Compound	$X_{(1)}$	$X_{(2)}$	$X_{(3)}$	$X_{(4)}$	$J_{2,3}$	$J_{3,4}$	$J_{2,4}$	$J_{1,4}$	$J_{1,2}$	$J_{1,3}$
CF$_3$CF:CF$_2$	CF$_3$	F	F	F	120	57	40	8	13	21
CF$_3$CCl:CF$_2$	CF$_3$	Cl	F	F				12		21
cis-CF$_3$ClC:CFCl	CF$_3$	Cl	F	Cl						23
CF$_2$ClCF:CF$_2$	CF$_2$Cl	F	F	F	118	56	39	6	19	31
CF$_3$CF:CFMn(CO)$_5$	CF$_3$	F	F	Mn	127				12	23
CF$_3$CF:CFFe(CO)$_2$C$_5$H$_5$	CF$_3$	F	F	Fe	131				13	22

‡ $X_{(1)}$, $X_{(2)}$, etc., refer to the structural formula.

11.11.2 Other Fluoroalkenes

Table 11.30 lists the ^{19}F chemical shifts, measured from the CF$_3$ absorption band in the reference compound CF$_3$CF$_2$COOH, of four halogenated propenes[67]. It is seen that fluorine atoms *trans* to CF$_3$ groups are less shielded than those

TABLE 11.30 ^{19}F CHEMICAL SHIFTS AND SPIN COUPLING CONSTANTS FOR SOME HALOGENATED PROPENES[67]

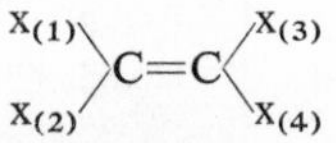

$$\begin{array}{c} X_{(1)} \\ \diagdown \\ X_{(2)} \end{array} C{=}C \begin{array}{c} X_{(3)} \\ \diagup \\ X_{(4)} \end{array}$$

X$_1$	X$_2$	X$_3$	X$_4$	ppm from external reference: CF$_3$ group in CF$_3$CF$_2$COOH††				Cycles per second					
				δ_1	δ_2	δ_3	δ_4	J_{12}	J_{13}	J_{14}	J_{23}	J_{24}	J_{34}
F	F	F	CF$_3$	11·6	25·1	110·6	−13·0	60·0	40·3	8·7	120·2	22·0	13·2
F	Cl	Cl	CF$_3$	−25·0			−23·7			10·4			
Cl	F	Cl	CF$_3$		−18·4		−23·5					24·3	
F	F	Cl	CF$_3$	−6·2	−5·9		−18·6	16·65		9·20		23·83	

†† $\delta_{\text{CF}_3\text{COOH}} = \delta_{\text{CF}_3\text{CF}_2\text{COOH}} - 7\cdot0$ ppm.

in the *cis* position. In $CF_3CF=CF_2$, the fluorine atom in the α-position to the CF_3 group is very highly shielded. Putman, Anderson and Sharkey[69] have reported that the ¹⁹F resonance spectrum of 1,1,4,4-tetrafluorobutadiene, $CF_2=CHCH=CF_2$ consists of a single broad absorption band (chemical shift from CF_3COOH reference of $+7.9$ to 14.4 ppm).

11.11.3 Coupling Constants in Fluoroalkenes

Coupling constants in fluorinated olefines have been more widely studied than the ¹⁹F chemical shifts in these molecules and theoretical interpretations of some of the observed coupling constants have been suggested (see Section

TABLE 11.31 ¹⁹F SPIN–SPIN COUPLING CONSTANTS (CYCLES SEC⁻¹) IN SOME FLUOROALKENES[33]

$$\begin{matrix} X_{(1)} & & & X_{(3)} \\ & \diagdown C=C \diagup & \\ X_{(2)} & & & X_{(4)} \end{matrix}$$

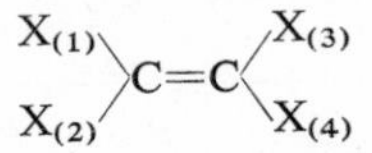

X_1	X_2	X_3	X_4	J_{12}	J_{13}	J_{23}	J_{14}	J_{24}	J_{34}
H	F	Cl	Cl	81					
H	H	F	F	~4	~1	34	34	~1	37
H	H	F	Cl	~3	8	40			
F	F	H	Cl	41	<3	13			
F	F	F	Cl	78	58	115			
F	F	F	Br	75	57	124			
F	F	F	CN	27	35	118			
F	F	F	H	87	33	119	12	<3	72
F	F	F	CF₃	57	39	116	8	22	13
F	F	Cl	CF₃				12	21	
Cl	F	Cl	CF₃					20	

5.8.1). Table 11.31 gives the various coupling constants extracted from analysis of the fluorine resonance spectra of several fluorinated ethylenes and propenes[33, 67]. Large variations in the magnitude of the F—F coupling constant between *geminal* fluorine atoms on a terminal carbon atom over a range 16–87 cycles sec⁻¹ are probably due in part to changes in the bond angle between the two C—F bonds. Attempts to correlate coupling constants with bond angles assume the Fermi contact term to dominate the coupling: McConnell[71] has shown that for fluorine–fluorine coupling the dipole–dipole term makes a large contribution to the mechanism and thus it is impossible to find a direct correlation of J_{F-F} values with molecular parameters such as bond angles.

Examination of Tables 11.30 and 11.31 reveals certain regular features of the observed coupling constants. For example the F—F coupling constants between atoms in *trans* positions to each other are found in the narrow range of 118 ± 6 cycles sec⁻¹ for all the molecules studied. In the halogenated propenes[67] the J_{CF_3-F} values for groups *trans* to each other are fairly constant ($\sim 9{\cdot}5$ cycles sec^{-1}) and the same is true for the groups when in *cis* positions ($J_{CF_3-F} \sim 23$ cycles sec^{-1}). It is also worth noting that the *cis* coupling is larger than the *trans* coupling, unlike the coupling between two fluorine or hydrogen nuclei directly bonded to two olefinic carbon atoms. There is some evidence that this reversal of coupling behaviour also occurs for the J_{CH_3-H} *cis*- and *trans* coupling constants in the ^1H spectra of propenes[72, 73].

Table 11.32 gives a list of F—F coupling constants measured for some *cis*- and *trans*-phenyl perfluoro-olefines[75]. The isomeric assignments are known

TABLE 11.32 F—F COUPLING CONSTANTS (CYCLES SEC^{-1}) OF *cis*- AND *trans*-PHENYL PERFLUOROALKENES[75]

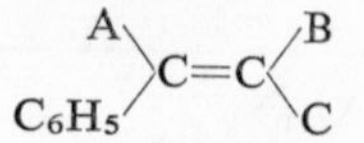

A	B	C	J_{AC}	J_{AB}	J_{BC}
F	CF_3	F	131	23	10
F	F	CF_3	13	9	9
CF_3	F	CF_3	1·5	28	7
CF_3	CF_3	F	12	12	7

TABLE 11.33 H—F COUPLING CONSTANTS (CYCLES SEC^{-1}) OF SOME FLUOROALKENES

Compound	J^{gem}_{HF}	J^{cis}_{HF}	J^{trans}_{HF}	Reference
$FHC{=}CH_2$	+84·7	+20·1	+52·4	77
$F_2C{=}CH_2$		~1	34	33
$FClC{=}CH_2$		8	40	33
$Cl_2C{=}CHF$	81			33
$F_2C{=}CHCl$		<3	13	33
$F_2C{=}CHF$	72	<3	12	33
cis $CHF{=}CHF$ †	+72·7‡		+20·4	188
trans $CHF{=}CHF$ ††	+74·3‡	+4·4		188

† $J^{cis}_{HH} = \mp 2{\cdot}0$, $J^{cis}_{FF} = \pm 18{\cdot}7$.
‡ Assumed to be positive.
†† $J^{trans}_{HH} = \pm 9{\cdot}5$, $J^{trans}_{FF} = \mp 124{\cdot}8$.

to be correct and thus the observed data confirmed the relative magnitudes of *cis* and *trans* F—F and F—CF_3 coupling constants in fluoroalkenes suggested by other workers, namely,

$$|J^{cis}_{F-F}| < |J^{trans}_{F-F}|$$

$$|J^{cis}_{F-CF_3}| > |J^{trans}_{F-CF_3}|$$

Several workers[76, 77, 78] have measured H—F coupling constants in fluoroalkenes in order to establish their relative magnitudes. From an examination of Table 11.33 it is apparent that J^{gem}_{HF} values fall in the range 72 to

85 cycles sec^{-1} while J_{HF}^{cis} are between 0 and 20 cycles sec^{-1} and J_{HF}^{trans} values are in the range 12 to 53 cycles sec^{-1}.

Reilly[(76)] has analysed the ^{1}H and ^{19}F spectra of *cis*- and *trans*-2-fluoro-3-chloropropene-2 and his results are shown in Table 11.34: it is seen that J_{HF}^{cis} is numerically less than J_{HF}^{trans}.

TABLE 11.34 ^{19}F AND ^{1}H SPECTRAL PARAMETERS[(79)] OF *cis*- AND *trans*-2-FLUORO-3-CHLOROPROPENE-2

	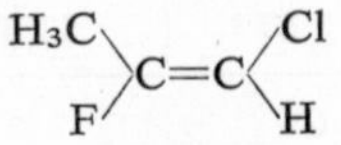 bp 30°C	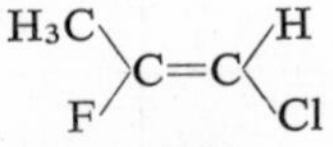 bp 60°C	
δ(=CH)	1·99 ppm	1·92 ppm	Ref. internal TMS
δ(—CH_3)	5·86 ppm	5·31 ppm	Ref. internal TMS
δ(—F)	12·66 ppm	10·18 ppm	Ref. external CF_3COOH
J_{FH}	10·8 cycles sec^{-1}	24·2 cycles sec^{-1}	
J_{FCH_3}	16·85 cycles sec^{-1}	16·3 cycles sec^{-1}	
J_{HCH_3}	1·14 cycles sec^{-1}	1·26 cycles sec^{-1}	

Coyle, Stafford and Stone[(74)] have analysed the ^{19}F spectrum of *cis*-1,2-difluoroethylene, CFH=CFH and they have reported the following parameters:

$$\delta_F(CFCl_3 \text{ internal reference}) = 168 \text{ ppm}$$

$$J_{FF}^{cis} = 18{\cdot}6 \quad J_{HF}^{trans} = 20{\cdot}1 \quad J_{HF}^{gem} = 71{\cdot}9 \text{ cycles sec}^{-1}$$

Baldeschwieler and co-workers[(188)] have examined the NMR spectra of *cis*- and *trans*-1,2-difluoroethylene in the gas phase and from a detailed analysis of the spectrum (which included considerations of the line widths) they were able to assign the relative signs of the coupling shown in Table 11.33.

By examining the ^{19}F resonance spectra of *cis*- and *trans*-2-chloroheptafluorobutene-2, one can differentiate between the *cis* and *trans* coupling constants involving CF_3 and F groups (see Table 11.35)[(82)]. The magnitudes of the coupling constants are in agreement with those previously found for fluoroalkenes. Coupling between two CF_3 groups separated by a double bond was also detected in the spectrum of these compounds and it was found that

$$|J_{CF_3-CF_3}^{trans}| \ll |J_{CF_3-CF_3}^{cis}|$$

The ^{1}H and ^{19}F resonance spectra of *cis*- and *trans*-1-fluoropropene have been fully analysed[(157)] and from the spectral parameters listed in Table 11.36 it is seen that

$$|J_{F-CH_3}^{trans}| > |J_{F-CH_3}^{cis}|$$

Several interesting F—F and H—F spin coupling constants have been measured in the resonance spectra of *cis*- and *trans*-1-fluoro-2-(perfluoroisopropyl)-

TABLE 11.35 ^{19}F CHEMICAL SHIFTS AND COUPLING CONSTANTS[82] OF *cis*- AND *trans*-2-CHLOROHEPTAFLUOROBUTENE-2

$CF_3CCl{=}CFCF_3$

	1-CF_3		
	$\varphi^{*\,a}$	$J(1,3)$	$J(1,4)$
trans	+64·804	24·72	1·27
cis	+62·180	8·67	11·32
	4-CF_3		
	$\varphi^{*\,a}$	$J(4,1)$	$J(4,3)$
trans	+68·350	1·33	5·49
cis	+66·274	11·43	7·74
	3-F		
	$\varphi^{*\,a}$	$J(3,1)$	$J(3,4)$
trans	+113·669	24·76	5·38
cis	+106·761	8·09	8·09

[a] Chemical shifts measured in ppm from CCl_3F internal reference in a solution containing 20 per cent by volume of the sample in CCl_3F.

TABLE 11.36 THE ^1H AND ^{19}F CHEMICAL SHIFTS AND SPIN COUPLING CONSTANTS FOR 1-FLUOROPROPENE[157]

	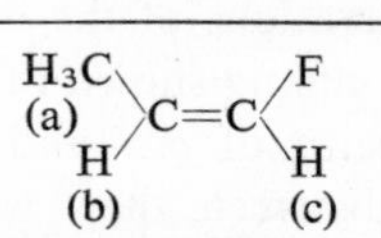	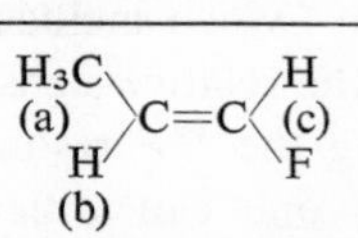	
δ_{CH_3}	−1·596 ppm	−1·498 ppm	to low fields of internal TMS
δ_{H_b}	−4·720 ppm	−5·300 ppm	
δ_{H_c}	−6·451 ppm	−6·450 ppm	
δ_F	131·4 ppm	129·5 ppm	to high fields of internal CCl_3F
$J_{H_bCH_3}$	7·0 cycles sec^{-1}	7·1 cycles sec^{-1}	
$J_{H_cCH_3}$	−1·8	−1·7	
J_{FCH_3}	2·6	3·3	
$J_{H_bH_c}$	+4·5	+11·1	
J_{H_bF}	+41·8	+19·9	
J_{H_cF}	+89·9†	+84·8†	

† Arbitrarily assumed to be positive.

TABLE 11.37 THE ^{1}H AND ^{19}F CHEMICAL SHIFTS AND SPIN COUPLING CONSTANTS OF *cis*- AND *trans*-1-FLUORO-2-(PERFLUOROISOPROPYL)ETHYLENE[78]

Coupling constants (cycles sec^{-1})	$(CF_3^a)_2CF_c(H_a)C{=}C(F_b)H_b$	$(CF_3^a)_2CF_c(H_a)C{=}C(H_b)F_b$
J_{HaHb}	5·9	11·3
J_{HbFc}	2·1	~0·0
J_{HbFb}	77·3	78·3
J_{HbFa}	~0·0	~0·0
J_{HaFa}	0·62	~0·15
J_{HaFc}	22·7	21·1
J_{HaFb}	37·0	16·0
J_{FaFc}	7·6	7·0
J_{FbFc}	31·0	5·0
J_{FaFb}	5·8	0·56
Chemical shifts † (ppm)		
δ_{Fa}	1·82	2·32
δ_{Fb}	32·31	40·50
δ_{Fc}	107·7	110·2
τ_{Ha}	5·10	4·41
τ_{Hb}	3·40	3·04

† ^{19}F chemical shifts measured from CF_3COOH external reference. ^{1}H chemical shifts are τ values.

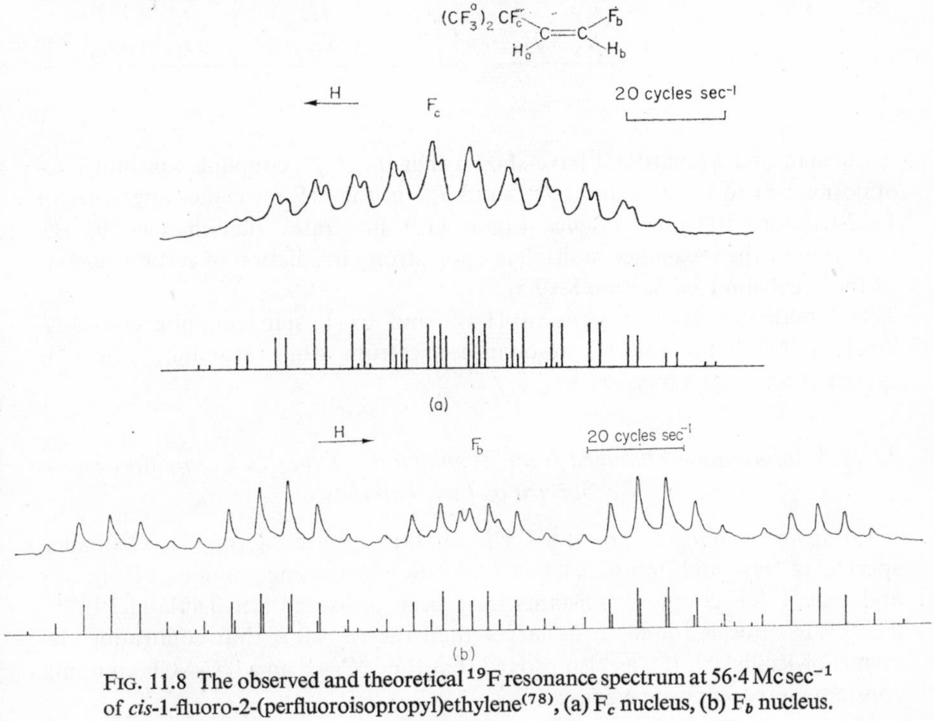

FIG. 11.8 The observed and theoretical ^{19}F resonance spectrum at 56·4 Mc sec^{-1} of *cis*-1-fluoro-2-(perfluoroisopropyl)ethylene[78], (a) F_c nucleus, (b) F_b nucleus.

ethylene (see Table 11.37)[78]. Although the ^1H and ^{19}F resonance spectra of the compounds are first order, they are complex because of the profusion of spin–spin interactions. Figure 11.8 shows the ^{19}F resonance spectra of two of the fluorine nuclei in the *cis* isomer: the F_c multiplet (Fig. 11.8a) is shown to be a doublet ($J_{F_bF_c} = 31{\cdot}0$) of doublets ($J_{H_aF_c} = 22{\cdot}7$) of septets ($J_{F_c(CF_3)_2} = 7{\cdot}6$) of doublets ($J_{H_bF_c} = 2{\cdot}1$ cycles sec^{-1}), while the F_b multiplet (Fig. 11.8b) is a doublet ($J_{H_bF_b} = 77{\cdot}3$) of doublets ($J_{H_aF_b} = 37{\cdot}0$) of doublets ($J_{F_bF_c} = 31{\cdot}0$) of septets ($J_{F_b(CF_3)_2} = 5{\cdot}8$ cycles sec^{-1})[195].

11.11.4 *Relative Signs of* ^{19}F *Coupling Constants in Fluoroalkenes*

Evans[161] has derived the relative signs of several ^{19}F coupling constants in fluoroalkenes using the spin decoupling method: a summary of his findings is given in Table 11.38. The relative signs are probably the same in most fluoroalkenes and from the data obtained for a variety of typical compounds[24] the signs are as given in Table 11.13.

TABLE 11.38 RELATIVE SIGNS OF ^{19}F COUPLING CONSTANTS IN SOME FLUOROALKENES[161, 24]

$CF_2 = CFCl$	$J_{12} = J_{FF}^{gem}$ ±	$J_{13} = J_{FF}^{cis}$ ±	$J_{23} = J_{FF}^{trans}$ ∓
$CF_2 = CFH$	$J_{12} = J_{FF}^{gem}$ ±	$J_{13} = J_{FF}^{cis}$ ±	$J_{23} = J_{FF}^{trans}$ ∓
	$J_{34} = J_{HF}^{gem}$ ±	$J_{24} = J_{HF}^{cis}$ ∓	$J_{14} = J_{HF}^{trans}$ ±
$CF_2 = CFCF_3$	$J_{12} = J_{FF}^{gem}$ ±	$J_{13} = J_{FF}^{cis}$ ±	$J_{23} = J_{FF}^{trans}$ ∓
	$J_{34} = J_{FF_3}^{gem}$ ∓	$J_{24} = J_{FF_3}^{cis}$ ±	$J_{14} = J_{FF_3}^{trans}$ ±

Elleman and Manatt[153] have shown that the J_{FF}^{trans} coupling constant is of opposite sign to those of both J_{FF}^{gem} and J_{FF}^{cis} in the ^{19}F resonance spectrum of 1,1,2-trifluoro-2-bromoethylene. Figure 11.9 illustrates the changes in the spectrum of the resonance multiplets upon strong irradiation of certain regions of the spectrum (see Section 8.19.5).

To obtain the relative signs of H—F and F—F spin coupling constants involves irradiating the ^1H resonance spectrum while examining the ^{19}F spectrum and vice versa.

11.11.5 *Information Obtained from Examination of the* ^{13}CF *Satellites in the* ^{19}F *Spectra of Fluoroalkenes*

From an examination of the ^{13}CF satellite spectra in the ^{19}F resonance spectra of *cis*- and *trans*-CFCl=CFCl, the relative magnitudes of the *cis* and *trans* F—F coupling constants have been measured (see Table 11.39)[80]. The *trans* value is found to be larger than the *cis* value thus confirming the results of Reilly[76]. It was also proved that the ^{13}C—F and ^{13}C—CF coupling constants have opposite signs.

Tiers[81] has analysed the complex ^{13}CF satellite multiplets in the ^{19}F resonance spectra of *cis*- and *trans*-2,3-dichlorohexafluorobutene-2 ($ClCF_3C{=}CCF_3Cl$), and his results are summarised in Table 11.40. Spin coupling between *cis* CF_3—CF_3 groups is about ten times larger than that between *trans* CF_3—CF_3 groups[81, 82].

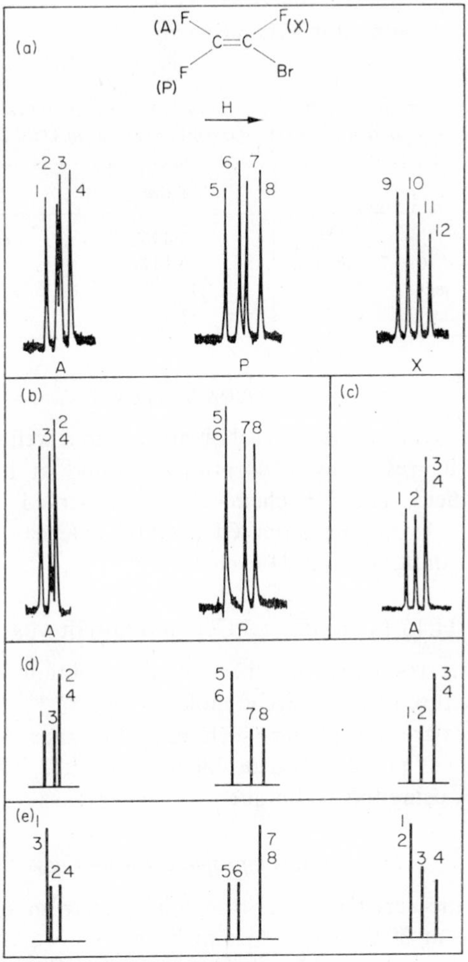

FIG. 11.9 ^{19}F NMR spectrum at 56·4 Mc sec^{-1} of 1,1,2-trifluoro-2-bromoethylene. *a*: phase detected undecoupled; *b*: A region when lines 5 and 6 irradiated and P region when lines 2 and 4 irradiated, $\Omega = 1008$ cycles sec^{-1}, $\gamma H_1/2\pi = 150$ cycles sec^{-1}; *c*: A region when lines 9 and 10 of region X irradiated, $\Omega = 2565$ cycles sec^{-1}, $\gamma H_1/2\pi = 150$ cycles sec^{-1}; *d*: changes predicted for double irradiation as described in *b* and *c* above if J_{AX} and J_{PX} are of different sign and J_{AX} and J_{PX} of different sign (far right); *e*: changes predicted in *b* and *c* if all the signs are the same. Elleman and Manatt[153].

TABLE 11.39 ^{19}F CHEMICAL SHIFTS AND SPIN COUPLING CONSTANTS FOR *cis*- AND *trans*-CFCl=CFCl[80]

	cis-CFCl=CFCl	*trans*-CFCl=CFCl	
φ	$+105{\cdot}079 \pm 0{\cdot}004$	$+119{\cdot}602 \pm 0{\cdot}003$	ppm
† $J_{^{13}C-^{19}F}$	$+299{\cdot}26 \pm 0{\cdot}27$	$+289{\cdot}57 \pm 0{\cdot}42$	cycles sec^{-1}
$J_{^{13}C-^{19}F}$	$-38{\cdot}10 \pm 0{\cdot}27$	$-53{\cdot}85 \pm 0{\cdot}42$	cycles sec^{-1}
$J_{FF'}$	$37{\cdot}50 \pm 0{\cdot}10$	$129{\cdot}57 \pm 0{\cdot}14$	cycles sec^{-1}

† $J_{^{13}C-^{19}F}$ has been arbitarily taken as positive.

TABLE 11.40 CHEMICAL SHIFTS AND SPIN COUPLING CONSTANTS[81] FOR *cis*- AND *trans*-2,3-DICHLOROHEXAFLUOROBUTENE-2

	Cis	*Trans*
φ ppm	$+60{\cdot}446$	$+63{\cdot}730$
$\Delta\varphi(^{13}CF_3—^{12}CF_3)$ ppm	$+0{\cdot}137$	$+0{\cdot}132$
$J_{^{13}CF}$ cycles sec^{-1}	275·3	275·7
$J_{CF_3-CF_3}$ cycles sec^{-1}	13·4	1·44

11.12 FLUOROACETYLENES

A fluorine atom on an acetylenic carbon atom is in a well shielded electronic environment and its resonance absorption is found at high values of the applied magnetic field. The ^{19}F chemical shift observed in fluoroacetylene, F—C≡C—H, is $+181{\cdot}3$ ppm from CF_3COOH external reference and the H—F coupling constant, J_{H-F}, is 21 cycles sec^{-1}[83].

11.13 FLUORINATED CYCLIC COMPOUNDS

Nuclear magnetic resonance has been used to obtain information about the molecular structure of many cyclic molecules[16, 84–89, 93]. In cases where the cyclic molecules are non-planar (such as cyclohexane derivatives) conformational isomerism is possible and problems associated with such isomerism can be investigated using this technique[16, 86–89, 93].

11.13.1 Cyclopropane Derivatives

Phillips[85] has measured the ^{19}F resonance spectrum of 1-methyl-2,2-difluorocyclopropane at 30·00 Mc sec^{-1} and he has shown the spectrum to be consistent with a cyclic structure for the molecule. The ^{19}F resonance spectrum of this molecule is shown in Fig. 11.10 (c). The two geminal fluorine nuclei are non-equivalent due to their different geometric configurations with respect to the methyl substituent and consequently they give rise to a pair of AB doublets (see Section 8.13.1) separated by a chemical shift of 16·8 ppm and having a *geminal* fluorine coupling constant of $J_{F-F} = 157$ cycles sec^{-1}. Further fine structure is evident on the absorption bands due to spin–spin coupling of the fluorine nuclei with the hydrogen nuclei in the neighbouring

—CH and —CH_2 groups: the components of the high field doublet have a pronounced doublet splitting from spin–spin interaction with the CH group while the components of the low field doublet are broadened, presumably because of coupling with both neighbouring groups. It was not possible to assign the two fluorine atoms to their respective absorption doublets.

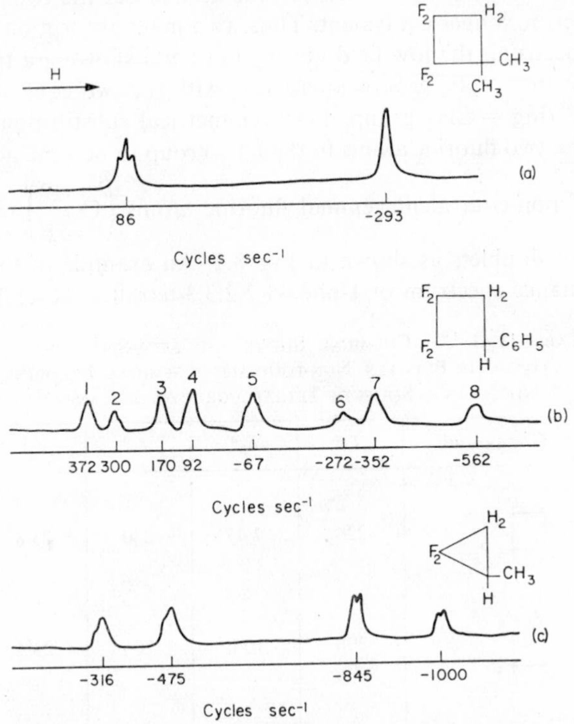

FIG. 11.10 The 30 Mc sec^{-1} ^{19}F resonance spectra of (a) 1,1-dimethyl-2,2,3,3-tetrafluorocyclobutane, (b) 1-phenyl-2,2,3,3-tetrafluorocyclobutane, (c) 1-methyl-2,2-difluorocyclopropane. Chemical shifts are measured in cycles sec^{-1} from the external reference tetrafluorocyclobutane. Phillips(85).

11.13.2 Mono- and Disubstituted Derivatives of Tetrafluorocyclobutane

The ^{19}F resonance spectrum of 1,1,2,2-tetrafluorocyclobutane consists of a single absorption band indicating that the four fluorine nuclei in this molecule are equivalently shielded(85). This would be expected if the molecule has a planar structure, or is rapidly interconverting between two non-planar structures.

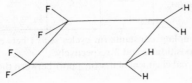

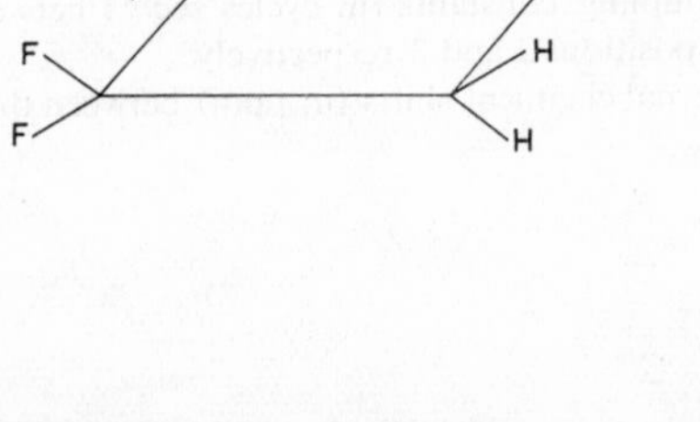

Measurements of the ^{19}F resonance spectra of derivatives of this cyclobutane show that the equivalence can be removed by suitable mono- or disubstitution. This point is illustrated by the ^{19}F spectrum of 1,1-dimethyl-2,2,3,3-tetrafluorocyclobutane reproduced in Fig. 11.10 (a). Disubstitution with two identical groups does not result in non-equivalence of the two fluorine atoms on the adjacent carbon atom (*geminal* fluorine atoms) but the two —CF_2 groups are themselves no longer equivalent. Thus, two main absorption bands appear in the ^{19}F spectrum, the low field absorption band showing a triplet splitting due to one of the —CF_2 groups interacting with the two equivalent hydrogen nuclei of the ring —CH_2 group. Less symmetrical substitution of the molecule causes the two fluorine atoms in the CF_2 group to become non-equivalent. Each pair of non-equivalent geminal fluorine atoms $\left(\mathrm{C}{<}^{\mathrm{F}}_{\mathrm{F}}\right)$ will give rise to an AB pair of doublets as shown in Fig. 8.7. An example of this is found in the ^{19}F resonance spectrum of 1-phenyl-2,2,3,3-tetrafluorocyclobutane shown

TABLE 11.41 ^{19}F CHEMICAL SHIFTS AND SPIN–SPIN COUPLING CONSTANTS BETWEEN NON-EQUIVALENT GEMINAL FLUORINE NUCLEI IN A SERIES OF TETRAFLUOROCYCLOBUTANES(85)

Compound	$J_3{}^a$	$\delta_3{}^a$	$J_2{}^b$	$\delta_2{}^b$
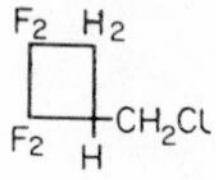	224	7·43	230	23·8
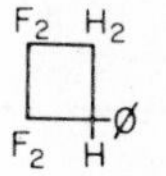	206	10·0	206	23·5
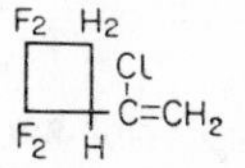	211	8·50	202	22·5
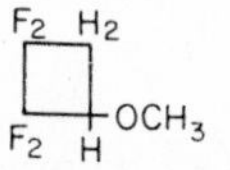	210	2·90	213	22·4
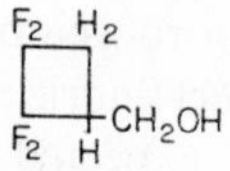	219	5·53	218	21·0
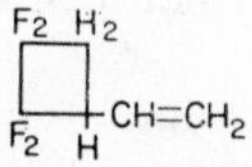	220	7·73	220	20·5

[a] J_2 and J_3 are the coupling constants (in cycles sec^{-1}) between the two non-equivalent *geminal* fluorine nuclei at positions 2 and 3 respectively.

[b] δ_2 and δ_3 are the internal chemical shifts (in ppm) between the two non-equivalent *geminal* fluorine nuclei.

in Fig. 11.10 (b). All four fluorine atoms are non-equivalent and the spectrum consists of two overlapping AB quartets. By examining a complete series of substituted tetrafluorocyclobutanes it was possible to obtain empirical information which allows one to assign the two CF_2 groups to their respective AB quartets. Thus, bands 1, 3, 7 and 8 in Fig. 11.10 (b) are due to the CF_2 group in the 2-position and bands 2, 4, 5 and 6 correspond to the CF_2 group in the 3-position. Table 11.41 contains data abstracted from the ^{19}F resonance spectra of several mono- and disubstituted tetrafluorocyclobutanes[85]. In a few cases, the fluorine absorption bands possess fine structure due to spin–spin coupling of the fluorine nuclei with neighbouring hydrogen nuclei.

The average value of the coupling constant between *geminal* fluorine atoms in tetrafluorocyclobutanes is 211 cycles sec^{-1}. From this investigation it was found that, generally, the difference in shielding between two non-equivalent *geminal* fluorine atoms in a —CF_2 group is larger in a monosubstituted than in a disubstituted derivative of tetrafluorocyclobutane. This is consistent with the view that the factors controlling the shielding of the fluorine nuclei in these molecules could be either (i) an asymmetrical inductive effect or (ii) a direct fluorine-substituent potential interaction, since in each case the chemical shifts of the fluorine nuclei in the disubstituted derivatives would be predicted to be approximately equal to the difference between the chemical shifts of the two related monosubstituted cyclobutanes.

Previous to these studies, Shoolery[84] had examined several substituted fluorocyclobutanes which have the following general structures

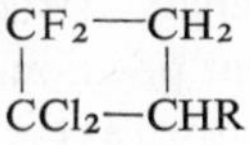

$$\begin{array}{cc} \begin{array}{cc} CF_2 & \!\!\!\!-CH_2 \\ | & | \\ CCl_2 & \!\!\!\!-CHR \end{array} & \begin{array}{cc} CF_2 & \!\!\!\!-CHR \\ | & | \\ CCl_2 & \!\!\!\!-CH_2 \end{array} \\ \text{(I)} & \text{(II)} \end{array}$$

where R is —$Si(OC_2H_5)_3$, —$Si(CH_3)_3$ and —$Si(CH_3)_2R'$ and he showed that the two *geminal* fluorine atoms are non-equivalent in all the molecules studied, due to the asymmetrical substitution of one of the carbon atoms in the planar ring structure. The derivative of formula

$$\begin{array}{cc} CF_2 & \!\!\!\!-CH_2 \\ | & | \\ CF_2 & \!\!\!\!-CH(Si(CH_3)_3) \end{array}$$

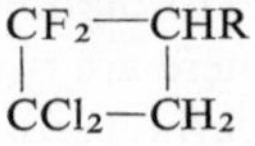

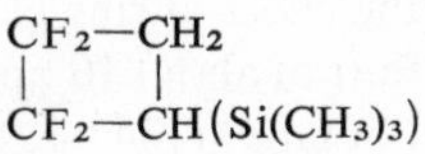

was shown to possess two different pairs of non-equivalent geminal fluorine atoms; the ^{19}F resonance spectrum of this molecule being very similar to that shown in Fig. 11.10 (b).

An interesting example of the occasional failure of H—F spin–spin coupling constants to decrease monotonically with the number of intervening bonds between the interacting nuclei is provided by a series of substituted cyclobutenes examined by Sharts and Roberts[18]. In molecules of the type

$$\begin{array}{ccc} \begin{array}{cc} C_6H_5C & \!\!\!\!-CFCl \\ \| & | \\ HC & \!\!\!\!-CF_2 \end{array} & \text{and} & \begin{array}{cc} C_6H_5C & \!\!\!\!-CH_2 \\ \| & | \\ FC & \!\!\!\!-CF_2 \end{array} \end{array}$$

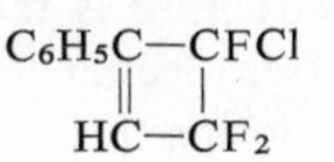

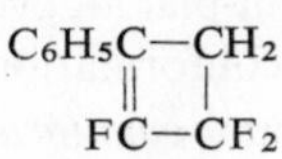

the cross-ring H—F coupling (four bonds between nuclei) of $J_{HF} = 8$ to 12 cycles sec^{-1} is much greater than that between adjacent hydrogen and fluorine nuclei of $J_{H-F} = 1$ to 2 cycles sec^{-1} (three bonds between nuclei).

NMR studies have also been conducted on fluorine-containing cyclobutane derivatives of general formula

$$\begin{array}{c} CH_2\!\!-\!\!CRR' \\ | \qquad | \\ CF_2\!\!-\!\!CFX \end{array}$$

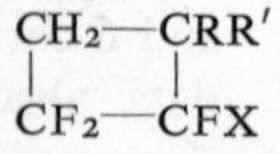

where R,R' and X are substituent groups[90].

Cyclobutane and substituted cyclobutanes have a slightly puckered structure[91] and this should be detectable in a NMR experiment. Phillips[92] has observed a temperature dependence of the ^{19}F resonance spectrum of 1-chloro-2,2,3,3-tetrafluorocyclobutane (III) which he has attributed to the temperature dependence of the populations of the higher vibrational states of the ring puckering fundamental.

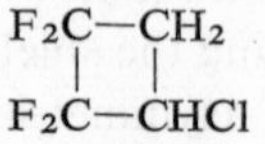

$$\begin{array}{c} F_2C\!\!-\!\!CH_2 \\ | \qquad | \\ F_2C\!\!-\!\!CHCl \end{array}$$
$$\text{(III)}$$

11.13.3 Fluorinated Cyclohexanes

Cyclohexane and its derivatives possess non-planar ring structures due to the ring carbon atoms attempting to take up positions which allow the C—C bonds to subtend tetrahedral bond angles to each other. The most stable manner of achieving this is by the formation of a "chair" structure (see Section 9.7.1). On each carbon atom there are two different positions for substitution: one in the plane of the ring of carbon atoms and known as the "*equatorial*" position (*e*) and the other either above or below the plane of the ring known as the "*axial*" position (*a*). Simultaneous partial rotation about each C—C bond will cause a substituent which was originally in an *axial* position to take up an *equatorial* position; that is, for a monosubstituted cyclohexane derivative there are two forms of the molecule each with a different spatial arrangement of atoms and these two forms are referred to as conformational isomers.

Tiers[94] has observed that the effect of ring closure on a —CF$_2$— resonance band is to produce an upfield shift of about 10 ppm. Thus perfluorocyclohexane (133·25φ) and perfluorocyclobutane (134·94φ) have higher shielded CF$_2$ groups than the midchain —CF$_2$— groups in long chain n-perfluoroalkyls ($\varphi \sim 122\cdot5$). Similar effects have been observed with cyclic fluorocarbon sulphides (see Table 11.18A).

Perfluorocyclohexane, C_6F_{12}. The room temperature ^{19}F spectrum of perfluorocyclohexane consists of a single broad absorption band. On cooling a solution of the sample in trichlorofluoromethane and trifluoromethylbenzene to $-66°C$ the broad band resolves itself into an AB quartet[86]. At room temperature the non-planar cyclohexane structure is rapidly interconverting between identical conformational forms (see Section 9.7), a process which results in the *axial* and *equatorial* positions losing their identity. Consequently each fluorine atom spends equal periods of time in *axial* and *equatorial* positions and the lifetime of a fluorine atom in either state is such that a single absorption band is observed at room temperature. On lowering the temperature, the lifetime of a fluorine atom in any particular position increases until at $-66°$C the interconversion is sufficiently slow to allow separate absorption bands to be observed for the fluorine atoms in the *axial* and *equatorial* positions. The chemical shift difference between fluorine nuclei in *axial* and *equatorial* positions is 18·2 ppm and the coupling constant between the *geminal* fluorine nuclei is 284 ± 1 cycles sec^{-1}. The *geminal* F—F coupling constant is considerably larger than similar coupling constants in fluorocyclobutanes[85] ($J_{FF} = 220$ cycles sec^{-1}) and fluorocyclopropanes[85] ($J_{FF} = 160$ cycles sec^{-1}).

Monosubstituted Perfluorocyclohexanes. Monosubstitution of a cyclohexane ring usually results in the substituted molecule existing in a preferred conformational form at room temperature with the substituent occupying an

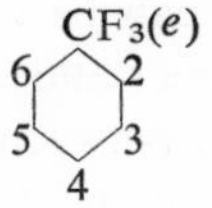

$C_6F_{11}\cdot CF_3$

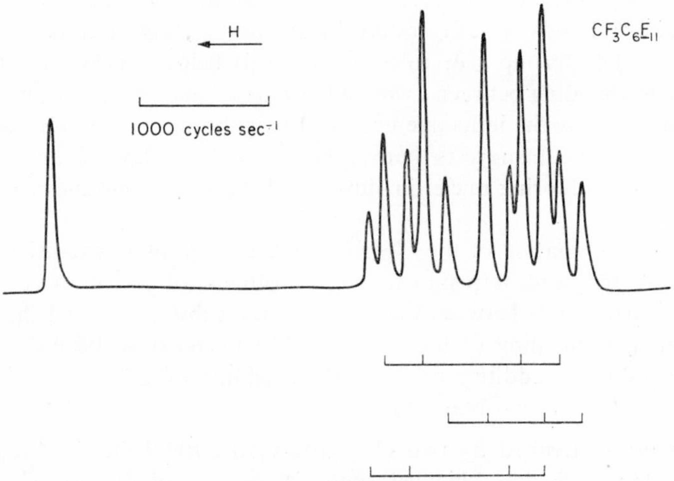

FIG. 11.11 The ^{19}F resonance spectrum of the ring fluorine nuclei in perfluoromethylcyclohexane at 56·4 Mc sec^{-1}.

equatorial position. A "fixed" conformer of this type would give rise to three different pairs of non-equivalent *geminal* fluorine nuclei. This can be seen by considering the structure of perfluoromethylcyclohexane shown above.

Fluorine atoms in the positions (2,6), (3,5) and 4 are obviously non-equivalent: furthermore, the two fluorine atoms on each carbon atom are themselves non-equivalent because they occupy *equatorial* and *axial* positions. Thus, each of the three sets of non-equivalent *geminal* fluorine atoms gives rise to an AB quartet in the ^{19}F resonance spectrum of this molecule[16] (see Fig. 11.11). Other monosubstituted derivatives such as the monohydro- and the monochloro derivatives show similar features in their ^{19}F resonance spectra (there is good evidence to show that the monohydroperfluorocyclohexane is rapidly interconverting at room temperature)[16, 87].

Dihydroperfluorocyclohexanes, $C_6F_{10}H_2$. The ^{19}F resonance spectra of the complete series of isomers of the dihydro derivatives have been investigated and interpreted in an analogous manner to those of the monosubstituted derivatives[16, 87, 93]. In some cases it is possible to decide unequivocally whether or not a molecule is undergoing rapid interconversion at room temperature. In this respect, it is found useful to apply the information obtained from the low temperature investigation of perfluorocyclohexane to assist in the assignments. The appearance in the ^{19}F resonance spectrum of an AB quartet containing a chemical shift of $\sim 18{\cdot}0$ ppm, as found for the *geminal* fluorine atoms in perfluorocyclohexane, can be taken as strong evidence for the absence of rapid interconversion. Homer and Thomas[93] have shown that the *cis*-1H:3H isomer is inverting rapidly between non-equivalent chair forms at room temperature. From the assignments made for the dihydrodecafluorocyclohexanes shown in Table 11.42 it can be seen that proximity to a hydrogen atom through bonds usually results in the deshielding of fluorine nuclei in an adjacent CF_2 group (see rules (ii) and (iii) below). However, the large difference in shielding between *axial* and *equatorial* fluorine atoms in perfluorocyclohexane, where the inductive effects of neighbouring groups would be expected to be identical, suggests that spatial interactions play a dominant part in the shielding of fluorine nuclei in substituted fluorocyclohexanes (see Section 4.4.4).

From an examination of the ^{19}F resonance spectra of an extensive series of mono-, di-, tri- and tetrasubstituted derivatives of perfluorocyclohexane, empirical correlations between the nature of the substituents and their contributions to the shielding of neighbouring ^{19}F nuclei have been deduced[93]. Thus the following additive rules for the shielding of CF_2 groups in fluorocyclohexanes have been obtained:

(i) In a group flanked by two CF_2 groups, the *axial* fluorine ($\delta_{CF_3COOH} = +47{\cdot}4$ ppm) is less shielded than the *equatorial* fluorine ($\delta_{CF_3COOH} = +65{\cdot}1$ ppm) by 17·7 ppm.

(ii) An α-*axial* hydrogen atom shields F_a by 2·3 ppm and deshields F_e by 15·0 ppm.

(iii) An α-*equatorial* hydrogen atom deshields F_a by 4·3 ppm and deshields F_e by 10·5 ppm.

(iv) A β-*axial* hydrogen atom shields F_e by about 4 ppm.

Cis- and Trans-perfluorodecalin. A NMR investigation of the ^{19}F resonance spectra of these compounds has confirmed that the *cis* isomer is rapidly interconverting at room temperature while the *trans* molecule forms a rigid conformer as shown in Fig. 11.12[88].

TABLE 11.42 THE ^{19}F CHEMICAL SHIFTS AT 40 MC SEC^{-1} AND ASSIGNMENTS FOR SOME DIHYDRO-DECAFLUOROCYCLOHEXANES[87]

Compound	Assignment[a]	Band	Chemical shift (cycles sec^{-1})
cis-1H:3H, b.p. 90·9°	2, 2′	1	1265
		2	1570
		4	1790
		6	2050
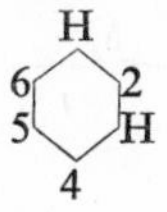		3	1650
	4, 6	5	1930
		6	2050
	4′, 6′	8	2330
	5, 5′	7	2250
	1′, 3′	10	5730
		11	5770
cis-1H:4H, b.p. 85·4°	2, 3, 5, 6	1	1670
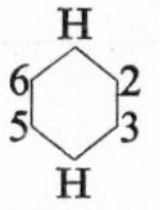		2	1950
		3	2080
	2′, 3′, 5′, 6′	4	2370
	1′, 4′	5	5940
		6	5980
trans-1H/2H, b.p. 70°		1	1790
	4*a*, 5*a*	3	2070
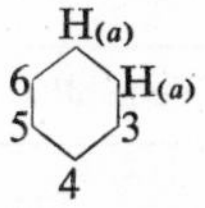		2	1860
	3*e*, 3*a*, 6*e*, 6*a*	4	2155
		5	2420
		6	2550
	4*e*, 5*e*	7	2840
		8	5850
	1*e*, 2*e*	9	5900
Mixture of *trans*-1H/3H and *trans*-1H/4H, b.p. 79°			
	2, 2′	1	1815
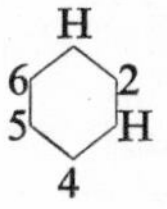		2	2010
	4, 4′, 6, 6′	3	2085
	5, 5′	5	2255
	1, 3	6	5860
		7	5905
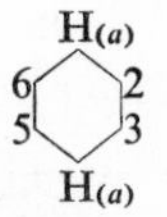	2*e*, 2*a*, 3*e*, 3*a*	4	2100
	5*e*, 5*a*, 6*e*, 6*a*	4	2100
		8	6120
	1*e*, 4*e*	9	6165

[a] Atoms marked with a prime are *trans* to the nearest hydrogen atom via the bonds in an interconverting molecule.

The bands bracketed together are components of a multiplet absorption band. C_6F_{12} has a chemical shift of +2200 cycles sec^{-1} (55 ppm) from CF_3COOH external reference. Some of the above assignments were obtained from reference 93.

In the fixed *trans* isomer there are two sets of non-equivalent *geminal* fluorine atoms each resulting in an AB quartet in the ^{19}F resonance spectrum of the molecule (Fig. 11.12(b)). One AB quartet (marked *a* in the spectrum) contains a chemical shift of 18·2 ppm (as found in the ^{19}F spectrum of the fixed conformer of

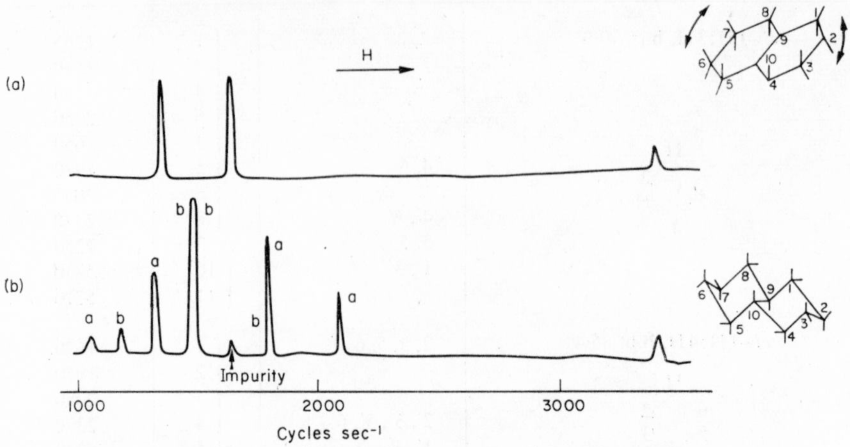

FIG. 11.12 The ^{19}F resonance spectra at 30·1 Mc sec^{-1} of (a) *cis*-perfluorodecalin and (b) *trans*-perfluorodecalin. Frequencies are measured from the external reference trifluoroacetic acid. Homer and Thomas(88).

TABLE 11.43 ^{19}F CHEMICAL SHIFTS OF SOME FLUOROCYCLOHEXENES(78)

Compound	Assignment	^{19}F Chemical shift (ppm)†
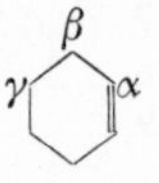 perfluorocyclohexene	β γ α	40·9 55·6 74·6
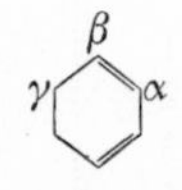 perfluorocyclohexa-1,3-diene	α‡ β‡ γ	76·9 86·0 48·6
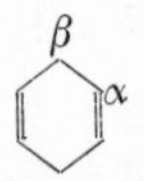 perfluorocyclohexa-1,4-diene	α β	80·9 36·6
 perfluorobenzene		88·0

† Chemical shifts measured in ppm from CF_3COOH external reference.
‡ These assignments are tentative.

C_6F_{12}) which confirms that this molecule is fixed, hence the remaining pair of doublets can be assigned to the fluorine atoms adjacent to the fused position. For the rapidly interconverting *cis* isomer there are two different sets of identical *geminal* fluorine atoms which give rise to two single absorption bands as shown in Fig. 11.12 (a).

Fluorinated Cyclohexenes. Perfluorocyclohexene and perfluorocyclohexadienes have very complicated ^{19}F resonance spectra due to the presence of strongly coupled chemically equivalent fluorine nuclei. Table 11.43 contains the ^{19}F chemical shifts for several molecules of this type: the chemical shift of perfluorobenzene has been included for comparison purposes(78). The structures of some transition metal complexes of perfluorocyclohexa-1,3-diene and 1,4-diene have been identified by means of NMR spectroscopy(70).

11.13.4 Fluorinated Heterocyclic Compounds

Perfluoropiperidine C_5NF_{11}. A rapidly interconverting molecule of perfluoropiperidine would give rise to four types of fluorine nuclei, α, β, γ and NF fluorine nuclei. Since averaged values of coupling constants of the type $J_{\alpha\beta}$

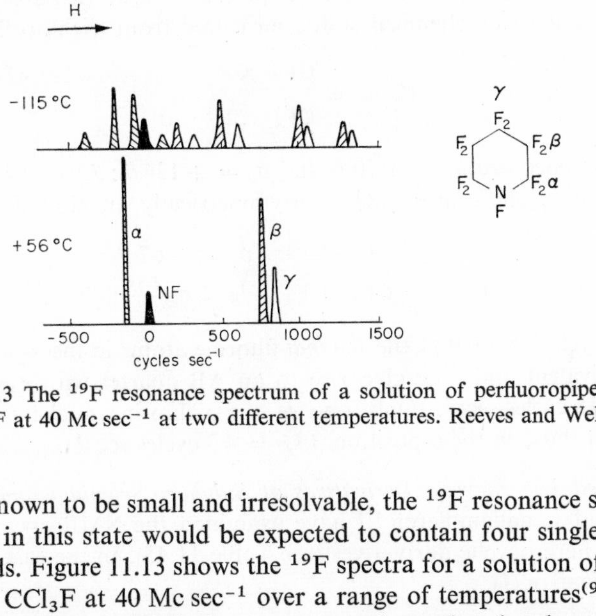

FIG. 11.13 The ^{19}F resonance spectrum of a solution of perfluoropiperidine in CCl_3F at 40 Mc sec^{-1} at two different temperatures. Reeves and Wells(95).

and $J_{\beta\gamma}$ are known to be small and irresolvable, the ^{19}F resonance spectrum of the molecule in this state would be expected to contain four single broad absorption bands. Figure 11.13 shows the ^{19}F spectra for a solution of perfluoropiperidine in CCl_3F at 40 Mc sec^{-1} over a range of temperatures(95). At high temperatures (above -40°C) four separate absorption bands are observed indicating the presence of rapid conformational interconversion in the molecule. On lowering the temperature, the NF absorption band remains unchanged but three AB quartets appear for the α, β and γ ring fluorine nuclei, indicating that the *geminal* fluorine nuclei at each ring position are no longer equivalent. The fact that the NF absorption band remains unchanged even at -115°C suggests that the NF fluorine atom is rapidly interconverting at this temperature.

Table 11.44 gives the ^{19}F chemical shifts and spin coupling constants measured for perfluoropiperidine: they are similar to the values measured for fluoro-cyclohexanes[16].

TABLE 11.44 ^{19}F Chemical Shifts and Geminal Coupling Constants of Perfluoro-piperidine[95]

	Fluorine nucleus	Coupling constant (cycles sec^{-1})	Chemical shift †		
		J_{ae}	F_a	F_e	NF
F$_2$γ, F$_2$, F$_2$β, F$_2$, N, F$_2$α, F	α	185	+113·7	+105·2	
	β	278	+140·9	+122·1	
	γ	284	+142·1	+125·1	
	NF				+112·9

† Chemical shifts measured in ppm from CCl_3F internal reference.

$(CF_2)_4Fe(CO)_4$[96]. In this cylic compound (I) the metal atom is symmetrically substituted and its ^{19}F resonance spectrum shows two absorption multiplets as expected (the chemical shifts, measured from trichlorofluoromethane

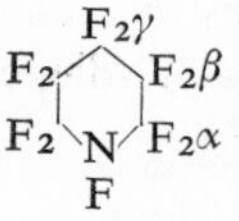

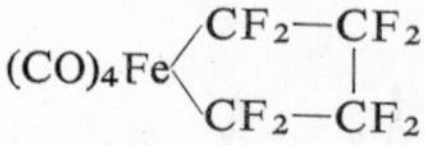

$$(CO)_4Fe \Big\langle \begin{matrix} CF_2-CF_2 \\ | \\ CF_2-CF_2 \end{matrix} \quad (I)$$

internal reference are $\delta_\alpha = +70·6$ and $\delta_\beta = +136·9 : J_{\alpha\beta} = 2·4$ cycles sec^{-1}). When heterocyclic compounds are asymmetrically substituted as in

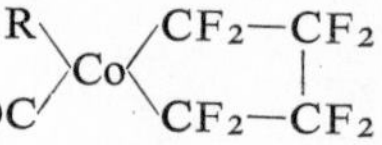

$$\begin{matrix} R \\ OC \end{matrix} \Big\rangle Co \Big\langle \begin{matrix} CF_2-CF_2 \\ | \\ CF_2-CF_2 \end{matrix} \quad \begin{matrix} \delta_\alpha = +67·5 \\ \delta_\beta = +135 \text{ ppm} \end{matrix}$$

where R is cyclopentadienyl, the *geminal* fluorine atoms in the α-position are no longer equivalent and they give rise to an AB quartet with $\delta_{AB} = 6·25$ ppm and $J = 218$ cycles sec^{-1}. Only one of the α-fluorine nuclei is observed to couple with those in the β-position, ($J_{\alpha\beta} = 4·3$ cycles sec^{-1}).

Fluorinated Heterocyclic Derivatives of Sulphur, Selenium and Phosphorus. Krespan and Langkammerer[97] have examined the NMR spectra of several fluorinated hererocyclic derivatives (see Table 11.45). In the case of the phosphorus derivative (I)

$$\begin{matrix} I \\ | \\ P \\ F_2C \quad CF_2 \\ | \qquad | \\ F_2C \quad CF_2 \\ P \\ | \\ I \end{matrix} \quad (I)$$

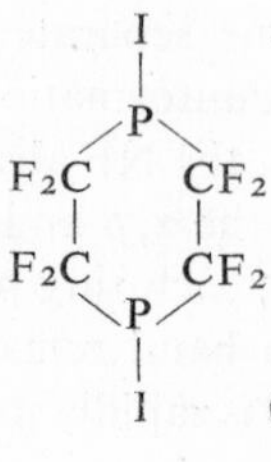

the ^{19}F resonance spectrum is consistent with the molecule being in a fixed conformation, so that the *geminal* fluorine nuclei in each CF_2 group are non-equivalent ($J_{F_1F_2}$ = 280 cycles sec^{-1}, J_{PF_1} = 128 cycles sec^{-1} and J_{PF_2} = 54 cycles sec^{-1}). No change in the spectrum was observed on heating the sample to 100°C indicating that the barrier to *axial/equatorial* interconversion is high.

TABLE 11.45 ^{19}F CHEMICAL SHIFTS OF SEVERAL FLUORINATED HETEROCYCLIC COMPOUNDS(97)

Compound	δ ppm† CF_2—M	δ ppm† —C—CF_2—C
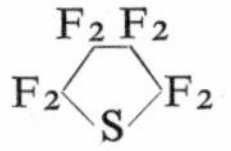	+19·7	+6·44
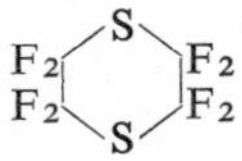	+23·4	
	+18·2	+64·9
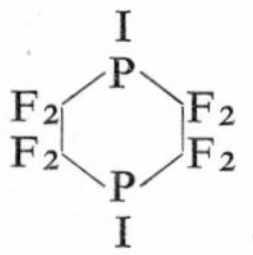	+24·4 +46·3	

† Chemical shifts measured in ppm from $CFCl_2CFCl_2$ external reference. $\delta_{CF_3COOH ext} = \delta_{Cl_2FCCFCl_2 ext} - 12{\cdot}0$ ppm (very approximate conversion).

Miscellaneous Cyclic Compounds. Ito and co-workers(156) have measured the ^{19}F chemical shifts of 2- and 3-fluoropyridines, 1-fluoropyrene and cyclohexyl fluoride and they have found that the shifts correlate most closely with the π-electron density on the ring carbon atom to which the fluorine is bonded. This suggests that the shielding variations are controlled mainly by the polarity of the CF σ-bond.

11.14 METHYL AND ETHYL FLUOROSILANES R_xSiF_{4-x}

Schnell and Rochow(98) have investigated the changes in the magnetic shielding of fluorine atoms in fluorosilanes with variation in the nature and number of alkyl substituents: their results are given in Fig. 11.14. They suggested that the two most important factors controlling the shielding of fluorine nuclei in fluorosilanes are (i) an inductive effect which would result in increased shielding when an electron releasing alkyl group is introduced into the molecule, (ii) an opposing effect due to the presence of Si—F $d\pi$—$p\pi$ bonding(99). It was not possible to resolve the relative importance of these two effects from the above measurements but the presence of a minimum in each curve indicates the two effects to be in opposition. The fluorine nuclei in the ethyl derivatives are more shielded than in the methyl derivatives as would be predicted from simple inductive considerations.

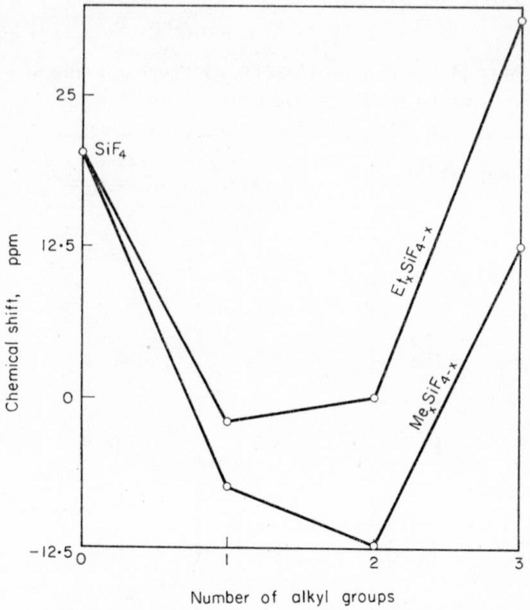

FIG. 11.14 Graph of ^{19}F chemical shifts in methyl and ethyl fluorosilanes (R_xSiF_{4-x}) against the number of alkyl substituents. $\delta_{CF_3COOH} = \delta_{Et_2SiF_2} + 66{\cdot}6$ ppm. Schnell and Rochow(98).

11.15 ANTIMONY PENTAFLUORIDE

At room temperature, antimony pentafluoride exists as a viscous polymeric liquid and a possible structure for this molecule has been suggested on the basis of NMR evidence(100). At -10°C, the ^{19}F resonance spectrum of this molecule consists of three absorption bands in the intensity ratio 1:2:2 indicating the presence of three non-equivalent types of fluorine nuclei in the molecule (see Fig. 11.15). Such a spectrum would result from a long chain molecule constructed from SbF_6^- units as shown in Fig. 11.16: each SbF_6^- group shares two of its fluorine atoms (type A) with neighbouring groups and this results in two of the remaining four fluorine atoms (type B) being in *trans* positions to type A atoms, while the other two fluorine atoms (type C) are *trans* to each other. Fine structure on the bands is due to spin–spin interaction between the three types of differently shielded fluorine nuclei, and the following coupling constants have been estimated from these splittings: $J_{AB} = \sim 70$ cycles sec^{-1}, $J_{BC} \sim 130$ cycles sec^{-1}, and $J_{AC} < 30$ cycles sec^{-1}. The single absorption band observed in the room temperature ^{19}F resonance

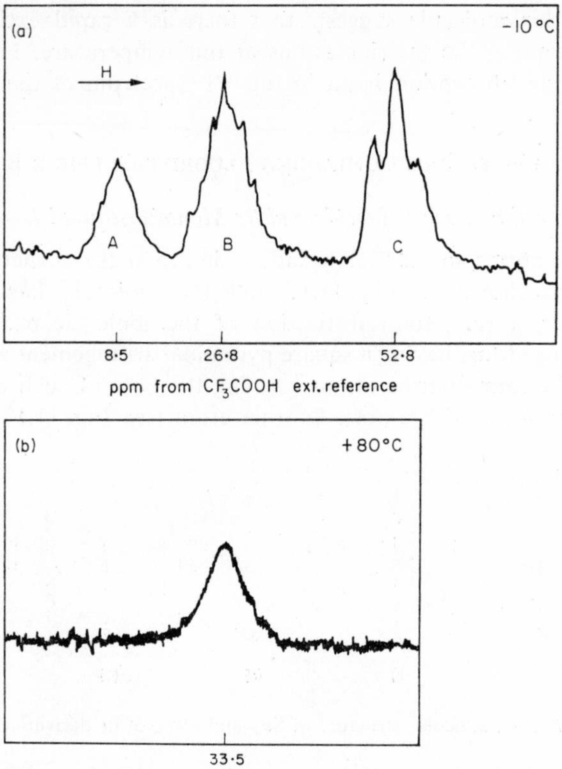

FIG. 11.15 The ^{19}F resonance spectrum of antimony pentafluoride at 40 Mc sec^{-1} (a) at about -10°C, (b) at about 80°C. Hoffman, Holder and Jolly(100).

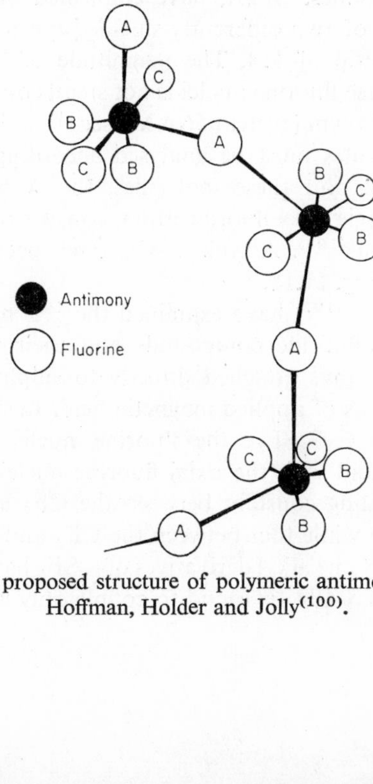

FIG. 11.16 The proposed structure of polymeric antimony pentafluoride. Hoffman, Holder and Jolly(100).

spectrum of this molecule suggests that there is a rapid exchange process taking place among the fluorine atoms at this temperature. Figure 11.15 (b) shows the single absorption band in the ^{19}F spectrum of the compound at about 80°C.

11.16 Compounds Containing Fluorine–Sulphur Bonds

11.16.1 Sulphur Hexafluoride and its Monosubstituted Derivatives

The fluorine atoms in sulphur hexafluoride are at the corners of a regular octahedron as shown in Fig. 11.17 and the molecule has a tetragonal bipyramidal structure. Monosubstitution of the molecule results in the remaining fluorine atoms having a square pyramidal arrangement with respect to each other. The four fluorine atoms forming the base of such a pyramid will be different from the single apex fluorine atom (see Fig. 11.17 (b)). Nuclear

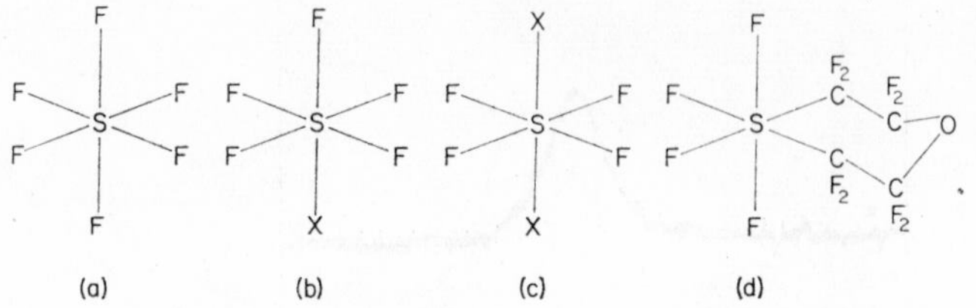

FIG. 11.17 The molecular structure of SF_6 and some of its derivatives.

magnetic resonance measurements of the ^{19}F spectra of monosubstituted sulphur hexafluoride molecules, SF_5X, have confirmed the above structure by indicating the presence of two differently shielded types of fluorine nucleus in the correct intensity ratio of 1:4. The magnitude of the coupling constant between the apex and base fluorine nuclei is not small compared to the chemical shift difference between them (even at 56·4 Mc sec^{-1}) and thus the observed ^{19}F spectra of SF_5X molecules must be analysed according to an AB_4 analysis (see Section 8.13.4)[101]. For these molecules, the A part of the spectrum, corresponding to the single apex fluorine atom, consists of 9 bands whilst the B region contains 12 bands[103]. A typical AB_4 type spectrum for this class of molecules is shown in Fig. 11.18.

Merrill and co-workers[102] have examined the ^{19}F resonance spectra of a series of sulphur pentafluoride compounds and their results are shown in Table 11.46. Fluorine atoms attached directly to sulphur atoms give resonance signals at low values of applied magnetic field. In fluoroalkyl derivatives such as $C_3F_7SF_5$ and $C_4F_9SF_5$, the fluorine nuclei in the α-CF_2 group couple with the basal and with the axial fluorine nuclei of the —SF_5 group. For CF_3SF_5, the coupling constant between the CF_3 and the basal fluorine nuclei is 22 cycles sec^{-1} while that between the CF_3 and the axial fluorine nucleus is 6·4 cycles sec^{-1}. Some alkyl derivatives of —SF_5 have been examined (e.g. $ClCH_2CH_2SF_5$) and the α-CH_2 is found to couple only with the basal fluorine nuclei in the SF_5 group ($J_{CH_2-FB} = 6$–8 cycles sec^{-1})(103). The spin coupling constant between the axial and basal fluorine nuclei is close to 150 cycles sec^{-1} in all the molecules examined. The apex fluorine nuclei are usually more shielded than the basal fluorine nuclei but this situation is reversed in the alkyl derivatives (see Table 11.47)(103, 104). By changing the substituent, large variations in the shielding of the basal fluorine nuclei occur. The variation in shielding of the basal fluorine nuclei with change in substituent is roughly similar to that observed when the same substituents are adjacent to a —CF_2 group in fluoro-

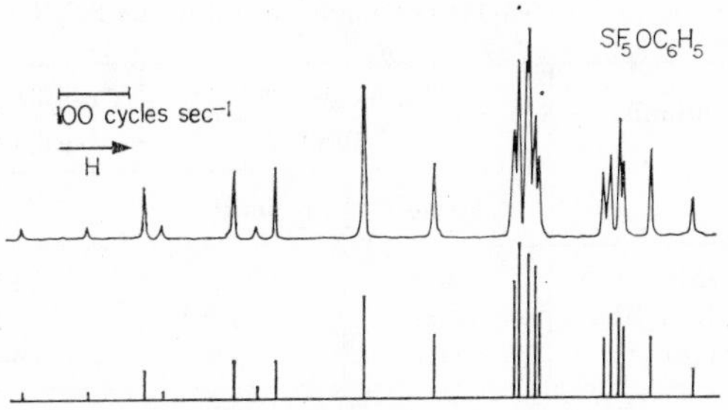

FIG. 11.18 The ^{19}F resonance spectrum of $SF_5OC_6H_5$ at 40 Mc sec^{-1}. Packer and Harris(105).

TABLE 11.46 ^{19}F CHEMICAL SHIFTS MEASURED IN PPM FROM AN INTERNAL SF_6 REFERENCE AND ^{19}F COUPLING CONSTANTS, IN CYCLES SEC^{-1}, BETWEEN APICAL AND BASAL FLUORINE NUCLEI, FOR A SERIES OF SF_5X COMPOUNDS(102)

Compound	δ ppm[a] Base F	δ ppm[a] Apex F	J_{AB}
SF_5Br	−88·2	−5·00	143·1
SF_5Cl	−68·4	−4·88	148·5
CF_3SF_5	18·4	−5·43	145·4
SF_5OSO_2F	−14·8	1·63	153·5
$(SF_5)_2SO_4$	−15·1	0·43	153·4
$FC_2H_4OSF_5$	−2·48	−17·98	153·8
$FClC_2H_3OSF_5$	−2·69	−15·93	154·7
$C_2F_5OSF_5$	−15·2	−3·35	152·8
$C_5F_9OSF_5$	−14·7	−4·00	154·9
$FC_2Cl_4OSF_5$	−14·8	−6·37	154·9
CF_3OSF_5	−11·4	−4·23	153·0
SF_5OSF_5	−14·0	−4·53	150
SF_5OOSF_5	0·75	0·16	

[a] Chemical shifts given here were obtained in about 50 per cent SF_6 solution and thus may have small errors associated with them. However, the related compounds SO_3F_2 and SF_5OF show less than 0·3 ppm change in shift in proceeding from 10 to 90 mole per cent SF_6. Positive shifts are at increased magnetic field from SF_6.

$$\delta_{CF_3COOH\,ext} = \delta_{SF_6} - 127 \text{ ppm (very approximate conversion).}$$

alkanes and is opposite to that expected from electronegativity considerations[8, 103]. Thus the order of shielding ability of the substituents is F > CF_3 > Cl > Br. Apex fluorine nuclei in —SF_5 groups suffer comparatively small irregular changes in shielding when the substituent is varied. Inductive effects would be expected to act equally on all five fluorine nuclei of

TABLE 11.47 ^{19}F CHEMICAL SHIFTS MEASURED IN PPM FROM AN INTERNAL $CFCl_3$ REFERENCE AND ^{19}F COUPLING CONSTANTS IN CYCLES SEC^{-1} BETWEEN APICAL AND BASAL FLUORINE NUCLEI FOR A SERIES OF ALKYL DERIVATIVES OF GENERAL FORMULA SF_5R[103]

Compound	Chemical shift φ^* ppm		Coupling constant J_{AB} cycles sec^{-1}
	Apical	Basal	
$CH_2{=}CHSF_5$	−80·9	−59·3	147·8
$CH_3CHClCH_2SF_5$	−82·2	−64·9	144·2
$ClCH_2CH_2SF_5$	−81·1	−64·3	144·4

φ^* is the chemical shift measured in ppm from $CFCl_3$ internal reference. $\delta_{CF_3COOH} = \varphi^*_{CFCl_3} - 78{\cdot}6$.

the —SF_5 group and since the basal fluorine nuclei are nearer to the substituent than is the fluorine nucleus in the apex position, it is tempting to suggest that the large variation in basal fluorine shielding is due to a spatial interaction with the substituent. However, a neighbour diamagnetic anisotropic effect would provide much smaller contributions to the shielding than those observed and

TABLE 11.48 ^{19}F CHEMICAL SHIFTS OF PERFLUOROALKYL DERIVATIVES OF SULPHUR HEXAFLUORIDE[101]

Group	$C_2F_5SF_5$	$C_3F_7SF_5$	$C_4F_9SF_5$	$(C_2F_5)_2SF_4$	$(C_3F_7)_2SF_4$	$O(CF_2CF_2)_2SF_4$
$-CF_3$	5·3	5·0	5·2	4·5	5·0	
$C{-}CF_2{-}S$	15·5	18·8	18·0	21·2	16·5	22·2
$C{-}CF_2{-}C$		50·7	46·5 49·5		50·0	
$O{-}CF_2{-}C$						2·4
SF_5	−118·7[a] −137·5	[b]	[b]			
SF_4				−104·0	−106·1	−123·0[c] −94·8

[a] These values are the δ-values for the base and apex fluorines of the SF_5 pyramid, derived from an analysis of the complex fine structure observed.

[b] SF_5 resonance essentially the same as for $C_2F_5SF_5$.

[c] These values are for the centres of the triplet resonances arising from the non-equivalence of the fluorines in the SF_4 group of this molecule.

TABLE 11.49 ^{19}F CHEMICAL SHIFTS OF PERFLUOROALKYL DERIVATIVES OF SULPHUR HEXAFLUORIDE[104]

Compound	δ_{SF}[a]	δ_{SF_4}	δ_{CF_3S}	δ_{CF_2-S}	δ_{CF_2-C}	δ_{CF_2C-S}	δ_{CF_2CC-S}
$(CF_3CF_2)_2SF_4$		−105·0		21·0	4·5		
$CF_3SF_4CF_2CF_3$		−99·7	−11·4	21·4	4·5		
$CF_3SF_4CF_2COOCH_3$		−99·7	−12·7	12·1			
$CF_3CF_2SF_5$	−138·0	−118·5		24·0	5·6		
γ β α $CF_3CF_2CF_2CF_2SF_5$	−136·9	−119·5		17·8 (α)	5·0	46·2 (β)	48·7 (γ)
$CF_3SF_4CF_2SF_5$	−141·6	−103·9 −125·8[b]	−11·9	−10·3			

[a] Chemical shift of apex fluorine atom of the SF_5 group.
[b] Chemical shift of base fluorine atoms of SF_5 group.
Chemical shifts are measured in ppm from the external reference CF_3COOH.

TABLE 11.50 F—F SPIN COUPLING CONSTANTS OF PERFLUOROALKYL DERIVATIVES OF SULPHUR HEXAFLUORIDE[(104)]

Compound[a]	$J_{CF_3-SF_4}$	$J_{CF_2-SF_4}$	$J_{CF_3C-SF_4}$	$J_{CF_3C-CF_2}$	$J_{CF_3CC-CF_2}$	J_{CF_3-SFa}[b]	J_{CF_2-Fa}[b]	J_{SFa-Fb}[c]	$J_{CF_3-CF_2}$
$(CF_3CF_2)SF_4$		15·70	9·33						≦1
$CF_3SF_4CF_2CF_3$	24·00	15·10	9·40						
$CF_3SF_4CF_2COOCH_3$	23·50	13·60							
$CF_3CF_2SF_5$		14·36	8·56			4·82		152·19	≦1
$CF_3CF_2CF_2CF_2SF_5$[d]		17·0		10·80	2·42	4·93	2·47	145·96	≦1
$CF_3SF_4CF_2SF_5$[e]	22·92	21·42				5·28		151·87	

[a] Coupling constants are given in units of cycles per second. [b] SF_a indicates the apex fluorine atom of the SF_5 group. [c] $J_{SF_a-F_b}$ is the coupling constant between the apex and base fluorine atoms in the SF_5 group. [d] $J_{CF_2-C-SF_4}$ must be about 8–9 cycles sec^{-1} in this compound to account for the SF_4 multiplet observed. Some assumptions concerning the relative magnitudes to be expected for certain of these coupling constants have been made in assigning them to particular pairs of groups. [e] $J_{SF_4-C-SF_4}$ must be about 10–12 cycles sec^{-1} in this compound to account for the SF_4 multiplet at −103·9 ppm.

it is more likely that the large basal fluorine deshielding arises from the presence of low-lying excited electronic states of the correct symmetry for mixing with the ground state(102, 56).

Tables 11.48 to 11.50 give the ^{19}F chemical shifts and spin coupling constants for some perfluoroalkyl derivatives of sulphur hexafluoride(101, 104). In these molecules F—F spin coupling between nuclei separated by 3 or 4 bonds seems to depend both on through-bond and through-space interactions, while coupling between fluorine nuclei separated by five bonds is largely determined by a spatial mechanism.

Several authors(103, 105, 106) have used a full analysis of the AB_4 system based on the complex particle method(107) to interpret the ^{19}F spectra of SF_5X derivatives. In the ^{19}F spectra of the compound $SF_5 \cdot O \cdot SO_2F$(105), the fluorine nuclei of the —SO_2F group couple with both the axial ($J = 0{\cdot}9$ cycles sec^{-1}) and the basal ($J = 7{\cdot}2$ cycles sec^{-1}) nuclei of the SF_5 group and this suggests that the large difference in the two coupling constants might be due to variation in the spatial contribution to F—F coupling(17, 20).

11.16.2 *Disubstituted Derivatives of Sulphur Hexafluoride*

Disubstitution of sulphur hexafluoride usually results in the *trans* positions being occupied and the remaining four fluorine nuclei adopting a square planar arrangement in which they are all equivalent (Fig. 11.17(c)). Their ^{19}F resonance spectra consist of a single absorption band in the absence of any coupling with the substituents. Perfluorodialkyl derivatives of sulphur hexafluoride have a molecular structure of this type. In some molecules the disubstitution takes place at two adjacent corners of the octahedron structure as shown in Fig. 11.17(d) for the cyclic molecule, $\overline{CF_2CF_2OCF_2CF_2SF_4}$. Here, the C—S—C bond angle is of the order of 90° and the remaining four fluorine nuclei are no longer equivalent since two of them are in the C—S—C plane while the other two are above and below it. Two triplets of equal intensity appear in the ^{19}F resonance spectrum of this molecule, the triplet splitting arising from spin–spin interaction of the two different pairs of equivalent fluorine nuclei with each other. The chemical shift data for this molecule is given in Table 11.48: it was not possible to assign the two pairs of fluorine atoms to their corresponding triplets(101).

The ^{19}F resonance spectrum of *cis*-$SF_4(SO_3F)_2$ (structure I) is typical of an $A_2B_2X_2$ system and confirms that the molecule has the unusual *cis* configuration(108).

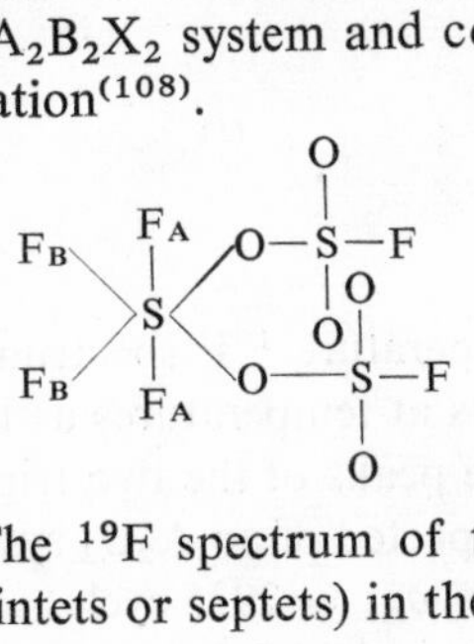

(I)

$$J_{AB} = 156 \text{ cycles sec}^{-1}$$

$$\delta_{AB} = 501 \text{ cycles sec}^{-1} \text{ at } 40 \text{ Mc sec}^{-1}$$

The ^{19}F spectrum of the molecule $CF_3SF_4SF_4CF_3$ shows two multiplets (quintets or septets) in the low field S—F region of the spectrum (δ_{CF_3COOH} =

– 95·5 and – 116 ppm)(109). No explanation of the origin of the non-equivalence of the S—F fluorine atoms in this compound has been put forward. The CF_3 absorption is a triplet at – 5·5 ppm from trifluoroacetic acid external reference.

11.16.3 Sulphur Tetrafluoride, SF_4

The ^{19}F NMR spectrum of this compound(110, 111) has been obtained at – 100°C and consists of two triplets separated by a chemical shift of 48 ppm and with a fine structure splitting of 78 cycles sec^{-1}. This indicates the presence of two different types of fluorine atom and is consistent with a non-planar

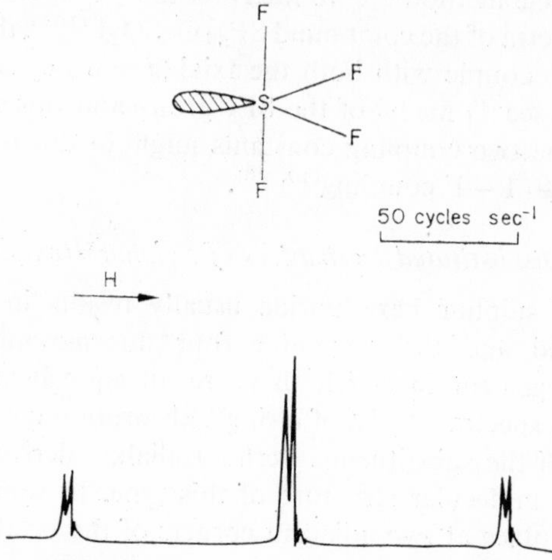

FIG. 11.19 The low field half of the ^{19}F resonance spectrum at 56·4 Mc sec^{-1} of sulphur tetrafluoride at – 101°C. Bacon, Gillespie and Quail(175).

structure (C_{2v}) for this molecule which has been suggested on the basis of infrared measurements(112). Structure I illustrates the trigonal bipyramidal structure which is postulated for this molecule: one of the equatorial positions is occupied by a lone pair of electrons

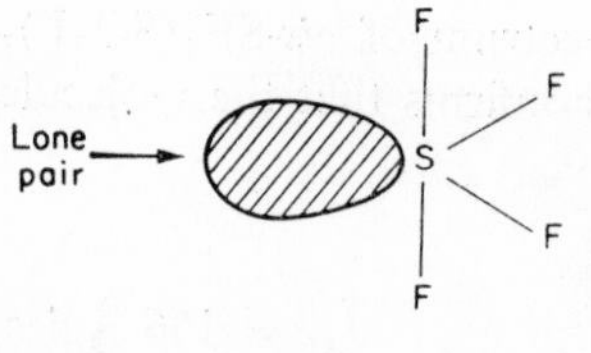

(I)

Other workers(175) have also examined the low temperature ^{19}F spectrum of sulphur tetrafluoride and observed the pair of triplets at temperatures as high as – 60°C. On cooling the sample to – 101°C all the peaks of the two triplets are split into doublets (see Fig. 11.19) as would be expected of an A_2B_2 system (see Section 8.13.8) with J_{AB} = 76·3 cycles sec^{-1} and $\nu_0\,\delta_{AB}$ = 2935 cycles sec^{-1}

at 56·4 Mc sec^{-1}. In view of the small value of the $J/\nu_0\,\delta$ ratio the appearance of second order splittings in the spectrum is somewhat surprising and arises because of the large absolute values of J and $\nu_0\,\delta$. At room temperature the fluorine atoms in SF_4 are undergoing rapid exchange and from a NMR investigation of this molecule over a range of temperatures the heat of activation for the exchange process has been estimated to be $4{\cdot}5 \pm 0{\cdot}8$ kcal mole^{-1}. NMR measurements(41, 110) have shown that SeF_4 has a similar molecular structure to SF_4.

11.16.4 Perfluoroalkyl Derivatives of SF_4

Tables 11.51 and 11.52 give the ^{19}F chemical shifts and spin coupling constants for a series of such compounds(113). Because of the symmetry of the molecules it is not possible from examination of their ^{19}F resonance spectra to decide whether monosubstitution (I) occurs at the *axial* or the *equatorial* positions of the SF_4 molecule. For the disubstituted derivative $[(CF_3)_2CF]_2SF_2$, the ^{19}F

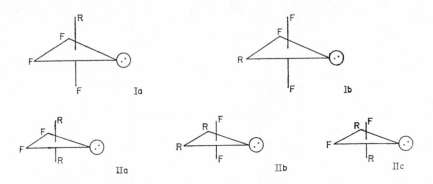

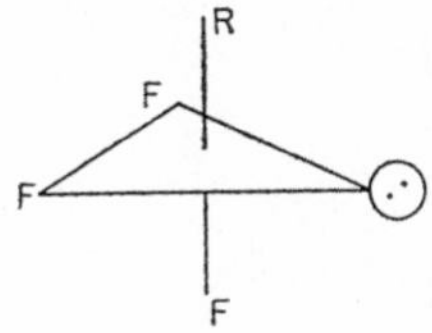

Ia

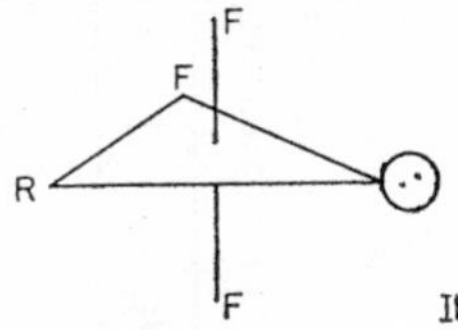

Ib

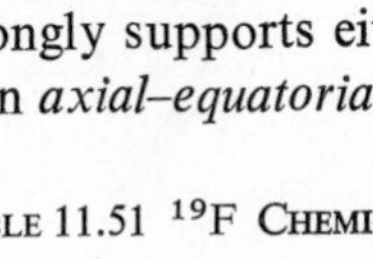

IIa

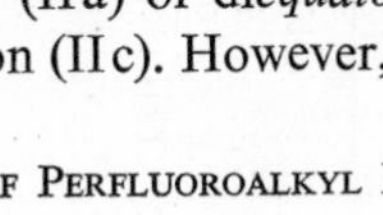

IIb

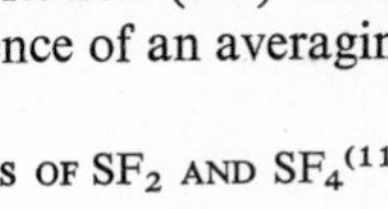

IIc

resonance spectrum contains a single multiplet for the SF fluorine nuclei, which strongly supports either di*axial* (IIa) or di*equatorial* substitution (IIb) rather than *axial–equatorial* substitution (IIc). However, the presence of an averaging

TABLE 11.51 ^{19}F CHEMICAL SHIFTS OF PERFLUOROALKYL DERIVATIVES OF SF_2 AND SF_4(113)

Compound	δ_{SF_2}	δ_{SF}	δ_{CF_3}	δ_{CF}
$[(CF_3)_2CF]_2SF_2$	−56·9		+4·97	+76·4
$(CF_3)_2CFSF_2CF_3$	−53·8		+8·25	+100
			+5·38 (i-C_3F_7)	
$(CF_3)_2CFSF_3$	−129	−13·5	+6·47	+97·4
$(CF_3)_2CFSF$		+293	+6·10	+91·1
$[(CF_3)_2CF]_2S$			+11·0	+99·0
$(CF_3)_2CFSOCF(CF_3)_2$			+7·87	+94·8
			+14·2	+71·8
$(CF_3)_2CFS(O)OH$			+5·33	+115
$(CF_3)_2CFS(O)OC_2H_5$			+4·76	+113

Chemical shifts are measured in ppm from a $CFCl_2CFCl_2$ reference.
$\delta_{CF_3COOH\,ext} = \delta_{Cl_2FCCFCl_2\,ext} - 12{\cdot}0$ ppm (very approximate conversion).

TABLE 11.52 F—F COUPLING CONSTANTS (CYCLES SEC^{-1}) OF PERFLUOROALKYL DERIVATIVES OF SF_2 AND SF_4[(113)]

Compound	J_{SF_2-SF}	$J_{SF_2-CF_3}$	J_{SF_2-CF}	J_{SF-CF_3}	J_{SF-CF}	$J_{CF_3-CF_3}$	J_{CF_3-CF}	J_{CF-CF}
$[(CF_3)_2CF]_2SF_2$		10	4·0				7·5	
$(CF_3)_2CFSF_3$	4·8	1	2·8	0·7	0·4		0·4	
$(CF_3)_2CFSF_2CF_3$		19	28			4·1	7·2	
		12(i-C_3H_7)					4·3(i-C_3H_7)	
$(CF_3)_2CFSF$				10	22		9·3	
$(CF_3)_2CFSOCF(CF_3)_2$							11(CF′–CF_3′)	20
							2(CF′–CF_3)	
$(CF_3)_2CFS(O)OH$							8·0	
$(CF_3)_2CFS(O)OC_2H_5$							8·0	

process, such as intermolecular exchange of substituent groups, would lead to the observed spectrum whichever structure prevails. Included in Tables 11.51 and 11.52 are the data for sulphenyl fluoride $(CF_3)_2CFSF$, a monosubstituted derivative of sulphur difluoride: the ^{19}F resonance shielding of the SF fluorine nuclei is extremely high (+281 ppm from CF_3COOH external reference). This large shift has been attributed to mixing of the ground state with low-lying excited states associated with the promotion of the non-bonding sulphur electrons.

11.17 Other Fluorine–Sulphur Containing Compounds

Gaseous samples of fluorine fluorosulphonate (SO_3F_2), thionyl tetrafluoride (SOF_4) and pentafluorosulphur hypofluorite (SOF_6) were condensed into sample tubes and their ^{19}F resonance spectra recorded at low temperatures, the ^{19}F chemical shifts being measured from perfluorocyclobutane[114].

(a) *Fluorine fluorosulphonate.* The ^{19}F resonance spectrum consists of two doublets of equal intensity which suggests that this molecule has the structure $SO_2F.OF$.[114]

(b) *Thionyl tetrafluoride.* The ^{19}F spectrum is a single absorption band indicating the molecular structure to be $F_4S{=}O$ rather than SF_3OF. The former structure would be square pyramidal. However, from the NMR data it is impossible to exclude the possibility of the structure being SF_3OF, the non-equivalence of the fluorine atoms being removed by a rapid exchange process[114]. NMR experiments over a range of temperatures might yield more positive information concerning the structure of thionyl tetrafluoride.

(c) *Pentafluorosulphur hypofluorite.* The ^{19}F resonance spectrum of this compound is that expected for an AB_4X system[103] which suggests that the molecule has the structure SF_5OF with a tetragonal pyramidal arrangement of the five fluorine atoms directly bonded to the sulphur atom (see Fig. 11.17(b))[114, 115].

(d) $S_3O_8F_2$. This compound, formed by the reaction of fluorine and sulphur dioxide on peroxydisulphuryl difluoride, was shown to have the probable struc-

O O O

ture F S O S O S F from its ^{19}F resonance spectrum, which consists of a single

O O O

absorption band with a chemical shift of −31·7 ppm from perfluorocyclopentane[116].

(e) *Thiocarboxylic acids.* The ^{19}F chemical shifts of the fluorine atoms in two fluoroalkyl thiocarboxylic acids[117] have been measured and they are given

Table 11.53 ^{19}F Chemical Shifts of some Fluoroalkyl Carboxylic Acids Measured in ppm from Trifluoroacetic Acid External Reference[117]

1 2 3	F_1	F_2	F_3	F_4
$CF_3CF_2CF_2COOH$	5·0	42·8	49·9	
$CF_3CF_2CF_2COSH$	4·4	38·7	48·8	
$H(CF_2)_4COOH$	41·8	47·0	51·8	60·8
$H(CF_2)_4COSH$	37·6	45·8	50·8	60·3

in Table 11.53 together with those of their hydrogen-containing anologues for comparative purposes.

(f) *Thioalcohols.* In the thioalcohols of formula $C_3F_7CH_2SH$ and $H(CF_2)_4CH_2SH$, the coupling constant between the SH hydrogen nucleus and the fluorine nuclei in the nearest CF_2 group is less than 1 cycle sec^{-1}[(118)].

Many other sulphur-containing compounds have been examined[(181)].

11.18 Interhalogen Compounds

Some of these substances were among the first fluorine-containing compounds to be examined by high resolution NMR[(6)]. The ^{19}F resonance spectra of BrF_5, IF_5 and IF_7 have already been discussed (see Section 11.4). For the pentafluorides it was postulated that the molecules have a tetragonal pyramidal structure. Iodine heptafluoride gives a complex ^{19}F spectrum which indicates that all the fluorine atoms are not equivalent but no further structural information could be obtained.

11.18.1 Chlorine Trifluoride

A ^{19}F NMR investigation of chlorine trifluoride (ClF_3) over a range of temperature has shown that the fluorine atoms in this molecule are rapidly exchanging with other fluorine atoms at room temperature[(119)]. It is known from microwave[(120)] and electron diffraction[(121)] studies that chlorine trifluoride has C_{2v} symmetry as shown in structure I, the planar molecule having

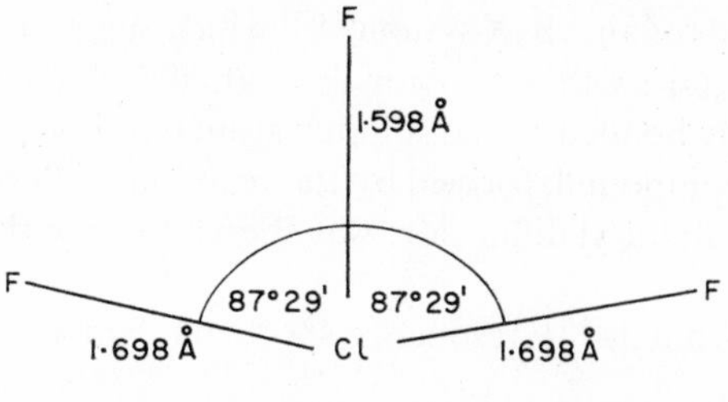

(I)

two long Cl—F bonds and one short Cl—F bond. One of the fluorine nuclei is thus in a different environment from the other two and it was hoped that the ^{19}F resonance spectrum of the molecule would support this structure by indicating the presence of two non-equivalent types of fluorine nucleus. The room temperature ^{19}F resonance spectrum consists of two very broad absorption bands which, on cooling to $-60°C$, resolve themselves into a typical AB_2 type spectrum (see Section 8.13.2). From a full analysis of the low temperature spectrum of the molecule (shown in Fig. 11.20) it was found that the two different types of fluorine nuclei in chlorine trifluoride have a chemical shift separation of ~ 110 ppm and a coupling constant of 403 cycles sec^{-1}.† At 40·00 Mc

† Recent studies of ClF_3 in the gas phase give a chemical shift of 125·9 ppm and a coupling constant of 441 cycles sec^{-1}[(194)].

sec^{-1} the ^{19}F resonance spectrum approximates to that expected of an AX_2 type system: the low field doublet corresponds to the two equivalent fluorine nuclei which interact with the remaining single non-equivalent fluorine nucleus to give a doublet splitting, while the single non-equivalent fluorine nucleus gives

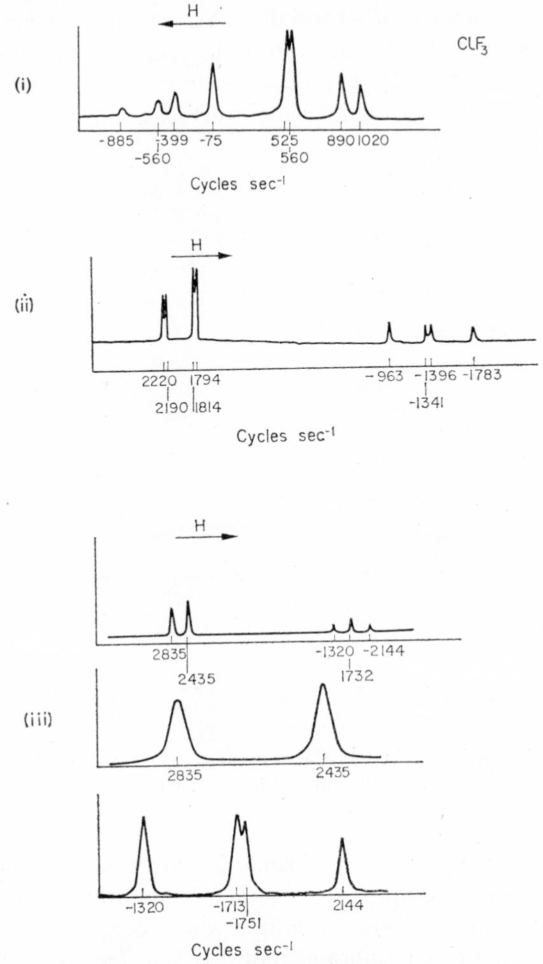

FIG. 11.20 The ^{19}F resonance spectra of chlorine trifluoride at $-60°C$ recorded at (i) 10·00 Mc sec^{-1}, (ii) 30·00 Mc sec^{-1}, (iii) 40·00 Mc sec^{-1}. Bands are measured from the reference SF_6. Muetterties and Phillips[119].

rise to a triplet arising from interaction with the other two fluorine nuclei. At the lower frequencies, 30·00 and 10·00 Mc sec^{-1}, the chemical shift separation between the two types of fluorine nucleus is comparable with the coupling constant between them, and complex AB_2 type spectra result.

Figure 11.21 shows the changes occurring in the spectrum of ClF_3 on raising the temperature from -40 to $+60°C$. First, the triplet and doublet splittings collapse and finally the two absorption bands coalesce. Rapid exchange of the fluorine atoms between different chemical environments is thought to be the cause of the observed spectral changes with temperature. One can estimate values of the average lifetime of a fluorine atom in a given environment at the temperature at which the multiplet structure disappears (− 15°C) and at the final coalescence temperature (+ 60°C) and thus obtain the heat of activation for the exchange process over this temperature range (4·8 kcal mole^{-1}). Hamer[122] has also investigated the exchange process in chlorine trifluoride and finds that the temperature at which the multiplet fine structure collapses varies from sample

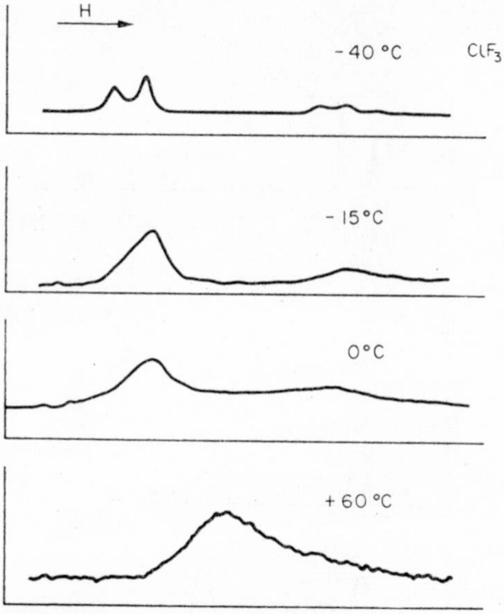

FIG. 11.21 The variation in the ^{19}F resonance spectrum of ClF_3 over the temperature range − 40 to + 60°C at 30 Mc sec^{-1}. Muetterties and Phillips[119].

to sample suggesting the presence of some impurity in the system (probably HF). For one particular sample the spin coupling multiplets were still present at 0°C. Whether or not chlorine trifluoride will undergo exchange in the absence of hydrogen fluoride is still uncertain but if it does occur the activation heat must be considerably greater than 4·8 kcal mole^{-1}[122]. ^{19}F resonance measurements on the system HF/ClF_3 indicate the presence of rapid exchange of fluorine atoms in this system. Similar experiments with binary mixtures of any pair of the fluorine-containing molecules HF, ClF_3, ClF and BrF_3 show that rapid mutual exchange of fluorine atoms occurs in all cases[122].

11.18.2 Bromine Trifluoride

The ^{19}F resonance spectrum of bromine trifluoride, BrF_3, consists of a single absorption band at room temperature, and if the molecule has a similar structure to ClF_3 then it is likely that it is showing similar exchange behaviour[119]. The high melting point of bromine trifluoride (8·8°C) prevented low temperature experiments from being conducted on the pure sample. It might be possible to study the exchange behaviour of the fluorine atoms in this system in the presence of a suitable inert solvent which would allow low temperature measurements to be made.

11.18.3 Iodine and Bromine Pentafluorides

Iodine and bromine pentafluorides, IF_5 and BrF_5, are known to have similar tetragonal pyramid structures.

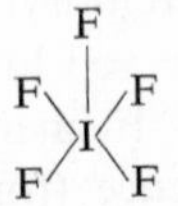

The four basal fluorine atoms are in a different environment from the single apex fluorine atom and this is reflected in their ^{19}F resonance spectra. In both cases, two multiplets are observed in the intensity ratio of 1 : 4. The low field quintet is assigned to the single apex fluorine nucleus which is coupled equally to the four equivalent basal fluorine nuclei, and the high field doublet is assigned to the four basal fluorine atoms. If any exchange is occurring at room temperature in iodine pentafluoride then it is sufficiently slow to allow the observation of the spin–spin multiplet splittings ($J_{F-F} = 81$ cycles sec^{-1}). On heating a sample of IF_5 to 115°C the fine structure disappears due to rapid exchange between the fluorine atoms and thus the lifetime of a fluorine atom at an apex or base site at 115°C is given by

$$\tau = 1/(4\pi\, J_{F-F}) = 1/(4\pi\, 81) = 9{\cdot}8 \times 10^{-4} \text{ sec.}$$

Attempts to observe the coalescence temperature (when only a single absorption band would be observed in the spectrum) failed due to the experimental difficulties encountered. An estimate of $\sim$ 195°C for the coalescence temperature was made by comparing the line broadening behaviour up to 175°C with that of ClF_3 and this leads to a heat of activation for the process of 13 kcal mole^{-1}. Bromine pentafluoride has a ^{19}F resonance spectrum similar to that of IF_5 but exhibits no line broadening on heating to 180°C indicating that there is a much higher activation energy for the exchange of fluorine atoms in the bromine derivative(119). Hamer(122) has shown that no rapid exchange of fluorine atoms takes place on mixing BrF_5 with other fluorides such as HF, ClF_3, ClF and BrF_3 since no change in the spectrum of BrF_5 accompanies the mixing.

11.18.4 Perchloryl Fluoride, $FClO_3$ *and Related Compounds*

The ^{19}F resonance spectrum of this compound is interesting in that it features spin–spin coupling between fluorine and chlorine nuclei (^{35}Cl and ^{37}Cl nuclei both have spin numbers $I = 3/2$)(123). Both ^{35}Cl and ^{37}Cl nuclei possess quadrupole moments and consequently they have short relaxation times due to interaction between their quadrupole moments and asymmetric electric field gradients within the molecule. The chlorine nucleus in perchloryl fluoride is tetrahedrally surrounded by the three oxygen atoms and the single fluorine atom, an arrangement which leads to the molecule having no dipole moment and the chlorine being surrounded by a symmetrical electric field. This removes the rapid relaxation mechanism of the chlorine nuclei so that F—Cl spin coupling may be observed. ($J_{F-^{35}Cl} \sim 310$ cycles sec^{-1}.) The ^{19}F resonance spectrum is consistent with the presence of two overlapping quartets from F—^{35}Cl and F—^{37}Cl spin coupling respectively. Perchloryl fluoride has a very low ^{19}F chemical shift ($\delta_{CF_3COOH\,ext} = -320$ ppm), almost as low as that of molecular fluorine. The lack of a dipole moment for the molecule suggests that the electronegativity of the perchloryl group is similar to that of fluorine and this is consistent with the observed low field ^{19}F chemical shift(6). Other workers(166) have measured the ^{19}F chemical shifts of related compounds using $CFCl_3$ as an internal reference (for example $FClO_4$, $-225{\cdot}9$; FOF, $-250{\cdot}0$; $FClO_3$, $-287{\cdot}0$ and $FOClO_3$, $-225{\cdot}9$ ppm from $CFCl_3$). There is quite a large discrepancy (~ 45 ppm) between the reported values for the ^{19}F chemical shift of $FClO_3$ when they are converted to a common reference scale(123, 166).

11.19 Compounds Containing Boron–Fluorine Bonds

11.19.1 Boron Trifluoride and Related Compounds

Early measurements of the fluorine resonance spectrum of BF_3 did not reveal any fine structure from B—F spin–spin interaction, a single absorption band being observed. The absence of spin–spin splittings was attributed to the interaction of the electric field gradients in BF_3 with the boron electric quadrupole moment(42, 124). However, later experiments on boron trifluoride(125) in the presence of other boron trihalides have shown the ^{19}F absorption band to be a quartet ($J_{BF} = 15 \pm 2$ cycles sec^{-1}) indicating the original failures to observe the fine structure to be due to lack of resolution. By examining a mixture of BCl_3 and BF_3 at room temperature, Coyle and Stone(125) were successful in observing the ^{19}F resonance spectra of the mixed halides BCl_2F and $BClF_2$ in addition to those of the two starting materials as shown in Fig. 11.22A and Table 11.54. Within this binary system there exists a labile equilibrium involving the four species and any attempt to isolate the mixed halides would fail due to their tendency to rapidly disproportionate to BF_3 and BCl_3. The binary system BBr_3/BF_3 has also been examined by NMR and similar results obtained (see Fig. 11.22B). When the ternary mixture $BF_3/BCl_3/BBr_3$ is examined, the hitherto unknown species BBrClF is observed, in addition to the mixed halides found previously in the binary mixtures (see Fig. 11.22C). Table 11.54 gives the B—F spin–spin coupling constants measured from the spectra of the mixed boron halides. The ^{19}F spectra of a number of organodifluoroboranes have also been examined(64, 126) and the fluorine nuclei in such molecules are found to be deshielded with respect to the fluorine nuclei in boron trifluoride, as can be observed from inspection of the ^{19}F chemical shifts in Table 11.54. This implies that electron withdrawal from the remaining two fluorine atoms accompanies the monosubstitution of boron trifluoride with an organic group. On normal electronegativity arguments one would not have predicted a trend of this sort and it is necessary to consider π bonding to explain the chemical shifts. When a fluorine atom in boron trifluoride is replaced by an organic group, the amount of π bonding donation of the fluorine atoms to the boron atoms is increased and this might well result in a deshielding of the fluorine atom concerned. There will also be a small amount of B—C π bonding in the organo difluoroboranes and for the molecules examined this has its smallest value in the vinyl derivative, which explains the larger ^{19}F shielding in the compound.

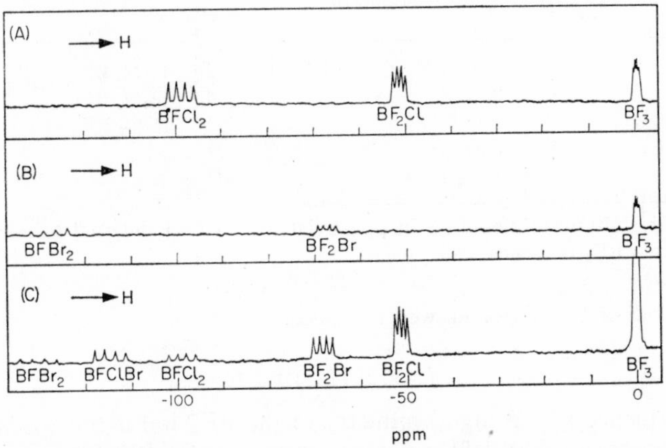

FIG. 11.22 (A) The ^{19}F resonance spectra at 40 Mc sec^{-1} of the boron mixed halides formed in a BF_3/BCl_3 mixture at room temperature. (B) The ^{19}F resonance spectra at 40 Mc sec^{-1} of the boron mixed halides formed in a BF_3/BBr_3 mixture at room temperature. (C) The ^{19}F resonance spectra at 40 Mc sec^{-1} of the boron mixed halides in a $BF_3/BCl_3/BBr_3$ mixture at room temperature. The BF_3 signal is 50·4 ppm to high fields of external CF_3COOH.

TABLE 11.54 ^{19}F CHEMICAL SHIFTS AND SPIN–SPIN COUPLING CONSTANTS OF COMPOUNDS WITH B—F BONDS[125, 126]

Compound	Chemical shifts			Coupling constants
	$\delta^{int}_{BF_3}$	φ ppm from CCl_3F at infinite dilution	$\delta^{ext}_{CF_3COOH}$†	$J_{^{11}B-^{19}F}$ (cycles sec^{-1})
CH_3BF_2 (126)		+68·8	−9·8	77
$C_2H_5BF_2$ (126)		+74·6	−4·0	81
n-$C_3H_7BF_2$ (126)		+72·8	−5·8	81
$CH_2{=}CHBF_2$(126)		+88·6	+10·0	67
BF_3 (125)	0	+127	+48·4	15 ± 2
BF_2Cl (125)	−51·5		−1·1	34
BF_2Br (125)	−68·4		−18·0	56
$BFCl_2$ (125)	−99·0		−48·6	74
$BFClBr$ (125)	−114·8		−64·4	92
$BFBr_2$ (125)	−130·4		−80·0	108

† The chemical shifts have been converted to the CF_3COOH external reference scale.

Coyle and co-workers(127, 207) have measured the ^{19}F chemical shifts of compounds containing boron–fluorine bonds and their data are summarised in Table 11.55. Because organic groups are generally poorer π-donors than fluorine atoms, the replacement of the latter by the former in boron trifluoride derivatives results in a withdrawal of electrons from around the remaining fluorine nuclei, which leads to the observed deshielding.

TABLE 11.55 ^{19}F CHEMICAL SHIFTS OF COMPOUNDS CONTAINING B—F BONDS(127)

Compound	Shift (ppm)[a]	Compound	Shift (ppm)[a]	Compound	Shift (ppm)[a]
BF_3	0	$CH_2{:}CH \cdot CH_2 \cdot BF_2$	−52	Me_3N, BF_3	+37
$Ph \cdot BF_2$	−35	Pr^nBF_2	−54	$Me_3N, BEtF_2$	+38
$CH_2{:}CH \cdot BF_2$	−38	$Bu \cdot BF_2$	−54	$Me_3N, BF_2 \cdot CH{:}CH_2$	+39
$CF_2{:}CF \cdot BF_2$	−40	EtBClF	−99		
		Me_2BF	−107		

[a] Chemical shifts were measured in ppm relative to CCl_3F internal reference and then transferred to a BF_3 reference scale

$$\delta_{BF_3} = 127 + \delta_{CFCl_3\,int}.$$

Dilute solutions of the compounds were examined.

11.19.2 The BF_4^- *Ion*

A consequence of the high symmetry of the BF_4^- ion is the absence of quadrupole broadening in the ^{19}F spectrum of this species. The ^{19}F resonance spectrum of the BF_4^- ion has been observed for an aqueous solution of $BF_4BF_3CF_3$, ($[BF_4]\,[BF_3CF_3]$) and consists of a quartet absorption ($J_{BF} = 4{\cdot}8$ cycles sec^{-1}) with the individual components of the quartet being much narrower than in other B—F compounds(128). The ^{19}F chemical shifts from CF_3COOH external reference and B—F coupling constants for the molecule, $[BF_4]^-[BF'_3CF''_3]^+$, are:

$$\delta_{BF_4^-} = 72{\cdot}3 \quad \delta_{BF_3} = 77{\cdot}3 \quad \delta_{CF_3} = -2{\cdot}06 \text{ ppm}$$

$$J_{BF} = 4{\cdot}8 \quad J_{BF'} = 39{\cdot}0 \quad J_{BF''} = 34{\cdot}0 \text{ cycles sec}^{-1}.$$

J_{BF} in the BF_4^- ion is dependent on concentration and the presence of cations(204).

11.20 COMPOUNDS CONTAINING NITROGEN–FLUORINE BONDS

Table 11.56 gives a list of fluorine chemical shifts in compounds containing nitrogen–fluorine bonds.

The molecular structure of nitryl fluoride (FNO_2) has been determined from an examination of the ^{19}F NMR spectrum of the compound warmed to just above its melting point(129). The spectrum consists of a triplet with components of equal intensity and separated by splittings of 113 cycles sec^{-1}: this splitting is similar to that found in nitrogen trifluoride ($J_{NF} = 160$ cycles sec^{-1}) and strongly suggests that the fluorine atom in nitryl fluoride is directly attached to the nitrogen atom. In cyanogen fluoride, FCN, where the fluorine is not directly attached to the nitrogen atom, the coupling constant J_{FN} is 33 cycles sec^{-1} (δ_{CF_3COOH} = +79·5 ppm)[111].

Both NF_3 and FCN show a temperature dependence in their ^{19}F spectra[41]. On cooling a sample of nitrogen trifluoride, the triplet splitting of the fluorine absorption band collapses at temperatures below −180°C and this has been attributed to the temperature dependence of the quadrupole relaxation time of the nitrogen nucleus[130].

TABLE 11.56 ^{19}F CHEMICAL SHIFTS IN COMPOUNDS CONTAINING N—F BONDS

Compound		^{19}F Chemical shifts † δ ppm	Reference
NF_3		−221·1	41
$ClNF_2$		−217·1	131
N_2F_4		−135·0	132
trans-N_2F_2		−167·3	133
cis-N_2F_2		−208·0	133
HNF_2		−72·5	132
CH_3CONF_2		−106·8	132
$(CH_3)_2C(CN)NF_2$		−118·1	132
FCN		+79·5	111
ONF (Nitrosyl fluoride)		−924	135
$(CH_3)_3CNF_2$		−105·6	132
$(C_6H_5)_3CNF_2$		−110·8	132
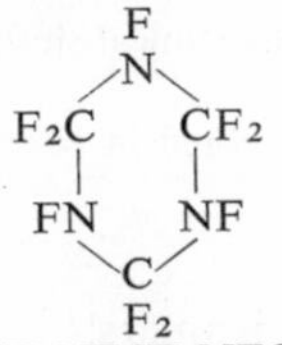	NF	+11·8	134
	CF_2	+12·8	
$CF_3NFCF_2NFCF_2NF_2$	NF_2	−95·2	134
	NF	+7·9	
	NF	+8·9	
	CF_2 (between 2NF)	+15·0	
	CF_2 (next to NF_2)	+25·6	
	CF_3	−7·4	
$CF_3NFCF_2NFCF_3$	NF	+8·7	134
	CF_3	−7·2	
	CF_2	+17·3	

† Measured in ppm from CF_3COOH external reference.

The ^{19}F chemical shift of nitrosyl fluoride, O=N—F, is one of the lowest recorded (−420 ppm from F_2 or −924 ppm from CF_3COOH external reference) which is surprising in view of the predominantly ionic nature of the N—F bond[135]. Chemiluminescence studies of nitrosyl fluoride have revealed the presence of a low-lying electronic state which must have the correct symmetry properties for "mixing" with the ground state by the magnetic field. This would explain why there is a large paramagnetic contribution to the fluorine shielding in the molecule. Thus, the qualitative correlation between bond ionic character and fluorine chemical shifts (see Section 11.4) to which reference has already been made, is only valid if the molecules in a series have similar energy separations between the ground state and low-lying excited electronic states.

An investigation of the ^{19}F resonance spectra of *trans*- and *cis*-N_2F_2 has confirmed that the molecules have structures I and II [133, 136]:

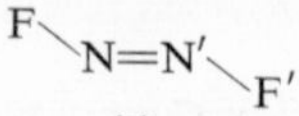

$$
\begin{array}{cc}
\overset{F}{\diagdown}N{=}N'\diagdown_{F'} & \underset{F}{\diagup}N{=}N'\diagdown_{F'} \\
(I) & (II)
\end{array}
$$

The observed spectra are characteristic of AA′XX′ systems and furthermore the changes which occur in the ^{19}F resonance spectra when the ^{14}N nuclei are irradiated are those expected for an AA′XX′ system. Table 11.57 contains a

TABLE 11.57 ^{19}F CHEMICAL SHIFTS AND COUPLING CONSTANTS FOR THE ISOMERS OF N_2F_2 AND RELATED MOLECULES[136]

Compound	Chemical shifts (ppm)†		Coupling constants (cycles sec^{-1})		
	^{19}F	^{14}N	J_{NF}	$J_{N'F}$	J_{FF}
N_2F_4‡	− 59·8	+ 39·8			
N_2F_2 (*trans*)	− 94·9	− 75·2	± 136	∓ 73	322
N_2F_2 (*cis*)	− 133·7	− 13·3	± 145	∓ 37	99
NF_3‡	− 146·9	0·0	155		

† ^{19}F chemical shifts measured in ppm from CCl_3F internal reference. ^{14}N chemical shifts measured in ppm from NF_3 reference.

‡ E. W. RANDALL and J. D. BALDESCHWIELER: private communication quoted in reference 136.

list of the chemical shifts and coupling constants of the N_2F_2 isomers[136]. The ^{14}N chemical shifts were measured using the double irradiation technique[137] and it was found that the molecules each contained only one type of nitrogen nucleus. It was thought originally that the molecule assigned as the *cis* isomer might be 1,1-difluorodiazine, $\underset{F}{\overset{F}{\diagdown}}N{=}N$. The double irradiation behaviour of the molecule does not support the diazine structure and furthermore a molecule with this structure is unlikely to have only a single ^{14}N resonance frequency.

From a comparison of the indirect N—F coupling constants given in Table 11.57 one can infer that the F—N—N bond angles are probably quite different in the *cis*- and *trans*-N_2F_2 isomers.

11.21 COMPOUNDS CONTAINING OXYGEN–FLUORINE BONDS

Table 11.58 gives the chemical shift and spin coupling data for a group of hypofluorites[115]. All the molecules give rise to first order spectra at 40·00 Mc sec^{-1} with the exception of SF_5OF (an AB_4X system). From the chemical

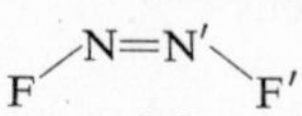

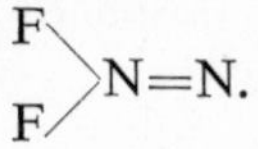

shift of the —OF group it is inferred that the charge on this fluorine atom is negative[115].

TABLE 11.58 CHEMICAL SHIFTS AND SPIN COUPLING CONSTANTS OBTAINED FROM ^{19}F RESONANCE SPECTRA AT 40 Mc sec^{-1} OF SOME HYPOFLUORITES[115]

Substance	Chemical shift, δ, compared to SF_6 as zero[a]		Spin–spin coupling constant, J (cycles sec^{-1})
	For F_2 or OF ppm	For SF or CF ppm	
F_2	−365·5		
OF_2	−217·0		Between
FSO_2OF	−187·5	SF 21·5	(SO_2F and OF) 6·1
SF_5OF	−131·5	SF 1·75	(SF and OF) 0·0
		SF_4 3·64	(SF_4 and OF) 17·4
			(SF_4 and SF[b]) 155·0
CF_3OF	−92·5	CF_3 128·5	(CF_3 and OF) 33·2

[a] Values are positive in the direction of increased magnetic field strength. In changing from high concentration to infinite dilution in SF_6 solution the SO_3F_2 resonance absorptions change about 0·4 ppm upfield with respect to the SF_6; SF_5OF absorptions change even less. Dilute SF_6 solutions of the other substances were used and not extrapolated to infinite dilution.

[b] Apex fluorine atom resonance in $—SF_5$ group.

$\delta_{CF_3COOH\,ext} = \delta_{SF_6} - 127$ ppm (approximate conversion).

11.22 COMPOUNDS CONTAINING PHOSPHORUS–FLUORINE BONDS

Phosphorus pentafluoride is known to have a trigonal bipyramidal structure[138, 139] and would therefore be expected to have a ^{19}F resonance spectrum showing the presence of two non-equivalent types of fluorine atom in the ratio 2:3. However, the fluorine resonance spectrum of PF_5 is found to consist of a single doublet, the doublet splitting being caused by spin–spin interaction with the phosphorus nucleus ($J_{PF} = 930$ cycles sec^{-1}, $\delta_{CF_3COOH} = -0{\cdot}68$ ppm)[42, 140]. Large ^{19}F chemical shifts between *axial* and *equatorial* fluorine nuclei have been observed in the ^{19}F resonance spectra of R_2PF_3 derivatives[140]. This suggests that the equivalence of the fluorine nuclei in PF_5 is probably due to intramolecular rearrangement of the fluorine nuclei between the *axial* and *equatorial* positions of a trigonal bipyramidal structure[140, 141]. Muetterties and co-workers[140] have examined the ^{19}F resonance spectra of an extensive series of mono-, di- and trisubstituted phosphorus (V) fluorides (see Tables 11.62f–i). In the spectra of the disubstituted alkyl and aryl derivatives, R_2PF_3, the presence of two different types of fluorine atom is indicated: this suggests that such compounds have a trigonal bipyramidal structure with the R groups in *equatorial* positions. For Cl_2PF_3 the fluorine nuclei show spectroscopic equivalence at 25°C but on cooling to −80°C a spectrum typical of the R_2PF_3 compounds is obtained[140]. All of the monosubstituted derivatives examined (RPF_4) were shown to possess spectroscopically equivalent fluorine nuclei: thus the R groups could occupy either the *axial* position of a tetragonal pyramid or an *equatorial* position of a trigonal bipyramidal structure in which there is rapid intramolecular positional exchange of the fluorine nuclei(140). ^{19}F chemical shifts for phosphorus chlorofluorides of general formula PCl_xF_{3-x} and PCl_xF_{5-x} are shown in Fig. 11.23: the trend in ^{19}F shielding with increasing chlorine substitution in phosphorus (III) chlorofluorides is opposite to that in phosphorus (V) chlorofluorides(178). No satisfactory explanation of this effect has been suggested.

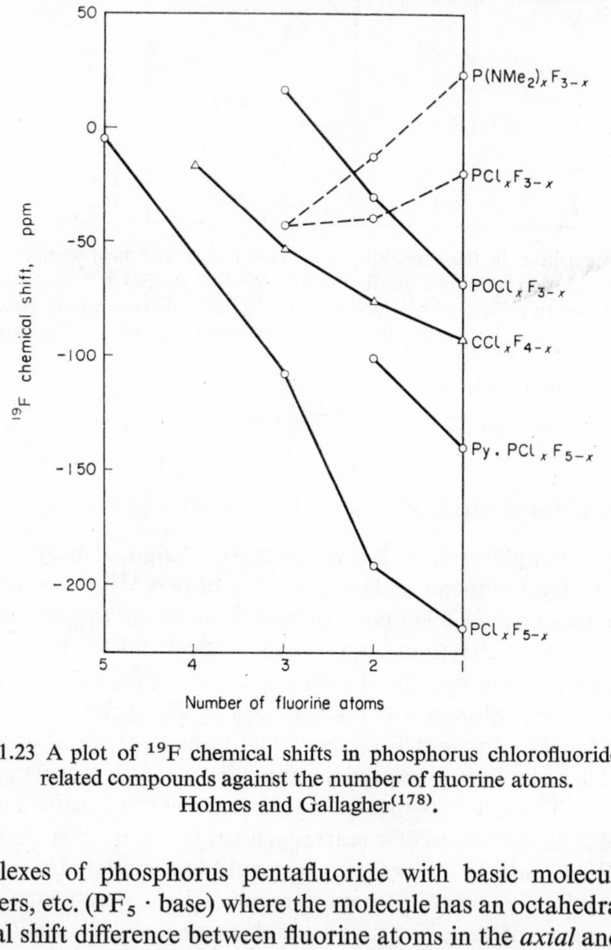

FIG. 11.23 A plot of ^{19}F chemical shifts in phosphorus chlorofluorides and related compounds against the number of fluorine atoms. Holmes and Gallagher(178).

In complexes of phosphorus pentafluoride with basic molecules such as amines, ethers, etc. ($PF_5 \cdot$ base) where the molecule has an octahedral structure, the chemical shift difference between fluorine atoms in the *axial* and *equatorial* positions is about 7 ppm and the F—F coupling constant 45–70 cycles sec^{-1}(142). The P—F coupling constants vary from compound to compound over the range 710–765 cycles sec^{-1} (for PF_6^-, J_{PF} = 710 cycles sec^{-1}). The similarity between the J_{PF} values for PF_6^- and the ($PF_5 \cdot$ base) compounds is assumed to be a consequence of the similar hybridisation in the molecules. Table 11.59 gives a collection of ^{19}F chemical shifts and coupling constants for a series of phosphorus–fluorine containing compounds. An attempt(42) to correlate J_{PF}

coupling constants with the ^{19}F chemical shifts in this series of compounds indicates a roughly linear relationship between the two parameters: a similar correlation is also found for J_{PF} values and ^{31}P chemical shifts[42].

The ^{19}F spectrum of the cyclic compound fluorochlorosubstituted tri-phosphonitrile (I)

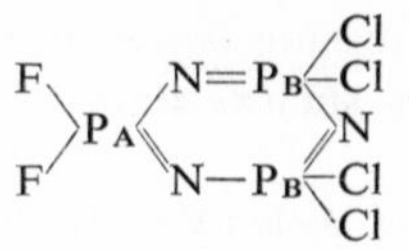

(I)

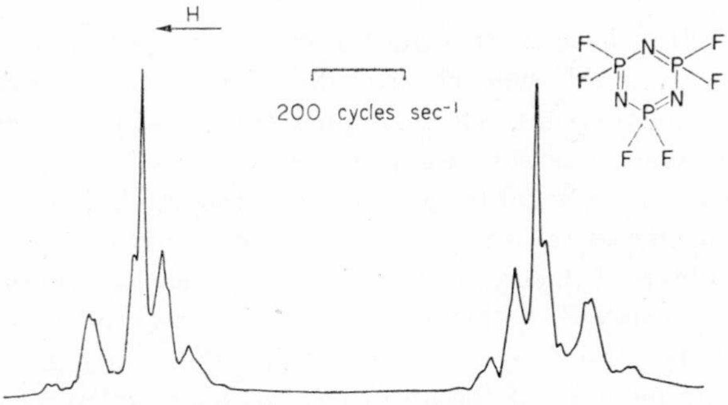

FIG. 11.24 The ^{19}F resonance spectrum of perfluorosubstituted tri-phosphonitrile, $N_3P_3F_6$ at 56·4 Mc sec^{-1} in CCl_4 solution[145].

TABLE 11.59 ^{19}F CHEMICAL SHIFTS AND SPIN–SPIN COUPLING CONSTANTS OF COMPOUNDS WITH P—F BONDS[42]

Compound	J_{PF} cycles sec^{-1}	Chemical shift δ ppm CF_3COOH reference (external)
PF_3	1400	−43·4
$POCl_2F$	1180	−69·0
$POClF_2$	1120	−30·4
POF_3	1060	+15·8
$F_2PO(OH)$	980	+9·0
$FPO(OH)_2$	955	−2·5
PF_5	930	−0·7
Na_2PO_3F (aq.)	783	+26·8
HPF_6	715	−5·5
KPF_6 (aq.)	706	−7·7
$C_2H_5POF_2$[143]	1132	−8·6
CH_3POF_2[143]	1100	−16·9

has been analysed and the coupling constants between the fluorine and phosphorus atoms calculated[144],

$$J_{FP_A} = 934 \text{ cycles sec}^{-1}$$
$$J_{FP_B} = -14 \text{ cycles sec}^{-1}$$
$$J_{P_AP_B} = -100 \text{ cycles sec}^{-1}$$

The perfluorosubstituted tri-phosphonitrile, $N_3P_3F_6$, constitutes an $AA'A''X_2X_2'X_2''$ system and gives rise to complex ^{19}F and ^{31}P resonance spectra(145). Figure 11.24 shows the ^{19}F resonance spectrum of the molecule at 56·4 Mc sec^{-1} and although an approximate value for the large P—F spin coupling constant (J_{PF} = 935 cycles sec^{-1}) can be obtained from the spectra, evaluation of the remaining coupling constants would necessitate a complete analysis. In non-cyclic molecules, such as Me_2NPF_2, $J_{PF} \approx 1200$ cycles sec^{-1}(202).

11.23 Complex Compounds

11.23.1 Complexes of Boron Trifluoride

Ogg and Diehl(146) have studied the ^{19}F resonance spectra of several complexes of boron trifluoride with electron donating molecules such as water, alcohols, ethers and ketones. They adopted the technique of examining a liquid mixture of two donor substances in the presence of an amount of boron trifluoride, which is insufficient to saturate both donors. At low temperatures, when the exchange processes involved are slow, two fairly narrow ^{19}F absorption bands are observed in such systems. For example, BF_3 forms complexes with a mixture of methyl and ethyl alcohol and gives rise to two separate ^{19}F resonance bands (separated by 2·0 ppm) for the coordinated BF_3 molecules. By measuring the intensity of the absorption bands in mixtures of different composition it was established that a reversible equilibrium exists between the two donors and their respective complexes. It was possible to obtain values for the equilibrium constants at different temperatures and thus to calculate the corresponding enthalpy and standard entropy changes. At higher temperatures, the two signals broaden and then coalesce, indicating that rapid exchange of BF_3 groups is taking place. The rate of exchange and the heat of activation for the process can be calculated from examination of the signal shapes at the coalescence temperature (see Section 9.1.3).

Large hydrogen resonance chemical shifts were also observed in the spectra of the donor molecules when BF_3 was introduced into the system. It is worth noting that in cases where the acceptor molecule contains hydrogen as its only magnetic nucleus, NMR spectroscopy cannot be used to study complex formation since changes in the ^1H chemical shifts are very small in the acceptor molecule (unlike the ^{19}F chemical shifts in BF_3).

11.23.2 Complexes of Metal Tetrafluorides

The ^{19}F spectra of several complexes formed between organic donor molecules and metal tetrafluorides of titanium, tin, silicon, germanium and molybdenum have been measured and they can be used to indicate the nature of the complex formation and the molecular structures of the complexes(147). In the fluorine resonance spectrum of TiF_4 and SnF_4 complexes with mono- and difunctional donor molecules (such as $(CH_3)_2SO$, amines and amides) two triplets of equal intensity appear. No change in the spectrum is observed over the temperature range + 15°C to the melting point of the solvent used (ethers, nitriles or excess base). The spectrum is consistent with the presence of two non-equivalent pairs of identical fluorine atoms in the molecules and provides strong evidence that the molecules have octahedral symmetry with two *cis* positions being substituted. Structures I and II indicate the octahedral structures for a 1:2 and a 1:1 complex of titanium: the two *equatorial* fluorine nuclei in the plane of substitution are differently shielded from the remaining two fluorine nuclei above and below the plane, and each pair of fluorine nuclei gives rise to a triplet (J_{FF} = 36 cycles sec^{-1} for $TiF_4 \cdot 2EtOH$).

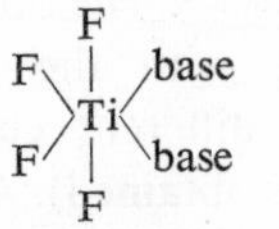

1:2 complex. (I)
E.g. base = $(CH_3)_2SO$

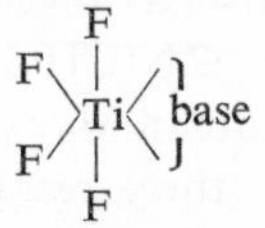

1:1 complex. (II)
E.g. base = en

On heating ethereal solutions of several SnF_4 and TiF_4 complexes to above room temperature the triplet structure on the absorption bands disappears, the bands broaden and finally coalesce indicating that the ligands are undergoing rapid exchange at and above room temperature.

Solutions of various complexes of SiF_4 and GeF_4 in ether or excess base show a single resonance band in their ^{19}F spectra over a wide range of temperatures, extending from the freezing point of the solvent to well above room temperature. The single band is thought to be due to a rapid ligand exchange process but it could also arise from a symmetrical molecule resulting from *trans* substitution of the octahedral structure.

The ^{19}F resonance spectra of complexes of SF_4 give little information since the tertiary amines are not sufficiently basic to cause this weak acceptor to change its characteristic ^{19}F spectrum (see Fig. 11.19). The tertiary amine complexes with SF_4 possess a single fluorine resonance absorption band, which is unchanged by variations of the temperature over the range -100 to $+50$°C.

The ^{19}F resonance spectra of $MoF_4 \cdot 2$ base complexes consist of a single broad band.

11.23.3 Other Metal Fluoride Complexes

Aqueous solutions of metal fluoride complexes (Th, Al and Zr) have been examined by NMR and attempts have been made to correlate the observed ^{19}F chemical shifts with various parameters[148, 149]. No simple correlation was found with either the electronegativity of the metal ion or the stability of the complex. Although ThF^{3+} and AlF^{2+} are far more stable species than ZrF^+, the ^{19}F resonance band of the latter is intermediate between those of the other two. However, the metal cations with high atomic numbers are generally associated with deshielded fluorine atoms and a rough correlation between ^{19}F chemical shifts and A/d values exists (where A is the atomic number of the metal cation and d is the interatomic distance within the complex). In the fluorine resonance spectra of some of the complexes there are several absorption bands, which is evidence for the presence of more than one species in the system. An equimolar mixture of $Al(NO_3)_3$ and NaF aqueous solutions shows two fluorine absorption bands for the two separate species AlF_2^+ and

AlF^{2+}. The fluorine atoms in the system are not involved in a rapid exchange process and from the chemical shift difference between the fluorine nuclei of AlF_2^+ and AlF^{2+} it is possible to set a lower limit of $8{\cdot}0 \times 10^{-3}$ sec on the lifetimes of the fluorine atom in each species. By measuring the intensities of the two separate absorption bands the relative amounts of the two complex ions can be found.

Complexes of tellurium hexafluoride with tertiary amines have been examined by NMR over a range of temperatures[154]. The observed ^{19}F resonance spectrum of $TeF_6{\cdot}2N(CH_3)_3$ is consistent with the molecule having an octahedral structure and existing in three different geometrically isomeric forms at $-180°C$ (three resonance bands are obtained). At room temperature, a single absorption band is observed which strongly suggests that rapid exchange of amine molecules occurs.

11.24 Fluorine-containing Polymers

It has already been seen that the study of hydrogen-containing polymers by NMR is seriously restricted by the excessive line widths observed in their ^{1}H resonance spectra, and by the problems of finding a suitable solvent for the polymer (see Section 10.37). By studying fluorinated polymers both these restrictions can be partially overcome since (i) ^{19}F chemical shifts extend over a much larger range than hydrogen chemical shifts and the magnitudes of the line widths are usually small compared with the chemical shifts, (ii) many hydrogen-containing solvents are available for fluorinated polymers which could not previously be used because of the ^{1}H resonance spectra of the solvent overlapping that of the polymer[150].

Table 11.60 ^{19}F Chemical Shifts of Fluorocarbon Groups in Polymers

Sample no.	Type of resonance	Sample	ppm from CF_3COOH (external)
1	$F-\overset{\vert}{\underset{\vert}{C}}-H$	Polytrifluoroethylene	131·7
2	$F-\overset{\vert}{\underset{\vert}{C}}-Cl$	Kel-F	50·0
3	$F-\overset{\vert}{\underset{\vert}{C}}-F$	Perfluorodecanoic acid	41·7
4	CF_3	Perfluorodecanoic acid	3·3
5	$F-\overset{\vert}{\underset{\vert}{C}}-H$	Polyvinyl fluoride	103·3
6	$F-\overset{\vert}{\underset{\vert}{C}}-F$	Polyvinylidene fluoride	13·3

^{19}F chemical shifts are accurate to 0·8 ppm.

Naylor and Lasoski[150] have exploited these features in a NMR study of a wide range of fluorinated polymers examined as 10 per cent solutions in either dimethyl formamide or butanone-2. Tables 11.60 and 11.61 list the ^{19}F chemical shifts of fluorine atoms in various environments within polymeric structures. The structure of a sample of polyvinylidene fluoride was shown to have a

TABLE 11.61 ^{19}F CHEMICAL SHIFTS OF FLUOROCARBON GROUPS IN POLYMERS

Sample no.	Type of resonance	Sample	ppm from CF$_3$COOH (external)
1	H F H / —C—C—C— / H H H	Polyvinyl fluoride	103·3
2	F F F / —C—C—C— / F H F	Polytrifluoroethylene	131·7
3	H F H / C—C—C / H F H	Polyvinylidene fluoride	13·3
4	F F F / —C—C—C— / H F H	Polytrifluoroethylene	38·3
5	F F F / —C—C—C— / F F F	Perfluorodecanoic acid	41·7
6	F F CH$_3$ H / —C—C—C=C— / F F	Poly(2-methyl-1,1,4,4-tetrafluorobutadiene)	30·0 35·0

^{19}F chemical shifts are accurate to 0·8 ppm.

"head-to-head" arrangement of its monomeric units on the basis of the ^{19}F resonance spectrum of the molecule.

Wilson[176] has examined the ^{19}F resonance spectrum at 56·4 Mc sec^{-1} of polyvinylidene fluoride in N,N-dimethylacetamide and he has observed separate absorption bands for the various CF$_2$ groups:

$$-CF_2-CH_2-CF_2^*-CH_2-CF_2 \qquad \varphi^* = +91.6 \text{ ppm}$$
$$-CH_2-CH_2-CF_2^*-CH_2-CF_2 \qquad \varphi^* = +94.8 \text{ ppm}$$
$$-CF_2-CH_2-CF_2^*-CF_2-CH_2 \qquad \varphi^* = +113.6 \text{ ppm}$$
$$-CH_2-CH_2-CF_2^*-CF_2-CH_2 \qquad \varphi^* = +115.9 \text{ ppm}$$

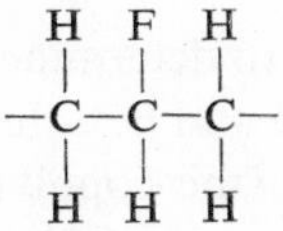

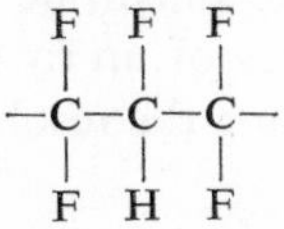

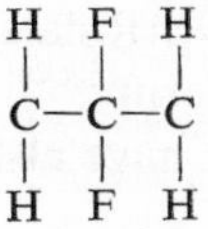

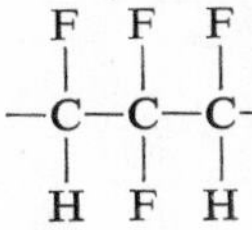

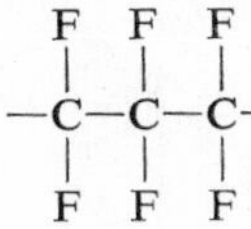

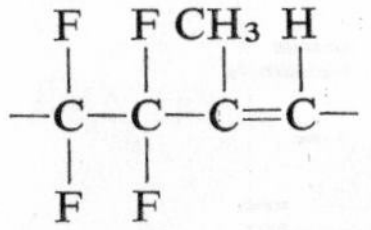

It is seen that the ^{19}F chemical shifts are influenced not only by nearest neighbours in the polymer chain but also by next nearest neighbours. Intensity measurements of the absorption bands give a measure of the relative amounts of head-to-head, tail-to-tail, and head-to-tail structures in the polymer chain. The ^{19}F resonance spectrum of polytrifluorochloroethylene in 3,3′-bistrifluoromethylbiphenyl solution at 150°C shows two doublets having components of unequal intensities(177). By comparing this spectrum with the similar ^{19}F resonance spectrum obtained for the model compounds *meso*- and *dl*-$CF_2ClCFClCF_2CFClCF_2Cl$ it was possible to assign the components of the doublets to fluorine nuclei in isotactic and syndiotactic sequences in the polymer chain.

Fluorine resonance measurements have been used to determine the structure of the linear copolymer formed by vinylidene fluoride and hexafluoropropylene and also to indicate the mole ratio of monomers in the copolymer(151). The solvents acetone, trifluoroacetic acid or trifluoroacetic anhydride were used for this investigation and it was found that sample tubes of up to 8 mm outside diameter could be employed without seriously affecting the resolution.

11.25 Miscellaneous Studies

Table 11.62 is a compilation of miscellaneous ^{19}F NMR data and Fig. 11.25 presents some important ^{19}F chemical shifts in chart form(155): these are given for the sake of completeness. Ito and co-workers(156) have also measured the

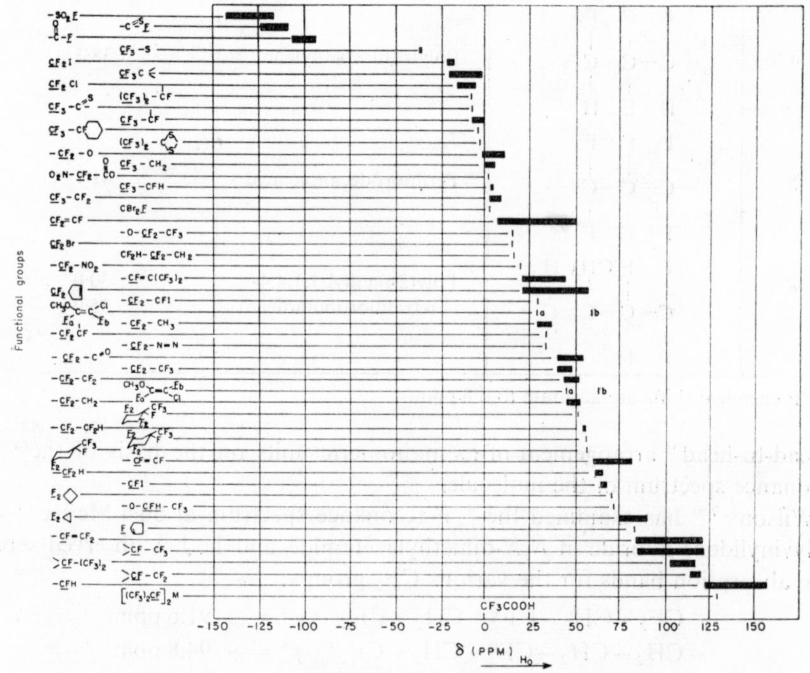

FIG. 11.25 Compilation of ^{19}F chemical shifts measured in ppm from trifluoroacetic acid external reference. Brame(155).

^{19}F resonance spectra of several miscellaneous monofluorinated compounds. ^{19}F chemical shifts in xenon fluorides and related compounds have been measured ($\delta_{XeF_2} = 629$, $\delta_{XeF_4} = 450$ and $\delta_{XeF_6} = 310$ ppm from a F_2 reference sample): ^{129}Xe chemical shifts have also been determined(185-187). Studies of krypton fluorides have also been reported(203).

TABLE 11.62 a ^{19}F CHEMICAL SHIFTS OF SOME FLUOROCARBONS(50)

Formula	Group	δ ppm †
1. Fluorocarbons		
$(CF_3)_4C$	CF_3	−13·8
$(CF_3)_3CF$	CF_3	−1·2
	CF	112·5
$CF_3CF_2CF_2CF_3$	CF_3	6·0
	CF_2	51·4
a b c d e $CF_3CF_2CF_2CF(CF_2CF_3)_2$	CF_3(a)	4·8
	CF_3(e)	3·2
	CF_2(b)	46·6
	CF_2(c)	34·4
	CF_2(d)	37·4
	CF	107·0
Perfluorocyclohexane	CF_2	55·0
2. Alkoxy derivatives of perfluoroisobutylene		
$(CF_3)_2CHCF_2OCH_3$	CF_3	−12·8
	CF_2	−3·0
$(CF_3)_2C{=}CFOCH_3$	CF_3	−18·9
	CF	−9·4
$(CF_3)_2C{=}CFOCH_2CH_2CH_3$	CF_3	−19·7
	CF	−11·8
$(CF_3)_3C{=}C(OCH_2CH{=}CH_2)_2$	CF_3	−11·1
$(CF_3)_2CHCF_2OCH_2CH_2F$	CF_3	−13·0
	CF_2	−6·2
	CF	149·5
a b $(CF_3)_2C{=}CFOCH_2CH_2F$	CF_3	−19·3
	CF(a)	−11·1
	CF(b)	149·5
3. Miscellaneous compounds		
CF_3CF_2COOH	CF_3	7·0
	CF_2	46·0
$(CF_3CF_2)_2O$	CF_3	11·9
	CF_2	12·9

† Chemical shifts measured in ppm from CF_3COOH external reference.

TABLE 11.62 b ^{19}F CHEMICAL SHIFTS OF SOME FLUOROETHANES[171]

Compound	φ ppm
CF_2BrCF_2Br	63·4
CF_2ClCF_2Cl	71·2
CF_2ICF_2Cl	59·6 (CF_2I) 67·0 (CF_2Cl)
$CF_2ClCFCl_2$	72·2 ($CFCl_2$) 68·05 (CF_2Cl)
CF_3CFCl_2	84·6 (CF_3) 76·8 ($CFCl_2$)

Chemical shifts measured in ppm from $CFCl_3$ internal reference (φ values).

TABLE 11.62 c ^{19}F CHEMICAL SHIFTS AND SPIN COUPLING CONSTANTS IN SOME PERFLUOROALKANE DERIVATIVES[78]

$(CF_3)_2CFBr$†	$\delta_{CF_3} = 1{\cdot}15$ $\delta_{CF} = 66{\cdot}9$
$(CF_3)_2CFI$	$\delta_{CF_3} = -2{\cdot}00$ $\delta_{CF} = 70{\cdot}4$
$CF_3CF_2CF_2I$	$\delta_{CF_3} = 2{\cdot}25$ $\delta_{CF_2} = 40{\cdot}6$ $\delta_{CF_2I} = -17{\cdot}2$
CF_3CFICF_2Cl	$\delta_{CF_3} = -5{\cdot}65$ $\delta_{CF_A} = -15{\cdot}8$ $\delta_{CF_B} = -12{\cdot}5$ $\delta_{CFI} = 38{\cdot}7$
CF_3 CF_3 CF·CF CF_2Cl $CFCl_2$	$\delta_{CF_3} = -8{\cdot}87$ $\delta_{CF_2} = -20{\cdot}6$ $\delta_{CF} = 84{\cdot}5$
$(CF_3)_2CF \cdot CF(CF_3)_2$	$\delta_{CF_3} = -5{\cdot}54$ $\delta_{CF} = 103{\cdot}3$

$(CF_3)_2CFBr$	$J_{CF_3-CF} = 8{\cdot}9 \pm 0{\cdot}5$ cycles sec^{-1}
$(CF_3)_2CFI$	$J_{CF_3-CF} = 12{\cdot}5 \pm 0{\cdot}1$
$CF_3CF_2CF_2I$	$J_{CF_3-CF_2} = 0{\cdot}8 \pm 0{\cdot}1$, $J_{CF_3-CF_2I} = 9{\cdot}4 \pm 0{\cdot}2$ $J_{CF_2-CF_2I} = 4{\cdot}7 \pm 0{\cdot}2$
CF_3CFICF_2Cl	$J_{CF_3-CF} = 11{\cdot}8 \pm 0{\cdot}1$, $J_{CF_3-CF_A} = 9{\cdot}4 \pm 0{\cdot}1$ $J_{CF_3-CF_B} = 11{\cdot}8 \pm 0{\cdot}1$, $J_{CF-CF_A} = 18{\cdot}8 \pm 0{\cdot}5$ $J_{CF-CF_B} = 18{\cdot}1 \pm 0{\cdot}5$, $J_{CF_A-CF_B} = 116 \pm 2$
$(CF_3)_2CF \cdot CF(CF_3)_2$	$J_{CF_3-CF} = 9{\cdot}0 \pm 0{\cdot}1$

† Chemical shifts in ppm measured from CF_3COOH: positive shifts are to high fields of the reference.

TABLE 11.62 d ^{19}F CHEMICAL SHIFTS OF SOME COMPOUNDS CONTAINING PERFLUOROMETHYL GROUPS(171)

Compound	φ ppm	J_{FF} cycles sec^{-1}†
$(CF_3)_2N{\cdot}NO_2$	59·20	10·8
$(CF_3)_2PCl$	61·4	8·93
$(CF_3)_2S$	38·64	9·68
$(CF_3S)_2$	46·88	4·47
$(CF_3S)_2Hg$	21·11	<0·2
$(CF_3)_2AsCl$	56·06	7·85
$(CF_3)_2Se$	—	8·48
$(CF_3Se)_2$	38·1	3·08
$(CF_3Se)_2Hg$	15·2	<0·2
CF_3I	4·78	—
$(CF_3)_2Hg$	36·4	5·3
Cyclo-C_4F_8	135·5	‡

† $^{13}C^{19}F$ satellite spectra were analysed to obtain the F–F coupling constants.
‡ $^{13}C^{19}F$ satellites are 1:1:1 triplets with a splitting of 3·0 cycles sec^{-1}.
Chemical shifts measured from $CFCl_3$ internal reference.

TABLE 11.62 e ^{19}F AND ^{31}P CHEMICAL SHIFTS AND COUPLING CONSTANTS IN A SERIES OF PERFLUOROALKYL PHOSPHORUS DERIVATIVES(170)

Compound	δ_P†‡	φ_F‡††	$J(P{-}CF_3)$‡‡
$(CF_3)_2PF$	$-123·9 \pm 0·6$	$66·5 \pm 0·05$	$89·6 \pm 0·20$
$(CF_3)_2PCl$	$-50·0 \pm 0·4$	$61·4 \pm 0·10$	$85·1 \pm 0·10$
$(CF_3)_2PBr$	$-33·7 \pm 0·1$	$59·5 \pm 0·02$	$80·6 \pm 0·05$
$(CF_3)_2PI$	$-0·8 \pm 0·04$	$55·4 \pm 0·05$	$73·2 \pm 0·03$
$(CF_3)_2P \cdot CN$	$40·7 \pm 0·2$	$51·3 \pm 0·20$	$85·6 \pm 0·10$
$(CF_3)_2P \cdot NCO$	$-34·5 \pm 0·2$	$63·2 \pm 0·20$	$88·0 \pm 0·10$
$(CF_3)_2P \cdot NCS$	—	$61·9 \pm 0·05$	$87·3 \pm 0·10$
$(CF_3)_2P \cdot OEt$	$-92·3 \pm 0·3$	$65·3 \pm 0·20$	$86·6 \pm 0·04$
$(CF_3)_2P \cdot NMe_2$	$-46·3 \pm 0·2$	$60·0 \pm 0·10$	$85·6 \pm 0·10$
$(CF_3)_2P \cdot S \cdot CF_3$	$-12·8 \pm 0·1$	$55·6 \pm 0·20$	$83·8 \pm 0·40$
$(CF_3)_2P \cdot Se \cdot CF_3$	$-14·1 \pm 0·1$	$53·7 \pm 0·10$	$77·2 \pm 0·10$
$(CF_3)_2PH$	—	$47·5 \pm 0·04$	$68·6 \pm 0·10$
$(CF_3)_3P$	$2·6 \pm 0·0$	$50·8 \pm 0·05$	$85·5 - 0·10$
$(CF_3)_2PCl_3$	—	$78·8 \pm 0·10$	$193·3 \pm 0·20$
$(CF_3)_3P{\rightarrow}O$	$-2·3 \pm 0·15$	$66·2 \pm 0·05$	$113·4 \pm 0·10$
$[(CF_3)_3P]_2Ni(CO)_2$	$-52·6 \pm 0·5$	$56·6 \pm 0·12$	$91·4 \pm 0·10$

† In ppm from H_3PO_4 (85 per cent).
‡ High-field shift positive.
†† In ppm from CCl_3F.
‡‡ In cycles sec^{-1}.

TABLE 11.62 f COUPLING CONSTANTS OF PHOSPHORUS (V) FLUORIDES(140)

Compound	J_{PF} cycles sec^{-1}	J_{HF} cycles sec^{-1}
PF_5	916	
CH_3PF_4	967	6—7
$ClCH_2PF_4$	997	6—7
$C_2H_5PF_4$	987	6—7
n-$C_4H_9PF_4$	990	6
$C_8H_{15}PF_4$ isomer A	955	6·5
isomer B	955	6·5
$C_6H_5CH_2PF_4$	1002	6—7
cis-$(C_6H_5)HC{=}CH(PF_4)$	940	6—7
$C_6H_5PF_4$	963	<0·5
m-$CH_3C_6H_4PF_4$	960	<0·5
p-$CH_3C_6H_4PF_4$	960	<0·5
m-$C_3H_7C_6H_4PF_4$	963	<0·5
p-$C_3H_7C_6H_4PF_4$	958	<0·5
m-$ClC_6H_4PF_4$	960	<0·5
p-$ClC_6H_4PF_4$	960	<0·5
2,5-$(CH_3)_2C_6H_3PF_4$	981	<0·5
CF_3PF_4	1103	12 (FC—PF)

TABLE 11.62 g ^{19}F CHEMICAL SHIFTS OF PHOSPHORUS (V) FLUORIDES(140)

Compound	δ_{CF_3} ppm	$\delta_{F(mono)}$ ppm	δ_{Fe} ppm	δ_{Fa} ppm
CF_3PF_4	−3·4	−10		
$(CF_3)_2PF_3$	−3·8		−7·5	
$(CF_3)_3PF_2$	−12			−16·8
CH_3PF_4		−31		
$(CH_3)_2PF_3$			+9·8	−74
$(CH_3)_3PF_2$				−73
$(CH_2)_5PF_3$			+6	−58
$C_2H_5PF_4$		−25		
$(C_2H_5)_2PF_3$			+16	−52
$(C_2H_5)_3PF_2$				−44
n-$C_4H_9PF_4$		−27		
(n-$C_4H_9)_2PF_3$			+13	−56
(n-$C_4H_9)_3PF_2$				−44
$C_6H_5PF_4$		−23		
$(C_6H_5)_2PF_3$			+1·2	−44
$(C_6H_5)_3PF_2$				−39
$C_6H_5(CH_3)PF_3$			+5·4	−60
$ClCH_2PF_4$		−24		
$C_8H_{15}PF_4$		−31		
$C_6H_5CH{=}CHPF_4$		−32		
2,5-$(CH_3)_2C_6H_3PF_4$		−25		

Chemical shifts measured from CF_3COOH external reference.

TABLE 11.62 h ^{19}F COUPLING CONSTANTS (IN CYCLES SEC^{-1}) FOR R_2PF_3 COMPOUNDS[(140)]

Compound	J_{PF_a}	J_{PF_e}	$J_{F_eF_a}$	J_{HF_e}	J_{HF_a}	$\lvert\delta_{F_e}-\delta_{F_a}\rvert$ ppm
$(CH_3)_2PF_3$	772	960	26	~2		61
$(C_2H_5)_2PF_3$	815	980	29		12	68
$(n\text{-}C_4H_9)_2PF_3$	810	985	28	~2	14	70
$CH_3(C_6H_5)PF_3$	785	935	33		14	60
$(C_6H_5)_2PF_3$	838	970	37		13·5	45
$(CH_2)_4PF_3$ (−100°)	865	990	50			
$(CH_2)_4PF_3$ (25°)	915[a]				8·6	
$(CH_2)_5PF_3$	800	1005	42			64
$(CF_3)_2PF_3$		1260		175_{P-CF}	16_{CF-PF}	
Cl_2PF_3	1050 (av.)					
Br_2PF_3	1140 (av.?)					

[a] This compares well with the value of 907 cycles sec^{-1} calculated by averaging the two J_{PF} obtained for $(CH_2)_4PF_3$ at −100°.

a and *e* refer to *apical* and *equatorial* positions.

TABLE 11.62 i ^{19}F COUPLING CONSTANTS (CYCLES SEC^{-1}) FOR R_3PF_2 COMPOUNDS[(140)]

Compound	J_{PF}	J_{FF}	J_{HF}
$(CH_3)_3PF_2$	545		11
$(C_2H_5)_3PF_2$	575		11
$(n\text{-}C_4H_9)_3PF_2$	585		16
$(C_6H_5)_3PF_2$	695		
$(CF_3)_3PF_2$	988	16	

Additional ^{19}F data for compounds containing PF bonds are given in references 205 and 206.

TABLE 11.62 j ^{19}F CHEMICAL SHIFTS AND J_{CF} COUPLING CONSTANTS FOR SEVERAL ORGANO-FLUORINE COMPOUNDS(190)

Compound	Coupling constants [a] (cycles sec^{-1})		δ_F ppm	Isotope shift [b] ppm
	J_{CF}	J_{CCF}		
CH_3F	158		276	0·067
$C_6H_5CH_2F$	165		207	0·107
$(CH_3)_3CF$	167		132	0·114
CH_2F_2	232		148	0·143
p-$CH_3OC_6H_4F$	237		125	
p-$CH_3C_6H_4F$	241		119	
o-ClC_6H_4F	244		116	
C_6H_5F	244 [c]		114	
p-BrC_6H_4F	247		116	
m-ClC_6H_4F	248		111	
p-$CF_3C_6H_4\mathbf{F}$	252 [c]		109	
p-$CH_3C(O)C_6H_4F$	253		107	
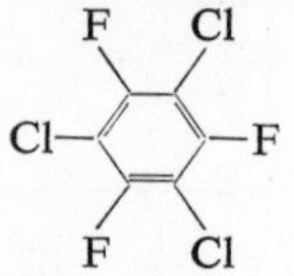	253	− 21·6	98	0·090
$CF_3—C≡C—CF_3$	256	− 57·2	57	0·142
CF_4	257		69	0·105
p-$NO_2C_6H_4F$	257		103	
$CF_3N{=}SF_2$	263		50	0·147
$(CF_3)_2\mathbf{CF_2}$	265	− 32·5	134	0·115
$(CF_3)_2O$	265		62	0·116
$(CF_3)_3N$	269		59	0·125
p-$NH_2C_6H_4CF_3$	270	− 32·4		
p-$FC_6H_4\mathbf{CF_3}$	271	− 33·2		
p-$(CF_3)_2C_6H_4$	271	− 32·9	65	0·128
CF_3CH_3	271		65	0·128
CF_3H	272		84	0·133
CF_3CH_2Br	272	− 38·5	71	0·129
m-$(CF_3)_2C_6H_4$	272		65	0·128
CF_3CH_2Cl	274		74	0·108
$CF_3CCl{=}CCl_2$	274	− 39·2	62	0·140
CF_3CH_2OH	278			0·116
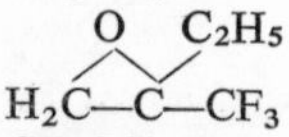	278		78	0·106
CF_3CCl_3	283 [d]	− 43·1 [d]	82 [d]	0·131 [d]
CF_3COOH	283	− 44·1 [d]	79	0·129 [d]
$CF_3COOC_2H_5$	284	− 44·1	78	0·130
$(\mathbf{CF_3})_2CF_2$	285	− 40·0	86	0·106
$CF_2{=}CD_2$	287		88	
CF_2ClCH_3	288		47	0·147
$CF_2{=}CCl_2$	289 [d]	− 44·2 [d]	89 [d]	0·103 [d]
$CF_3C(O)CH_3$	289		83	0·120
Cyclic C_4F_8	298	− 25·8	138	
CF_3Cl	299		33	0·152
Cyclic $C_4F_4Cl_4$	300		114	0·152

(continued)

Compound	Coupling constants[a] (cycles sec^{-1}) J_{CF}	J_{CCF}	δ_F ppm	Isotope shift[b] ppm
$CFCl{=}CCl_2$	303[d]	−43·7[d]	79[d]	0·112[d]
CF_3Br	324		21	0·152
CF_2Cl_2	325		8	0·164
$CFCl_3$	337		0	0·192
$C_6H_5C(O)F$	344	−61·0	−17	0·118
CF_3I	344		5	0·132
$CH_3C(O)F$	353	−59·7	−47	0·125
CF_2Br_2	358		−7	0·168
HC(O)F	369		−41	0·128
$CFBr_3$	372[f]		−7[e]	

[a] Negative signs have been chosen for J_{CCF} on the basis of conclusions reported in ref. 80.
[b] δ_F is greater for the ^{13}C-containing molecules.
[c] ±5 cycles sec^{-1}. Other values are ±1 cycles sec^{-1} or better.
[d] From reference 13.
[e] From reference 2.
[f] From reference 92.
Additional ^{13}C–F coupling constants are given in reference 182.
Chemical shifts were measured using an external $CFCl_3$ reference.

TABLE 11.62 k ^{19}F CHEMICAL SHIFTS AND COUPLING CONSTANTS IN SOME ALKYL AND SILYL SELENIDES[(39)]

Compound	^{19}F Chemical shift φ^* ppm	J_{HF} cycles sec^{-1}
$CF_3 \cdot Se \cdot SiH_3$	+25·5	1·6
$CF_3 \cdot Se \cdot C_2H_5$	+35·2	
$C_3F_7 \cdot Se \cdot SiH_3$	+77·9 (α-CF_2)	3·0, 1·5
	+121·3 (β-CF_2)	
	+79·5 (CF_3)	
$C_3F_7 \cdot Se \cdot C_2H_5$	+88·6 (α-CF_2)	
	+123·7 (β-CF_2)	
	+82·5 (CF_3)	

φ^* Measured in ppm from $CFCl_3$ used as an internal reference.

REFERENCES

1. D. F. Evans, *J. Chem. Soc.*, 877 (1960).
2. G. Filipovich and G. V. D. Tiers, *J. Phys. Chem.*, **63**, 761 (1959).
3. R. E. Glick and S. J. Ehrenson, *J. Phys. Chem.*, **62**, 1599 (1958).
4. B. B. Howard, B. Linder and M. T. Emerson, *J. Chem. Phys.*, **36**, 485 (1962).
5. A. Saika and C. P. Slichter, *J. Chem. Phys.*, **22**, 26 (1954).
6. H. S. Gutowsky and C. J. Hoffman, *J. Chem. Phys.*, **19**, 1259 (1951).
7. J. R. Holmes, B. B. Stewart and J. S. MacKenzie, *J. Chem. Phys.*, **37**, 2728 (1962).
8. G. V. D. Tiers, *J. Amer. Chem. Soc.*, **78**, 2914 (1956).
9. L. H. Meyer and H. S. Gutowsky, *J. Phys. Chem.*, **57**, 481 (1953).
10. T. S. Smith and E. A. Smith, *J. Phys. Chem.*, **63**, 1701 (1959).
11. G. V. D. Tiers, *J. Amer. Chem. Soc.*, **79**, 5585 (1957).
12. H. S. Gutowsky, *J. Chem. Phys.*, **31**, 1683 (1959).
13. G. V. D. Tiers, *J. Phys. Soc. Japan*, **15**, 354 (1960).
14. G. V. D. Tiers, *J. Inorg. Nuc. Chem.*, **16**, 363 (1961).
15. A. Saika and H. S. Gutowsky, *J. Amer. Chem. Soc.*, **78**, 4818 (1956).
16. J. Feeney and L. H. Sutcliffe, *Trans. Faraday Soc.*, **56**, 1559 (1960).
17. L. Petrakis and C. H. Sederholm, *J. Chem. Phys.*, **35**, 1243 (1961).
18. C. M. Sharts and J. D. Roberts, *J. Amer. Chem. Soc.*, **79**, 1008 (1957).
19. H. S. Gutowsky, C. H. Holm, A. Saika and G. A. Williams, *J. Amer. Chem. Soc.*, **79**, 4596 (1957).
20. L. M. Crapo and C. H. Sederholm, *J. Chem. Phys.*, **33**, 1583 (1960).
21. J. I. Musher, *J. Chem. Phys.*, **36**, 1086 (1962).
22. D. F. Evans, *Discuss. Faraday Soc.*, **34**, 139 (1962).
23. S. L. Manatt and D. D. Elleman, *J. Amer. Chem. Soc.*, **84**, 1305 (1962).
24. D. F. Evans, S. L. Manatt and D. D. Elleman, *J. Amer. Chem. Soc.*, **85**, 238 (1963).
25. B. H. Arison, T. Y. Shen and N. R. Trenner, *J. Chem. Soc.*, 3828 (1962).
26. H. S. Gutowsky, G. G. Belford and P. E. McMahon, *J. Chem. Phys.*, **36**, 3353 (1962).
27. H. S. Gutowsky, *Techniques of Organic Chemistry*, Editor A. Weissberger, Interscience, N.Y. (1960), Chapt. XLI, Vol. 1, Part IV, 3rd Edn.
28. D. S. Thompson, R. A. Newmark and C. H. Sederholm, *J. Chem. Phys.*, **37**, 411 (1962).
29. B. Bak, J. N. Shoolery and G. A. Williams, *J. Mol. Spect.*, **2**, 525 (1958).
30. S. Fujiwara and H. Shimizu, *J. Chem. Phys.*, **32**, 1636 (1960).
31. G. A. Williams and H. S. Gutowsky, *J. Chem. Phys.*, **30**, 717 (1959).
32. I. Solomon and N. Bloembergen, *J. Chem. Phys.*, **25**, 261 (1956).
33. H. M. McConnell, C. A. Reilly and A. D. McLean, *J. Chem. Phys.* **24**, 479 (1956).
34. J. J. Drysdale and W. D. Phillips, *J. Amer. Chem. Soc.*, **79**, 319 (1957).
35. T. Schaefer, *Can. J. Chem.*, **37**, 882 (1959).
36. R. J. Abraham and H. J. Bernstein, *Can. J. Chem.*, **39**, 216 (1961).
37. M. Takahashi, D. R. Davies and J. D. Roberts, *J. Amer. Chem. Soc.*, **84**, 2935 (1962).
38. A. D. Cross and P. W. Landis, *J. Amer. Chem. Soc.*, **84**, 1736 (1962).
39. E. A. V. Ebsworth, H. J. Emeléus and N. Welcman, *J. Chem. Soc.*, 2290 (1962).
40. R. C. Lord, M. A. Lynch, W. C. Schumb and E. J. Slowinski, *J. Amer. Chem. Soc.*, **72**, 522 (1950).
41. E. L. Muetterties and W. D. Phillips, *J. Amer. Chem. Soc.*, **81**, 1084 (1959).
42. H. S. Gutowsky, D. W. McCall and C. P. Slichter, *J. Chem. Phys.*, **21**, 279 (1953).
43. J. N. Shoolery, Varian Technical Bulletin, No. 1, (3), (1955).
44. G. Silbiger and S. H. Bauer, *J. Amer. Chem. Soc.*, **68**, 312 (1946).
45. W. D. Phillips, *Ann. N.Y. Acad. Sci.*, **70**, 817 (1958).
46. J. Lee and L. H. Sutcliffe, *Trans. Faraday Soc.*, **54**, 308 (1958).
47. P. M. Nair and J. D. Roberts, *J. Amer. Chem. Soc.*, **79**, 4565 (1957).
48. J. N. Shoolery and B. Crawford, *J. Mol. Spect.*, **1**, 270 (1957).
49. J. Lee and L. H. Sutcliffe, *Trans. Faraday Soc.*, **55**, 880 (1959).
50. D. D. Elleman, L. C. Brown and D. Williams, *J. Mol. Spect.*, **7**, 307 (1961).
51. D. D. Elleman, L. C. Brown and D. Williams, *J. Mol. Spect.*, **7**, 322 (1961).

52. J. A. Young, W. S. Durrell and R. D. Dresdner, *J. Amer. Chem. Soc.*, **84**, 2105 (1962).
53. H. Schroeder, E. Kober, H. Ulrich, R. Rätz, H. Agahigian and C. Grundmann, *J. Org. Chem.*, **27**, 2580 (1962).
54. N. Muller, P. C. Lauterbur and G. F. Svatos, *J. Amer. Chem. Soc.*, **79**, 1807 (1957).
55. J. Bigeleisen and M. Wolfsberg, *J. Chem. Phys.*, **23**, 1535 (1955).
56. E. Pitcher, A. D. Buckingham and F. G. A. Stone, *J. Chem. Phys.*, **36**, 124 (1962).
57. W. R. McClellan, *J. Amer. Chem. Soc.*, **83**, 1598 (1961).
58. L. P. Hammett, *Chem. Rev.*, **17**, 125 (1935).
59. H. S. Gutowsky, D. W. McCall, B. R. McGarvey and L. H. Meyer, *J. Amer. Chem. Soc.*, **74**, 4809 (1952).
60. R. W. Taft, *J. Amer. Chem. Soc.*, **79**, 1045 (1957).
61. M. Karplus and T. P. Das, *J. Chem. Phys.*, **34**, 1683 (1961).
62. T. Isobe, K. Inukai and K. Ito, *J. Chem. Phys.*, **27**, 1215 (1957).
63. R. E. Richards and T. Schaefer, *Trans. Faraday Soc.*, **54**, 1447 (1958).
64. A. J. R. Bourn, D. G. Gillies and E. W. Randall. *Proc. Chem. Soc.*, 200 (1963).
65. G. M. Brooke, J. Burdon and J. C. Tatlow, *J. Chem. Soc.*, 802 (1961).
66. T. D. Coyle, S. L. Stafford and F. G. A. Stone, *Spect. Acta.*, **17**, 968 (1961).
67. C. A. Reilly and J. D. Swalen, *J. Chem. Phys.*, **34**, 2122 (1961).
68. J. D. Roberts, *An Introduction to the Analysis of Spin–Spin Splitting in Nuclear Magnetic Resonance*, W. A. Benjamin, New York (1961).
69. J. L. Anderson, R. E. Putnam and W. H. Sharkey, *J. Amer. Chem. Soc.*, **83**, 382 (1961).
70. H. H. Hoehn, L. Pratt, K. F. Watterson and G. Wilkinson, *J. Chem. Soc.*, 2738 (1961).
71. H. M. McConnell, *J. Chem. Phys.*, **24**, 460 (1956).
72. S. Alexander, *J. Chem. Phys.*, **28**, 358 (1958).
73. E. B. Whipple, J. H. Goldstein and L. Mandell, *J. Amer. Chem. Soc.*, **82**, 3010 (1960).
74. T. D. Coyle, S. L. Stafford and F. G. A. Stone, *J. Chem. Soc.*, 743 (1961).
75. S. Andreades, *J. Amer. Chem. Soc.*, **84**, 864 (1962).
76. C. A. Reilly, *J. Chem. Phys.*, **37**, 456 (1962).
77. C. N. Banwell and N. Sheppard, *Proc. Roy. Soc.*, **A 263**, 136 (1961).
78. N. Boden, J. W. Emsley, J. Feeney and L. H. Sutcliffe, unpublished results.
79. T. D. Coyle, S. L. Stafford and F. G. A. Stone, *Spect. Acta*, **17**, 1244 (1961).
80. T. G. V. D. Tiers and P. C. Lauterbur, *J. Chem. Phys.*, **36**, 1110 (1962).
81. G. V. D. Tiers, *J. Chem. Phys.*, **35**, 2263 (1961).
82. G. V. D. Tiers, *J. Phys. Chem.*, **66**, 1192 (1962).
83. W. J. Middleton and W. H. Sharkey, *J. Amer. Chem. Soc.*, **81**, 803 (1959).
84. J. N. Shoolery, *Discuss. Faraday Soc.*, **19**, 215 (1956).
85. W. D. Phillips, *J. Chem. Phys.*, **25**, 949 (1956).
86. G. V. D. Tiers, *Proc. Chem. Soc.*, 389 (1960).
87. J. Feeney and L. H. Sutcliffe, *J. Phys. Chem.*, **65**, 1894 (1961).
88. L. F. Thomas and J. Homer, *Proc. Chem. Soc.*, 139 (1961).
89. N. Sheppard and R. K. Harris, *Proc. Chem. Soc.*, 418 (1961).
90. P. Tarrant, R. W. Johnson and W. S. Brey, *J. Org. Chem.*, **27**, 602 (1962).
91. J. D. Dunitz and V. J. Schomaker, *J. Chem. Phys.*, **20**, 1703 (1952).
92. W. D. Phillips, *Determination of Organic Structures by Physical Methods*, Vol. 2, Chapt. 6, Editors F. C. Nachod and W. D. Phillips, Academic Press, New York (1962).
93. J. Homer and L. F. Thomas, *Trans. Faraday Soc.*, **59**, 2431 (1963).
94. G. V. D. Tiers, *J. Phys. Chem.*, **66**, 764 (1962).
95. L. W. Reeves and E. J. Wells, *Discuss. Faraday Soc.*, **34**, 177 (1962).
96. T. D. Coyle, R. B. King, E. Pitcher, S. L. Stafford, P. Treichel and F. G. A. Stone, *J. Inorg. Nuc. Chem.*, **20**, 172 (1961).
97. C. G. Krespan and C. M. Langkammerer, *J. Org. Chem.*, **27**, 3584 (1962).
98. E. Schnell and E. G. Rochow, *J. Amer. Chem. Soc.*, **78**, 4178 (1956).
99. F. G. A. Stone and D. Seyferth, *J. Inorg. Nuc. Chem.*, **1**, 112 (1955).
100. C. J. Hoffman, B. E. Holder and W. L. Jolly, *J. Phys. Chem.*, **62**, 364 (1958).
101. N. Muller, P. C. Lauterbur and G. F. Svatos, *J. Amer. Chem. Soc.*, **79**, 1043 (1957).

102. C. I. Merrill, S. M. Williamson, G. H. Cady and D. F. Eggers, *Inorg. Chem.*, **1**, 215 (1962).
103. N. Boden, J. Feeney, J. W. Emsley and L. H. Sutcliffe, *Trans. Faraday Soc.*, **59**, 620 (1963).
104. M. T. Rogers and J. D. Graham, *J. Amer. Chem. Soc.*, **84**, 3666 (1962).
105. K. J. Packer and R. K. Harris, *J. Chem. Soc.*, 4736 (1961), 3077 (1962).
106. D. Chapman, *J. Chem. Soc.*, 131 (1963).
107. D. R. Whitman, L. Onsager, M. Saunders and H. E. Dubb, *J. Chem. Phys.*, **32**, 67 (1960).
108. J. M. Shreeve and G. H. Cady, *J. Amer. Chem. Soc.*, **83**, 4521 (1961).
109. J. A. Young and R. D. Dresdner, *J. Org. Chem.*, **24**, 1021 (1959).
110. F. A. Cotton, J. W. George and J. S. Waugh, *J. Chem. Phys.*, **28**, 994 (1958).
111. F. S. Fawcett and R. D. Lipscomb, *J. Amer. Chem. Soc.*, **82**, 1509 (1960).
112. R. E. Dodd, L. A. Woodward and H. L. Roberts, *Trans. Faraday Soc.*, **52**, 1052 (1956).
113. R. M. Rosenberg and E. L. Muetterties, *Inorg. Chem.*, **1**, 756 (1962).
114. F. B. Dudley, J. N. Shoolery and G. H. Cady, *J. Amer. Chem. Soc.*, **78**, 568 (1956).
115. G. H. Cady and C. I. Merrill, *J. Amer. Chem. Soc.*, **84**, 2260 (1962).
116. J. E. Roberts and G. H. Cady, *J. Amer. Chem. Soc.*, **81**, 4166 (1959).
117. W. A. Sheppard and E. L. Muetterties, *J. Org. Chem.*, **25**, 180 (1960).
118. J. F. Harris and W. A. Sheppard, *J. Org. Chem.*, **26**, 354 (1961).
119. E. L. Muetterties and W. D. Phillips, *J. Amer. Chem. Soc.*, **79**, 322 (1957).
120. D. F. Smith, *J. Chem. Phys.*, **21**, 609 (1953).
121. R. D. Burbank and F. N. Bensey, *J. Chem. Phys.*, **21**, 602 (1953).
122. A. N. Hamer, *J. Inorg. Nuc. Chem.*, **9**, 98 (1959).
123. S. Brownstein, *Can. J. Chem.*, **38**, 1597 (1960).
124. R. A. Ogg, *Discuss. Faraday Soc.*, **17**, 215 (1954).
125. T. D. Coyle and F. G. A. Stone, *J. Chem. Phys.*, **32**, 1892 (1960).
126. T. D. Coyle and F. G. A. Stone, *J. Amer. Chem. Soc.*, **82**, 6223 (1960).
127. T. D. Coyle, S. L. Stafford and F. G. A. Stone, *J. Chem. Soc.*, 3103 (1961).
128. R. D. Chambers, H. C. Clark, L. W. Reeves and C. J. Willis, *Can. J. Chem.*, **39**, 258 (1961).
129. R. A. Ogg and J. D. Ray, *J. Chem. Phys.*, **25**, 797 (1956).
130. J. A. Pople, *Mol. Phys.*, **1**, 168 (1958).
131. R. C. Petry, *J. Amer. Chem. Soc.*, **82**, 2400 (1960).
132. R. C. Petry and J. P. Freeman, *J. Amer. Chem. Soc.*, **83**, 3912 (1961).
133. C. B. Colburn, F. A. Johnson, A. Kennedy, K. McCallum, L. C. Metzger and C. O. Parker, *J. Amer. Chem. Soc.*, **81**, 6397 (1959).
134. J. B. Hynes and L. A. Bigelow, *J. Amer. Chem. Soc.*, **84**, 2751 (1962).
135. J. R. Holmes, B. B. Stewart and J. S. MacKenzie, *J. Chem. Phys.*, **37**, 2728 (1962).
136. J. H. Noggle, J. D. Baldeschwieler and C. B. Colburn, *J. Chem. Phys.*, **37**, 182 (1962).
137. J. D. Baldeschwieler and E. W. Randall, *Proc. Chem. Soc.*, 303 (1961).
138. H. Braune and P. Pinnow, *Z. Phys. Chem.*, **B 35**, 239 (1937).
139. L. O. Brockway and J. Y. Beach, *J. Amer. Chem. Soc.*, **60**, 1836 (1938).
140. W. Mahler, R. Schmutzler and E. L. Muetterties, *Inorg. Chem.*, **2**, 613 (1963).
141. R. S. Berry, *J. Chem. Phys.*, **32**, 933 (1960).
142. E. L. Muetterties, T. A. Bither, M. W. Farlow and D. D. Coffman, *J. Inorg. Nuc. Chem.*, **16**, 52 (1960).
143. J. Feeney and L. H. Sutcliffe, unpublished results.
144. M. L. Heffernan and R. F. M. White, *J. Chem. Soc.*, 1382 (1961).
145. N. Boden, J. Feeney and L. H. Sutcliffe, unpublished results.
146. R. A. Ogg and P. Diehl, *Nature*, **180**, 1114 (1957).
147. E. L. Muetterties, *J. Amer. Chem. Soc.*, **82**, 1082 (1960).
148. R. E. Paulson and R. E. Connick, *J. Phys. Chem.*, **63**, 568 (1959).
149. R. E. Paulson and R. E. Connick, *J. Amer. Chem. Soc.*, **79**, 5153 (1957).
150. R. E. Naylor and S. W. Lasoski, *J. Polymer Sci.*, **44**, 1 (1960).

151. R. C. FERGUSON, *J. Amer. Chem. Soc.*, **82**, 2416 (1960).
152. C. G. KRESPAN, *J. Org. Chem.*, **25**, 105 (1960).
153. D. D. ELLEMAN and S. L. MANATT, *J. Chem. Phys.*, **36**, 1945 (1962).
154. E. L. MUETTERTIES and W. D. PHILLIPS, *J. Amer. Chem. Soc.*, **79**, 2975, (1957).
155. E. G. BRAME, *Anal. Chem.*, **34**, 591 (1962).
156. K. ITO, K. INUKAI and T. ISOBE. *Bull. Chem. Soc. Japan*, **33**, 315 (1960).
157. R. A. BEAUDET and J. D. BALDESCHWIELER, *J. Mol. Spect.*, **9**, 30 (1962).
158. S. G. FRANKISS, *J. Phys. Chem.*, **67**, 752 (1963).
159. S. BROWNSTEIN, *Chem. Rev.*, **59**, 463 (1959).
160. D. D. ELLEMAN and S. L. MANATT, private communication quoted in reference 22.
161. D. F. EVANS, *Mol. Phys.*, **5**, 183 (1962).
162. C. A. REILLY, *J. Chem. Phys.*, **25**, 604 (1956).
163. J. A. POPLE, W. G. SCHNEIDER and H. J. BERNSTEIN, *High Resolution Nuclear Magnetic Resonance*, McGraw-Hill, New York (1959).
164. J. A. POPLE, *Mol. Phys.*, **1**, 216 (1958).
165. D. F. EVANS, *Mol. Phys.*, **6**, 179 (1963).
166. H. AGAHIGIAN, A. P. GRAY and G. D. VICKERS, *Can. J. Chem.*, **40**, 157 (1962).
167. D. D. ELLEMAN, S. L. MANATT and C. D. PEARCE, private communication.
168. G. V. D. TIERS, *J. Amer. Chem. Soc.*, **84**, 3972 (1962).
169. G. V. D. TIERS, *J. Phys. Chem.*, **67**, 928 (1963).
170. K. J. PACKER, *J. Chem. Soc.*, 960 (1963).
171. R. K. HARRIS, private communication (1963).
172. F. PROSSER and L. GOODMAN, *J. Chem. Phys.*, **38**, 374 (1963).
173. R. W. TAFT, F. PROSSER, L. GOODMAN and G. T. DAVIS. *J. Chem. Phys.*, **38**, 380 (1963).
174. M. T. ROGERS and R. G. SUMMITT, private communication.
175. J. BACON, R. J. GILLESPIE and J. W. QUAIL, *Can. J. Chem.*, **41**, 1016 (1963).
176. C. W. WILSON, *J. Polymer Sci.*, **A1**, 1305 (1963).
177. G. V. D. TIERS and F. A. BOVEY, *J. Polymer Sci.*, **A1**, 833 (1963).
178. R. R. HOLMES and W. P. GALLAGHER, *Inorg. Chem.*, **2**, 443 (1963).
179. G. V. D. TIERS, *J. Amer. Chem. Soc.*, **79**, 5585 (1957).
180. R. J. GILLESPIE and J. W. QUAIL, *J. Chem. Phys.*, **39**, 2555 (1963).
181. G. H. CADY, *Chem. Can.*, **15**, 22 (1963).
182. G. P. VAN DER KELEN, *Bull. Soc. Chim. Belg.*, **72**, 644 (1963).
183. G. ARULDHAS and P. VENKATESWARLU, *Mol. Phys.*, **7**, 65, 77 (1964).
184. H. S. GUTOWSKY and V. D. MOCHEL, *J. Chem. Phys.*, **39**, 1195 (1963).
185. T. H. BROWN, E. B. WHIPPLE and P. H. VERDIER, *Science*, **140**, 178 (1963).
186. D. LAZDINS, C. W. KERN and M. KARPLUS, *J. Chem. Phys.*, **39**, 1611 (1963).
187. T. H. BROWN, E. B. WHIPPLE and P. H. VERDIER, *J. Chem. Phys.*, **38**, 3029 (1963).
188. G. W. FLYNN, M. MATSUSHIMA, N. C. CRAIG and J. D. BALDESCHWIELER, *J. Chem. Phys.*, **38**, 2295 (1963).
189. N. BODEN, J. W. EMSLEY, J. FEENEY and L. H. SUTCLIFFE, *Mol. Phys.*, **8**, 133 (1964).
190. N. MULLER and D. T. CARR, *J. Phys. Chem.*, **67**, 112 (1963).
191. W. S. BREY and K. C. RAMEY, *J. Chem. Phys.*, **39**, 844 (1963).
192. J. C. SCHUG, P. E. MCMAHON and H. S. GUTOWSKY, *J. Chem. Phys.*, **33**, 843 (1960).
193. R. W. TAFT, E. PRICE, I. R. FOX, I. C. LEWIS, K. K. ANDERSON and G. T. DAVIS, *J. Amer. Chem. Soc.*, **85**, 3146 (1963).
194. L. G. ALEXAKOS and C. D. CORNWELL, *J. Chem. Phys.*, **41**, 2098 (1964).
195. N. BODEN, J. W. EMSLEY, J. FEENEY and L. H. SUTCLIFFE, *Proc. Roy. Soc.*, **A282**, 559 (1964).
196. R. D. CHAMBERS and T. CHIVERS, *J. Chem. Soc.*, **47**, 82 (1964).
197. D. E. FENTON and A. G. MASSEY, *J. Inorg. Nuc. Chem.*, **27**, 329 (1965).
198. S. NG and C. H. SEDERHOLM, *J. Chem. Phys.*, **40**, 2090 (1964).
199. C. J. JAMESON and H. S. GUTOWSKY, *J. Chem. Phys.*, **40**, 2285 (1964).
200. R. J. GILLESPIE and J. W. QUAIL, *Can. J. Chem.*, **42**, 2671 (1964).
201. S. NG, J. TANG and C. H. SEDERHOLM, *J. Chem. Phys.*, **42**, 79 (1965).
202. R. G. CAVELL, *J. Chem. Soc.*, 1992 (1964).

203. F. Schreiner, J. G. Malm and J. C. Hindman, *J. Amer. Chem. Soc.*, **87**, 25 (1965).
204. K. Kuhlmann and D. M. Grant, *J. Phys. Chem.*, **68**, 3208 (1964).
205. R. R. Holmes, R. P. Carter and G. E. Peterson, *Inorg. Chem.*, **3**, 1748 (1964).
206. E. L. Muetterties, W. Mahler, K. J. Packer and R. Schmutzler, *Inorg. Chem.*, **3**, 1298 (1964).
207. T. C. Farrar and T. D. Coyle, *J. Chem. Phys.*, **41**, 2612 (1964).

CHAPTER 12

NMR SPECTRA OF NUCLEI OTHER THAN HYDROGEN AND FLUORINE

IN PRINCIPLE, nuclear magnetic resonance can be used to investigate any isotope which has a nucleus with non-zero spin. Most of the known isotopes fulfilling this requirement have not been examined by this technique under high resolution conditions due to their unsuitability from other points of view. To show a high resolution spectrum, a magnetic nucleus must be present in a state where direct dipole–dipole interactions are averaged to zero (this usually implies that it is in the liquid or gaseous state) and must also possess several other desirable features if the NMR investigation is to be successful. The following properties of a nucleus favour successful high resolution NMR studies:

(1) The nucleus must possess a large magnetic moment, since the relative sensitivity of nuclei to NMR detection is proportional to the cubes of the magnetic moments at constant field strength.

(2) It should have a spin number $I = \frac{1}{2}$: higher spin numbers usually have quadrupole moments associated with them which lead to quadrupolar broadening of absorption lines. Simpler interpretation of spectra also results from examination of nuclei with spin numbers equal to one half.

(3) The natural abundance of the isotope must be sufficiently large for the nucleus to be detected by NMR.

(4) Values of spin–lattice relaxation times for the nucleus in its various environments must be short enough to avoid saturation effects.

(5) The substance under examination must be free from strong interactions between the magnetic nuclei and unpaired electrons: this does not preclude the examination of some paramagnetic species.

It is also necessary to examine the substance in the liquid or gaseous state: ideally the substance should be a liquid since gases must be studied at high pressures (even then the less sensitive nuclei cannot be detected) and solids require dissolving in a suitable solvent or alternatively melting before examination.

Absence of any of these features does not necessarily mean that it is impossible to carry out high resolution NMR measurements since careful choice of samples and experimental conditions can very often offset such difficulties. All the problems associated with lack of sensitivity can be improved by operating at the highest possible value of applied magnetic field with the available fixed frequency R.F. units and also by increasing the size of the sample. Each of these factors results in a decrease in the resolution of the equipment and generally one must come to some compromise with regard to the sample size. Quadrupolar broadening effects of one magnetic nucleus on another can be removed by double irradiation: the nucleus with the quadrupole moment is effectively decoupled from the other magnetic nucleus by this technique (see Section 8.19.5). Replacement of a nucleus with a quadrupole moment by an isotope of the same element which has zero spin has also been used to achieve the same object. Line narrowing of the absorption bands from a nucleus which has a quadrupole moment can be obtained by examining the nucleus in a molecule where it is present in a symmetrical electric field. This is because quadrupolar broadening operates via interactions between the quadrupole moment and electric field gradients in the molecule (see Section 2.5.2), and if the electric field gradient is zero (as in the tetrahedral NH_4^+ ion) broadening is removed.

Low natural abundance of the magnetic isotope concerned can best be remedied by enriching the molecule with this isotope. This process has the additional advantage that the enrichment can be made specific to certain groups within the molecule, thus enabling unequivocal assignments of chemical shifts to be made.

Nuclei with long relaxation times are usually examined in the dispersion mode under rapid passage conditions: under these conditions much higher values of the radiofrequency field, H_1, can be used before saturation effects become obvious. Another technique to avoid saturation is to decrease the relaxation times of the nuclei being examined by introducing paramagnetic ions or free radicals into the system. Saturation effects can also be minimised by continuously supplying unsaturated nuclei to the region of the receiver coil using a flow technique.

More details of the manner in which high resolution measurements can be conducted under unfavourable conditions will be discussed under the sections on the particular nuclei concerned.

Most of the published NMR studies to date have involved either ^{1}H or ^{19}F resonance since both these nuclei satisfy all the conditions required for a successful NMR investigation, and furthermore, many compounds containing these nuclei are readily available. Of the remaining nuclei with magnetic moments, ^{11}B, ^{13}C and ^{31}P are the only nuclei with have been studied in any detail although several studies involving other nuclei have been reported.

All the examined magnetic nuclei other than those of hydrogen and fluorine possess some feature which militates against the technique to varying extents, but which can either be tolerated or remedied. A table of magnetic properties of common nuclei is given in Appendix A.

In this chapter, all chemical shifts are quoted as positive if they correspond to signals at higher field values than that of the reference compound.

12.1 Boron

Both the naturally occurring isotopes of this element possess nuclei with magnetic moments: boron—10 has a natural abundance of 18·8 per cent and a spin value $I = 3$, and boron—11, of 81·2 per cent natural abundance, has a spin value $I = \frac{3}{2}$. High resolution NMR investigations of boron resonance invariably feature the more abundant ^{11}B isotope since this is easier to detect both from the point of view of larger natural abundance, and also in that it has a higher natural sensitivity to NMR detection due to its larger magnetic moment, e.g. for ^{10}B, $\mu = 1{\cdot}8006$ and for ^{11}B, $\mu = 2{\cdot}6880$ nuclear magnetons. For an external magnetic field strength of 14,000 gauss, the respective resonance frequencies of ^{10}B and ^{11}B are 6·405 and 19·124 Mc sec^{-1}. Although boron—11 has a quadrupole moment, line broadening resulting from its interaction with electric field gradients is usually not excessive, and since the natural sensitivity to NMR detection is reasonable (16·5 per cent of that of hydrogen nuclei at a constant field value) it is possible to obtain strong ^{11}B resonance absorption signals from liquid samples contained in 5 mm o.d. sample tubes. However, the observed bands are generally much broader than those obtained in hydrogen and fluorine spectra and consequently small coupling constants are not observed. This probably accounts for the fact that only a few coupling constants for interaction between a boron atom and a hydrogen atom separated by more than one bond have been reported(7). A source of line broadening frequently encountered in liquid boron compounds arises from their viscous nature: in such cases the addition of an inert solvent narrows the absorption bands. It has been found that solvent effects on the shielding of boron nuclei are negligible in the absence of any chemical reaction(2). The most commonly used reference compounds in boron studies are methyl borate and boron trifluoride etherate, both of which are readily available substances and give rise to sharp ^{11}B absorption bands. An external referencing procedure is usually adopted and bulk diamagnetic susceptibility corrections neglected.

12.1.1 ^{11}B *Chemical Shifts*

Several workers have examined the NMR spectra of boron compounds with a view to correlating chemical shifts of the boron nuclei with their electronic environment. Table 12.1 lists a selection of ^{11}B chemical shifts measured from methyl borate external reference. Phillips, Miller and Muetterties(1) have pointed out that the general trend of ^{11}B chemical shifts can be explained qualitatively in terms of variations in the paramagnetic contribution to the nuclear shielding as is found in the cases of ^{19}F(3) and ^{31}P(4, 5) shielding. Almost all ^{11}B chemical shifts fall between the low field resonance band of $B(CH_3)_3$, where the boron atom is sp^2 hybridised and has a vacant p_z atomic orbital, and the higher field absorption band of BH_4^- where the boron atom is sp^3 hybridised. This state of affairs would be expected if the contribution of the paramagnetic term dominates the overall shielding since the extent of deshielding depends upon the number of imbalanced p electrons. Thus BH_3 adduct formation results in the ^{11}B nucleus becoming more shielded, reflecting the reduced paramagnetic contribution to the shielding which accompanies electron donation to the empty boron p_z orbital and the change in hybridisation from sp^2 to sp^3.

In the series BCl_3, BBr_3 and BI_3 the ^{11}B shielding increases with decreasing halogen electronegativity as can be seen from Table 12.2. BF_3 has an anomalous

TABLE 12.1 ^{11}B CHEMICAL SHIFTS AND ^{11}B—^{1}H SPIN COUPLING CONSTANTS IN BORON COMPOUNDS[1]

Compound	δ ppm	J_{B-H} (cycles sec^{-1})
$B(CH_3)_3$	$-68{\cdot}2$	
$B(C_2H_5)_3$	$-66{\cdot}6$	
$C_6H_5BCl_2$	$-35{\cdot}9$	
$C_6H_5B(OH)_2$ (in pyridine)	$-15{\cdot}2$	
$C_4H_9B(OH)_2$ (in acetone)	$-14{\cdot}3$	
$C_6H_5B(OC_2H_5)_2$	$-10{\cdot}4$	
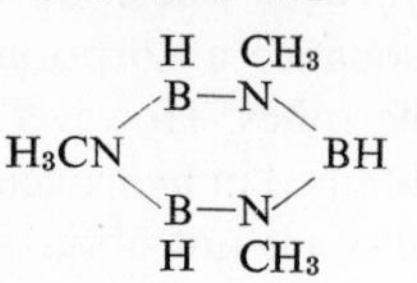	$-14{\cdot}3$	134
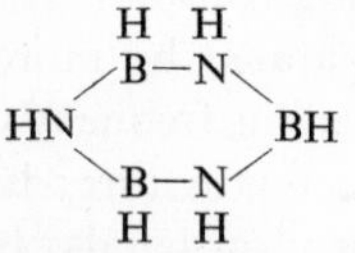	$-12{\cdot}3$	136
$B[N(C_2H_5)_2]_3$	$-12{\cdot}9$	
$B(OCH_3)_3$	0	
$B(OC_2H_5)_3$	$+0{\cdot}6$	
$B(O\text{-}n\text{-}C_3H_7)_3$	$+0{\cdot}5$	
$B(O\text{-}n\text{-}C_4H_9)_3$	$-0{\cdot}1$	
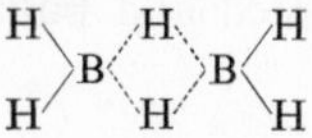	$+0{\cdot}5$	137 (terminal) 48 (bridge)
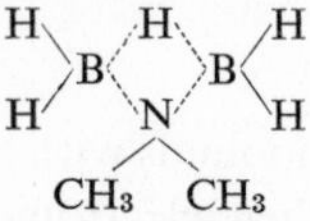	$+36{\cdot}7$	130 (terminal) 29 (bridge)
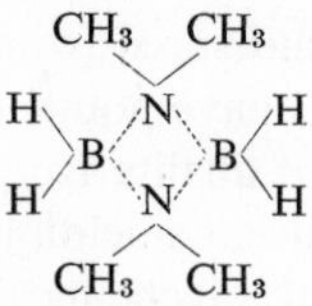	$+14{\cdot}5$	116
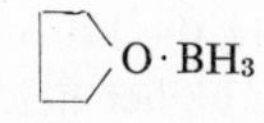	$+19{\cdot}0$	103
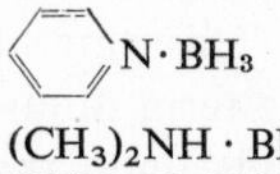	$+31{\cdot}4$	90
$(CH_3)_2NH \cdot BH_3$	$+32{\cdot}8$	94
$(CH_3)_3N \cdot BH_3$	$+24{\cdot}9$	97
$(CH_3)_2PH \cdot BH_3$	$+55{\cdot}6$	96
$NaBC_6H_4$ (in H_2O)	$+16{\cdot}1$	
$NaB(OCH_3)_4$ (in CH_3OH)	$+15{\cdot}2$	
$Al(BH_4)_3$	$+55{\cdot}1$	86
$NaBH_4$ (in $0{\cdot}1$ *N* NaOH)	$+61{\cdot}0$	81
$LiB(C{\equiv}CC_6H_5)_4$	$+49{\cdot}4$	

(continued)

Compound	δ ppm	J_{B-H} (cycles sec^{-1})
O·BF_3	+19·0	
$NH_3 \cdot BF_3(H_2O)$	+20·2	
$(CH_3)_3N \cdot BF_3(C_6H_6—CH_3OH)$	+18·6	
$TlBF_4$ (H_2O)	+18·8	
$AgBF_4$ (H_2O)	+20·3	
$(C_2H_5)_2O \cdot BF_3$	+18·2	
$CH_3OH \cdot BF_3$	+19·1	
$H_3BO_2F_2$	+18·7	
$BI_3:PCl_3$ †	+82·4	
$BI_3:C_5H_5N$ †	+77·4 ± 5	
$(n\text{-}C_4H_9)_3NH:B(C_6H_5)_4$ †	+23·9	
$BBr_3:C_5H_5N$ †	+23·6	
$BBr_3:(C_2H_5)_2O$ †	+23·5	
$BF_3:PCl_3$ †	17·4	
$BF_3:H_2O$ †	−17·2	
$B(C_2H_5)_3:(CH_3)_2NH$ †	−13·4	
$BCl_3:C_5H_5N$ †	−8·4	
$BCl_3:(C_2H_5)_2O$ †	−6·9	
$(C_2H_5O)_2BBr$ †	−1·1	
$(C_6H_5)_3B$ †	−42·6	

δ is the chemical shift measured in ppm from $B(OCH_3)_3$ external reference.

† These chemical shifts were measured originally in ppm from $BF_3:O(C_2H_5)_2$ external reference. They have been transferred to the $B(OCH_3)_3$ reference scale using the conversion $\delta_{B(OCH_3)_3} = \delta_{BF_3.O(C_2H_5)_2} + 17{\cdot}4$ (approximate conversion).

^{11}B chemical shift which has been attributed to the presence of a significant amount of "back-donation" (double bond character) from the filled p_z orbital of the fluorine to the empty p_z orbital of the boron atom[(6)].

Included in Tables 12.2, 12.3 and 12.4 are the ^{11}B chemical shifts of several planar boron compounds each of which contains a different amount of double bond character in its B—X bonds. Examination of Tables 12.2 and 12.3 indicates that the shielding of the boron nucleus increases with increase in double

TABLE 12.2 ^{11}B CHEMICAL SHIFTS OF BORON TRIHALIDES[(6)]

Compound	Chemical shift δ ppm
BF_3	+6·6
BCl_3	−29·2
BBr_3	−22·7
BI_3	+23·3

Chemical shifts measured in ppm from BF_3 etherate external reference.

$$\delta_{B(OCH_3)_3\ ext} = \delta_{BF_3O(C_2H_5)_2\ ext} + 17{\cdot}4\ \text{ppm}.$$

TABLE 12.3 ^{11}B CHEMICAL SHIFTS AND SPIN COUPLING CONSTANTS OF SOME BORON COMPOUNDS[2]

Compound	δ (ppm)	J (cycles sec^{-1})
B_5H_8I (apex boron) (CS_2 soln.)	55·0	
B_5H_{11} (apex boron)	53·5	170 (BH) ± 5
B_5H_9 (apex boron)	51·8	173 (BH) ± 5
B_6H_{10} (apex boron)	51·2	182 (BH) ± 5
B_4H_{10} (BH)	40·0	154 (BH) ± 5
$NaBH_4$ (aq. soln.)	38·7	82 (BH_4) ± 3
$LiBH_4$ (ether soln.)	38·2	75 (BH_4) ± 3
B_5H_8Br (apex boron) (CS_2 soln.)	36·4	
$B_{10}H_{14}$ (2,4 pos.) (CS_2 soln.)	34·9	158 (BH) ± 5
$(CH_3)_2HNBH_3$ (benzene soln.)	15·1	91 (BH_3) ± 3
B_5H_9 (base borons)	12·5	160 (BH) ± 1
B_5H_8Br (base borons) (CS_2 soln.)	12·5	161 (BH)± 5
B_5H_8I (base borons) (CS_2 soln.)	11·8	160 (BH) ± 5
$C_5H_5NBH_3$ (pure liquid)	11·5	96 (BH_3) ± 3
$(CH_3)_3NBH_3$ (benzene soln.)	9·1	101 (BH_3) ± 3
$NaB(C_6H_5)_4$ (aq. soln.)	8·2	
B_4H_{10} (BH_2)	6·5	123 (BH_2) ± 3
BI_3 (liquid melt)	5·5	
B_5H_{11} (base B—H)	2·3	133 (BH)
$NaBF_4$ (aq. soln.)	2·3	
$BF_3 \cdot$ piperidine (CS_2 soln.)	2·3	
NH_4BF_4 (aq. soln.)	1·8	
$BF_3 \cdot$ hexamethylenetetramine	1·4	
$BF_3 \cdot O(n\text{-}C_4H_9)_2$	0·0	
$BF_3 \cdot O(C_2H_5)_2$	0·0	
HBF_4 (50% aq. soln.)	−0·1	
$BF_3 \cdot P(C_6H_5)_3$ ($CHCl_3$ soln.)	−0·4	
$BF_3 \cdot S(C_2H_4—C_6H_5)_2$ ($CHCl_3$ soln.)	−0·5	
$B_{10}H_{14}$ (5,7,8,10 pos.) (CS_2 soln.)	−0·5	141 (BH)
Tetraacetyl diborate ($CHCl_3$ soln.)	−1·1 ± 1·0	
$NaBO_2$ ($B(OH)_4^-$) (aq. soln.)	−1·3	
NaB_5O_8 (aq. soln.)	−1·3 ± 1·0	
B_5H_{11} (base BH_2)	−2·9	130 (BH_2)
$LiB(OCH_3)_4$ (methanol soln.)	−2·9	
$NaBO_3$ (aq. soln.)	−5·5	
$K_2B_4O_7$ (aq. soln.)	−7·5 ± 1·0	
$HBCl_2 \cdot O(C_2H_5)_2$	−7·9	152 (BH) ± 5
$DBCl_2 \cdot O(C_2H_5)_2$	−8·0	? (BD)
$Na_2B_4O_7$ (aq. soln.)	−8·9	
BF_3 (gas)	−9·4 ± 1·0	
$(NH_4)_2B_4O_7$ (aq. soln.)	−10·3	
$BCl_3 \cdot O(C_2H_5)_2$ (ether soln.)	−10·5	
$N(CH_2CH_2O)_3B$ (aq. soln.)	−10·7	
$B_{10}H_{14}$ (1,3,6,9 pos.) (CS_2 soln.)	−12·4	138 (BH)
KB_5O_8 (aq. soln.)	−13·0	
Tri-*o*-chlorophenyl borate (ether soln.)	−13·7 ± 2·0	
NaB_5O_8 (aq. soln.)	−14·4 ± 1·0	
B_6H_{10} (base borons)	−15·0	160 (BH) ± 5
Tri-*o*-cresyl borate (ether soln.)	−15·0 ± 1·0	
B_2H_6 (gas)	−16·6	128 (BH_2) ± 4

(continued)

Compound	δ (ppm)	J (cycles sec^{-1})
Methyl metaborate (benzene soln.)	−17·3	
n-Butyl metaborate (benzene soln.)	−17·5	
$B(OCH_2CH{=}CH_2)_3$	−17·5	
$B(OCH_3)_3$	−18·1	
$B(OC_2H_5)_3$	−18·1	
$B(OH)_3$ (aq. soln.)	−18·8 ± 1·0	
$B(OC_2H_5)_2Cl$	−23·3 ± 1·0	
$HB(OCH_3)_2$	−26·1	141 (BH) ± 5
$DB(OCH_3)_2$	−26·7	24 (BD) ± 4
$B(OH)_2(n\text{-}C_9H_{19})$ (ether soln.)	−29·3 ± 1·0	
$B(OC_2H_5)Cl_2$	−32·5 ± 1·0	
$B_2H_2O_3$	−33·6 ± 3·0	169 (BH) ± 5
BBr_3	−40·1	
BCl_3	−47·7	
$B(C_2H_5)_3$	−85 ± 1·0	

$\delta_{B(OCH_3)_3} = \delta_{BF_3O(C_2H_5)_2} + 17{\cdot}4$ ppm (approximate conversion).

TABLE 12.4 ^{11}B CHEMICAL SHIFTS OF SOME TRIGONAL BORON COMPOUNDS(8)

Compound	Chemical shift ppm
$B(CH_3)_3$	−68·2
S—CH$_2$ i-C$_4$H$_9$B | S—CH$_2$	−51·9
$n\text{-}C_4H_9B(S\text{-}n\text{-}C_4H_9)_2$	−51·3
$B(S\text{-}n\text{-}C_4H_9)_3$	−47·9
$n\text{-}C_4H_9B(OH)_2$	−14·3
$B(OCH_3)_3$	0

$B(OCH_3)_3$ used as an external reference. ^{11}B chemical shifts compiled from the literature by M. F. Hawthorne(8).

bond character in the B—X bond(2). Trigonal thioborane derivatives have ^{11}B resonance absorptions at lower fields than those in analogous B—O compounds despite the fact that oxygen is more electronegative than sulphur: this has been attributed to the relatively small amount of back-donation in the sulphur containing compounds(8). In the absence of changes in hybridisation, an increase in the electronegativity of atoms directly attached to the boron atom results generally in deshielding of the boron nucleus i.e. chemical shifts become more negative (however, this must not be taken as evidence that changes in the diamagnetic shielding term are dominant in controlling ^{11}B chemical shifts(2, 9)). In the tetravalent boron series BH_4^-, $B(C_6H_5)_4^-$ and $B(OMe)_4^-$ the shielding abilities of the groups directly attached to the boron atom are found to be in the order H > $C_{aromatic}$ > O which would be predicted from normal electronegativity considerations if inductive effects are operative. A similar state of affairs is found in the ^{1}H spectra of the carbon analogues[10] and also in the ^{31}P spectra of the phosphorus analogues[5] of these species.

From the observed values of ^{11}B chemical shifts it appears that the shielding of a boron nucleus is partially dependent on the degree to which the vacant *p*-orbital of the trigonal boron atom is occupied, this being at a maximum in the tetrahedrally substituted boron compounds[11]. Table 12.5 gives the ^{11}B

TABLE 12.5 ^{11}B CHEMICAL SHIFTS OF SOME BORON TRIHALIDE DERIVATIVES[11]

Compound	Shift (ppm)[a]	Compound	Shift (ppm)[a]	Compound	Shift (ppm)[a]	Compound	Shift (ppm)[a]
$Et \cdot BCl_2$	−16·0	$CH_2{:}CH \cdot BCl_2$	−6·2	EtBClF	1·7	$CH_2{:}CH \cdot BF_2$	24·2
$Ph \cdot BCl_2$	−6·7	BCl_3	0	$EtBF_2$	18·9		

[a] Chemical shifts measured in ppm from BCl_3 external reference.

$$\delta_{B(OCH_3)_3} = \delta_{BCl_3} - 29{\cdot}6 \text{ ppm.}$$

chemical shifts of some vinyl and ethyl boron trihalides and it is seen that in the vinyl derivatives of boron trichloride and trifluoride, the boron nuclei are more shielded than in the ethyl compounds, suggesting that boron–carbon π-bonding in the former case might be an important shielding factor.

12.1.2 ^{11}B–^{1}H *Spin–Spin Interaction*

Spin coupling between a hydrogen nucleus and another magnetic nucleus to which it is directly bonded has been predicted to be dependent on the *s* character in the bond between the two species[12]. This is supported by

TABLE 12.6 ^{11}B CHEMICAL SHIFTS AND ^{11}B—^{1}H SPIN COUPLING CONSTANTS IN BORON HYDRIDES[1]

Compound	^{11}B Chemical shifts ppm		Coupling constants J_{B-H} (cycles sec^{-1})	
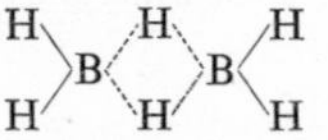	+0·5		137·48	
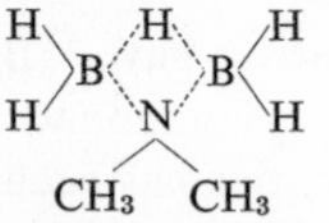	+36·7		130·29	
$B_3H_7 \cdot O(C_2H_5)_2$	+25·8		31 ± 5	
NaB_3H_8 (in H_2O)	+46·5		32	
B_4H_{10}	BH_2	BH	BH_2	BH
	+25·0	+59·9	132	156
B_5H_9	base	apex	base	apex
	+30·8	+69·6	168	176
$B_{10}H_{14}$	+6·9, +19·5, +53·9		124, 128, 159	
$B_{10}H_{12}I_2$	+4·0, +17·6, +60·7		136, 137	
B_5H_{11}	−16·2, +0·7, +49·8		134, 162, 142	

Chemical shifts measured in ppm from $B(OCH_3)_3$ external reference.

the ^{11}B–^{1}H spin coupling constants given in Table 12.6 where it is seen that sp^3 hybridised boron is associated with smaller coupling constants than sp^2 hybridised boron: (for example, in $(CH_3)_3NBH_3$ $J_{B-H} = 97$ cycles sec^{-1}, while in borazole[222] $J_{B-H} = 136$ cycles sec^{-1}) Muller and Pritchard[13] have measured $J_{^{13}C-^{1}H}$ coupling constants between directly bonded nuclei in several compounds and they find the ratio $J_{C_{sp^2}-H}/J_{C_{sp^3}-H}$ to be 1·33 as predicted theoretically (see Section 12.2.11). This ratio has the value of 1·37 for B—H coupling constants in good agreement with that for the C—H spin coupling constants.

12.1.3 Boron Hydrides

The ^{1}H and ^{11}B resonance spectra of several boron hydrides have been measured and in most cases are shown to be consistent with the molecular structures of the molecules as determined by other physical methods[2, 6, 9, 14–17]. Extensive use of double irradiation techniques has been adopted to remove unwanted multiplet splittings from both the ^{1}H and ^{11}B resonance spectra of the boron hydrides.

Table 12.6 gives the ^{11}B chemical shifts and B—H spin coupling constants for several boranes. Spin coupling between boron atoms and bridge hydrogen atoms has been observed only in the diboranes. The coupling constants

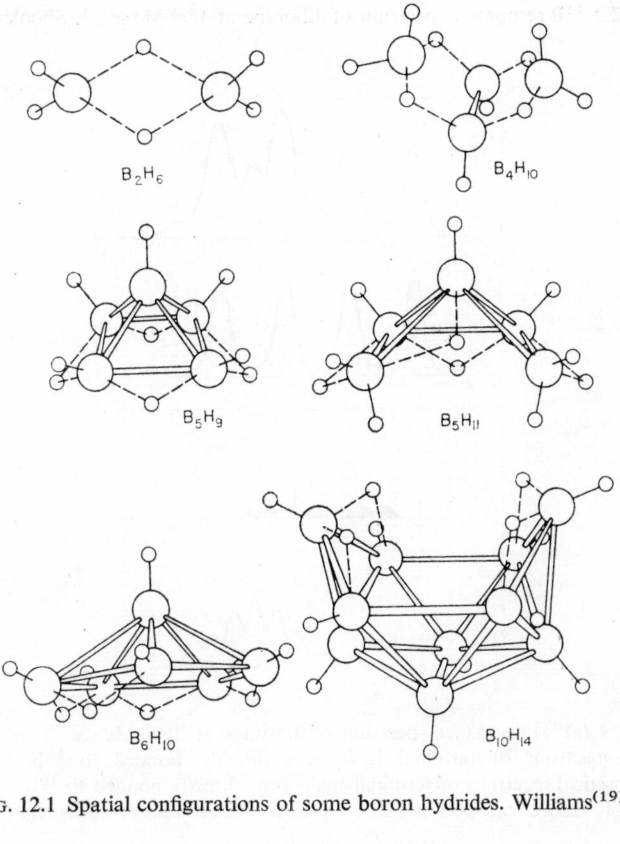

FIG. 12.1 Spatial configurations of some boron hydrides. Williams[19].

between boron atoms and attached terminal hydrogen atoms can be correlated with bond properties, and the measured *J* values indicate the bonds to vary over the range *sp* to sp^2 for the molecules examined[(2)].

Diborane, B_2H_6. Electron diffraction[(18)] and infrared absorption studies[(21)] have established that the electron deficient diborane molecule possesses a bridged structure (see Fig. 12.1). In this structure, four of the hydrogen atoms are directly attached to the boron atoms by means of conventional two-electron covalent bonds while the other two hydrogen atoms are held in bridging positions sharing the remaining boron valencies as shown (I)

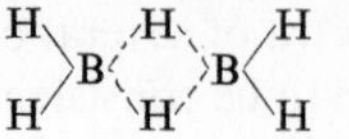

(I)

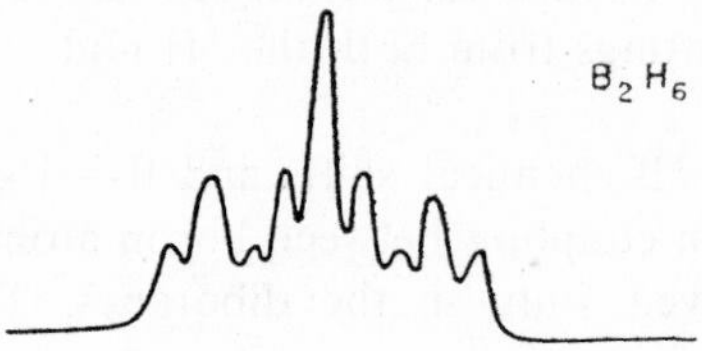

FIG. 12.2 ^{11}B resonance spectrum of diborane at 12·3 Mc sec^{-1}. Shoolery[(15)].

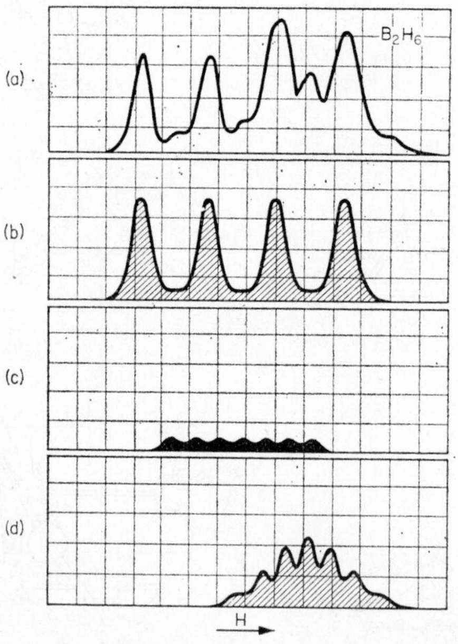

FIG. 12.3 (a) ^1H resonance spectrum of diborane at 30·00 Mc sec^{-1}; (b) theoretical spectrum of terminal hydrogens directly bonded to ^{11}B atoms; (c) theoretical spectrum of terminal hydrogens directly bonded to ^{10}B atoms; (d) H_1 theoretical spectrum of the bridge hydrogen atoms. Shoolery[(15)].

The ^1H and ^{11}B resonance spectra of liquid diborane (see Figs. 12.2, 12.3 and 12.4) support the bridge model for the molecule. The ^{11}B spectrum consists of a single multiplet composed of a triplet of triplets: the larger triplet splitting is thought to arise from spin coupling of each boron atom with the two equivalent terminal hydrogen atoms to which they are bonded and the small triplet splitting from coupling of the boron atom with the pair of shared bridged hydrogen atoms. Further support for the bridge model structure for diborane is found in the ^1H resonance spectrum of the molecule, where direct evidence for the two different types of hydrogen atom is obtained. Figure 12.3 indicates the origin of the components of the spectrum: terminal hydrogen atoms attached to a

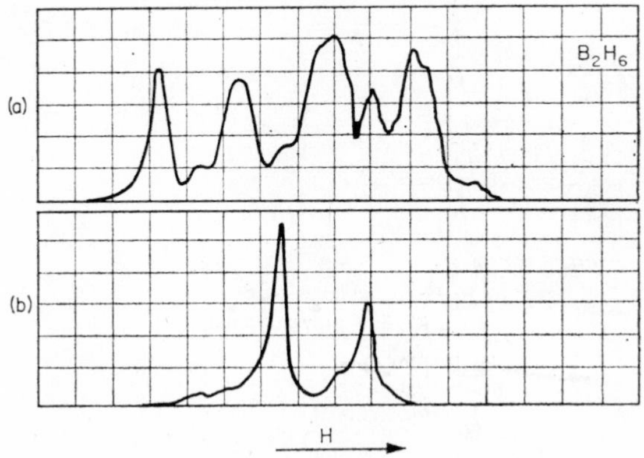

FIG. 12.4 (a) ^1H resonance spectrum of diborane at 30 Mc sec^{-1}. (b) The ^1H resonance spectrum of diborane at 30 Mc sec^{-1} decoupled from the ^{11}B nuclei by simultaneous irradiation with 9·6257 Mc sec^{-1}. Shoolery[15].

single boron atom of spin number $I = \frac{3}{2}$ will result in quartet absorption bands, while the bridge hydrogen atoms attached to two boron atoms give rise to a septet. By observing the ^1H resonance spectrum with the ^{11}B nucleus decoupled by double irradiation, the absorption bands for the two different types of hydrogen atom are reduced to two single resonance bands in the intensity ratio of 2:1 (see Fig. 12.4)[15]. Hydrogen atoms attached to ^{10}B atoms ($I = 3$) are responsible for the weak septet which overlays the remainder of the ^1H resonance spectrum.

Substituted diboranes. Williams and co-workers[20] have investigated a series of alkyl diboranes in an unsuccessful attempt to measure the ^{11}B—^{10}B spin–spin interaction constants between directly-bonded non-equivalent boron atoms. Figure 12.5 shows the ^{11}B resonance spectra of several methyl diboranes measured at 12·8 Mc sec^{-1}. Methyl substitution causes the boron atom to which it is attached to suffer a deshielding effect: similar effects were observed for the analogous ethyl derivatives. The failure to observe ^{11}B—^{10}B spin–spin coupling indicates such coupling either to be very small in these molecules[22] or to be obscured by quadrupolar interactions[23].

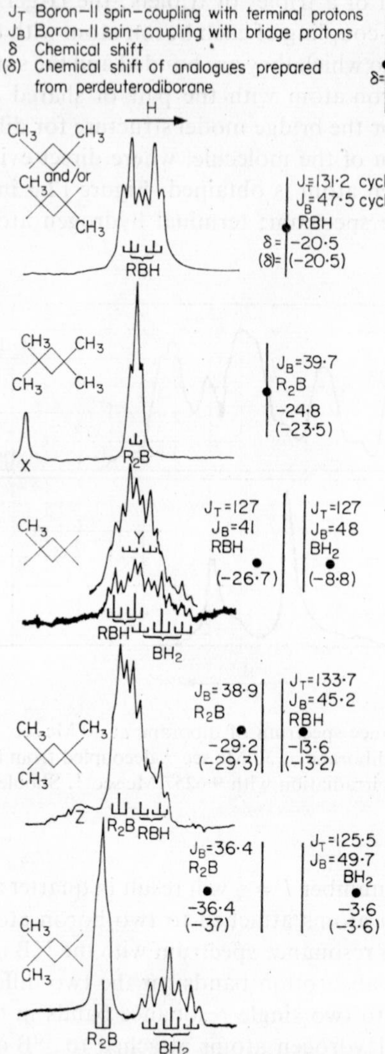

FIG. 12.5 The ^{11}B resonance spectra of several methyl boranes at 12·8 Mc sec^{-1}. Chemical shifts, δ (ppm from BF_3 etherate), are represented as dots. Bands X and Z are impurities, Y is 1,2-dimethyldiborane—a disproportionation product of methyl borane. Williams, Fisher and Wilson[20].

In monobromodiborane, substitution has been shown to take place at a terminal position[288].

Other boranes. The molecular structures and the ^{11}B resonance spectra of several other boranes are shown in Figs. 12.6 to 12.9. The ^{1}H resonance spectra of the molecules have also been measured but they are not given here: in all cases the ^{1}H resonance spectra support the assignments made for the ^{11}B resonance spectra.

Tetraborane, B_4H_{10}. Electron diffraction[24] and X-ray studies[25] have indicated the molecular structure of tetraborane to be as shown in Fig. 12.1. Two

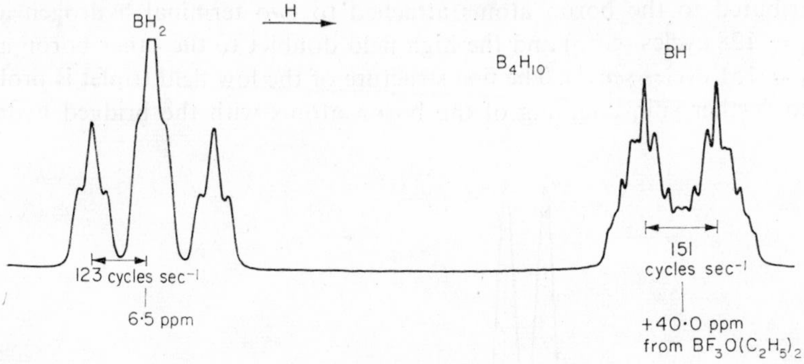

FIG. 12.6 The ^{11}B resonance spectrum of tetraborane (B_4H_{10}) at 32·1 Mc sec^{-1} (23,500 gauss). Pier[277] (Varian Associates).

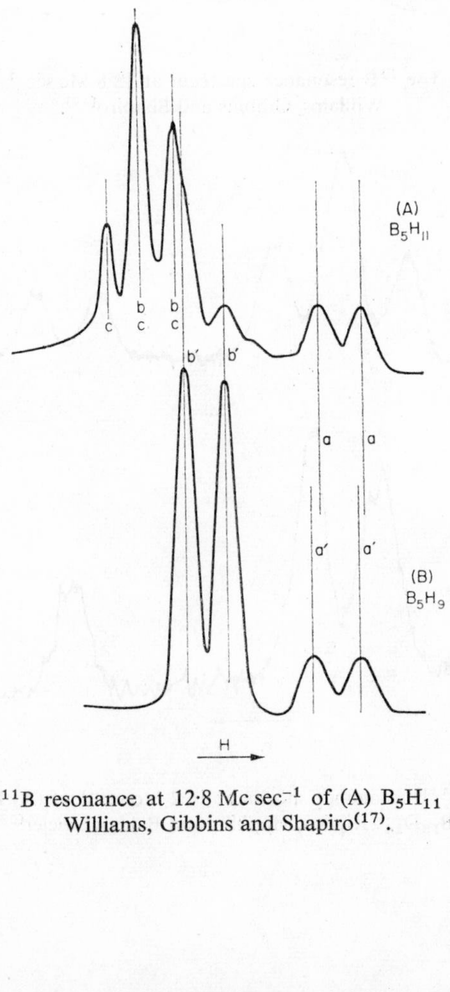

FIG. 12.7 The ^{11}B resonance at 12·8 Mc sec^{-1} of (A) B_5H_{11} and (B) B_5H_9. Williams, Gibbins and Shapiro[17].

of the boron atoms are bonded to two terminal hydrogen atoms and the other two boron atoms are each bonded to a single terminal hydrogen atom. Each pair of boron atoms has a bridged hydrogen atom connecting the boron atoms. NMR measurements can be shown to support such a structure for the molecule[22, 26]. In the ^{11}B resonance spectrum (see Fig. 12.6) the low field triplet is attributed to the boron atoms attached to two terminal hydrogen atoms (J_{B-H} = 128 cycles sec^{-1}) and the high field doublet to the other boron atoms (J_{B-H} = 151 cycles sec^{-1}). The fine structure of the low field triplet is probably due to further spin coupling of the boron atoms with the bridged hydrogen

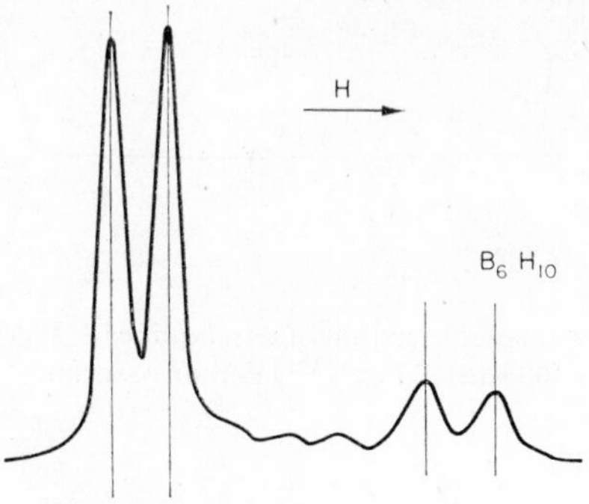

FIG. 12.8 The ^{11}B resonance spectrum at 12·8 Mc sec^{-1} of B_6H_{10}. Williams, Gibbins and Shapiro[17].

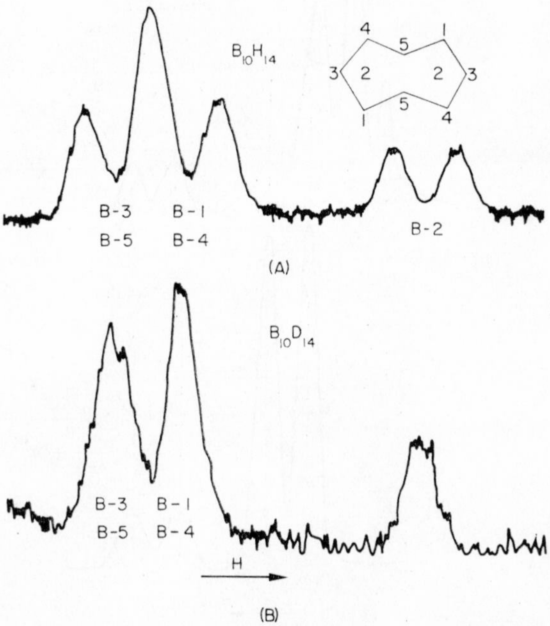

FIG. 12.9 The ^{11}B resonance spectra at 16·2 Mc sec^{-1} of (A) $B_{10}H_{14}$ and (B) $B_{10}D_{14}$. Rigden, Hopkins and Baldeschwieler[23].

atoms (J_{B-H} = 29 cycles sec^{-1}). This type of coupling also features in the high field doublet but it is more complex because of the magnetic non-equivalence of the hydrogen nuclei. It was thought originally that $^{10}B—^{11}B$ spin–spin interaction in 20 per cent of the molecules also makes a significant contribution to the fine structure. However, a later experiment in which the ^{11}B resonance spectrum of tetraborane was found to be unaffected by simultaneously irradiating the sample with the ^{10}B resonance frequency has shown that a $^{10}B—^{11}B$ spin–spin coupling constant does not feature in the ^{11}B spectrum of tetraborane(23). Confirmation of this point has been obtained by examining the ^{11}B resonance spectrum of deuterated tetraborane, B_4D_{10} which gives two broad resonance bands in the intensity ratio of 2:1 showing no indication of $^{10}B—^{11}B$ fine structure.

In the ^1H resonance spectrum of B_4H_{10}, the hydrogen atoms attached to the more shielded boron atoms are found to be more shielded than the other hydrogen atoms(22).

Schaeffer and Tebbe(27) have succeeded in labelling tetraborane with ^{10}B isotopes in a specific position in the molecule, by reacting labelled sodium triborohydride with a mixture of isotopically normal diborane and hydrogen chloride. The ^{11}B resonance spectrum of tetraborane prepared in this manner shows that the high field doublet has almost disappeared indicating that the ^{10}B nuclei are almost exclusively occupying the BH positions.

Pentaborane-9, B_5H_9. Hedberg and co-workers(28) have suggested that this molecule has a tetragonal pyramidal structure. Such a structure has one apical boron atom and four basal boron atoms: to each boron atom is attached a terminal hydrogen atom and the four basal boron atoms have a bridged hydrogen atom between each pair of them.

Shoolery(15) and other workers(17) have measured the ^{11}B resonance spectrum of pentaborane-9 (see Fig. 12.7B) and shown it to be consistent with the tetragonal pyramidal structure. Two doublets of relative intensity 4:1 arise from the basal and apical boron atoms respectively. The doublet splitting arises from B—H spin–spin interaction between the boron atoms and the single terminal hydrogen atom to which each is attached.

Pentaborane-11, B_5H_{11}. X-ray(29) and electron diffraction(30) studies have shown this unstable hydride to have a structure as shown in Fig. 12.1. The molecule contains three types of boron atom: type I is an apical boron atom connected to a terminal hydrogen atom and a unique hydrogen atom, type II are two basal boron atoms, each attached to a terminal hydrogen atom, and type III are the two remaining basal boron atoms attached to two terminal hydrogen atoms. The high field doublet in the ^{11}B resonance spectrum of B_5H_{11} (Fig. 12.7A) has been assigned to the apical boron atom: only the terminal hydrogen atom couples with the boron atoms(9). Williams *et al.*(17) have shown that the bands marked a′ and b′ in the ^{11}B spectrum originate from some B_5H_9 impurity in the sample. The remaining three bands in the ^{11}B resonance spectrum are attributed to the overlap of a low field triplet (bands c from BH_2 type III) with a doublet (bands b from BH type II).

Hexaborane, B_6H_{10}. Hexaborane is thought to have an irregular pentagonal pyramidal structure with one apical boron atom and five basal boron atoms[31] (see Fig. 12.1). Each boron atom is attached to a single terminal hydrogen atom with the four remaining hydrogen atoms in bridged positions between the basal boron atoms. Thus two of the basal boron atoms are not joined by a hydrogen bridge. Such a structure would have four different types of boron atom. The ^{11}B resonance spectrum (see Fig. 12.8) indicates the presence of only two types of boron present in the ratio of 5:1, a low field doublet from the five basal boron atoms and a high field doublet from the apical boron atom[29]. The doublet splitting is due to B—H spin coupling between the boron atoms and their terminal hydrogen atoms. Absence of triplets in the ^{11}B spectrum confirms the absence of BH_2 groups in the molecule. Thus, although the NMR measurements support the general picture of the proposed structure for hexaborane they do not distinguish between the different types of basal boron atoms. No spin–spin interaction between the boron atoms and the bridge hydrogen atoms was detected in the ^{11}B spectrum.

Decaborane, $B_{10}H_{14}$. An X-ray investigation of decaborane has established that the molecular structure of this molecule is as shown in Fig. 12.1[32]. It can be visualised as two irregular pentagonal pyramidal structures whose bases share a common edge. Each boron atom is bonded to a single terminal hydrogen atom and the remaining four hydrogen atoms are in bridge positions and so distributed as to give rise to four different types of boron atom. The ^{11}B resonance spectrum of decaborane consists of a low field triplet and a high field doublet[9, 15, 16] in the intensity ratio of 4:1 as shown in Fig. 12.9A.† This spectrum has been shown to be consistent with the proposed structure of decaborane (see Fig. 12.1). Only the terminal hydrogen atoms are involved in spin–spin interactions with the boron atoms and thus the low field triplet can be assigned to three overlapping doublets from the three different types of non-apical boron atoms (detailed assignments are given in the spectrum). The high field doublet is assigned to apical boron atoms. Deuterated decaborane[7] gives a ^{11}B resonance spectrum with four chemically shifted absorption bands (Fig. 12.9B) which supports the low field assignments made for the normally substituted molecule. The ^{11}B spectrum of deuterated decaborane is simple since ^2H—B spin coupling is much smaller than ^1H—B spin coupling and can therefore be neglected in the spectrum.

The $B_3H_8^-$ *ion.* NMR measurements on the $B_3H_8^-$ ion casts no further light on the structure of this species. The ^{11}B resonance spectrum indicates that there is only one type of boron nucleus in the ion[2].

The $B_{11}H_{14}^-$ *ion.* The ^{11}B spectrum of a solution containing $B_{11}H_{14}^-$ ions consists of a symmetrical doublet having a field independent separation of 140 cycles sec^{-1}[33]. Double irradiation experiments designed to remove B—H spin coupling indicate that there are, in fact, two slightly differently shielded types of boron nucleus in the molecule. Hence, the ^{11}B spectrum consists of two

† The ^{11}B spectrum of $B_{10}H_{14}$ at 43,900 gauss shows three separate multiplets[310].

overlapping doublets separated by a very small irresolvable chemical shift suggesting that the two types of boron nucleus present in the molecule are directly bonded to hydrogen nuclei. The B—H coupling constant is ~ 130 cycles sec^{-1}.

B_9H_{15} *and* $B_{10}H_{15}$. The ^{11}B resonance spectra of B_9H_{15}[34] and $B_{10}H_{15}$[35] have been obtained but could not be analysed because of their complexity.

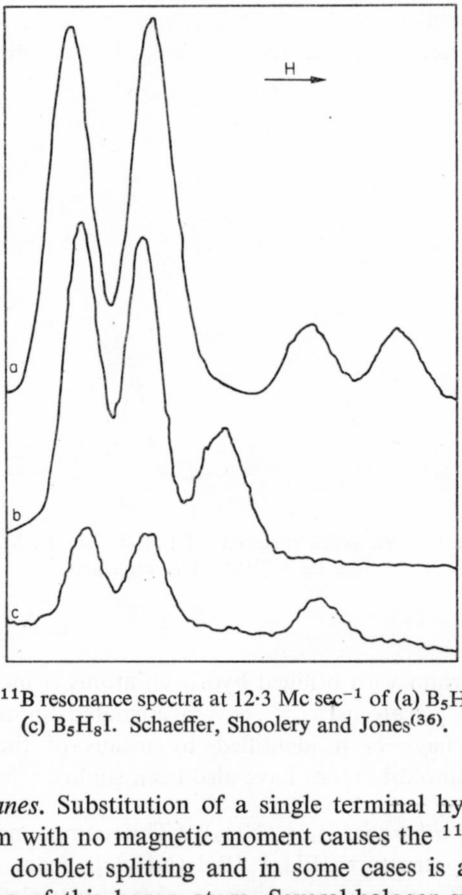

FIG. 12.10 The ^{11}B resonance spectra at 12·3 Mc sec^{-1} of (a) B_5H_9, (b) B_5H_8Br, (c) B_5H_8I. Schaeffer, Shoolery and Jones[36].

Substituted boranes. Substitution of a single terminal hydrogen atom in a borane by an atom with no magnetic moment causes the ^{11}B absorption concerned to lose its doublet splitting and in some cases is accompanied by a change in shielding of this boron atom. Several halogen substituted boranes have been examined by the NMR technique[36] and in most cases the position of substitution in the molecule can be determined. A monoiodide and monobromide of pentaborane-9 were shown to be substituted in the apex position. This can be seen from a comparison of their ^{11}B spectra (shown in Fig. 12.10) with that of the parent molecule: the doublet splitting of the high field band of pentaborane-9 is absent in the spectra of the monosubstituted molecules. In the monochloro derivative, B_5H_8Cl, the chlorine atom has been shown to be substituted at a basal position (see Fig. 12.11)[277]. The high field doublet characteristic of the apical boron atom in B_5H_9 is retained in the spectrum of

B_5H_8Cl. Similar derivatives of decaborane $B_{10}H_{13}I$ and $B_{10}H_{13}Br$ have been shown to be substituted in one of their two apical positions. For these molecules only one of the two high field doublets is affected. Substitution of decaboranes does not always occur at the apex sites as is shown by the ^{11}B resonance spectrum of benzyl decaborane, $B_{10}H_{13}CH_2C_6H_5$[37]. The originally identical high field doublets from the two apical boron atoms of the parent molecule are displaced slightly but still retain their doublet splitting, thus indicating that substitution has occurred at some non-apical position in the molecule in such a manner as to render the two apical boron atoms non-equivalent. NMR studies of the deuteration of decaborane using D_2O in dioxane confirm that

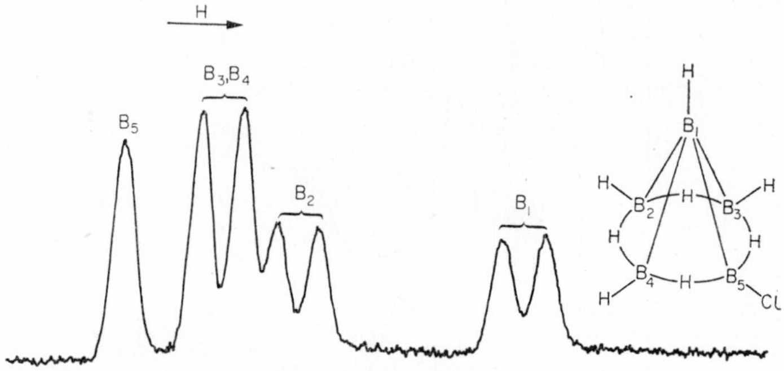

FIG. 12.11 The ^{11}B resonance spectrum of B_5H_8Cl at 32·1 Mc sec^{-1} (23,500 gauss). Pier[277] (Varian Associates).

exchange of deuterium with bridged hydrogen atoms is more rapid than it is with terminal hydrogen atoms[38, 39]. Several ethylated diboranes, pentaboranes and decaboranes have been identified by means of their ^{11}B resonance spectra[40–42]. Amino diboranes have also been studied[286].

Diammoniate of diborane, $B_2H_6(NH_3)_2$. This compound has been shown to have the ionic structure $[BH_4]^-$ $[BH_2(NH_3)_2]^+$ from an NMR investigation[43]. The ^{11}B resonance spectrum consists of a triplet (from the cation) and a quintet (from the anion) of equal intensity. Besides having the characteristic chemical shift of the borohydride ion (+39·3 ppm from $BF_3O(C_2H_5)_2$ external reference) the quintet features a coupling constant (J_{B-H} = 80 cycles sec^{-1}) similar to that in other borohydrides (e.g. $NaBH_4$, J_{B-H} = 82 cycles sec^{-1}; $LiBH_4$, J_{B-H} = 75 cycles sec^{-1})[1]. A similar argument can be used to characterise the cation as the species $[BH_2(NH_3)_2]^+$, (δ = + 14·6 ppm and J_{B-H} = 120 cycles sec^{-1}). A noteworthy experimental feature of this investigation is that the sample was dissolved in liquid ammonia contained in a sealed glass tube at room temperature.

12.1.4 Borohydrides

Sodium Borohydride, $NaBH_4$. The ^1H resonance spectrum of this molecule consists of a single multiplet of four equal intensity components: this is attributed to the spin–coupling of the four equivalent hydrogen nuclei with the single boron nucleus (J_{B-H} = 82 cycles sec^{-1})[14, 15]. Double irradiation techniques have been used to confirm the origin of the fine structure[15].

Aluminium Borohydride, AlB_3H_{12}. The proposed structure for aluminium borohydride, based on electron diffraction[44] and infrared[45] measurements, locates the aluminium atom at the centre of an equilateral triangle of boron atoms: four hydrogen atoms are bonded in a tetrahedral arrangement to each boron atom and two of these hydrogen atoms are bridged between the aluminium and the boron atoms. Measurement of the ^1H and ^{11}B resonance spectra of the compound does not readily support this structure, since the four hydrogen atoms are indicated to be equivalent. In the ^{11}B spectrum a single quintet arises from coupling of the four equivalent hydrogen atoms with the boron atom[46]. The ^1H resonance spectrum of the molecule suffers extensive line broadening due to the quadrupolar field of the aluminium-27 nucleus. When the line broadening is removed by using a double irradiation technique, the ^1H resonance spectrum clearly indicates all the hydrogen nuclei to be equivalent. Any intermolecular exchange process involving terminal and bridged hydrogen atoms, sufficiently rapid to cause averaging of their electronic environments, would almost certainly result in the collapse of the spin coupling fine structure (see Section 9.1.3). Ogg[46] has suggested that an exchange process could proceed via a quantum mechanical tunnelling mechanism which would not affect the bonding electronic system, and would consequently maintain the B—H spin coupling. However, there is no necessity to invoke this mechanism since the observed spectrum is consistent with the existence of a rapid intramolecular exchange of bridge and terminal hydrogen atoms within individual BH_4 groups (see Section 9.4.5). Similar intramolecular exchange processes prevail in the boron hydrides and their Lewis base adducts[19].

12.1.5 Other Boron Resonance Studies

The BF_4^- *ion.* The ^{11}B absorption band of BF_4^- is 41 ppm to the low field side of that of the BH_4^- ion. Because both ions have the same symmetry this shift has been interpreted in terms of changes in diamagnetic shielding which would be reduced in the case of BF_4^-. It could also arise from the presence of low-lying electronic states of different energy in the two species (see Section 11.2). Little change from the ^{11}B chemical shift of the BF_4^- ion is found for BF_3 adducts with ethers and amines, indicating that the hybridisation of the boron orbitals in the complex compounds are similar to that in BF_4^- ions[2].

$(CH_3)_2PHBH_3$. Shoolery[15] has examined the resonance spectra of all three magnetic nuclei in the compound $(CH_3)_2PH'BH_3''$ and his results are summarised in Table 12.7.

TABLE 12.7 SPIN COUPLING CONSTANTS IN $(CH_3)_2PH'BH_3''$ (15)

Spectrum	Coupling constants (cycles sec^{-1})					
	J_{HP}	$J_{HH'}$	$J_{PH'}$	$J_{BH''}$	J_{BP}	$J_{PH''}$
^1H	12	6	350	90		12
^{11}B				93	50	
^{31}P			350			

12.2 CARBON

^{13}C is the only naturally occurring isotope of carbon which possesses a magnetic moment (spin number $I = \frac{1}{2}$), and this nucleus has proved itself capable of being successfully studied by NMR(47). Despite its low natural abundance (1·1 per cent), long values of relaxation time and poor natural sensitivity to NMR detection (1·59 per cent of that of the hydrogen nucleus at the same value of field strength), by suitable choice of apparatus and experimental conditions quite large signal to noise ratios have been obtained. Although the published studies on this nucleus have not been as extensive as those on ^{19}F and ^{31}P resonance, sufficient has been done to indicate the vast potential of this branch of NMR spectroscopy. Shielding constants for ^{13}C nuclei have been found to extend over a wide range ($\sim$ 350 ppm) and to be very sensitive to slight changes in electronic environment, and furthermore, coupling constants between directly bonded carbon and hydrogen atoms are also large ($\sim$ 120 to 269 cycles sec^{-1}). Both these features have enabled useful ^{13}C investigations to be carried out under conditions which favour sensitivity at the expense of resolution. The important position of carbon in chemistry combined with the availability of carbon-containing compounds will no doubt stimulate a rapid growth in ^{13}C studies when the experimental techniques are more widely mastered. Advances in this field will probably be twofold, (a) improvements in resolution under the necessary conditions of high sensitivity, and (b) more extensive use of ^{13}C-labelled compounds(266).

Certain trends in ^{13}C chemical shifts have been noticed by several workers(48, 49). For example, Lauterbur(50) has found that in substituted methanes and ethanes the shielding of a carbon atom decreases when the number of electronegative substituents on that carbon atom increases. The order of decreasing shielding ability is usually I > Br > H > C > Cl > O.

12.2.1 Experimental Procedures for ^{13}C Resonance Measurements

To overcome the low natural abundance of the isotope, large sample tubes (15 mm outside diameter) and high values of radiofrequency power ($H_1 = 10$ milligauss for absorption mode signals and up to 200 milligauss for dispersion mode signals) are used(47). Optimum values of H_1 are selected to give the maximum sensitivity compatible with reasonable resolution. When high R.F. fields are used, it is necessary to sweep the signal very rapidly if saturation is to be avoided (values of 50 to 100 milligauss sec^{-1} are employed)[47]. Distortion of the signal caused by using rapid sweep rates and high R.F. power levels results in errors in the chemical shifts which can be corrected for readily by taking the mean of the chemical shifts measured from two spectra recorded at increasing and decreasing sweep-field[48]. A few minutes are allowed to elapse between each sweep to allow the nuclei to relax and thus re-establish a Boltzmann distribution. It is usual to observe the dispersion mode of the signal since under these conditions the nuclei are more difficult to saturate[47, 48, 51]. However, under rapid passage conditions the high R.F. power causes some saturation which distorts the signal, often removing the second half of the dispersion signal. This gives the spectrum the appearance of an ordinary absorption signal. Most workers have used external magnetic fields of 10,000 gauss or less (at 10,000 gauss the resonance frequency of the ^{13}C nucleus is 10·705 Mc sec^{-1}):

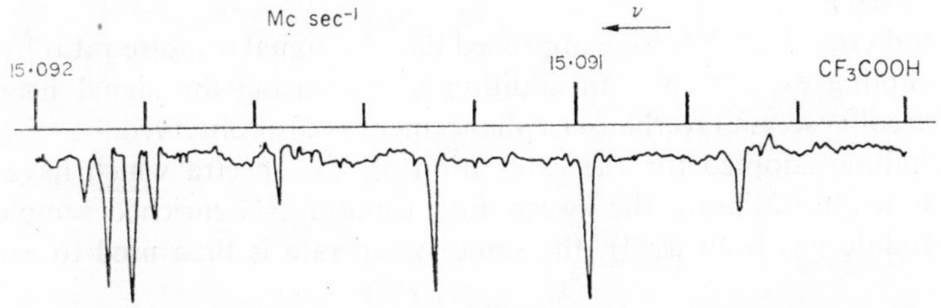

FIG. 12.12 The ^{13}C INDOR spectrum of neat CF_3COOH (4 mm i.d. sample tube). The high frequency quartet is due to $CF_3{}^{13}COOH$ (second irradiation at 56·460944 Mc sec^{-1}) and the low frequency quartet is due to $^{13}CF_3COOH$ (second irradiation frequency at 56·460816 Mc sec^{-1}). Baker[55].

fields of up to 24,500 gauss are now being employed with a corresponding increase in sensitivity[57]. Lauterbur has found that by operating under rapid passage dispersion conditions at a radiofrequency of 8·5 Mc sec^{-1} it is possible to detect ^{13}C resonance in a system containing one gram atom of carbon per litre in a 12 mm diameter sample. Flow techniques have been used successfully to avoid saturation difficulties in the examination of ^{13}C resonance[53]. By continuously supplying unsaturated nuclei to the region of energy absorption, up to five-fold increase in intensity can be achieved. A successful attempt to enhance ^{13}C signals by examining molecules in the presence of free radicals (Overhauser Effect, see Section 3.17) has been made[54]. Improved sensitivity can also be achieved by use of an internuclear double resonance technique (INDOR spectra)[55]. If a molecule possesses two nuclei of different species, A and X, coupled by spin–spin interaction, then by supplying low R.F. power of the resonance frequency of the A nucleus and simultaneously frequency sweeping through the X resonance frequencies at a higher power level, changes in the intensity of the A spectrum are observed. This gives rise to an INDOR spectrum which is an exact duplicate of the direct X spectrum, providing that the power level in the X spectrum is not too large. Figure 12.12 shows the

^{13}C INDOR spectrum for a non-enriched sample of CF_3COOH and there is a considerable improvement in the signal to noise ratio compared with that for a direct ^{13}C spectrum. The ^{19}F resonance spectrum of the molecule consists of a large single absorption band (from $^{12}CF_3{}^{12}COOH$ molecules) and two pairs of ^{13}CF satellites from $^{13}CF_3{}^{12}COOH$ ($J_{CF} = 283{\cdot}1$ cycles sec^{-1}) and $^{12}CF_3{}^{13}COOH$ ($J_{CF} = 43{\cdot}53$ cycles sec^{-1}). Each of the two multiplets shown in Fig. 12.12 was obtained by irradiating one of the corresponding ^{13}CF satellites in the ^{19}F spectrum and then frequency sweeping the ^{13}C resonance spectrum.

Signals arising from ^{13}C atoms attached to chlorine or nitrogen atoms (e.g. in CCl_4) are very weak and can only be observed by sweeping rapidly under high R.F. power conditions. The line broadening in the spectra of such molecules is due to the quadrupolar interactions of the chlorine or nitrogen nuclei (^{13}C has a spin number of one half and consequently has no quadrupole moment itself)(48).

Paul and Grant(303, 304) have improved the ^{13}C signal to noise ratio by using ^1H decoupling experiments: in addition to increasing the signal height by multiplet collapse, an Overhauser enhancement is also observed.

A technique adopted for the calibration of ^{13}C spectra which have weak signals is to pre-calibrate the sweep rate using a ^{13}C enriched sample (e.g. methyl iodide has been used): the same sweep rate is then used to examine

TABLE 12.8 ^{13}C CHEMICAL SHIFTS IN SOME SIMPLE COMPOUNDS(51)

Compound	Chemical shifts ppm		Compound	Chemical shifts ppm	
	$\delta_{C_6H_6}$	$\delta_{CH_3\overset{*}{C}OOH}$		$\delta_{C_6H_6}$	$\delta_{CH_3\overset{*}{C}OOH}$
CH_2I_2	197	247	n-Alkanes	107–127	157–177
CH_3I	153	203	Cycloalkanes	95–105	145–155
CH_3Br	126	176	Ethylene oxide	92	142
CH_3NH_2	116	166	Dioxane	55	105
CH_2Br_2	111	161	R—S—C≡N	15	65
$(CH_3S)_2$	109	159	Nitriles	−2 to 14	48 to 64
CH_3Cl	107	157	Aromatic and olefinic	−10 to 10	40 to 60
CH_3OH	81	131	$(COOR)_2$	−31	19
CH_2Cl_2	76	126	ROCOOR	−36	14
CH_3NO_2	53	103	$RCONR_2$	−45	5
$CHCl_3$	52	102	RCOOH	−52	−2
CCl_4	35	85	RCOR	−79	−29
C_6H_6	0	50	α-Hydroxy acid (carbonyl carbon)	−90	−40
HCOOH	−37	13			
KCN (saturated aqueous solution)	−49	1			

Chemical shifts measured from benzene reference and extrapolated to the $CH_3\overset{*}{C}OOH$ external reference scale

$$\delta_{CH_3\overset{*}{C}OOH} = \delta_{C_6H_6} + 50 \text{ ppm}.$$

the non-enriched sample under investigation. The absorption mode of the enriched sample is used for this purpose since it gives rise to narrower lines than the dispersion mode and thus leads to more accurate measurements.

Both internal and external referencing procedures can be used. Dioxane and carbon disulphide have both been used as internal reference compounds and it is found that unless they are enriched in ^{13}C atoms, then 20–30 per cent by volume of the reference material is required[49]. It is more usual to reference the spectra externally without making any correction for bulk diamagnetic susceptibility effects. Carbon disulphide, aqueous potassium carbonate solution, dimethyl carbonate and acetic acid are convenient compounds for this purpose. The ^{13}C chemical shifts reported here have been measured from a variety of reference compounds: where possible they have been extrapolated to acetic

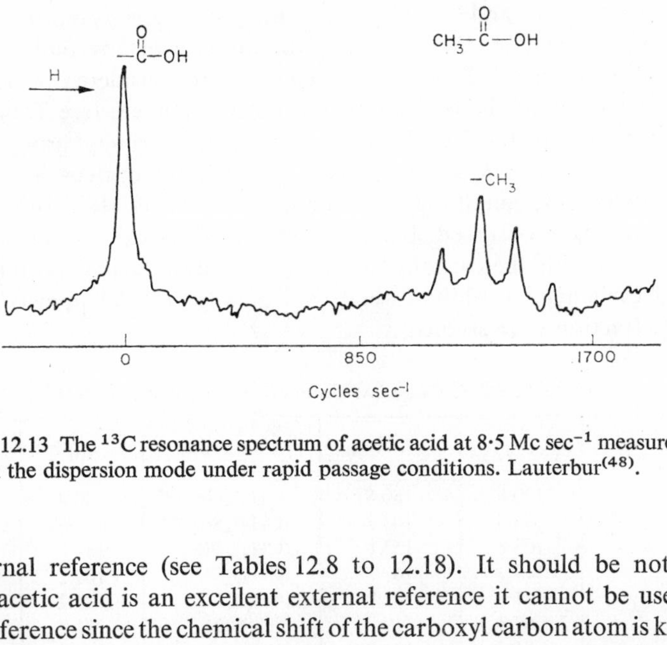

FIG. 12.13 The ^{13}C resonance spectrum of acetic acid at 8·5 Mc sec^{-1} measured in the dispersion mode under rapid passage conditions. Lauterbur[48].

acid external reference (see Tables 12.8 to 12.18). It should be noted that although acetic acid is an excellent external reference it cannot be used as an internal reference since the chemical shift of the carboxyl carbon atom is known to be solvent dependent. Carbon disulphide is probably the best external reference since its sharp absorption band is at lower fields than most ^{13}C resonance bands: it can also be used as an internal reference. Chemical shifts measured from acetic acid can be converted to those on the carbon disulphide scale using the formula[49]

$$\delta_{CS_2} = \delta^{\text{ext}}_{CH_3\overset{*}{C}OOH} + 15{\cdot}6 \text{ ppm}. \qquad (12.1)$$

Aqueous potassium carbonate solution is sometimes employed as a reference material: one of its advantages is that a ^{13}C enriched sample of this compound is relatively inexpensive.

$$\delta_{CS_2} = \delta^{\text{ext}}_{K_2CO_3} \text{ aq.} + 23{\cdot}2 \text{ ppm}. \qquad (12.2)$$

Spiesecke and Schneider(52) used a sample of ^{13}C enriched dimethyl carbonate as an external reference contained in the inner of two concentric spherical bulbs. A small amount of Fe(III) acetylacetonate was added to the reference compound to reduce the value of T_1 thus enabling the use of high-powered audiomodulation. The outer cell contained the sample under investigation and the complete system was designed so that it could be spun within the radio-frequency coils. When spherical samples are used, the bulk diamagnetic effects normally associated with external referencing do not influence the measured chemical shift (see Section 7.3.2).

Solvent effects in ^{13}C spectra have been estimated to be relatively small in molecules which do not contain highly polarisable groups (< 1 ppm)(52). For compounds such as methyl iodide and bromide where this effect would be expected to be greatest, dilution experiments using cyclohexane as the solvent, and ^{13}C enriched samples of the two substituted methanes give dilution shifts between neat liquid and 5 mole per cent cyclohexane solution of 7·3 and 3·6 ppm respectively to high fields, in the absence of any bulk diamagnetic susceptibility effects(52). These solvent effects were considered to be negligible in the ^{13}C spectra of the remaining substituted methanes (see Table 12.9)(52). However, a study of the ^{13}C chemical shifts for the carbonyl group of acetone in the presence of protic solvents has shown that the nucleus is strongly deshielded under these conditions(276). For aprotic solvents, shifts over a range of only 3·1 ppm were observed, but for protic solvents capable of forming hydrogen bonds with the carbonyl group or of causing actual protonation, the observed carbonyl ^{13}C shifts extend over a range of 35·8 ppm (solutions of 1:6 mole fraction were studied).

TABLE 12.9 ^{13}C CHEMICAL SHIFTS OF CH_3X COMPOUNDS(52)

Compound	$\delta_{C_6H_6}$ †	$\delta_{CH_3\overset{*}{C}OOH}$	Compound	$\delta_{C_6H_6}$ †	$\delta_{CH_3\overset{*}{C}OOH}$
CH_4	130·8	180·8	$(CH_3)_4Ge$	130·4	180·4
CH_3F	53·3	103·3	$(CH_3)_4Sn$	137·6	187·6
CH_3Cl	103·8	153·8	$(CH_3)_4Pb$	131·6	181·6
CH_3Br	119·3	169·3	$(CH_3)_2S$	109·2	159·2
CH_3I	151·0	201·0	$(CH_3)_2SO$	85·2	135·2
$(CH_3)_2O$	69·3	119·3	CH_3NO_2	71·4	121·4
$(CH_3)_3N$	81·2	131·2	$(CH_3)_2CO$	104	154
$(CH_3)_4N^+Br^-$	72·0	122·9	CH_3CN	124	174
$(CH_3)_4C$	97·1	147·1	CH_3CHO	99·1	149·1
$(CH_3)_4Si$	129·0	174·0			

† δ expressed in ppm from benzene external reference

$$\delta^{ext}_{CH_3COOH} = \delta^{ext}_{C_6H_6} + 50 \text{ ppm}.$$

12.2.2 ^{13}C *Chemical Shifts*

The work of Lauterbur(48) and Holm(51) has shown the potential value of ^{13}C NMR studies in the determination of molecular structures. It is evident that the carbon atoms in molecules are often sufficiently isolated to be outside the influence of intermolecular interactions and consequently the shielding of carbon nuclei is controlled mainly by their electronic environments within the molecule[51, 52]. No detailed account of the exact origin of ^{13}C chemical shifts has been put forward† but Lauterbur[47] has concluded from the observed ^{13}C chemical shifts in the series CBr_4, $C(CH_3)_4$ and CCl_4 that the paramagnetic contribution to the shielding of the carbon can be large even in the presence of tetrahedral symmetry. A similar state of affairs is found for ^{29}Si chemical shifts[56]. Other workers who have considered ^{31}P chemical shifts make the incorrect basic assumption that there would only be a small paramagnetic contribution to the shielding of an atom with tetrahedral symmetry[4].

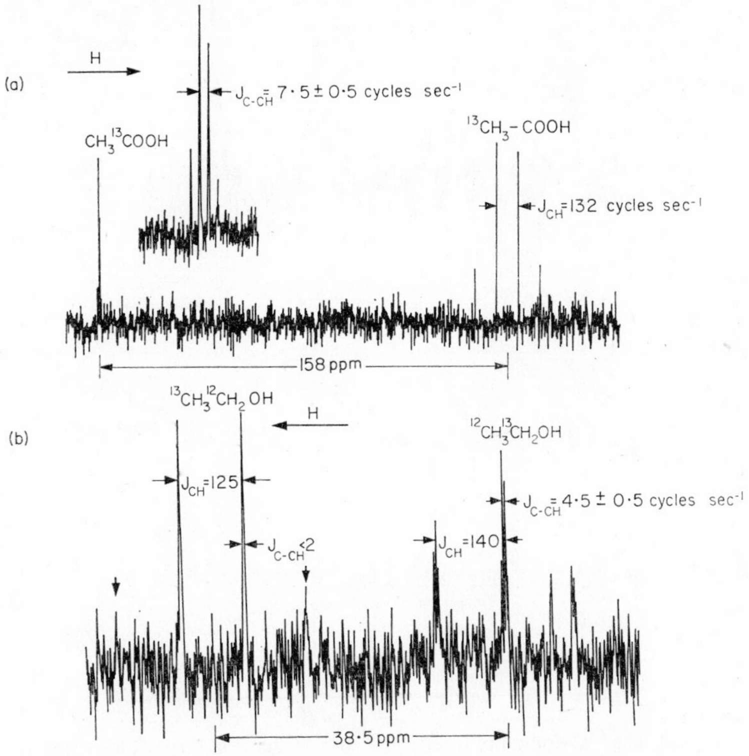

FIG. 12.14 The ^{13}C (natural abundance) resonance spectra at 15·085 Mc sec^{-1} of (a) acetic acid, (b) ethyl alcohol. Shoolery[57].

A typical ^{13}C spectrum is shown in Fig. 12.13 where the ^{13}C resonance spectrum of acetic acid is reproduced[48]. Because of the poor resolution conditions which usually prevail, the only indirect spin–spin coupling observed is that between directly bonded carbon and hydrogen atoms, where such coupling constants are large. Hence the methyl carbon atom of acetic acid gives rise to a high field quartet due to indirect spin coupling between the ^{13}C atom and the

† Pople *et al.*[284, 313] have used a MO approach to calculate the paramagnetic contribution to ^{13}C shielding for several characteristic groups.

three equivalent hydrogen atoms to which it is attached: the carboxylic carbon atom gives a single low field absorption band.

Shoolery[57] has succeeded in recording ^{13}C spectra in the absorption mode by applying a 2000 cycles sec^{-1} field modulation and observing the ^{13}C side-band signals after phasing out the main central band. This method allows the use of a lower radiofrequency power level than that adopted in the adiabatic rapid passage method and thus removes much of the line broadening observed under these conditions. Sweep rates of about 1 cycle sec^{-2} were employed

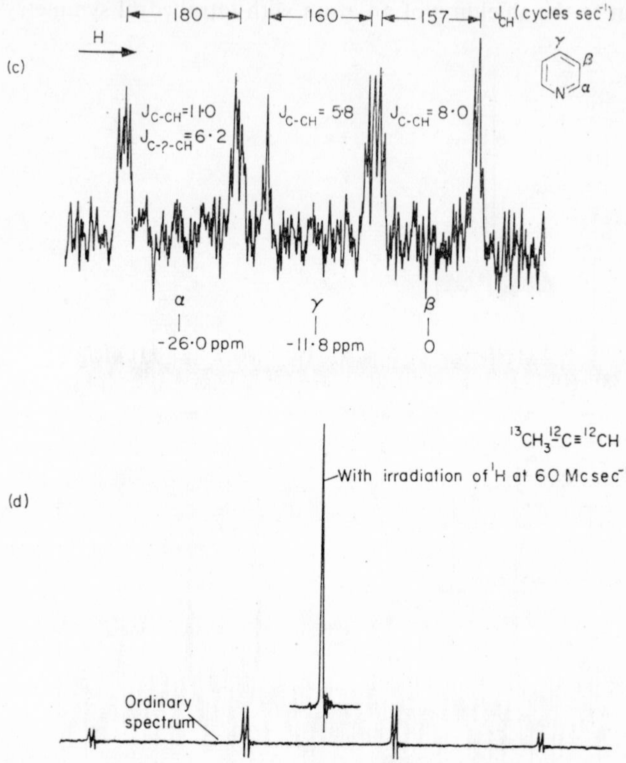

FIG. 12.14 The ^{13}C resonance spectra at 15·085 Mc sec^{-1} of (c) pyridine (natural abundance), (d) $^{13}CH_3{}^{12}C\equiv{}^{12}CH$. Shoolery[57].

and hyperfine splittings of ~ 3 cycles sec^{-1} can thus be resolved in ^{13}C spectra recorded for compounds containing only the natural abundance of ^{13}C nuclei. An added improvement in the line widths was achieved by spinning the large sample tubes (see Section 7.3.3). By this method it is possible to detect long range coupling constants between non-directly bonded nuclei in the ^{13}C resonance spectra. Some of the excellent spectra obtained using the technique are illustrated in Fig. 12.14[57]. Figure 12.14 (a) shows the ^{13}C resonance spectrum of acetic acid: the carboxyl absorption band is resolved into a quartet (J = 7·5 ± 0·5 cycles sec^{-1}) attributable to long range coupling with the hydrogen nuclei of the methyl group. The direct C—H coupling constant, as measured from the large quartet splitting on the methyl absorption, is 132 cycles sec^{-1}. The ^{13}C resonance spectrum of ethanol (Fig. 12.14 (b)) reveals not only the quartet splitting of the methyl absorption band and the triplet splitting of the methylene absorption band (arising from spin coupling between the directly bonded carbon and hydrogen nuclei) but also further fine structure due to long range C—H spin coupling. Similar fine structure is observed in the ^{13}C resonance spectra of pyridine and methyl acetylene (see Fig. 12.14 (c) and (d))(57).

12.2.3 *Correlation of ^{13}C Chemical Shifts with Electronegativities of Groups Attached to Carbon Atoms*

Tables 12.9 and 12.10 give the ^{13}C chemical shifts of the methyl groups in several monosubstituted methanes(48, 52). Lauterbur has shown that a linear relationship exists between the ^{13}C chemical shifts in a series of CH_3X compounds and the electronegativity of the group X for a series of similar compounds

TABLE 12.10 (a) ^{13}C CHEMICAL SHIFTS IN CHLOROBROMOMETHANES(48)

Compound	δ ppm	Compound	δ ppm	Compound	δ ppm
CCl_4	81	$CHCl_3$	98	CH_2Cl_2	124
CCl_3Br	109	$CHCl_2Br$	120	CH_2ClBr	139
CCl_2Br_2	142	$CHClBr_2$	143	CH_2Br_2	156
$CClBr_3$	170	$CHBr_3$	168		
CBr_4	205				

TABLE 12.10 (b) ^{13}C CHEMICAL SHIFTS IN SUBSTITUTED METHANES(48)

Compound	δ ppm
CHI_3	316
CH_2I_2	240
$C^*(OC_2H_5)_4$	38
$C^*H(OC_2H_5)_3$	50
$C^*H_2(OCH_3)_2$	83
$(C^*H_3O)_2CH_2$	130

^{13}C chemical shifts expressed in ppm from $CH_3\overset{*}{C}OOH$ external reference.

such as the methyl halides. As was found for ^{19}F nuclei in binary fluorides(58), the shielding decreases with increase in the electronegativity of the attached group. This linear correlation was taken as indicating that the changes in shielding are caused by changes in the ionicity of the C—X bond(48). Spiesecke and Schneider(52) have examined the ^{13}C chemical shifts of a wide range of methyl compounds, CH_3X (see Table 12.9), and by plotting a graph of the ^{13}C chemical shifts against the electronegativities of the group X (as shown in Fig. 12.15) it is seen that two distinct linear correlations are present. When the substituent is a halogen atom, they observed a marked deviation from the correlation line obtained for the other derivatives: these deviations have been interpreted in terms of an increased shielding contribution from neighbour anisotropic effects in the molecules in which they occur (see Section 4.7). Similar arguments have been applied to explain such deviations found in halogen substituted ethanes (see Fig. 12.16). However, Buckingham and co-workers[240] have pointed out that anisotropic shielding effects can only pro-

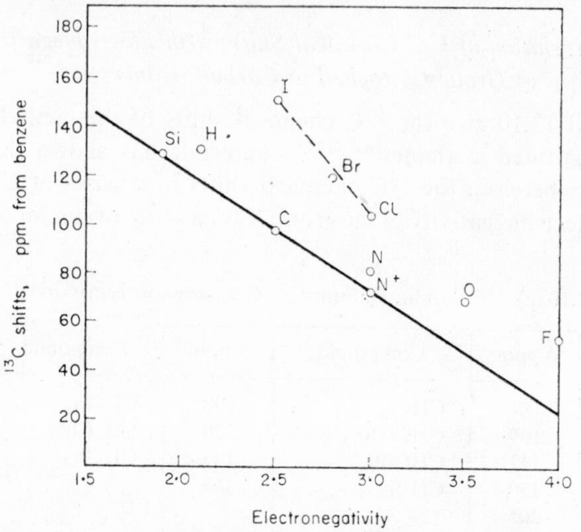

FIG. 12.15 Graph of ^{13}C chemical shifts of CH_3X compounds against the electronegativities of the X atoms. Spiesecke and Schneider[52].

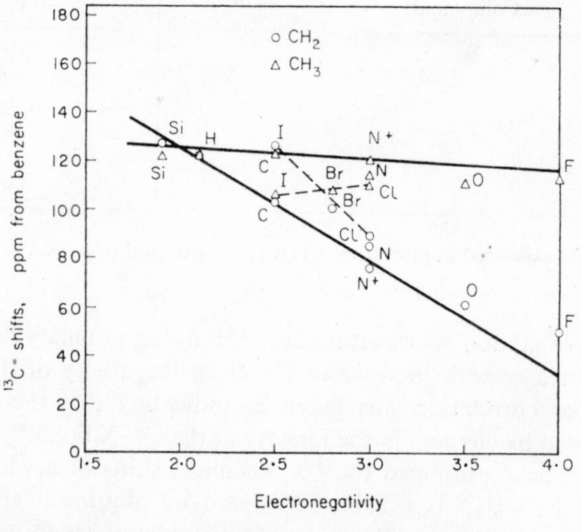

FIG. 12.16 Graph of ^{13}C chemical shifts of CH_3CH_2X compounds against the electronegativities of the X atoms. Spiesecke and Schneider[52].

vide comparatively small shielding contributions for all magnetic nuclei since the parameters on which they depend are associated mainly with the molecular geometry. Schneider[255] now believes that the anisotropic model is insufficient to account for the observed deviations in ^{13}C chemical shifts and suggests that effects from dispersion forces and highly polarisable groups are probably

TABLE 12.11 (a) ^{13}C CHEMICAL SHIFTS OF THE METHYL GROUPS OF t-BUTYL, i-PROPYL AND ETHYL DERIVATIVES[48]

Compound	δ ppm	Compound	δ ppm	Compound	δ ppm
$C^*H_3CH_2Cl$	159·9	$(C^*H_3)_2CHCl$	150·2	$(C^*H_3)_3CCl$	143·6
$C^*H_3CH_2Br$	158·1	$(C^*H_3)_2CHBr$	149·0	$(C^*H_3)_3CBr$	140·7
$C^*H_3CH_2I$	155·2	$(C^*H_3)_2CHI$	145·2	$(C^*H_3)_3CI$	136·6
$C^*H_3CH_2OH$	159·8	$(C^*H_3)_2CHOH$	152·6	$(C^*H_3)_3COH$	146·4
$C^*H_3CH_2NO_2$	166·6	$(C^*H_3)_2CHNO_2$	158·1	$(C^*H_3)_3CNO_2$	150·3

TABLE 12.11 (b) ^{13}C CHEMICAL SHIFTS OF THE METHYL GROUPS OF CHLORO- AND BROMO-ETHANES[48]

Compound	δ ppm
$C^*H_3CH_2Cl$	159·9
$C^*H_3CHCl_2$	145·7
$C^*H_3CCl_3$	131·7
$C^*H_3CH_2Br$	158·1
$C^*H_3CHBr_2$	142·3

TABLE 12.11 (c) ^{13}C CHEMICAL SHIFTS OF THE SUBSTITUTED CARBON ATOM IN t-BUTYL, i-PROPYL, AND ETHYL DERIVATIVES[48]

Compound	δ ppm	Compound	δ ppm	Compound	δ ppm
$CH_3C^*H_2Cl$	138·0	$(CH_3)_2C^*HCl$	123·3	$(CH_3)_3C^*Cl$	11·9
$CH_3C^*H_2Br$	150·1	$(CH_3)_2C^*HBr$	133·0	$(CH_3)_3C^*Br$	116·5
$CH_3C^*H_2I$	177·3	$(CH_3)_2C^*HI$	156·1	$(CH_3)_3C^*I$	135·2
$CH_3C^*H_2OH$	119·6	$(CH_3)_2C^*HOH$	114·4	$(CH_3)_3C^*OH$	109·4
$CH_3C^*H_2NO_2$	106·8	$(CH_3)_2C^*HNO_2$	98·1	$(CH_3)_3C^*NO_2$	92·0

^{13}C chemical shifts expressed in ppm from $CH_3\overset{*}{C}OOH$ external reference.

important. In general, an increase in dispersion effects results in a decrease in shielding[275]. There is usually also a reasonable correlation between ^1H and ^{13}C chemical shifts when these atoms are directly bonded to each other and this is substantiated in Fig. 10.2 where the ^1H chemical shifts of methyl derivatives are shown to vary with the electronegativity of the substituent X in an analogous manner to the ^{13}C chemical shifts.

^{13}C chemical shifts of the α-carbon atom of compounds of formula $(CH_3)_nCH_{3-n}X$ show a correlation with the C—X bond lengths[269].

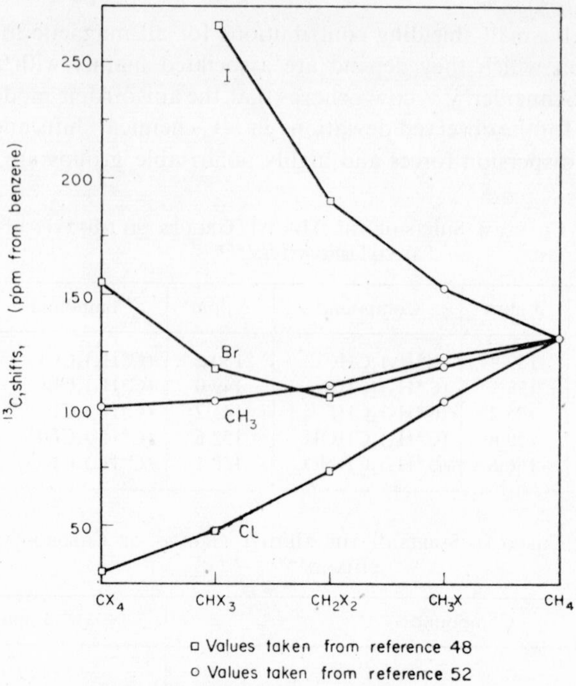

FIG. 12.17 Graph of the ^{13}C chemical shifts of some substituted methanes (CH_xX_{4-x}), against the number of substituent atoms X. Spiesecke and Schneider(52).

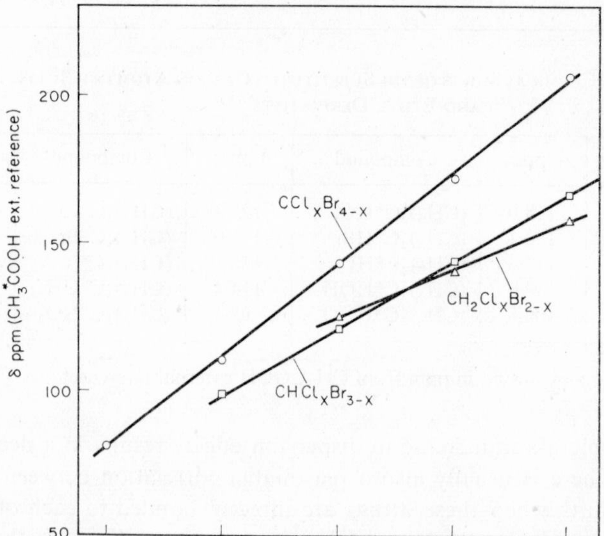

FIG. 12.18 Graphs of the ^{13}C chemical shifts in three series of chlorobromo-ethanes, CCl_xBr_{4-x}, $CHCl_xBr_{3-x}$ and $CH_2Cl_xBr_{2-x}$, against the number of chlorine atoms. Lauterbur(48).

Progressive replacement of hydrogen atoms in methane with halogen atoms results in a smooth gradation in the ^{13}C chemical shifts as can be seen from the data given in Table 12.10 (a) and the graphs in Fig. 12.17. All the graphs converge to the chemical shift value of methane. None of the plots is linear, a negative curvature being found in all cases (as observed in analogous ^{31}P[143] and ^{29}Si studies[50]).

The ^{13}C chemical shifts of the chloro and methyl-substituted methanes (viz. $CH_{4-x}X_x$, where $X = Cl$ or CH_3) decrease with progressive substitution as would be expected on normal electronegativity grounds (i.e. shielding decreases). However, in the case of the bromo and iodo derivatives this state of affairs no longer exists.

Three series of chlorobromomethanes have been examined[48] (CCl_xBr_{4-x}, $CHCl_xBr_{3-x}$ and $CH_2Cl_xBr_{2-x}$) and the results are reproduced in graphical form in Fig. 12.18 from the chemical shifts given in Table 12.10(a). A perfectly linear relationship was found between ^{13}C chemical shifts and the number of substituents in all cases. Similar linear relationships were found for the ^{13}C chemical shifts of CH_3 groups in halogenated ethanes.

From the ^{13}C studies reported here it can be seen that any attempt to correlate a molecular parameter with ^{13}C shielding constants in halogenated compounds must be treated with caution until the shielding effects are better understood.

12.2.4 Methyl and Ethyl Derivatives of Group IV Elements

Since there will be no magnetic anisotropic contribution to the shielding of carbon nuclei from the central atom in the tetrahedral methyls and ethyls of C, Si, Ge, Sn and Pb, variations in ^{13}C shielding constants might be expected to be related to the electronegativity of the Group IV element concerned[52]. The ^{1}H and ^{13}C resonance spectra of compounds of this type have been measured and the ^{13}C chemical shifts are given in Table 12.9. However, using methods employed previously to determine electronegativities from NMR data[59, 60], it was not possible to obtain reliable values for the electronegativities of Group IV elements.

12.2.5 Alkenes

^{13}C chemical shifts in alkenes are very similar to those in aromatic compounds, unlike the corresponding hydrogen resonance shifts.[50, 57] Thus, the large anisotropic shielding effect from induced ring currents which operates on aromatic ring hydrogen nuclei must obviously be small for ^{13}C nuclei. Although the ^{13}C spectra of only a few alkenes have been studied, it appears that the effects of substituents on the shielding are similar to those observed in the spectra of aromatic molecules[50]. The ^{13}C and ^{1}H spectra of enriched ethylene itself have been investigated, and from a detailed analysis the H—H coupling constants have been determined[279].

Figure 12.19 shows the ^{13}C resonance spectra of several olefinic systems[232]. It is found that $=CH_2$, $=\overset{|}{C}H$ and $=\overset{|}{\underset{|}{C}}$ groups can be assigned readily to triplets, doublets and singlets respectively in their ^{13}C resonance spectra. This is particularly useful for the identification of fully substituted olefines which cannot be studied easily by infrared or ^{1}H NMR techniques. Friedel *et al.*(232) have examined some di-olefines, both conjugated and cumulative, and they have discovered that conjugation has little effect on the ^{13}C chemical shifts of the terminal olefines. However, for cumulative olefines, such as methylallene,

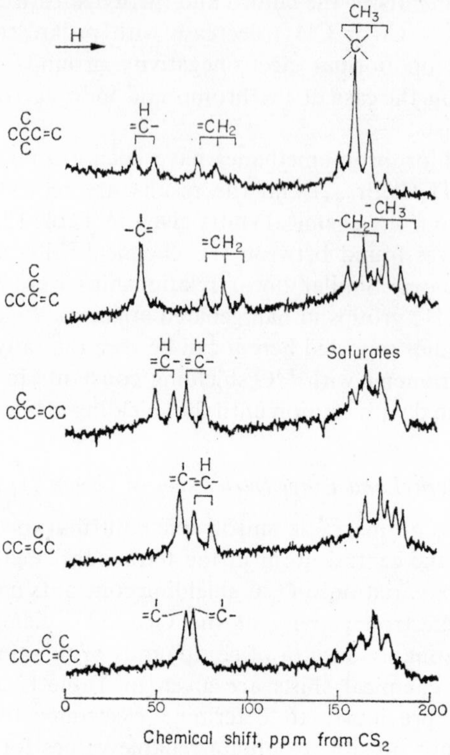

$\delta_{CH_3\overset{*}{C}OOH} = \delta_{CS_2} - 15{\cdot}6$ ppm

FIG. 12.19 The ^{13}C resonance spectra of some olefinic systems at 15·085 Mc sec^{-1}. Friedel and Retcofsky(232).

the 1 and 3 carbon nuclei experience increased shielding while the fully substituted 2 carbon nucleus experiences a large decreased shielding as compared with the shielding of ordinary olefinic carbon nuclei. Savitsky and co-workers(273) have measured the differential shielding ($\delta_{cis} - \delta_{trans}$) for the ethylenic carbon atoms in *cis*- and *trans*-CHX : CHX isomers where X is Cl, Br, I or $COOC_2H_5$. The differential shielding is of the same sign and follows the same order as that for the ^{1}H nuclei in the same compounds. However, the ^{13}C differential shielding values are an order of magnitude larger and cannot be accounted for by neighbour anisotropic shielding effects.

Savitsky *et al.*(301) have made empirical calculations of ^{13}C chemical shifts in unsaturated compounds.

12.2.6 *Acetylenes*

Lauterbur[50] has measured the ^{13}C chemical shifts and spin coupling constants in a series of substituted acetylenes and his results are shown in Table 12.12. Alkyne carbon nuclei and their resonance absorptions fall within a narrow range of a characteristic region of the ^{13}C spectrum (+ 104 to + 123 ppm from CS_2 reference). The effects of substituents on ^{13}C nuclear shielding in alkynes are similar to those observed in substituted alkanes except that the former are somewhat smaller.

TABLE 12.12 ^{13}C CHEMICAL SHIFTS AND SPIN–SPIN COUPLING CONSTANTS OF TRIPLY BONDED CARBON ATOMS[50]

Compound	δ_c† (ppm)	J†($^{13}C{\equiv}^{12}C$—H) (cycles sec^{-1})	δ_c‡ (ppm)	J‡(^{13}CH) (cycles sec^{-1})
$CH_3CH_2C†{\equiv}C†CH_2CH_3$	111·8			
$CH_3OC(=O)C†{\equiv}C†C(=O)OCH_3$	118·2			
$HOCH_2C†{\equiv}C‡H$	110·5	49	118·6	248
$ClCH_2C†{\equiv}C‡H$	114·1	45	118·1	256
$BrCH_2C†{\equiv}C‡H$	112·6	47	116·6	252
$C_6H_5C†{\equiv}C‡H$	108·9	44	115·3	252
$(CH_3)_2C(OH)C†{\equiv}C†H$	104·0	††	122·5	253
$(C_2H_5)(CH_3)C(OH)C†{\equiv}C‡H$	104·5	††	121·3	247

†† Could not be measured accurately because of overlapping peaks. Approximately 50 ± 10 cycles sec^{-1}.

‡ Chemical shifts measured in ppm from CS_2 reference.

12.2.7 *Aromatic Compounds*

The ^{13}C spectra of several substituted aromatic compounds have been examined and the chemical shifts of the ring carbon atoms in such molecules have been well characterised[48, 49, 61]. Benzene itself gives rise to a single doublet in its ^{13}C resonance spectrum (see Fig. 12.20), the doublet splitting arising from spin–spin interaction between the directly bonded carbon and hydrogen atoms (J_{C-H} = 160 cycles sec^{-1}). Monosubstitution of a benzene ring results in four different types of ring carbon atom, viz. *ortho, meta, para* and the substituted carbon atom. The substituted carbon atom will show a single absorption band in its ^{13}C resonance spectrum while the remaining carbon atoms will all be doublets. When an aromatic ring is monosubstituted with a methyl group the carbon atoms in the *ortho-*, *meta-*, and *para*-positions are not shielded very differently and under the prevailing resolution conditions they give rise to a single doublet with the same splitting as the benzene doublet: the substituted ring carbon atom appears as a single absorption band displaced to the low field side of the other ring absorption bands (see Fig. 12.20) and overlaps the low field component of the single doublet from the remaining ring carbon atoms. Of the three xylenes, only in the ^{13}C resonance spectrum of the *ortho-*

derivative is there evidence of two different types of non-substituted ring carbon atoms and even in this molecule the chemical shift difference between the two doublets is very small. In general, the methyl substituted benzenes are found to have ^{13}C chemical shifts very similar to that of benzene(49) and to show little difference from one molecule to the other. This can be seen from examination of the ^{13}C resonance spectra of toluene, the xylenes, durene, mesitylene and hexamethylbenzene, shown in Fig. 12.20, and from the chemical shift data given

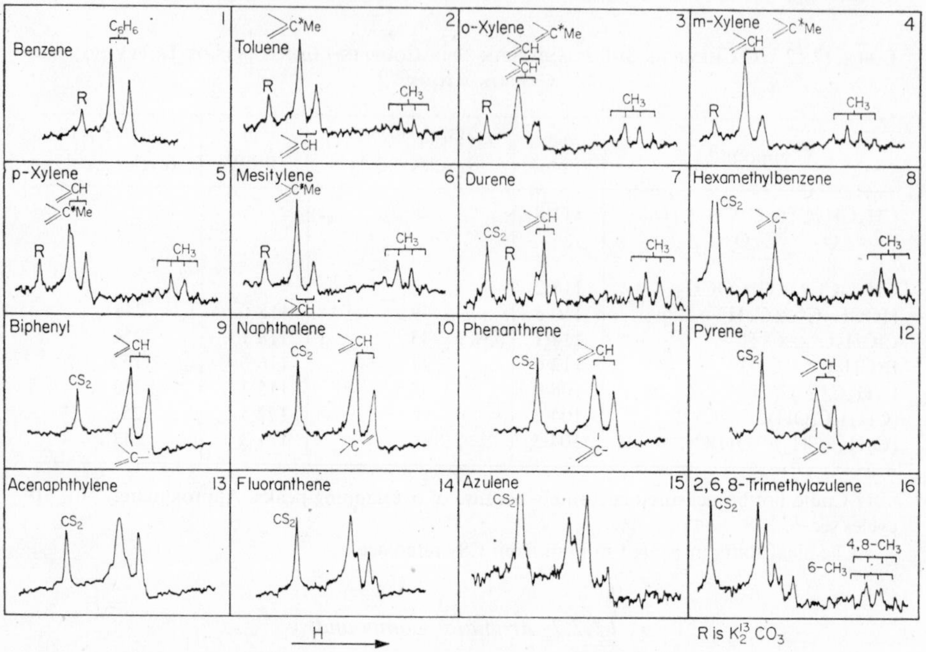

FIG. 12.20 The ^{13}C resonance spectra of aromatic molecules at 8·50 Mc sec^{-1}. Lauterbur(49).

in Table 12.13. Because the differences in chemical shifts are small in these compounds it is impossible to correlate them with the extent of methyl substitution(49).

Monosubstituted benzenes. Spiesecke and Schneider(62) have carried out both ^{1}H and ^{13}C resonance studies on a series of monosubstituted benzenes. Table 12.14 gives the ^{13}C chemical shifts of the various carbon atoms in such compounds measured relative to benzene. By examining deuterated samples of the monosubstituted benzenes, unequivocal assignments for the carbon atoms in the *ortho*-, *meta*- and *para*-positions in these compounds could be made. The effect of deuterium substitution is to increase the relaxation time, T_1, of the carbon nucleus to which it is attached to such an extent that the normal values of H_1 demanded by the low abundance of the carbon-13 nucleus, saturate the signal from the deutero substituted carbon nuclei. For such nuclei,

TABLE 12.13 ^{13}C CHEMICAL SHIFTS AND SPIN COUPLING CONSTANTS IN BENZENE AND SOME METHYL BENZENES[49]

Compound	CH			C^*-CH_3		CH_3		
	δ_{CS_2} ppm	$\delta_{CH_3\overset{*}{C}OOH}$ ppm	J_{CH} cycles sec^{-1}	δ_{CS_2} ppm	$\delta_{CH_3\overset{*}{C}OOH}$ ppm	δ_{CS_2} ppm	$\delta_{CH_3\overset{*}{C}OOH}$ ppm	J_{CH} cycles sec^{-1}
Benzene	65·0	49·4	159					
Toluene	65·2	49·6	156	56·0	40·4	171·8	156·2	122
o-Xylene (CH–3,6)	63·6	48·0	154	56·6	41·0	173·6	158·0	128
(CH–4,5)	67·2	51·6	154					
m-Xylene	65·8	50·2	160	56·4	40·8	172·6	157	127
p-Xylene	64·5	48·9	150	58·0	42·4	172·1	156·5	124
Mesitylene	66·1	50·5	154	56·4	40·8	172·2	156·6	128
Durene	62·0	46·4	142	59·6	44·0	173·6	158·0	127
Hexamethylbenzene				60·4	44·8	174·9	159·3	124

Chemical shifts measured in ppm from CS_2 internal reference and extrapolated to the CH_3COOH external reference scale.

$$\delta_{CH_3COOH\,ext} = \delta_{CS_2\,int} - 15{\cdot}6 \text{ ppm}.$$

the ^{13}C absorption band is not observed. The relaxation effect is via a dipolar relaxation mechanism and is assumed to be greater than any opposing quadrupolar relaxation effects which the deuterium ($I = 1$) would have on the carbon atom.

In monosubstituted benzenes the chemical shifts of the substituted carbon atoms are affected most by the substituent as might be expected. If a correction is made to the ^{13}C chemical shifts to allow for anomalous shielding effects of halogen substituents (as observed in the ^{13}C spectra of substituted methanes), then the resulting ^{13}C chemical shifts of the substituted carbon atoms show a reasonably linear relationship with the electronegativity of the substituents. The ^{13}C chemical shift of the substituted carbon atom decreases with increase in electronegativity of the substituent.

TABLE 12.14 ^{13}C CHEMICAL SHIFTS OF A SERIES OF MONOSUBSTITUTED BENZENES (IN PPM RELATIVE TO BENZENE REFERENCE)[52]

Substituent	C—X	*ortho*	*meta*	*para*
F	−35·1	+14·3	−0·9	+4·4
Cl	−6·4	−0·16	−1·0	+2·0
Br	+5·4	−3·3	−2·2	+1·0
I	+32·3	−9·9	−2·6	+0·4
CH_3	−9·1	−0·3	−0·3	+2·8
OCH_3	−30·2	+14·7	−0·9	+8·1
NH_2	−19·2	+12·4	−1·3	+9·5
$N(CH_3)_2$	−22·4	+15·7	−0·8	+11·8
CHO	−9·0	−1·2	−1·2	−6·0
$COCH_3$	−9·3	−0·2	−0·2	−4·2
NO_2	−19·6	+5·3	−0·8	−6·0

Positive shifts indicate greater nuclear screening than that of the carbon atoms in benzene, negative shifts indicate lower screening.

The anomalous shielding effects observed for ^{13}C nuclei in *ortho*-positions to certain substituents (such as halogens) are much too large to be explained in terms of anisotropic shielding effects. For iodobenzenes, Lauterbur[253] suggests that the large shielding contribution is associated with the high polarisability of the iodine atom (see Section 4.4.3). Small uniform shifts are observed for the carbon atoms in the *meta*-positions in the various compounds, indicating that for such carbon atoms the magnetic anisotropic and inductive shielding effects are almost negligible. Both the inductive and magnetic anisotropic contributions to the shielding of carbon atoms in *para*-positions would be expected to be small and variations in shielding have been attributed to changes in π-electron density at the *para*-positions as a result of resonance effects of the substituents. Electron releasing substituents increase the shielding of the carbon atoms in the *para*-position while electron withdrawing groups decrease the shielding with respect to the pure benzene absorption band. A plot of *para*-^{13}C chemical shifts against *para*-^{1}H chemical shifts for this series of substituted benzenes shows a linear relationship, indicating that the shielding of the two different nuclei responds similarly to changes in resonance effects. Although some correlation of this type is found for the nuclei in the *ortho*-position it is not as pronounced as for those in *para*-positions. No correlation is found between the ^{13}C and ^{1}H chemical shifts for the nuclei in the *meta*-positions. The *para*-carbon atoms also have chemical shifts which show a close linear relationship with the corresponding Hammett σ constants: no such correlation is found for the *meta*-carbon atoms.

Other aromatic compounds. Lauterbur[49] has examined the ^{13}C resonance spectra of several other aromatic derivatives including biphenyl, naphthalene, phenanthrene, pyrene, acenaphthylene and fluoranthene, and has succeeded

TABLE 12.15 ^{13}C CHEMICAL SHIFTS AND SPIN COUPLING CONSTANTS IN BIPHENYL AND SOME ALTERNANT HYDROCARBONS[49]

Compound	CH			CC	
	δ_{CS_2} ppm	$\delta_{CH_3\overset{*}{C}OOH}$ ppm	J_{CH} cycles sec^{-1}	δ_{CS_2} ppm	$\delta_{CH_3\overset{*}{C}OOH}$ ppm
Biphenyl	64·6	49·0	162	55·0	39·4
Naphthalene	65·9	50·3	158	56·6	41·0
Phenanthrene	65·6	50·0	158	60·2	44·6
Pyrene	66·0	50·4	154	56·9	41·30
				60·6	45·0

Chemical shifts are measured from a CS_2 reference (in ppm) and extrapolated to the $CH_3\overset{*}{C}OOH$ external reference scale.

$$\delta_{CH_3\overset{*}{C}OOH\,ext} = \delta_{CS_2\,int} - 15\cdot6 \text{ ppm}.$$

in partially analysing their spectra (shown in Figure 12.20). Other compounds, such as azulene and 4, 6, 8-trimethylazulene, possess ^{13}C resonance spectra which could only be assigned tentatively. In these latter non-alternant hydrocarbons, the range of ^{13}C chemical shifts is found to be much larger than that for alternant hydrocarbons which suggests that the origin of the shielding of the carbon nuclei in alternant hydrocarbons is governed largely by variations in π electron densities at the carbon atoms of the aromatic rings. This arises because in alternant hydrocarbons the π electron densities are very similar on all the ring carbon atoms, whereas this is not the case in a non-alternant molecule such as azulene. Lauterbur[49] has calculated the π electron densities at the various carbon atoms in azulene and found them to correlate well with the observed ^{13}C chemical shifts. By using an approach similar to that adopted by Saika and Slichter[3] to explain ^{19}F chemical shifts, he succeeded in obtaining an approximate estimate of the effects of changes in the π electron densities on the shielding of the carbon atoms concerned (a value of 240 ppm per electron was found).

Biphenyl and naphthalene each have a single doublet in their ^{13}C spectra with a splitting similar to that for benzene: the junction carbon atoms give rise to a single absorption band which overlaps the low field component of the doublet. Pyrene and phenanthrene have similar ^{13}C spectra to the above compounds except that the absorption signals for the junction carbon atoms are clearly resolved. Generally, the ^{13}C chemical shifts of the condensed aromatic compounds are at slightly higher fields than the benzene absorption band (see Fig. 12.20 and Table 12.15).

The ^{13}C chemical shifts of the methyl groups in a series of substituted toluenes have been measured and in the *ortho*-methyl series a correlation has been found between the carbon chemical shifts and those of ^{19}F nuclei in the same

TABLE 12.16 ^{13}C CHEMICAL SHIFTS AND SPIN COUPLING CONSTANTS FOR PHENOL, METHYL PHENOLS AND ANISOLE[61]

Compound	Group	Chemical shift † ppm		J_{CH} cycles sec^{-1}
		δ_{CS_2}	δ_{CH_3COOH}	
Phenol	C-1	37·4	21·8	
	CH-2,6	76·8	61·2	161
	CH-3,5	62·4	46·8	159
	CH-4	71·1	55·5	162
o-Cresol	C-1	39·0	23·4	
	C-2	68·5	52·9	
	CH-3	61·5	45·9	160
	CH-4	71·1	55·5	158
	CH-5	64·8	49·2	163
	CH-6	76·6	61·0	160
	CH_3	175·8	160·2	124
m-Cresol	C-1	37·6	22·0	
	CH-2	76·4	60·8	158
	C-3	53·2	37·6	
	CH-4	70·3	54·7	159
	CH-5	62·2	46·6	154
	CH-6	79·8	64·2	160
	CH_3	171·6	156·0	128
p-Cresol	C-1	39·9	24·3	
	CH-2,6	77·2	61·6	158
	CH-3,5	62·3	46·7	156
	C-4	62·0	46·4	
	CH_3	171·9	156·3	126
2,6-Dimethylphenol	C-1	40·2	24·6	
	C-2,6	68·9	53·3	
	CH-3,5	63·7	48·1	156
	CH-4	71·9	56·3	158
	CH_3	177·1	161·5	126
3,5-Dimethylphenol	C-1	38·0	22·4	
	CH-2,6	79·7	64·1	156
	C-3,5	53·6	38·0	
	CH-4	70·6	55·0	158
	CH_3	172·1	156·5	129
Anisole	C-1	32·7	17·1	
	CH-2,6	79·0	63·4	156
	CH-3,5	63·0	47·4	158
	CH-4	72·0	56·4	162
	OCH_3	138·4	122·8	145

† Chemical shifts measured in ppm from CS_2 internal reference and extrapolated to $CH_3\overset{*}{C}OOH$ reference using $\delta_{CH_3\overset{*}{C}OOH} = \delta_{CS_2} - 15{\cdot}6$ ppm.

position in analogous molecules. Correlations of these ^{13}C shifts with Hammett σ values are found to be not as good as the correlation of the latter with the ^{19}F chemical shifts[48].

Lauterbur[61] has examined the ^{13}C resonance spectra of a series of phenols, several dimethoxybenzenes and anisole: their chemical shifts and assignments are given in Table 12.16 and their ^{13}C spectra shown in Fig. 12.21. The ^{13}C resonance spectrum of *ortho*-dimethoxybenzene is shown in Fig. 12.22. In this compound, the methyl carbon atoms give rise to a high field quartet (bands 6 to 9) and the substituted ring carbon atoms produce a single absorption band

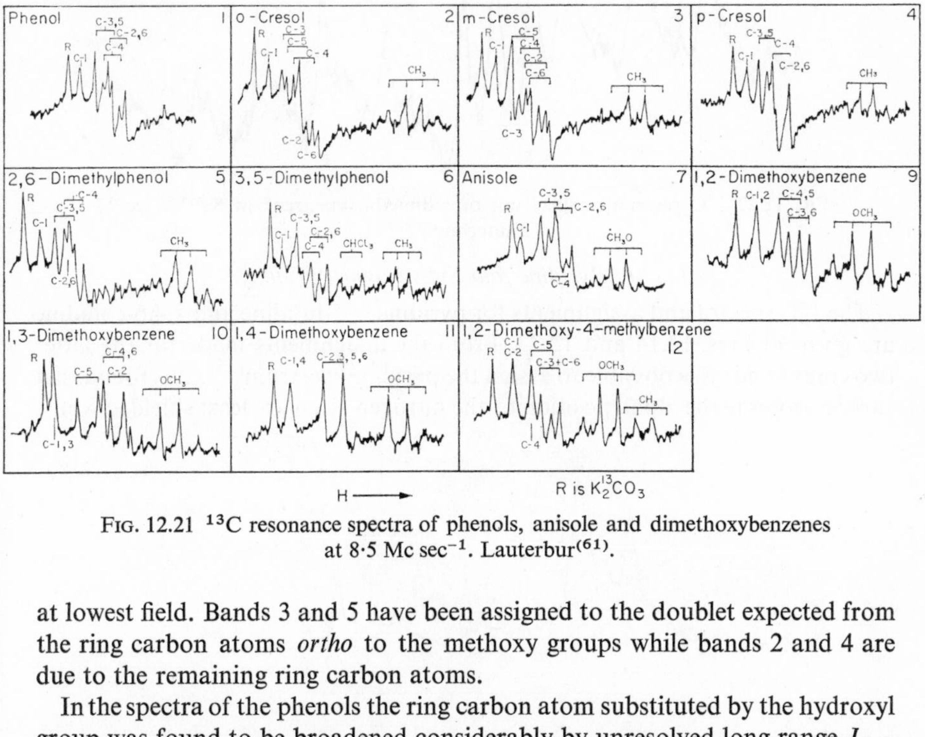

FIG. 12.21 ^{13}C resonance spectra of phenols, anisole and dimethoxybenzenes at 8·5 Mc sec^{-1}. Lauterbur[61].

at lowest field. Bands 3 and 5 have been assigned to the doublet expected from the ring carbon atoms *ortho* to the methoxy groups while bands 2 and 4 are due to the remaining ring carbon atoms.

In the spectra of the phenols the ring carbon atom substituted by the hydroxyl group was found to be broadened considerably by unresolved long range J_{C-H} coupling. As was found in methyl benzenes, the methyl substituted ring carbon atoms in cresols are deshielded by about 8 ppm as compared with an unsubstituted ring carbon atom. The indirect shielding effects of the methyl groups on other ring carbon atoms have also been classified by Lauterbur. It was found that the average shielding of a ring carbon atom *para* to a methyl group is $+2{\cdot}7$ ppm: the average shift contributions from *meta*- and *ortho*-methyl groups are $-0{\cdot}4$ ppm and $+0{\cdot}2$ ppm respectively. Using these values for the direct and indirect shielding effects of methyl groups it is possible to calculate the expected shifts for the carbon atoms in methyl benzenes: in every case, good agreement with the experimental values was obtained.

^{13}C chemical shifts in *para*-disubstituted benzenes have been found to obey additivity relationships[272].

Lauterbur has also examined the ^{13}C spectra of several anilines, *N,N*-dimethylanilines(252), methylnitrobenzenes(254) and methyliodobenzenes(253). Substituted acetophenones have also been studied(282).

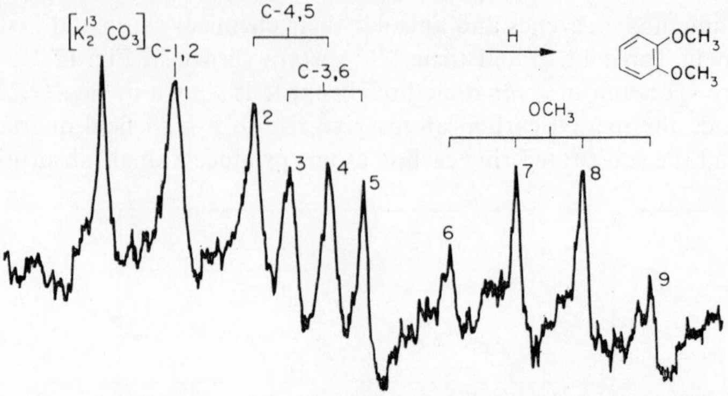

FIG. 12.22 ^{13}C resonance spectrum of *o*-dimethoxybenzene at 8·5 Mc sec^{-1}. Lauterbur(63).

12.2.8 *Pyridine and Substituted Pyridines*

The ^{13}C spectra and assignments for pyridine, 3,5-lutidine and 2,4,6-collidine are given in Figs. 12.14 and 12.23. From the assignments made for the latter two compounds it is possible to assign the pyridine spectrum(48). It is found that carbon atoms in the alpha position to the nitrogen atom are least shielded whilst

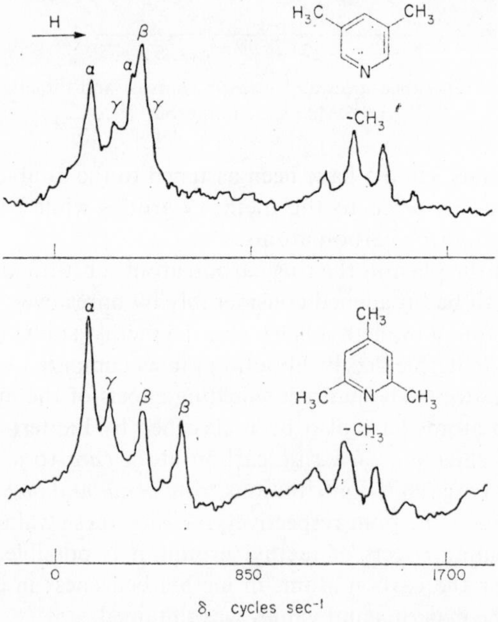

FIG. 12.23 ^{13}C resonance spectra of 3,5-lutidine and 2,4,6-collidine at 8·5 Mc sec^{-1}. Chemical shifts measured from external $CF_3\overset{*}{C}OOH$. Lauterbur(48).

those in the beta positions are shielded most: a similar state of affairs prevails in the ^{1}H resonance spectrum of pyridine.

The ^{13}C spectra of the picolines and several pyrazines[(63)], aromatic amines and imines[(287)] have been examined.

12.2.9 ^{13}C *Chemical Shifts of Carbonyl Groups*

Table 12.17 gives the ^{13}C chemical shifts in a series of compounds containing carbonyl groups: the carbonyl carbon nuclei in ketones are significantly less shielded than those in esters, a fact which could prove useful in differentiating between the two groupings in molecules of unknown structure[(50)]. In a large series of compounds containing carbonyl groups, the ^{13}C shielding is influenced mainly by the local electrons on the carbon[(290)].

TABLE 12.17 CARBONYL GROUP ^{13}C CHEMICAL SHIFTS

Compound	δ (ppm)†	Reference
Formic acid (88% aqueous solution)	27	47
Acrylic acid	20	50
Acetic acid	16	47
RCOOH	(13)	51
α-Hydroxy acid	−25	51
Acetic anhydride	27	47
Potassium acetate (saturated aqueous solution)	11	47
Dimethylacetylene dicarboxylate	40	48
Diethyl carbonate	39	47
Dimethyl carbonate	36	50
RO_2CCO_2R	(34)	51
$(RO)_2CO$	(29)	51
Methyl benzoate	27	48
Vinyl acetate	25	50
Isopropenyl acetate	25	50
Methyl acetate	23	50
Methyl salicylate	22	48
Methyl oleate	18	50
Ethyl lactate	17	50
Butyrolactone	15	50
Acetophenone	−4	47
Acetylacetone (keto form)	−9	50
(enol form)	2	50
Acetone	−12	47
2-Nonanone	−13	50
2,4,6-Trimethylacetophenone	−13	50
R_2CO	(−14)	51
Cyclohexanone	−16	50
Cyclopentanone	−26	50
Acetaldehyde	−6	47
Dimethylformamide	30	47
$RCONR_2$	(20)	51

Values for classes of compounds as given by Holm (51) are given in parentheses.
† Chemical shifts measured in ppm from CS_2 reference.
Intramolecular H-bonding can have large effects on the ^{13}C shielding in carbonyl groups[(289)].

12.2.10 Miscellaneous Studies

Gaseous samples of carbon monoxide and dioxide, enriched in ^{13}C, have been investigated and have been found to have ^{13}C chemical shifts relative to a carbon disulphide external reference of $+11 \cdot 5$ and $+68 \cdot 6$ ppm respectively[(64)]. The chemical shifts in these simple linear molecules might be important in the understanding of ^{13}C shielding constants[(64)]. High concentrations of the gases were obtained by cooling samples with liquid nitrogen prior to sealing the sample tubes: in the gas phase the ^{13}C relaxation time will be short and consequently saturation problems will be less serious. The chemical shift of the gaseous carbon dioxide is the same as that found for liquid carbon dioxide and also for ^{13}C enriched carbon dioxide dissolved in neutral and aqueous media[(65)].

In an aqueous solution of ^{13}C enriched carbon dioxide, separate absorption bands have been observed in the ^{13}C resonance spectra for the dissolved and hydrated forms of carbon dioxide. Addition of the catalyst, carbonic anhydrase,

TABLE 12.18 ^{13}C CHEMICAL SHIFTS OF SOME METAL CARBONYLS[(125)]

Compound	Reference	Chemical shift ppm
$Fe(CO)_5$	C_6H_6 ext	$-84 \cdot 6$
$Ni(CO)_4$	C_6H_6 int	$-64 \cdot 0$
$Fe(CO)_2(NO)_2$	C_6H_6 ext	$-79 \cdot 0$

causes the signals to collapse as a result of line broadening accompanying the rapid exchange process between the two forms[(64)]. An attempt to detect a ^{13}C resonance spectrum for carbonic acid was unsuccessful on account of the sensitivity limitations of the instrument used[(65)].

The ^{13}C resonance spectrum of iron pentacarbonyl, $Fe(CO)_5$, has been measured with a view to determining its molecular structure[(66)]. It is still uncertain whether the molecule has a square based pyramidal structure[(67)] or a trigonal bipyramidal structure[(68)]: the ^{13}C spectrum of the square based pyramid structure would have been expected to consist of two bands of relative intensities 4 : 1 whilst that of the trigonal bipyramid would give two bands of relative intensities 3 : 2. The observed spectrum consists of a single absorption band thus favouring neither structure. This could be due to chemical exchange of the carbon monoxide molecules or to the different carbon atoms having largely differing relaxation times but the most probable explanation of the single peak is that the chemical shifts of the carbon atoms in the two environments are the same[(66)]. No change in the ^{13}C spectrum is observed when the compound is cooled to $-60°C$ which suggests that the presence of an exchange process is unlikely[(125)].

Table 12.18 gives the ^{13}C chemical shifts for some metal carbonyls. The shifts are insensitive to a change in the metal atom and no evidence could be obtained to indicate whether the bonding of the CO molecules to the metal atom is via the O or the C atom in any of the compounds considered[(125)].

12.2.11 *Spin–Spin Interaction Between ^{1}H and ^{13}C Nuclei*

Several workers have reported coupling constants between directly bonded carbon and hydrogen atoms[47, 49, 51, 73–78] and in most cases the values of J_{CH} are obtained from examination of hydrogen resonance spectra where such measurements can be made with greater accuracy than from ^{13}C studies[13, 73–78]. Long range coupling constants between hydrogen and carbon atoms which are not directly bonded to each other have been observed in the ^{1}H resonance spectra of several ^{13}C enriched samples[57, 70, 99] (in favourable cases such coupling constants can be measured in the ^{1}H spectra of non-enriched samples[71]).

Tiers has measured the relative signs of the "direct" ^{13}C—^{1}H and ^{13}C—^{19}F coupling constants in dichlorofluoromethane $CHCl_2F$, using a spin-decoupling method. Surprisingly, the coupling constants are found to be opposite in sign ($J_{C-H} = +220{\cdot}0 \pm 0{\cdot}1$ and $J_{C-F} = -293{\cdot}8 \pm 0{\cdot}2$ cycles sec^{-1}), the high field ^{13}CF satellite doublet in the ^{19}F resonance spectrum collapsing when the low field ^{13}CH doublet in the ^{1}H resonance spectrum is irradiated. For this type of double irradiation experiment an instrument† was employed capable of strongly irradiating hydrogen nuclei at 42·50 Mc sec^{-1} whilst examining the fluorine resonance spectrum at 40·00 Mc sec^{-1}.

Coupling between Directly Bonded Atoms. From Ramsey's theory of indirect spin coupling[72] it can be shown that if the Fermi contact term dominates the spin–spin coupling interaction then the magnitude of the coupling constant

TABLE 12.19 ^{13}C—^{1}H SPIN COUPLING CONSTANTS IN A RANGE OF MOLECULES[74] WHERE THE CARBON HYBRIDISATION VARIES FROM *sp* TO *sp*^{3}

Compound	Hybridisation	J_{CH} Coupling constant (cycles sec^{-1})	Reference
$C(CH_3)_4$	sp^3	120	47
$Si(CH_3)_4$	sp^3	120	47
Cyclohexene	sp^2	170	47
Benzene	sp^2	159	47
$CH_3C(=O)H$	sp^2	174	47
Methyl acetylene	*sp*	248	74

between directly bonded nuclei should show a direct dependence on the amount of *s* character in the bond between them (see Section 5.9). For coupling between directly bonded carbon and hydrogen nuclei, a correlation of this type has been observed, indicating that the Fermi contact term is the controlling factor in this system[13, 69, 73–75, 300].

† Model SD–60 Spin Decoupler manufactured by NMR Specialities Co. Inc., Box 145, Greensbury Road, New Kensington, Pa., U.S.A.

Shoolery[74] has compiled a table of typical J_{CH} coupling constants in a range of compounds where the carbon hybridisation varies from *sp* to sp^3 (see Table 12.19). By assuming that the amount of 2*s* character in the C—H bonds depends directly on the squares of the coefficients of the 2*s* wavefunction in the L.C.A.O. description of sp^3, sp^2 and *sp* hybrid orbitals, he showed that the respective J_{CH} coupling constants between atoms using the above

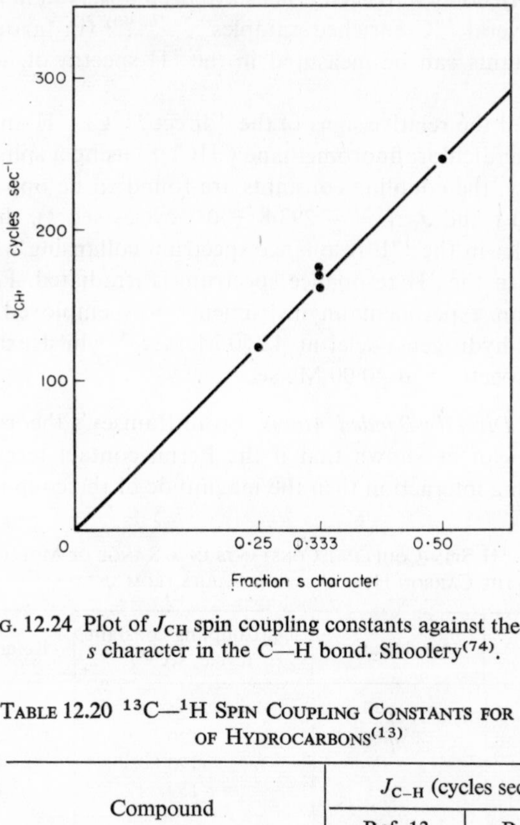

FIG. 12.24 Plot of J_{CH} spin coupling constants against the fraction of *s* character in the C—H bond. Shoolery[74].

TABLE 12.20 $^{13}C-^{1}H$ SPIN COUPLING CONSTANTS FOR A SERIES OF HYDROCARBONS[13]

Compound	J_{C-H} (cycles sec^{-1})	
	Ref. 13	Ref. 47
Cyclohexane	123	140
$(CH_3)_2C{=}C(CH_3)_2$	124	
CH_4	125	
$(CH_3)_4C$	124	120
Mesitylene (CH_3 groups)	126	126
Cyclopentane	128	
$CH_3-C{\equiv}C-CH_3$	131	
$^{13}CH_3-C{\equiv}C-H$	132	
Mesitylene (ring C—H)	154	160
Benzene	159	159
Cyclopropane	161	
$CH_3-C{\equiv}{}^{13}C-H$	248	
$C_6H_5-C{\equiv}{}^{13}C-H$	251	

orbitals would be equal to $\frac{1}{4}$, $\frac{1}{3}$ and $\frac{1}{2}$ of the coupling expected if the bonding were completely s in character and if the Fermi contact term dominates the coupling. Figure 12.24 shows a plot of J_{CH} coupling constants against the fractions of s character in the bonds concerned: as predicted, the plot is linear and has no intercept. Similar results to those of Shoolery have been published by Muller and Pritchard[13, 73] who had been working concurrently on this topic. They examined the ^1H spectra of a series of hydrocarbons and obtained the J_{CH} coupling constants shown in Table 12.20[13]. In addition to correlating

TABLE 12.21 J_{CH} COUPLING CONSTANTS IN SUBSTITUTED METHANES[73]

Compound	J_{C-H} (cycles sec^{-1})
$(CH_3)_3SiCN$	122
$(CH_3)_2C{=}CH_2$	126[a]
C_2H_6	126[b]
$(CH_3)_2C{=}O$	126
$CH_3{-}C_6H_5$	126[c]
$CH_3{-}CHO$	127[d]
p-$CH_3{-}C_6H_4{-}NO_2$	127
$(CH_3)_4Sn$	128[e]
$(CH_3)_3C{-}CN$	129
$CH_3{-}COOH$	130
$(CH_3)_3N$	131
$(CH_3)_2NH$	132
CH_3NH_2	133
CH_3CCl_3	134
CH_3CN	136
$(CH_3)_2SO$	138
$(CH_3)_2NH(BH_3)$	139
CH_3OH	141
$CH_3OC_6H_5$	143
$H_2C(CN)_2$	145
p-$CH_3O{-}C_6H_4{-}CHO$	145
CH_3NO_2	147
$(CH_3{-}O{-}C(O)CH_2{-})_2$	147[f]
CH_3F	149[g]
CH_3Cl	150
CH_3I	151
CH_3Br	152
CH_2I_2	173
CH_2Cl_2	178
$CHBr_3$	206
$CHCl_3$	209

[a] J_{C-H} (ethylenic) = 155; $J_{H-H} = 1{\cdot}2 \pm 0{\cdot}1$.
[b] $J_{H-H} = 7{\cdot}7 \pm 0{\cdot}2$.
[c] J_{C-H} (ring) Av = 155.
[d] J_{C-H} (aldehyde) = 173.
[e] $J_{H-Sn} = 53$ (sidebands due to ^{117}Sn and ^{119}Sn overlap).
[f] J_{C-H} (CH_2 groups) = 155;
J_{H-H} ($-CH_2-CH_2-$) = $7{\cdot}1 \pm 0{\cdot}4$.
[g] $J_{H-F} = 45{\cdot}8 \pm 0{\cdot}5$.

the coupling constants with the amount of *s* character in the bond they formulated a semi-empirical equation to describe their results (see equation (5.48)).

The effect of bond polarities on J_{CH} coupling constants between the directly bonded atoms has been considered by several workers[13, 73, 75, 77, 78]. Muller and Pritchard[13, 73, 75] consider this effect to be quite small and cite the similar coupling constants found in methyl halides, where the bond polari-

TABLE 12.22 J_{CH} COUPLING CONSTANTS IN FORMYL COMPOUNDS[75]

Compound	J_{CH} (cycles sec^{-1})	J_{C-CH} (cycles sec^{-1})	$r(C—H)_{calc}$ (Å)	$r(C—H)_{obs}$ (Å)	$r(C{=}O)$ (Å)	<HCO
CH_3CHO	173		1·088	1·114	1·216	118° 36′
p-$CH_3OC_6H_4CHO$	173		1·088			
C_6H_5CHO	174	24·1	1·088			
o-HOC_6H_4CHO	177	19·8	1·086			
$(CH_3)_2NCHO$	192		1·080			
CCl_3CHO	207	46·3	1·073			
HOCHO	222		1·067	1·097	1·202	124° 8′
CH_3OCHO	226		1·065	1·101	1·200	124° 50′
FCHO	267		1·049	1·095	1·181	127° 20′

TABLE 12.23 J_{CH} COUPLING CONSTANTS C—H BOND LENGTHS AND H—C—X BOND ANGLES OF SEVERAL SUBSTITUTED METHANES[73]

Compound	J_{C-H} (cycles sec^{-1})	$r(C—H)_{calc}$ (Å)	$r(C—H)_{obs}$ (Å)	<HCX
$CH_3—C{\equiv}C—H$	132	1·1046	1·1046	110° 16′
$CH_3—C{\equiv}N$	136	1·1030	1·1025	109° 30′
$CH_3—F$	149	1·0975	1·097	108° 27′
$CH_3—Cl$	150	1·0971	1·0959	108° 00′
$CH_3—I$	151	1·0967	1·0958	106° 58′
$CH_3—Br$	152	1·0963	1·0954	107° 14′
CH_2Cl_2	178	1·0854	1·082	
$CHBr_3$	206	1·0725	1·068	
$CHCl_3$	209	1·0737	1·073	

ties are very different, as support for this idea (see Table 12.21). Table 12.21 contains J_{CH} coupling constants for an extensive series of substituted methanes.

Muller[75] has examined a series of formyl compounds i.e. molecules of general formula $X{-}C\genfrac{}{}{0pt}{}{\diagup O}{\diagdown H}$ and has reported the J_{CH} coupling constants within the formyl group (see Table 12.22). It was found that increasing the electronegativity of the substituent X results in an increase in the J_{CH} coupling constant and decreases the C—H bond length in the formyl group. Muller attributed these effects to the change in carbon hybridisation with change of substituent X. If the bond angle data can be used as a measure of hybridisation then the measured values indicate that there is little change in hybridisation from molecule to molecule within this series of compounds: however, Muller claims that such correlations can be misleading since observed bond angles can be quite different from inter-orbital angles which are a true reflection of the state of hybridisation of an atom[13]. In a series of substituted methanes, the J_{CH} coupling constants can be seen from examination of Table 12.23 to vary markedly from one compound to the other even though the bond angles in every case indicate the molecule to be tetrahedral. Muller considers that the variations in the J_{CH} values are too great to be explained in terms of bond polarities and postulates the presence of bent bonds in these compounds (due to the difference between inter-orbital bond angles and observed bond angles)[73]. However, Gutowsky and Juan[69] believe such effects to be unimportant. Other workers[77, 78] have correlated the J_{CH} coupling constant in methane itself with bond polarisation parameters: theoretically, J_{CH} was shown to decrease with increase in $C^{-}H^{+}$ ionic character if this contribution is important. The later work of Muller[75] concerning formyl compounds suggests that this effect is negligible since the observed trend in J_{CH} coupling constants found in this series of compounds is opposite to that expected if the bond polarity effect were dominant. However, it is obvious that the origin of the variations in J_{CH} is not completely clear at the present time.

If the J_{CH} coupling constant is solely a function of the state of hybridisation of the carbon atom, it should also bear some simple relationship to the C—H bond length[13, 73, 75]. Muller and Pritchard[13] have suggested a semi-empirical equation relating these two parameters for simple hydrocarbons: the equation cannot be applied to any class of compounds other than hydrocarbons since consistently low predicted values were obtained for the C—H bond lengths in the formyl derivatives using this equation[75]. For substituted methanes, the equation relating the C—H bond length, r(C—H), and the J_{CH} coupling constant is

$$r(\text{C—H}) = 1{\cdot}1597 - 4{\cdot}17 \times 10^{-4} J_{CH} \qquad (12.3)$$

and this equation was found to yield C—H bond lengths in good agreement with measured values (see Table 12.23). The same authors also derived an empirical equation relating the electronegativity of the substituent in monosubstituted methanes with the J_{CH} coupling constant and the C—X bond length, r(C—X): for a series of substituted methanes CH_3X the equation is

$$J_{CH} = 22{\cdot}6 E_X + 40{\cdot}1\, r(\text{C—X}) + 5{\cdot}5 \qquad (12.4)$$

where E_X is the electronegativity of substituent X on the Huggins scale[79].

Care should be taken in applying such relationships to solutions because it has been found that the J_{CH} value in chloroform varies over a wide range depending on the solvent (from 208·1 cycles sec^{-1} in a cyclohexane solution to 217·7 cycles sec^{-1} in dimethyl sulphoxide)[262]. The increase in coupling constants accompanies an increase in the ability of the solvent molecules to form hydrogen bonds with the chloroform. Smaller solvent effects have been observed for the H—F coupling constant in bromochlorofluoromethane: here, hydrogen bonding produces a decrease in the coupling constant[262].

Reeves *et al.*[291–293] have pointed out a useful linear relationship between $|J_{XY}/\gamma_X\gamma_Y|^{1/2}$ and Z_X (the atomic number) for Group IV elements: it is valid for J_{XH}, $J_{X\text{-}C\text{-}H}$, J_{XF} and $J_{X\text{-}C\text{-}F}$ values.

TABLE 12.24 MALINOWSKI'S ζ_X VALUES FOR A LIST OF COMMON SUBSTITUENTS AS OBTAINED FROM THE J_{CH} COUPLING CONSTANTS OF THE CORRESPONDING METHYL DERIVATIVES[80]

Substituent	[a] J_{CH} (cycles sec^{-1})	ζ_X (cycles sec^{-1}) (av. value)
—H	125	41·7
—F	149	65·6
—Cl	150	68·6
—Br	152	68·6
—I	151	67·6
—OC_6H_5	143	59·6
—OH	141, 144	59·6
—$S(O)CH_3$	138	54·6
—NH_2	133	49·6
—$NHCH_3$	132	48·6
—$N(CH_3)_2$	131	47·6
—CN	136	52·6
—CCl_3	134	50·6
—CH_2I	132	48·6
—C≡CH	132	48·6
—$CHCl_2$	131	47·6
—COOH	103, 131	47·1
—CH_2Br	128	44·6
—CH_2Cl	128	44·6
—CHO	127	43·6
—CH_3	126	42·6
—C_6H_5	126	42·6
—$CH(CH_3)Br$	126	42·6
—$C(O)CH_3$	126, 122	40·6
—$C(CH_3)_3$	124, 120	38·6

[a] J_{CH} values taken from references 13, 73, 85 and 241.

TABLE 12.25 A COMPARISON OF OBSERVED J_{CH} COUPLING CONSTANTS IN SATURATED MOLECULES WITH COUPLING CONSTANTS CALCULATED USING MALINOWSKI'S ζ_X VALUES[80]

Compound	J_{CH} (calcd.)	[a] J_{CH} (exp.)	Diff.
$C_6H_5\mathbf{CH_2}C_6H_5$	127	127	0
$(CH_3)_2C\mathbf{CH_2}OH$	139	132	+7
$CH_3\mathbf{CH_2}I$	152	149	+3
$CH_3\mathbf{CH_2}Br$	153	151	+2
$C_6H_5\mathbf{CH_2}Cl$	153	152	+1
$C_6H_5\mathbf{CH_2}Br$	153	153	0
$(CH_3)_2\mathbf{CH}Br$	154	151	+3
$BrCH_2CH_2Br$	155	157	−2
$ClCH_2CH_2Cl$	155	154	+1
CH_2ClCN	163	161	+2
CH_2I_2	177	173	+4
CH_2Br_2	179	178	+1
CH_2Cl_2	179	178	+1
$Cl_2CHCHCl_2$	185	182	+3
$CHCl_2CN$	190	189	+1
$CHCl_3$	206	209	−3

[a] J_{CH} values taken from references 13, 70, 73, 85 and 241.

12.2.12 *Additivity Effects in* $^1H—^{13}C$ *and in* $^{19}F—^{13}C$ *Coupling Constants*

Malinowski[80] has observed that for molecules of the type CHXYZ, the J_{CH} coupling constants can be predicted using the simple additivity relationship

$$J_{CH} = \zeta_X + \zeta_Y + \zeta_Z \qquad (12.5)$$

TABLE 12.26 J_{CF} COUPLING CONSTANTS AND ζ_X VALUES OBTAINED FROM EXAMINATION OF THE $^{19}F—^{13}C$ SATELLITE RESONANCE SPECTRA OF SUBSTITUTED FLUOROALKANES[81]

Molecule†	$J_{^{13}CF}$	Atom directly bonded to ^{13}C	ζ
(a) Trifluoromethyl compounds			
CF_4	259·2[236]	F	86·4[a]
CF_3H	274·3[236]	H	101·5
CF_3CCl_3	282·5[237]	C	109·7
CF_3CO_2H	283·2[237]	C	110·4
$(CF_3)_2NNO_2$	273·6	N	100·8
$(CF_3)_2PCl$	320·2	P	147·4
$(CF_3S)_2$	313·8	S	141·0
$(CF_3S)_2Hg$	308·3	S	135·5
CF_3SNCO	309	S	136·0
$(CF_3)_2Se$	331·3	Se	158·5
$(CF_3Se)_2$	337·1	Se	164·3
$(CF_3Se)_2Hg$	332·5	Se	159·7
(b) Other compounds			
CF_2H_2	234·8[236]	H	74·2
CFH_3	157·4[236]	H	52·5
cyclo-C_4F_8[c]	298·0	C	105·8
CCl_3F	336·5	Cl	112·2
$(CF_2Cl)_2$	299·0	Cl	104·4[b]
$(CF_2Br)_2$	311·6	Br	115·7[b]

[a] This value is used in the derivation of all the others.
[b] Assuming $\zeta_c = 108$.
[c] The ^{13}C satellite bands of this compound have a broadened triplet structure (with 1:1:1 relative intensities), the splitting being 3·0 cycles sec^{-1}.

† The compounds are arranged in the order of the atomic number of the element for which zeta is quoted.

where ζ_X, ζ_Y and ζ_Z are contributions to the coupling from the X, Y, Z substituents respectively. These zeta values for various substituents can be calculated from the C—H coupling constants in the corresponding methyl derivatives, for example

$$\zeta_x = J_{CH}(CH_3X) - 2\zeta_H \qquad (12.6)$$

where ζ_H is 41·7 cycles sec^{-1} (evaluated from the observed J_{CH} value for methane; $J_{CH}(CH_4) = 3\,\zeta_H = 125$ cycles sec^{-1}). Table 12.24 gives a list of calculated zeta values and Table 12.25 presents a comparison of predicted and observed J_{CH} values in saturated molecules obtained by using equation (12.5): excellent agreement is found in nearly all cases. The zeta values appear to depend primarily on the atom of the substituent to which the carbon is directly attached. Similar attempts to predict J_{CF} coupling constants have also been reasonably successful[81, 307]. Table 12.26 gives a list of J_{CF} coupling constants together with the appropriate zeta contributions for a series of compounds. It is seen that fairly constant zeta values are obtained for substituents other than hydrogen. The J_{CF} values are all larger than the analogous J_{CH} values and the former are observed to increase when the atomic number of the directly bonded substituent atom is increased within a given group of the periodic table. The characteristic

TABLE 12.27 COMPARISON OF OBSERVED J_{CH} COUPLING CONSTANTS WITH COUPLING CONSTANTS CALCULATED USING MALINOWSKI'S ζ_X VALUES[100]

Compound	J_{CH} (cycles sec^{-1})		
	Observed	Predicted	Difference
C_6H_5**CH_2**F	151 [a]	150	+1
CH_2F_2	185 [b]	173	+12
CHF_3	238	197	+41
$CHFCl_2$	220	203	+17
CHF_2Cl	231	200	+31
$CH_2(COOH)_2$	132 [b]	136	−4
$CH_2ClCOOH$	152	157	−5
$CHCl_2COOH$	181	184	−3
CH_3OCH_3	140	[140] [c]	[0]
CH_2 $(OCH_3)_2$	162	155	+7
CH$(OCH_3)_3$	186	170	+16

[a] D. T. Carr, Thesis, Purdue University, 1962.
[b] Reference 75.
[c] Used to evaluate zeta for the methoxy group as 56·6 cycles sec^{-1}.

C—F coupling constants can sometimes be used to confirm proposed molecular structures[81].

Gutowsky and Juan[69, 82] have considered the theoretical implication of the observed additivity of substituent effects on J_{CH} coupling constants. Using a valence bond approach and assuming the Fermi contact term to dominate C—H spin coupling interactions they were able to show that each substituent has a characteristic affinity for *s* character, which controls the manner in which the carbon 2*s* orbital is distributed over the bonds (see Section 5.9).

The general validity of the simple additivity relationship for C—H coupling constants has been questioned by Muller and Rose[100] and by Frankiss[236]. Table 12.27 presents a comparison of some observed J_{CH} coupling constants with the values predicted using Malinowski's zeta values[80]; large deviations from the predicted values occur especially when the substituents on the interacting carbon atom are highly electronegative[100]. This suggests that the *s* character of the carbon atomic orbital used in the C—H bond does not vary linearly upon the introduction of additional substituents.

Frankiss[236] has pointed out that C—H coupling constants in fluoro (and to some extent in alkoxy and chloro) methane derivatives do not conform to the additivity rule of Malinowski (see Table 12.28). Deviations from the rule appear to be found for molecules containing highly electronegative substituents with lone pair electrons on the atom bonded directly to the interacting carbon atom. The deviations are too large to be attributable to changes in the *s* character of the C—H bond even though the groups concerned are of high electronegativity. Interactions between lone pair electrons of the oxygen and fluorine atoms and the other substituents are thought to be important.

TABLE 12.28 OBSERVED AND CALCULATED J_{CH} COUPLING CONSTANTS IN SOME SUBSTITUTED METHANES[236]

Compound	J_{CH} observed (cycles sec^{-1})	J_{CH} calculated (cycles sec^{-1})
$CH_2(NMe_2)_2$	136·6	137
$CH_2(OEt)_2$	161·1	155
$CH_2(NO_2)_2$	169·4	169
CH_2Cl_2	178·0	175
CH_2F_2	184·5	173
$CH(NO_2)_3$	195·8	191
$CHCl_3$	209·0	200
CHF_3	239·1	197
$CH(OEt)_3$	185·2	170

12.2.13 J_{CH} Additivity Relationship for sp² Hybridised Carbon Atoms

Malinowski[83] has extended his additivity relationship in substituted methanes to molecules containing substituted sp^2 hybridised carbon atoms. The zeta values ζ_X obtained for substituted methanes are found to show a direct linear correlation with the J_{CH} coupling constants observed in the corresponding substituted aldehydes, XCHO. Thus, J_{CH} values in XCHO molecules can be predicted using the relationship

$$J_{CH}(XCHO) = 5{\cdot}3 + 4{\cdot}01\,\zeta_X \qquad (12.7)$$

Table 12.29 gives a list of calculated and observed ^{13}C—^{1}H coupling constants for some substituted aldehydes. The carbonyl oxygen of the aldehyde group makes a common contribution to all the observed coupling constants and the additivity relationship expressed in equation (12.7) is not unexpected. Calculations of coupling constants based on a dominant Fermi contact term would predict that zeta values for sp^3 hybridised carbon atoms will also feature in the equation for sp^2 hybridised carbon atoms if the overlap integrals are independent of the state of hybridisation of the carbon atom. An additivity relationship has also been observed for the C—H coupling constants involving sp^2 hybridised carbon atoms in benzene, substituted pyridines and pyrimidines[83], and in heteroaromatic compounds[309].

TABLE 12.29 CALCULATED AND OBSERVED J_{CH} COUPLING CONSTANTS FOR SOME SUBSTITUTED ALDEHYDES[83], XCHO

Substituent	ζ,[a] (cycles sec^{-1})	J_{CH}, cycles sec^{-1} calcd.	J_{CH},[e] cycles sec^{-1} exptl.	Diff.
—H	41·7	172·5	172	−0·5
—$C(CH_3)_3$	40·6	168·1	168·6	−0·5
—$CH(CH_3)_2$	39·0[b]	161·7	168·9	+7·2
—CH_2CH_3	41·0[c]	169·7	170·6	+0·9
—CH_3	42·6	176·1	172·4	−3·7
—C_6H_5	42·6	176·1	173·7	−2·4
—*p*-C_6H_4Cl	42·9	177·3	175·2	−2·1
—*m*-C_6H_4Cl	43·4	179·3	177·5	−1·8
—*o*-C_6H_4Cl	44·1	182·1	182·8	+0·7
—CCl_3	50·6	208·2	207·2	−1·0
—$N(CH_3)_2$	47·6	196·2	191·2	−5·0
—OCH_3	54·6	224·2	226·2	+2·0
—OCH_2CH_3	53·4[d]	219·4	225·6	+6·2
—F	65·6	268·4	267·0	−1·4

[a] Calculated from data for methyl derivatives except where indicated otherwise, see ref. 80.
[b] Calculated from $J_{CH}((CH_3)_2CH\mathbf{CH_2}Cl) = 147{\cdot}3$ cycles sec^{-1}.
[c] Calculated from $J_{CH}(CH_3CH_2\mathbf{CH_2}Cl) = 149{\cdot}3$ cycles sec^{-1}.
[d] Calculated from $J_{CH}((CH_3\mathbf{CH_2})_2O) = 137{\cdot}7$ cycles sec^{-1}.
[e] From hydrogen spectra.

12.2.14 *Relationship of J_{CH} with J_{HH}^{vic} and J_{HH}^{gem} Values in Ethylenes*

For alkyls and alkenes, J_{HH} and J_{CH} coupling constants have both been shown to depend to some extent on the electron density at the hydrogen nucleus and also on the carbon hybridisation[82, 84–86]. Thus, it is not surprising that linear relationships exist between J_{CH} and J_{HH} spin coupling constants. When the J_{CH} values for several CH_3X compounds are plotted against the three H—H coupling constants in the corresponding $CH_2{=}CHX$ compounds roughly linear correlations are observed[82]: J_{HH} values are found to increase while J_{CH} decrease (assuming J_{HH}^{trans} to be positive). This is consistent with the fact that a decrease in J_{CH} corresponds to a decrease in *s* character of the C—H bond and this also implies a decrease in the C—C—H bond angle. Such a decrease would increase both J_{HH}^{cis} and J_{HH}^{trans} as observed.

12.2.15 *Correlation between ^{1}H—^{13}C Coupling Constants and ^{1}H Chemical Shifts*

Because CH coupling constants depend mainly on the *s* character of the carbon bonding orbital, there exists a close linear correlation between J_{CH} coupling constants and ^{1}H chemical shifts when the latter are controlled predominantly by the electron density surrounding the hydrogen nucleus in the isolated molecule (i.e. in the absence of diamagnetic anisotropy, medium and self-association effects)[87]. This is illustrated in Fig. 12.25 which is a plot of the CH coupling constants against the ^1H chemical shifts (given in Table 12.30) for ethylenic and heterocyclic hydrogen nuclei[87]. A similar plot is observed for saturated compounds. Since the CH coupling constants are insensitive to medium and magnetic anisotropy effects, such effects, when present, will cause deviations from the linear curve shown in Fig. 12.25. In fact, by noting the

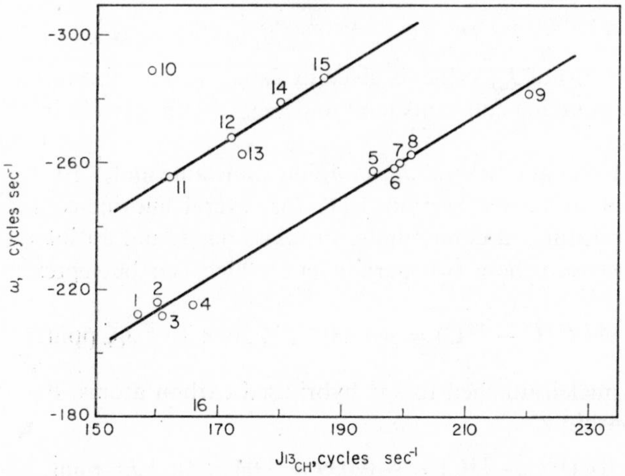

FIG. 12.25 Graph of ^1H chemical shifts (ω) against J_{CH} values for some ethylenic and heterocyclic compounds. The numbers correspond to those given in Table 12.30. Goldstein and Reddy[87].

TABLE 12.30 ^1H CHEMICAL SHIFTS AND ^{13}C—^1H COUPLING CONSTANTS (IN CYCLES SEC^{-1} AT 40 MC SEC^{-1}) FOR ETHYLENIC AND HETEROCYCLIC HYDROGEN NUCLEI

	Compound[a]	ω[b]	$J(^{13}C—H)$
1	Ethylene	−212·0	157·0
2	Vinyl chloride (*cis*)	−216·3	160·0
3	Vinyl chloride (*trans*)	−211·2	161·0
4	Vinylidene chloride	−215·3	166·0
5	Vinyl chloride (α)	−247·5	195·0
6	*cis*-Dichloroethylene	−249·9	198·5
7	*trans*-Dichloroethylene	−249·5	199·1
8	Trichloroethylene	−252·9	201·2
9	Vinylidene carbonate	−281·0	220·1
10	Benzene	−278·5	159·0
11	2,5-Dimethylthiophene	−255·3	162·0
12	2,5-Dibromothiophene	−268·4	172·0
13	2,5-Dichlorothiophene	−262·5	174·3
14	Thiophene (β)	−279·3	180·0
15	Thiophene (α)	−286·4	187·0
16	Allene	−181·9	168·2

[a] Where there is more than one hydrogen, the values refer to the hydrogen specified in parentheses.

[b] In cycles per second at 40 Mc sec^{-1} relative toTMS (internal).

deviation from linearity for a particular compound one can make an empirical estimate of the diamagnetic anisotropy effect. This method has been used to measure the anisotropy effects for benzene, thiophene, acetylene, allene and the chloride group, and good agreement is observed when it is possible to compare these estimates of anisotropy contributions with values obtained by other means.

12.2.16 ^{13}C—^{19}F *Coupling Constants*

An extensive list of J_{CF} values is given in Table 11.62j[270]. For directly bonded nuclei, the coupling constants tend to decrease with increase in ^{19}F chemical shifts.

Table 12.31 contains several J_{CF} coupling constants and $^{19}F(^{13}C—^{12}C)$ isotopic chemical shifts (see Section 3.11) for several fluorine-containing molecules[236]. For saturated compounds, Frankiss has found an interesting linear correlation between these two parameters, which can be represented by the equation

$$\Delta\varphi(^{13}C - {}^{12}C) = +0{\cdot}007 + 4{\cdot}36 \times 10^{-4} J_{CF} \text{ ppm}.$$

For fluorine nuclei attached to sp^2 hybridised carbon atoms, the appropriate linear relationship is

$$\Delta\varphi(^{13}C - {}^{12}C) = -0{\cdot}039 + 5{\cdot}04 \times 10^{-4} J_{CF} \text{ ppm}.$$

The significance of these correlations is not understood.

TABLE 12.31 VALUES OF SOME (^{13}C—^{19}F) COUPLING CONSTANTS AND $^{19}F(^{13}C—^{12}C)$ ISOTOPIC CHEMICAL SHIFTS[236]

Compound	J_{CF} (cycles sec^{-1})	$\Phi\, ^{19}F(^{13}C—^{12}C)$ ppm
CF_3CCl_3[237]	282·5	0·131
CF_3COOH[237]	283·2	0·129
$(CF_3)_2S$	309·4[81]	0·148[238]
$^{13}CF_3SCFS$[239]	312·4	0·141
$(CF_3)_2Se$	331·3[81]	0·145[238]
CF_3I[238]	344·8	0·149
CF_2Br_2	357·0[81]	0·168[238]
$CF_2{=}CCl_2$[237]	288·9	0·103
$CFCl{=}CCl_2$[237]	303·1	0·112
COF_2[239]	308·35	0·121
CSF_2[239]	366·0	0·143
CF_3SCFS[237]	395 ± 4	0·16 ± 0·05

12.2.17 ^{13}CH *Satellite Spectra of Symmetrically Substituted Benzenes*

By examining the ^{13}CH satellites in the ^{1}H resonance spectra of symmetrically substituted benzenes, H—H coupling constants between ring hydrogen nuclei can be obtained[88]. Table 12.32 gives a list of the spectral parameters measured in this way and Fig. 12.26 shows the ^{13}CH satellite spectra of three substituted

TABLE 12.32 COUPLING CONSTANTS (CYCLES SEC^{-1}) IN SOME SYMMETRICALLY SUBSTITUTED BENZENES(88)

Compound	State	$J_{^{13}CH}$†	Other coupling constants†
2,3,5,6-Tetrachloronitrobenzene	In CCl_4	$175 \cdot 0 \pm 0 \cdot 4$	$J_{^{13}CCH} = 4 \cdot 9 \pm 0 \cdot 3$
	In acetone	$176 \cdot 9 \pm 0 \cdot 6$	or $J_{^{13}CCCH} = 4 \cdot 9 \pm 0 \cdot 3$
2,4,6-Tribromophenol	In acetone	$172 \cdot 5 \pm 0 \cdot 8$	$J_m^{HH} = 2 \cdot 3 \pm 0 \cdot 2$
2,4,6-Trichlorophenol	In acetone	$171 \cdot 3 \pm 0 \cdot 5$	$J_m^{HH} = 2 \cdot 5 \pm 0 \cdot 2$
2,4,6-Trinitrophenol	In acetone	$175 \cdot 8 \pm 0 \cdot 5$	$J_m^{HH} = 2 \cdot 8 \pm 0 \cdot 2$
2,6-Dinitro-4-chlorophenol	In ether	$174 \cdot 1 \pm 0 \cdot 4$	$J_m^{HH} = 2 \cdot 8 \pm 0 \cdot 2$
2,6-Dibromo-4-nitrophenol	In acetone	$172 \cdot 8 \pm 1 \cdot 3$	$J_m^{HH} = 3 \cdot 3 \pm 0 \cdot 3$
1,3,5-Trichlorobenzene	In CCl_3Br	$172 \cdot 2 \pm 0 \cdot 4$	$J_m^{HH} = 2 \cdot 1 \pm 0 \cdot 2$
1,3,5-Tribromobenzene	In CCl_3Br	$174 \cdot 3 \pm 0 \cdot 5$	$J_m^{HH} = 1 \cdot 7 \pm 0 \cdot 3$
1,3,5-Trinitrobenzene	In acetone	$179 \cdot 5 \pm 1 \cdot 5$	$J_m^{HH} = 1 \cdot 9 \pm 0 \cdot 2$
p-Dichlorobenzene	In acetone	$169 \cdot 0 \pm 1 \cdot 0$	
p-Dimethoxybenzene	In acetone	$161 \cdot 1 \pm 1 \cdot 0$	
Benzene	Liquid	$158 \cdot 7 \pm 0 \cdot 8$	
2,4,6-Trimethylpyridine	Liquid	$158 \cdot 5 \pm 0 \cdot 7$	$J_{^{13}CH}(CH_3) = 126 \cdot 4 \pm 0 \cdot 5$

† Errors given are standard deviations.

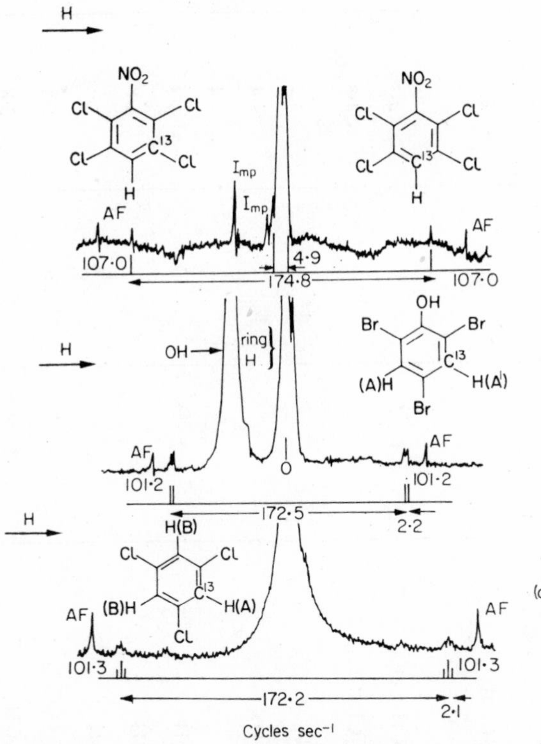

FIG. 12.26 The ^1H resonance spectra at 60 Mc sec^{-1} at high radiofrequency power, showing the ^{13}CH side bands in saturated solutions of (a) 2,3,5,6-tetrachloronitrobenzene in acetone, (b) 2,4,6-tribromophenol in acetone, (c) 1,3,5-trichlorobenzene in trichlorobromomethane. Band separations are given in cycles sec^{-1}. Hutton, Reynolds and Schaefer(88).

TABLE 12.33 LONG RANGE J_{C-H} COUPLING CONSTANTS (IN CYCLES SEC^{-1}) FOR A SERIES OF COMPOUNDS[70]

Compound	${}^{a}J_{^{13}C-H}$	${}^{b}J_{^{13}C-C-H}$	${}^{b}J_{^{13}C-C-C-H}$	${}^{b}J_{^{13}C-O-C-H}$	$J_{H-C-C-H}$	$\frac{J_{^{13}C-C-CH}}{J_{H-C-C-H}} \times 100$
$(CH_3)_2CH\underset{13}{\overset{\overset{O}{\|}}{C}}CH(CH_3)_2$		4·1	5·1		7·2	71
$(CH_3)_2CH\underset{13}{\overset{\overset{OH}{\vert}}{C}}HCH(CH_3)_2$	136		4·5		6·7	67
$(CH_3)_2CH\underset{13}{C}H_2CH(CH_3)_2$			~4·8		6·1	79
$(CH_3)_3C\overset{13}{C}O_2H$			4·2			
$(CH_3)_3C\overset{13}{C}O_2CH_3$			4·4	3·5		
$(CH_3)_3C\overset{13}{C}O_2^-$			4·4			
$(CH_3)_3C\overset{13}{C}H_2OH$	132		4·8			
$(CH_3)_3C\overset{13}{C}D_2OH$			4·8			
$(CH_3)_2CH\overset{13}{C}O_2H$		5·2	5·4		7·2	75
$(CH_3)_2CH\overset{13}{C}O-O_2CH_3$		5·6	5·8	3·5		
$(CH_3)_2CH\overset{13}{C}H_2OH$	140		3·8		4·8	79
$(CH_3)_2CH\overset{13}{C}D_2OH$			3·8			

[a] Values are precise to ± 2 cycles sec^{-1}. [b] Values are precise to $\pm 0·1$ cycles sec^{-1}.

TABLE 12.34 LONG RANGE $^{13}C—^{1}H$ COUPLING CONSTANTS FOR A SERIES OF COMPOUNDS[96]

Compound	$J_{^{13}C-H}$	$J_{^{13}C-C-H}$	$J_{^{13}C-C-C-H}$	$J_{^{13}C-O-C-H}$	$J_{^{13}C-O-C-C-H}$	$J_{H-C-C-H}$
$CH_3CH_2\overset{13}{C}D_2OH$		~4	6·4 ± 0·2			7·3 ± 0·3
$(CH_3CH_2)_2\overset{13}{C}DOH$		4·0 ± 0·1	5·3 ± 0·2			7·3 ± 0·3
$(CH_3CH_2)_3\overset{13}{C}OH$		3·8 ± 0·2	4·5 ± 0·2			7·5 ± 0·3
$CH_3\overset{\alpha}{C}H_2\overset{13}{C}(OH)(\overset{\beta}{C}H_3)_2$		(α)4·0 ± 0·1 (β)4·1 ± 0·1	4·0 ± 0·2			7·3 ± 0·3
$CH_3\overset{\alpha}{C}H_2\overset{13}{C}(Cl)(\overset{\beta}{C}H_3)_2$		(α)3·7 ± 0·2 (β)3·9 ± 0·1	5·7 ± 0·1			7·5 ± 0·3
$^{13}CH_3-C(\alpha CH_3)(OH)\overset{\beta}{C}H_2CH_3$	129 ± 3		(α)3·2 ± 0·2 (β)3·0 ± 0·2			
$\overset{13}{C}H_3C(\alpha CH_3)(Cl)\overset{\beta}{C}H_2CH_3$	132 ± 3		(α)4·2 ± 0·2 (β)3·2 ± 0·2			

(continued)

TABLE 12.34. (*continued*)

Compound	$J_{^{13}C-H}$	$J_{^{13}C-C-H}$	$J_{^{13}C-C-C-H}$	$J_{^{13}C-O-C-H}$	$J_{^{13}C-O-C-C-H}$	$J_{H-C-C-H}$
$CH_3\overset{13}{C}OOCH_2CH_3$		6·0 ± 0·1		3·1 ± 0·1	0	
$(CH_3CH_2)_2\overset{13}{C}{=}O$		5·7 ± 0·1	4·7 ± 0·1			7·5 ± 0·1
$CH_3CH_2\overset{13}{C}O_2H$		6·4 ± 0·2	5·5 ± 0·2			7·4 ± 0·1
$CH_3CH_2\overset{13}{C}O_2CH_3$		6·5 ± 0·3	5·3 ± 0·1	4·0 ± 0·05		7·4 ± 0·1
$(CH_3CH_2)_2\overset{13}{C}{=}NNH\varphi(NO_2)_2$		6·5 ± 0·3	4·8 ± 0·4			7·2 ± 0·2
$(CH_3CH_2)_2\overset{13}{C}{=}NNHCONH_2$		4·0 ± 0·4	4·0 ± 0·3			7·5 ± 0·2
$\overset{13}{C}H_3C{\equiv}CH$ [a]	131·4		3·6			
$CH_3C{\equiv}\overset{13}{C}H$ [a]	247·6		4·8			
$\overset{\alpha}{C}H_3\overset{13}{C}{\equiv}\overset{\beta}{C}H$ [a]		(α)10·6 (β)50·8				
$\overset{13}{C}H_3COH$ [b]		26·6				

[a] Values taken from reference 99. [b] P. C. LAUTERBUR, private communication.

benzenes. All the benzenes listed in Table 12.32 give rise to a single aromatic ^{1}H resonance band for the isotopically normal molecules. An examination of Table 12.32 reveals that the C—H coupling constants of the substituted benzenes are all greater than that of benzene itself but the variations do not indicate any large deviation from sp^2 hybridisation of the carbon atoms. Most of the substituents in these compounds are electron withdrawing groups which increase the *s* character of the CH bond and thus produce an increase in the $J_{^{13}CH}$ value(88).

12.2.18 *Long Range* ^{13}C—^{1}H *Coupling Constants*

Spin coupling constants, between carbon and hydrogen nuclei which are separated by more than one bond are much smaller than those between the directly bonded nuclei and consequently they are much more difficult to resolve. By examining the ^{1}H resonance spectra of ^{13}C enriched samples, several long range J_{CH} coupling constants have been measured(70, 89, 96, 99) and their values are given in Tables 12.33 to 12.37.

For saturated compounds, the values of J_{CH} are found to be in the range 0 to 6·5 cycles sec^{-1} and they show no regular attenuation with increase in the number of bonds separating the two nuclei. In fact, some of the measured values of $J_{^{13}C-C-H}$ are smaller than those of $J_{^{13}C-C-C-H}$ in the cases where it is possible to observe both coupling constants in the same molecule. Similar coupling behaviour is observed in the ^{1}H resonance spectra of lead(90) and mercury(91, 92) alkyls for J_{M-H} values and also in the ^{19}F spectra of fluoroalkyls and fluorocyclobutanes(93).

Several values of spin coupling constants between carbon and hydrogen atoms separated by one bond have been measured and the values are included in Table 12.34(94, 95, 96). The average $J_{^{13}C-CH}$ coupling constants for sp^3, sp^2 and sp hybridised carbon are 4·0, 5·9 and 10·6 cycles sec^{-1} and if a plot of $J_{^{13}C-CH}$ values against the percentage *s* character in the ^{13}C—C bond is examined then a linear relationship is found. Unlike the linear plot which was obtained for a similar correlation for directly bonded C and H atoms, in this case an intercept is observed. By carrying out theoretical calculations it has been found (i) that the Fermi contact term is the important factor in such coupling and (ii) that replacing a hydrogen atom by a carbon—13 atom does not change the coefficient of the ground state wavefunction.†

When the two carbon atoms in the grouping ^{13}C—^{12}C—H are singly bonded the long range $J_{^{13}C-C-H}$ coupling constants(70, 75, 242) vary over the range 0 to 6·5 cycles sec^{-1} while for substituted acetylenes, X—$^{13}C \equiv {}^{12}C$—H the $J_{^{13}C-C-H}$ values(50, 89) are in the range 44 to 51 cycles sec^{-1}. Muller (242) has found values for $J_{^{13}C-C-H}$ in ethlyenic systems, —$^{13}C = {}^{12}CH$ of 0·0 to 15·7 cycles sec^{-1} as indicated for the substituted ethylenes in Table 12.35. The results indicate that the C—C bond order is not a dominant factor controlling $J_{^{13}C-C-H}$ coupling constants. In the geometric isomers of dichloroethylene, the bond order and

† More recent studies indicate that $J_{^{13}C-CH}$ values do not always correlate with the *s* character in the C—C bonds(306).

hybridisation of the carbon atoms will be fairly constant yet the $J_{^{13}C-CH}$ values are widely different[242].

While the $J_{^{13}C-H}$ and $J_{^{13}C-C-H}$ spin coupling constants show a linear correlation with the degree of *sp* hybridisation of the carbon atomic orbitals, no such correlation is evident for $J_{^{13}C-C-CH}$ coupling constants. Table 12.34 gives a list of such long range coupling constants measured in a series of compounds enriched in carbon-13. No correlation exists between the magnitude of the coupling constant and either the hybridisation of the carbon atomic orbitals or the electronegativity of the substituent attached to the ^{13}C atom. The lack of correlation is not due to conformational effects since the $J_{H-C-C-H}$ values indicate these

TABLE 12.35 ^{13}C—^{1}H COUPLING CONSTANTS IN SOME OLEFINIC COMPOUNDS[242]

Compound	$J_{^{13}CH}$ (cycles sec^{-1})	$J_{^{13}C-C-H}$ (cycles sec^{-1})
cis-Dichloroethylene	198·3	15·7
trans-Dichloroethylene	199·1	0·0
Diethyl maleate	167·6	1·5
Diethyl fumarate	168·6	4·4

to be similar in all the molecules examined (see Table 12.34). Hence the Fermi contact term is not the only important factor controlling the spin coupling in ^{13}C—C—CH systems although an appreciable fraction of the coupling is estimated to come from this source. For sp^3 hybridised carbon the $J_{^{13}C-C-CH}$ values are always equal to or greater than the $J_{^{13}C-CH}$ values measured in the same molecule. The reason for this appears to be that the $J_{^{13}C-C-CH}$ values are abnormally large: similar coupling anomalies observed in metal alkyls[91, 92, 90], and previously thought to arise from abnormally small J_{M-C-H} coupling constants, might also be explained in this way. Similar findings have been observed for the $J_{^{13}C-C-CH}$ coupling constants in a series of compounds containing the $CH_3CH_2{}^{13}C$ group (see Table 12.34)[96]. Examination of Table 12.33 reveals that there is a roughly linear correlation between $J_{^{13}C-C-CH}$ coupling constants and the corresponding $J_{H-C-C-H}$ values in molecules with an isopropyl group bonded to the ^{13}C atom[94]. This was thought originally to indicate either that the Fermi contact term controls both coupling constants or that conformational effects on the ^{13}CCC—H coupling are important. However, the foregoing results shown in Tables 12.34 suggest that the observed correlation in the isopropyl derivatives is fortuitous[96].

Measurement of long range ^{13}C—^{1}H *coupling constants.* If the principal central ^{1}H absorption band (corresponding to hydrogen attached to non-magnetic carbon-12 atoms) is narrow ($<1{\cdot}5$ cycles sec^{-1}) then it is possible to detect long range ^{13}C—^{1}H spin coupling constants in the ^{1}H resonance spectra of non-enriched samples using an unmodified commercial spectrometer[71]. Table 12.36 lists some long range C—H coupling constants obtained in this manner.

If one could remove the central intense signal of the hydrogen nuclei attached to ^{12}C atoms then the ^{13}C—H satellite spectra could be observed more easily.

Anderson[97] has succeeded in achieving this by frequency modulating a strong radiofrequency field near the carbon-13 resonance frequency with a 2 kc sec^{-1} modulation and then observing the effects of the modulation on the hydrogen resonance signal after passing the output through a 2 kc sec^{-1} audiofrequency phase detector. Using this technique it is possible to measure ^{13}C chemical shifts, and ^{13}C—H spin coupling constants with higher sensitivity than by other methods.

TABLE 12.36 LONG RANGE ^{13}C—^{1}H SPIN COUPLING CONSTANTS MEASURED IN NON-ENRICHED SAMPLES[71]

Compound	^{1}H species	J (long range ^{13}C—^{1}H) (cycles sec^{-1})
Acetonitrile		9·8—10·0
Sodium acetate		5·8—6·0
Methyl acetate	acetate	6·8—6·9
Acetophenone	methyl	5·7
Acetaldehyde	methyl	6·0
Toluene	methyl	5 (broad)

12.2.19 ^{13}C—^{13}C *Spin Coupling Constants*

From an examination of the ^{1}H resonance spectra of carbon-13 enriched samples of ethane, ethylene and acetylene it is possible to measure the C—C spin coupling constants[98] (the introduction of the carbon-13 nuclei causes the hydrogen nuclei to become magnetically non-equivalent: thus $H^{13}C{\equiv}^{13}CH$ is a typical AA′XX′ spin system). The C—C coupling constants given in Table 12.37 were mostly measured in the ^{13}C resonance spectra of carbon-13 enriched asymmetrically substituted compounds[98, 249]. The J_{CC} values of ethane and ethylene are of the approximate magnitude expected if the contact term dominates the coupling. However, the much larger C—C coupling constant observed for acetylene is thought to have an additional positive contribution from some other source[98]. Conjugated acyclic compounds have smaller C—C coupling constants than other compounds with π-electron bonds[249].

By using a similar approach to that adopted by Muller and Pritchard[13] to interpret C—H coupling constants (see Section 5.9), Bernstein and Frei[249] have shown that, for hydrocarbons, the J_{CC} values are directly proportional to the products of the *s* characters of the two carbon atoms in the bond in question. For substituted hydrocarbons, "modified *s* characters" of the appropriate orbitals were obtained by using an empirical relationship[74] involving J_{CH} values in related compounds[249].

Although there is no general, simple correlation between C—C coupling constants and C—C bond distances, a relationship of this type has been noted for hydrocarbons having single C—C bonds[249].

TABLE 12.37 ^{13}C COUPLING CONSTANTS (INCLUDING SOME ^{13}C—^{13}C COUPLING CONSTANTS) OF SOME CARBON-13 ENRICHED COMPOUNDS[98, 249]

Compound x–y	^{13}C coupling constants (cycles sec^{-1})					Chemical shifts ppm from benzene reference		Reference
	$^JC_xC_y$	^JC_xH	^JC_yH	$^JC_xC_yH$	$^JC_yC_xH$	δ_x	δ_y	
C_6H_5—$^{13}CH_2$—$^{13}CH_3$	34 ± 1	~127	~127					249
C_6H_5—$^{13}CH(HO)$—$^{13}CH_3$	38·1 ± 0·1	142·5 ± 0·1	126·9 ± 0·1	4·1 ± 0·2	2·0 ± 0·2	58·2	102·9	249
C_6H_5—^{13}CO—$^{13}CH_3$	43·3 ± 0·1		125·7 ± 0·5	6·2 ± 0·1		−68·6	103·2	249
 ^{13}C—$^{13}CH_3$	44·2 ± 0·3		136·2 ± 0·1	6·0 ± 0·1		−9·2	106·5	249
N≡^{13}C—$^{13}CH_3$	57·3 ± 0·3			10·1 ± 0·1		10·4	127·8	249
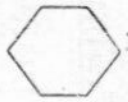 ^{13}C—$^{13}COCl$	74·1 ± 0·2					−4·8	−39·8	249
C_6H_5—CH=^{13}CH—$^{13}COOC_2H_5$	76·3 ± 0·2	160·9 ± 0·5						249
 ^{13}C—^{13}C≡N	80·3 ± 0·5					13·8	9·2	249
C_6H_5—^{13}C—$^{13}CCOC_2H_5$	126·8 ± 0·1					46·9	−25·5	249
C_6H_5—C≡^{13}C—^{13}C≡N	155·8 ± 0·2					64·2	21·8	249
C_6H_5—$H^{13}C$=$^{13}CH_2$	70 ± 3							249
C_6H_5—^{13}C≡^{13}C—H	175·9 ± 0·3	251·1 ± 0·2	49·9 ± 0·2			45·4	51·4	249
C_6H_5—C≡^{13}C—$^{13}CH_3$	68·6 ± 0·1	131·3 ± 0·1	10·5 ± 0·1			41·9	123·8	249
^{13}CH≡^{13}CH	171·5							98
$^{13}CH_2$=$^{13}CH_2$	67·6							98
$^{13}CH_3$—$^{13}CH_3$	34·6							98

12.2.20 *Miscellaneous* ^{13}C—^{1}H *Coupling Constants*

Table 12.38 lists several miscellaneous J_{CH} values and is given for the sake of completeness[75, 87].

Shoolery and co-workers[89] have measured six C—H coupling constants in the ^{1}H resonance spectrum of a sample of methyl acetylene enriched in carbon-13 nuclei. The observed coupling constants (in cycles sec^{-1}) are shown on structure I

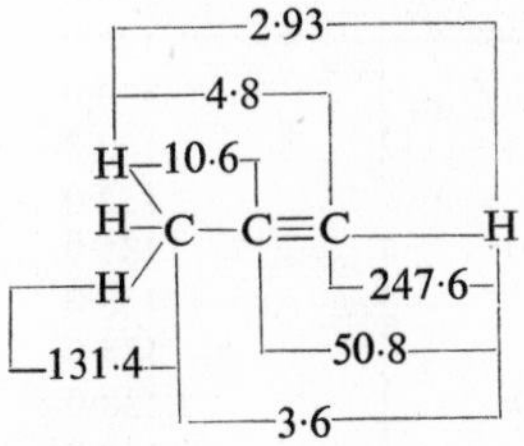

(I)

No simple correlation appears to exist between the various coupling constants.

12.3 Nitrogen

Both naturally occurring isotopes of nitrogen, ^{14}N (99·635 per cent abundant) and ^{15}N (0·365 per cent), have non-zero values of spin and are therefore capable of being investigated by nuclear magnetic resonance. However, the

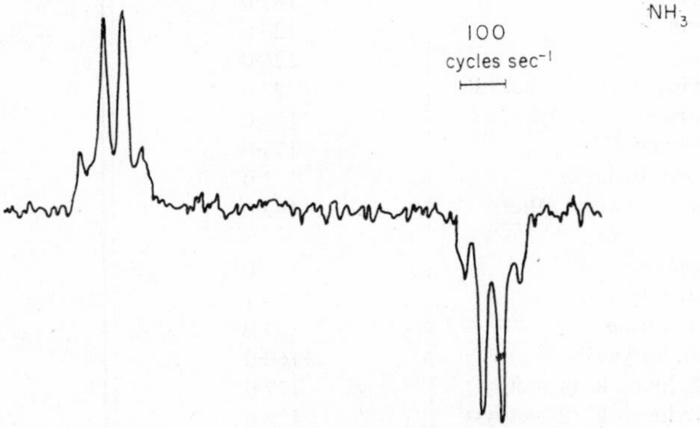

FIG. 12.27 ^{14}N magnetic resonance spectrum of liquid ammonia at 3·076 Mc sec^{-1}. Modulation frequency = 392 cycles sec^{-1}. The two quartets are side bands of a central signal which has been eliminated by phase adjustment. Acrivos[101].

low natural abundance of the ^{15}N isotope prohibits high resolution NMR studies of this nucleus, and the following section will be concerned mainly with the ^{14}N isotope. Nitrogen-14 has a spin number $I = 1$ and consequently possesses a quadrupole moment. Its low magnetic moment ($\mu = 0{\cdot}40357$ nuclear magnetons) causes the natural sensitivity of the nucleus to NMR detection to be very poor ($1{\cdot}01 \times 10^{-3}$ per cent that of the ^{1}H nucleus at constant

TABLE 12.38 ^{13}C—^{1}H COUPLING CONSTANTS FOR SEVERAL MISCELLANEOUS COMPOUNDS (75, 87)

Compound	J_{C-H} (cycles sec^{-1})	Reference
$Al_2(CH_3)_6$	113·0	
$Si(CH_3)_4$	118·0	
$Ga(CH_3)_3$	122·0	
$In(CH_3)_3$ (benzene soln.)	126·0	
Paraldehyde (CH_3 group)	127·0	
$Hg(CH_3)_2$	130·0	
CF_3CH_3	130·0	
$H_2C(COOH)_2$	132·0	
$C_6H_5N(CH_3)_2$ (CH_3 group)	135·0	
$(CH_3)_2S$	138·0	
CH_3SH	138·0	
$(CH_3)_2NCHO$ (CH_3 group)	138·0	
$(CH_3)_2SO_2$ (aq.)	140·0	75
$Na[B(OCH_3)_4]$ (aq.)	142·0	
1,4-Dioxane	142·0	
$B(OCH_3)_3$	143·0	
$(CH_3)_4NOH$ (aq.)	144·0	
$H_2C(CN)_2$	145·0	
$(CH_3O)_2CO$	147·0	
Ethylene carbonate	157·0	
Paraldehyde (ring C—H)	159·0	
Trioxane (benzene soln.)	166·0	
Ferrocene (CS_2 soln.)	175·0	
CH_2F_2	185·0	
Cyclohexane	123·0	
Isobutylene	126·0	
α-Methyl vinyl methyl ether (α)	127·0	
cis-Crotonitrile	128·0	
Crotonaldehyde	129·0	
α-Methacrylonitrile	132·0	
α-Methyl vinyl methyl ether (methoxy)	143·0	
Methylacetylene	132·0	
1,4-Dichlorobutyne-2	158·1	
Propargyl chloride	159·0	
1,4-Dibromobutyne-2	160·0	
2,4-Dimethylpyrrole (4-methyl)	127·0	
2,4-Dimethylpyrrole (2-methyl)	128·0	87
2-Methylfuran	129·0	
1,2,5-Trimethylpyrrole (*N*-methyl)	137·0	
N-Methylpyrrole	139·5	
4-Methylimidazole	126·5	
3-Methylpyrazole	129·0	
2-Methylimidazole	128·5	
N-Methylimidazole	140·0	
3-Methylthiophene	126·5	
2-Methylthiophene	128·5	
Tetramethylallene	127·0	
Toluene	126·0	

field strength). Poor natural sensitivity and quadrupolar line broadening effects have together been responsible for the comparatively little interest in ^{14}N nuclear magnetic resonance studies.

Acrivos[101] has measured the ^{14}N resonance spectrum (shown in Fig. 12.27) of dry liquid ammonia using a wide-line NMR spectrometer operating at 3·076 Mc sec^{-1}. Instead of examining the derivative mode, he used a modulation frequency of 392 cycles sec^{-1} ($\gg |\gamma|\, H_1$) and phased out the central band: Figure 12.27 shows the two remaining side-bands in the absorption mode. Better resolution is thus obtained since there is none of the line broadening which would arise from the finite modulation amplitude used in the derivative method. The spectrum has a quartet splitting due to N—H spin–spin interaction (J_{NH} $= 40 \pm 1$ cycles sec^{-1}).

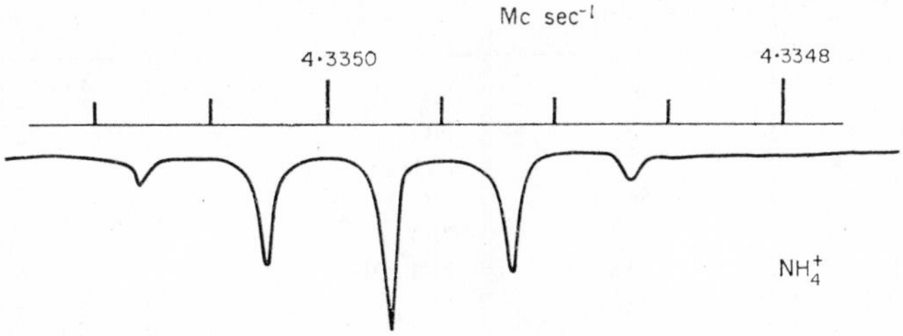

FIG. 12.28 ^{14}N INDOR spectrum of NH_4^+ in acidified NH_4NO_3 (4 mm i.d. sample tube). ^1H nuclei irradiated at 60·0099293 Mc sec^{-1}. Baker[55].

Baker[55] has improved the signal to noise ratio in ^{14}N spectra by using the internuclear double resonance (INDOR) technique (see Sections 12.2.1 and 6.8) to examine the NH_4^+ ion in an acid solution of NH_4NO_3 (see Fig. 12.28).

An ingenious method for measuring ^{14}N chemical shifts involving a double resonance technique has been proposed by Baldeschwieler and Randall[108] and it is particularly useful for molecules containing nitrogen attached directly to hydrogen. One observes the ^1H resonance spectrum of the nitrogen containing compound and simultaneously irradiates the ^{14}N nucleus at its resonance frequency using a variable frequency oscillator: removal of the fine structure on the NH hydrogen spectrum indicates when spin decoupling has been achieved (see Fig. 12.30). The ^{14}N chemical shifts are obtained by measuring the differences in the frequencies required for decoupling in various compounds. Very short ^{14}N relaxation times or the presence of proton exchange processes will both lead to line broadening and render the method less accurate. Some typical ^{14}N chemical shifts measured by this method are

NH_3	−16·8 ppm
NH_4^+	0·0
Pyridine C_5H_5N	−293·3
Pyridinium ion $C_5H_6N^+$	−175·6

12.3.1 ^{14}N *Chemical Shifts*

Nitrogen chemical shifts [102–106, 119, 299] have been observed in many compounds and some typical values, measured from the resonance band of the NO_2^- ion in aqueous solution, are given in Table 12.39. Variations in the paramagnetic term in Ramsey's expression for nuclear shielding[72] are thought to be the dominant cause of the large chemical shift differences observed for nitrogen-containing compounds. Changes in the ionic character of the nitrogen atom will influence the orbital angular momentum, which controls the magnitude of the paramagnetic term[3] (see fluorine chemical shifts, Section 4.6). If the

TABLE 12.39 ^{14}N CHEMICAL SHIFTS[103, 104]

Formula	Chemical shift† δ ppm	Formula	Chemical shift† δ ppm
NH_4^+	602	N_2	268
$(C_3H_7)_2NH$	575	NO_3^-	254
$(C_2H_5)_3N$	575	$C_6H_5 \cdot NO_2$‡	252
N_2H_4	566	n-$C_3H_7NO_2$	228
$(CH_3)_4NBr$	552	NO_2^-	0
$O{=}C(NH_2)_2$	536	NH_4OH	626
$NH_2OH \cdot HCl$	520	NH_4^+	600
$CH_3C{=}O$ with NH_2 on C	498	$N_2H_4 \cdot H_2O$	600
$(SCN)^-$	406	$(NH_2)_2CO$	600
CH_3CN	385	$(SCN)^-$	405
CN^-	380	CN^-	366
CH_3CSN	380	HNO_3 (100%)	306
$C(NO_2)_4$	300	NO_3^-	254
$C_2(NO_2)_6$	300	CH_3NO_2	254
Pyridine	276	NO_2^- (Reference)	0

† Chemical shifts measured in ppm from the NO_2^- ion external reference in aqueous solution.

All samples which are non-liquids were examined as aqueous solutions.

‡ Many ^{14}N shifts for nitro compounds are given in reference 298.

atom has a closed-shell, inert gas configuration, then the orbital angular momentum is zero and the paramagnetic term has a very low value (this is the case for the nitrogen atom in the ammonium ion). An increase in the electronegativity of an atom or group attached directly to a nitrogen atom causes the ionic character of the latter to decrease and the paramagnetic contribution to the shielding to increase, resulting in shifts to low fields. The ^{14}N chemical shifts presented in Table 12.39 are largely consistent with the above considerations. It is interesting to note that the ^{14}N chemical shift between the NO_3^- and the NO_2^- ions is almost identical with the ^{17}O chemical shift between these species (see Section 12.4.1).

Schmidt, Brown and Williams[105] have also measured ^{14}N chemical shifts in a series of nitrogen-containing compounds using as a reference signal the absorption band of the NH_4^+ ion in a saturated aqueous solution of ammonium nitrate. This reference material serves a dual purpose since it gives rise to two sharp ^{14}N absorption bands separated by 352 ppm which can be used for spectral calibration. Table 12.40 lists the ^{14}N chemical shifts for the compounds they examined together with the relative line widths (measured at half the signal amplitude and rendered "relative" by the field inhomogeneity contribution). Saturated solutions of the following ammonium salts possess a ^{14}N ab-

TABLE 12.40 ^{14}N CHEMICAL SHIFTS AND LINE WIDTHS FOR AMMONIA AND RELATED COMPOUNDS[(105)] (OBTAINED AT 10,700 GAUSS)

Compound	Sample [a]	Line width (milligauss)	$\delta\dagger$ (ppm)	δ (ppm)
NH_4^{+b}	S	35 ± 10	0	601
NH_4SCN	S	35 ± 10	$-9{\cdot}3$	592
NH_4OH	(28% NH_3)	320 ± 50	$+12$	613
NH_3	L	200	$+21$	622
NH_3	S (Ethanol)	360 ± 50	$+10$	611
$Ag(NH_3)_2NO_2$	—	730 ± 100	$+30$	631
$Zn(NH_3)_5Cl$	—	550 ± 100	$+20$	621
$Ca(NH_3)_8Cl_2$	—	1500 ± 200	$+20$	621
$N(CH_3)_4Cl$	S	40 ± 5	-20	581
$N(CH_3)_4Br$	S	40 ± 5	-20	581
$NH(CH_3)_2$	L	250 ± 50	$+5{\cdot}1$	606
$N(CH_3)_3$	L	250 ± 50	$+16$	617

[a] S indicates saturated solution—aqueous unless otherwise indicated. L indicates pure liquid.

[b] NH_4NO_3, NH_4Cl, NH_4Br, NH_4I, $NH_4H_2PO_4$, $NH_4C_2H_3O_2$, $(NH_4)_2SO_4$, $(NH_4)_2S$, and $(NH_4)_2SO_4 \cdot ZnSO_4 \cdot 6H_2O$.

High field shifts are positive.

$\delta\dagger$ is the chemical shift referred to NH_4^+.

δ is the chemical shift referred to NO_2^-.

sorption at the same position to within $\pm$ 10 milligauss: NH_4NO_3, NH_4Cl, NH_4Br, NH_4I, $NH_4H_2PO_4$, $NH_4C_2H_3O_2$, $(NH_4)_2SO_4$, $(NH_4)_2S$ and $(NH_4)_2SO_4 . ZnSO_4 . 4H_2O$. No change in chemical shift was observed on diluting the solutions. A saturated solution of NH_4SCN has a ^{14}N resonance position for the NH_4^+ group at 100 milligauss to low fields of the other ammonium salts, but on progressive dilution of the aqueous solution its ^{14}N chemical shift approaches that of the other ammonium salts.

From Table 12.40 it is seen that in ammonia and related molecules, the ^{14}N chemical shifts extend over the very narrow range of $\sim$ 50 ppm suggesting that the electronic environment of the nitrogen nucleus is similar in all the compounds. The small chemical shifts which do occur between ammonia and related compounds are probably caused by slight variations in the paramagnetic contribution to the shielding, and appear to depend in a roughly regular manner on the predicted bond ionicities. The high shielding of the nitrogen nucleus in these molecules indicates the nitrogen to be more ionic than in most other nitrogen-containing compounds. Although the nitrogen chemical shifts of ammonia and related compounds do not vary over a wide range, the line widths vary from 35 to 1500 milligauss, indicating that the electric field asymmetry around the nitrogen nucleus, which controls the extent of the quadrupolar broadening, can vary even though the electronic environment remains almost unchanged. This is consistent with the idea that the nitrogen atom in ammonia and related molecules is sp^3 hybridised as in the NH_4^+ ion: this would result in similar electronic configurations around the nitrogen in NH_3 and NH_4^+ species but very different electric field gradients.

TABLE 12.41 ^{14}N CHEMICAL SHIFTS IN A SERIES OF NITRATES, NITRITES AND NITRO COMPOUNDS[106]

Compound	Chemical shift[a] δ ppm	Line width[e] (milligauss)	Sample
NO_3^- [b]	0	60 ± 10	S[c] aqueous
HNO_3	28·3	60 ± 10	70%
$Cu(NO_3)_2 \cdot 3H_2O$	81	480 ± 50	5·8 M aqueous
$Cu(NO_3)_2 \cdot 3H_2O$	145	600 ± 200	3·5 M ethanol
$C_6H_5NO_2$	21	300 ± 50	L[d]
$NO_2C_6H_4COOH$	20	260 ± 80	S ethanol
$(NO_2)_2C_6H_3COCl$	15	200 ± 50	S ether
$NaNO_2$	−240	1200 ± 200	S aqueous

[a] Chemical shifts measured in ppm from the NO_3^- ion external reference.
[b] NH_4NO_3, $LiNO_3$, $NaNO_3$, KNO_3, $AgNO_3$, $Ag(NH_3)_2NO_3$, $Zn(NO_3)_2$, $Pb(NO_3)_2$, $Cd(NO_3)_2$, $UO_2(NO_3)_2$, and $Al(NO_3)_3$.
[c] S indicates saturated solution.
[d] L indicates pure liquid.
[e] Measurements made at a field strength of 10,729 gauss.

The above workers observed a small chemical shift difference between the ^{14}N resonance absorption in an aqueous solution of ammonia and that of liquid ammonia: the interaction between water and ammonia might be capable of being studied by this method.

The ^{14}N signal observed for a 28 per cent aqueous solution of ammonium hydroxide is about ten times as wide as that of other ammonium salts. Its chemical shift (+ 12 ppm from NH_4^+ reference) and line width are independent of concentration and this is taken as evidence that there might well be structural differences between the NH_4^+ group in NH_4OH and in other normal ammonium compounds. When an ammonium salt is added to ammonium hydroxide solution, a single broad ^{14}N absorption band for the NH_4^+ is recorded, and the chemical shift of the absorption band approaches that of the added ammonium salt as the amount of the latter in the system increases. If ammonium hydroxide is added to an aqueous solution of an ammonium salt, the signal gradually broadens but shows no change in resonance position. This is in contrast with the results obtained from mixing $N(CH_3)_4Br$ and ammonium hydroxide, where two peaks are observed. The two observations provide evidence for the presence and absence respectively of chemical exchange (see Chapter 9).

^{14}N resonance studies have led to the elucidation of the kinetics of the exchange of ammonia between nickel ammine complexes and ammonia in aqueous and anhydrous ammonia solutions[(257)].

Schmidt, Brown and Williams[(106)] have investigated the ^{14}N resonance spectra of a series of nitrates, nitrites and nitro compounds and a summary of their results is given in Table 12.41. They found the ^{14}N resonance absorptions for the nitrate groups in $LiNO_3$, $NaNO_3$, KNO_3, $AgNO_3$, $Ag(NH_3)_2NO_3$, $Zn(NO_3)_2$, $Pb(NO_3)_2$, $Cd(NO_3)_2$, $UO_2(NO_3)_2$ and $Al(NO_3)_3$ have the same chemical shift and line width as the nitrate resonance band in a saturated solution of NH_4NO_3. They found no concentration dependence of the NO_3^- signal in these compounds, contrary to the earlier findings of Holder and Klein[(104)]. For the paramagnetic salt, $Cu(NO_3)_2$, a large, concentration dependent, diamagnetic shift to high fields was observed. A shift in the same direction was also measured for $Fe(NO_3)_2$, while manganese salts show negative ^{14}N chemical shifts. With the exception of the paramagnetic salts, the ^{14}N chemical shifts of the various nitrate and nitro groups examined extend over a very narrow range of the total chemical shifts found in ^{14}N chemical shift measurements. This suggests the electronic structure of the nitrogen atom to be similar in the NO_3^- and NO_2 groups. Both groups have planar structures and the hybridisation of the four orbitals of the nitrogen atom should be similar in each case. The fact that oxygen atoms are more electronegative than nitrogen atoms reduces the electron density around the nitrogen nucleus and causes the ^{14}N resonance absorption bands to be at low fields for these groups. The increased covalent bond character in the HNO_3 molecule causes an increased electronic shielding of the nitrogen atom, the resonance band of which is shifted to higher fields.

The line widths of the ^{14}N resonance signals of the nitrite compounds are about four times greater than those of the nitrates.

^{14}N resonance studies of the azide ion (N_3^-) in sodium azide solution indicate the presence of two end nitrogen atoms and a single central nitrogen atom (their respective ^{14}N chemical shifts are $+278$ and $+129$ ppm from NO_3^- ion external reference)[(261)].

A few ^{15}N studies have been reported[(295-297)].

12.3.2 NMR Effects Associated with the Quadrupole Moment of the Nitrogen Nucleus

Quadrupolar line broadening has its origin in the relaxation process involving the interaction of the quadrupole moment of the nucleus with the electric field gradients within the molecule. If the nucleus is surrounded by a highly symmetrical arrangement of substituents, such electric field gradients are small and quadrupolar line broadening is diminished (see Section 2.5.2). Ogg and Ray[(107)] have demonstrated this by examining the ^{14}N spectrum of the tetrahedrally symmetrical NH_4^+ ion (acid was added to suppress hydrolysis ex-

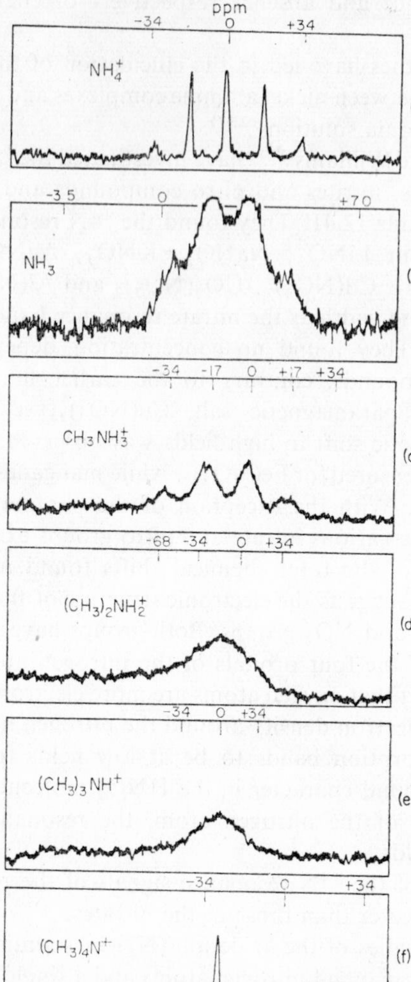

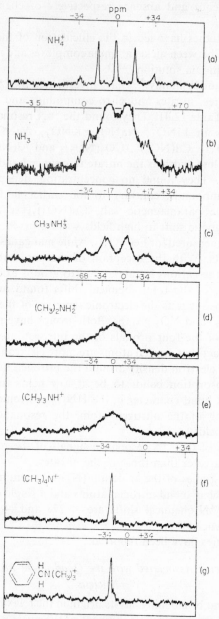

FIG. 12.29 The ^{14}N resonance spectra of (a) NH_4^+, (b) NH_3, (c) $CH_3NH_3^+$, (d) $(CH_3)_2NH_2^+$, (e) $(CH_3)_3NH^+$, (f) $(CH_3)_4N^+$ and (g) $C_6H_5CH_2N(CH_3)_3^+$ at 3 Mc sec^{-1}. Scales are ppm relative to the ^{14}N resonance signal of the ammonium ion in saturated aqueous ammonium nitrate. Ogg and Ray[107].

change reactions which would also lead to line broadening) and showing it to be composed of a multiplet absorption of five narrow components from J_{NH} coupling as shown in Fig. 12.29 (a). Also shown in Fig. 12.29 are the ^{14}N spectra of NH_3, $CH_3NH_3^+$, $(CH_3)_2NH_2^+$, $(CH_3)_3NH^+$, $(CH_3)_4N^+$ and $C_6H_5CH_2N(CH_3)_3^+$ ions. By comparing the line widths of the absorption bands of the various tertiary ammonium cations, some indication of the effects of substitution on the asymmetry of the electric fields can be obtained. Hence, the effect of the nitrogen lone pair electrons in the NH_3 molecule causes greater field asymmetry than does a methyl substituent, as can be seen from the relative line widths in Fig. 12.29 (b) and (c). The tetrahedrally symmetric $(CH_3)_4N^+$ ion gives rise to a single narrow absorption band as expected (Fig. 12.29 (f)). A narrow absorption band is also observed for $C_6H_5CH_2N(CH_3)_3^+$, which emphasises the short range nature of the effect of field asymmetry on quadrupolar relaxation (see Fig. 12.29 (g))[107].

Removal of quadrupolar broadening can be achieved completely by substituting the ^{14}N atoms with ^{15}N atoms, which possess no quadrupole moment (for ^{15}N, $I = \frac{1}{2}$). Such an experiment has been performed on the methylammonium ion $(CH_3{}^{15}NH_3^+)$ to establish that the line broadening of the hydrogen resonance absorption for the ^{14}N—H hydrogen nuclei in acid solution is due to electric quadrupole relaxation brought about by the ^{14}N nucleus[107].

Double resonance techniques have been used to remove ^{14}N quadrupolar relaxation line broadening effects in the 1H resonance spectra of compounds containing nitrogen and hydrogen. For the pyrrole molecule, strong irradiation at the resonance frequency of nitrogen-14 removes the line broadening from the NH hydrogen absorption band and enables fine structure arising from H—H spin–spin interaction with the ring hydrogen nuclei to be observed (see Fig. 8.52)[109]. Use of this technique has also been made in the analysis of the 1H resonance spectrum of formamide[110]. The absorption bands in the 1H resonance spectrum of formamide (I)

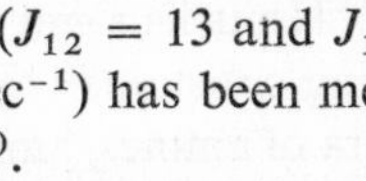

$$\begin{array}{c} O \\ \diagdown \\ \end{array} \begin{array}{c} \\ C—N \\ \diagup \end{array} \begin{array}{c} H_2 \\ \diagup \\ \end{array}$$
$$H_1 \qquad\qquad H_3 \qquad (I)$$

at 40 Mc sec^{-1} are considerably broadened by ^{14}N—1H spin–spin interaction[110, 244] and quadrupolar effects. Piette and co-workers[110] have removed this broadening by using a 1H—$\{^{14}N\}$ double irradiation technique and from the improved spectrum they were able to measure two of the H—H spin coupling constants in the molecule ($J_{12} = 13$ and $J_{13} = 2\cdot1$ cycles sec^{-1}). The J_{23} coupling constant ($2\cdot4$ cycles sec^{-1}) has been measured in the 1H spectrum of ^{15}N-substituted formamide[245].

Tiers and Bovey[111] have measured the 1H resonance spectra of a series of N-substituted amides, and they found that in some cases narrow NH absorption bands were obtained even in the absence of proton exchange processes (for example, N-acetyl-DL-valine, $CH_3CONHCH \cdot COOH$, gives a very narrow

$$\overset{|}{CH(CH_3)_2}$$

hydrogen resonance band for the NH group). In the asymmetric compounds where this effect is observed, one would expect to find strong electric field gradients around the nitrogen nucleus and there are theoretical reasons to justify the suggestion that such strong fields can remove the quadrupolar line broadening[112].

Rapid proton exchange involving the NH hydrogen atoms is known to cause both the removal of fine structure and the narrowing of lines in the hydrogen resonance spectra of such hydrogen nuclei. Even small traces of water (1 part in 10^7) will cause the triplet fine structure in the ^{1}H resonance spectrum of anhydrous ammonia to collapse by this mechanism. The triplet splitting due

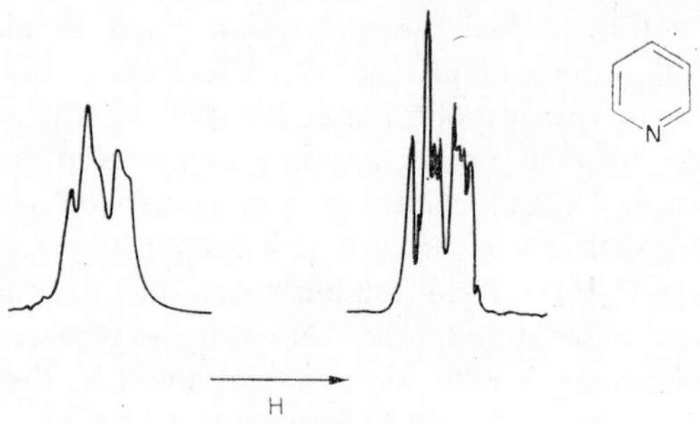

FIG. 12.30 The ^{1}H resonance at 40 Mc sec^{-1} of the α-hydrogen nucleus in neat pyridine without and with double irradiation of the ^{14}N nucleus. Baldeschwieler and Randall[108].

to ^{14}N—^{1}H spin–spin interaction has been observed in the ^{1}H spectra of rigorously dried liquid ammonia[113], in acid solutions of alkylamines[114, 115], in n-butylamine in trifluoroacetic acid solution[111], and in pure liquid formamide, acetamide and *N*-methylacetamide at high temperatures[115].

12.3.3 Long Range ^{1}H—^{14}N *Spin Coupling Constants*

Long range ^{1}H—^{14}N spin coupling constants have been observed in the ^{1}H resonance spectra of several isonitriles (see Table 12.42)[116]. This suggests that there is a small electric field gradient near the nitrogen nucleus and that the spin lattice relaxation time of the ^{14}N nucleus must be comparable with the times associated with the NH coupling constants[112]. Such splittings have not been observed in the resonance spectra of amines, amides, nitroalkanes, nitrogen-containing heterocyclic molecules, nitriles, *N*-oxides and alkyl azides. Only in the isonitriles is the electronic symmetry about the nitrogen nucleus sufficient to give the small electric field gradient necessary to avoid losing the ^{1}H—^{14}N fine structure due to quadrupolar relaxation. The measured NH coupling constants are particularly interesting for isopropylisonitrile, $(CH_3)_2CHNC$, where the β-coupling is stronger than the α-coupling as is found in several metal alkyls[90, 117].

TABLE 12.42 ^{1}H CHEMICAL SHIFTS AND ^{1}H—^{14}N SPIN COUPLING CONSTANTS OF SEVERAL ISONITRILES[(116)]

Compound	$\tau \pm 0{\cdot}02$	Multiplicity	J_{NH} (cycles sec^{-1}) $\pm 0{\cdot}2$	J_{HH} (cycles sec^{-1}) $\pm 0{\cdot}2$
$(CH_3)_3CNC^a$	8·56	triplet	3·5	
CH_3NC^a	7·15	triplet	2·7	
$C_6H_5CH_2NC$	5·72	triplet	1·3	
$(CH_3)_2CHNC$				
CH_3	8·55	tripled doublet	2·6	7·0
CH	6·13	tripled septet	1·8	7·0
$CH_3(CH_2)_3NC$				
α-CH_2	6·70	tripled triplet	2·0	6·7
β-CH_2		shows splitting		
$C_6H_{11}NC^bCH$	6·42	broad peak		

40 Mc sec^{-1}; $SiMe_4$ internal standard.
[a] CCl_4 solutions; the other compounds were run neat.
[b] Cyclohexyl isonitrile.

12.3.4 Structure Determinations Using ^{14}N Resonance

Cyanamides and Carbodi-imides. NMR measurements of the ^{14}N spectrum of diethylcyanamide[(118)] indicate that the molecule has a nitrile structure

$$Et_2N{-}C{\equiv}N$$

and not an isonitrile structure,

$$Et_2N{-}N{\equiv}C$$

The ^{14}N spectrum consists of two absorption bands at $+149$ and $+285$ ppm from the NO_3^- absorption line of an ammonium nitrate reference solution: the high field peak is assigned to the amino type nitrogen atom on the basis of its chemical shift[(104)]. Methyl isonitrile, CH_3NC, has a ^{14}N chemical shift of $+240$ ppm on this scale, which supports the view that the band in diethyl cyanamide at $+149$ ppm does not originate from an isonitrile nitrogen atom.

The ^{14}N NMR spectrum of *N,N'*-dicyclohexylcarbodi-imide consists of a single absorption band at $+240$ ppm from the NO_3^- reference and this is consistent with the symmetrical molecular structure, ($C_6H_{11}{-}N{=}C{=}N{-}C_6H_{11}$), which contains two equivalent nitrogen atoms[(118)].

12.4 OXYGEN

Oxygen-17 (natural abundance $3{\cdot}7 \times 10^{-2}$ per cent) is the only known oxygen isotope with non-zero spin (spin number $I = \frac{5}{2}$). This nucleus does not lend itself to convenient NMR investigation since in addition to its low natural abundance it has a considerable quadrupole moment and a poor natural sensitivity to NMR detection. Therefore, it is not surprising that few nuclear magnetic resonance studies of the nucleus have been reported.

Weaver, Tolbert and La Force[120] have examined the ^{17}O resonance dispersion mode spectra of a series of compounds and they found that the relaxation time, T_1 of oxygen is usually sufficiently short to allow conditions of "slow passage" to be employed. Table 12.43 gives a list of ^{17}O chemical shifts measured from the resonance band of a water reference sample. In ethyl nitrate, two absorption bands in the intensity ratio 1:2 are observed and they have been assigned to the two types of oxygen, >C—O—N< and —N<(O)(O). It is interesting to note that the ^{14}N chemical shift difference

TABLE 12.43 ^{17}O CHEMICAL SHIFTS OF SOME COMMON COMPOUNDS[120]

Compound	Chemical shift ppm	Compound	Chemical shift ppm
Tetramethylorthosilicate	−20	Ethyl nitrate	−340 −470
		$NaNO_3$	−430
Octamethylcyclo-tetrasiloxane	−80	SO_2 (liquid)	−540
n-Butylnitrite	−170 −380	Acetone	−600
H_2O_2 (30%)	−190	Nitroethane	−640
Acetic acid	−220	$NaNO_2$	−690
Formic acid	−270	H_2O	0
Sodium formate	−300		
Formamide	−320		

Chemical shifts measured in ppm from an H_2O external reference.

between NO_3^- and NO_2^- (see Table 12.39) is almost identical with the ^{17}O chemical shift difference for the species: the full significance of this observation is not yet understood.

12.4.1 ^{17}O Chemical Shifts

The resonance absorption of water occurs at the highest field value, and this is attributed to the partial ionic character of the OH bond causing the valency electrons on the oxygen atom to form a system of high symmetry. The paramagnetic shielding of an oxygen nucleus surrounded by an electronic system of high symmetry would be small and lead to the diamagnetic shielding observed. A later investigation of the ^{17}O resonance spectra of a series of organic compounds showed that alcohols and ethers have similar chemical shifts to that of water (see Table 12.44), thus indicating that the shielding of oxygen nuclei is very similar in molecules where the oxygen forms single bonds with either carbon or hydrogen[121]. The factors controlling the shielding of oxygen atoms involved in single bond formation appear to be diamagnetic in type and to be similar for oxygens bound to hydrogen and carbon.

Figgis and co-workers[122] have measured the chemical shifts of ^{17}O in several inorganic compounds (see Tables 12.45 and 12.46). For the "closed shell" oxyanions of transition metals, and for carbonyl oxygen atoms in organic molecules, they find a linear relationship between the observed ^{17}O chemical shifts and the lowest energy electronic transitions as measured from U.V. and visible spectra. This linear relationship is illustrated in Figure 12.31 and

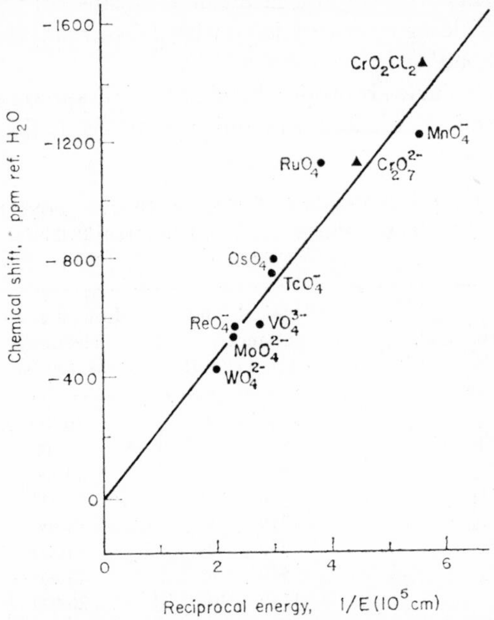

FIG. 12.31 Correlation between chemical shift and lowest energy electronic transition for compounds containing oxygen bonded to a transition metal: ● signifies a symmetrical tetrahedral species; ▲ signifies a species of other than tetrahedral symmetry. Figgis, Kidd and Nyholm(122).

TABLE 12.44 ^{17}O CHEMICAL SHIFTS IN ORGANIC MOLECULES(121)

Compound	Chemical shift ppm	Remarks
Methanol †	+40·0	
Ethanol	0	98% pure
Water	0·0	Reference sample
Ether	0	
Propionic acid	−210	
Acetic acid	−220	
Formic acid	−270	
Propionic anhydride	−240	Stronger signal
	−420	Weaker signal
Acetyl acetone	−235	
Ethyl acetate	−310	
Conc. nitric acid	−460	Very strong signal
Acetone	−600	
Methyl ethyl ketone	−600	
Acetoacetic ester	−620	Broad signal
Ethyl malonate	−625	

Chemical shifts measured in ppm from an H_2O external reference.
† The ^{17}O resonance in CH_3OH is displaced −3·7 ppm upon dilution with CCl_4(271).

is in accord with the proposed origin of ^{17}O chemical shifts in these compounds as arising from the paramagnetic term in Ramsey's equation (see Section 3.5).

Oxygen nuclei in ketonic carbonyl groups (acetone and methyl ethyl ketone) are much less shielded than those in alcohols because of an increase in the paramagnetic deshielding term associated with the *p*-orbital contribution to the carbonyl double bond[(121)].

The presence of a single absorption band in the ^{17}O spectra of the carboxylic acid groups in formic, acetic and propionic acid, suggests that the two oxygen

TABLE 12.45 ^{17}O CHEMICAL SHIFTS OF OXYGEN BONDED TO TRANSITION METALS. SHIFTS ARE MEASURED FROM INTERNAL H_2O REFERENCE[(122)]

Compound	Chemical shift and mean deviation (ppm)	Lowest energy electronic transition (cm^{-1})
Na_3VO_4	-571 ± 4	36900
Na_2CrO_4	-835 ± 5	26800
K_2MoO_4	-540 ± 2	44000
Na_2WO_4	-420 ± 2	50300
$NaMnO_4$	-1219 ± 8	18300
$NaTcO_4$	-749 ± 7	34000
$NaReO_4$	-569 ± 4	43500
RuO_4	-1119 ± 10	26400
OsO_4	-796 ± 3	33500
$Na_2Cr_2O_7$	-1125 ± 6	22700
CrO_2Cl_2	-1460 ± 8	18000

TABLE 12.46 ^{17}O CHEMICAL SHIFTS OF OXYGEN BONDED TO NON-TRANSITION ELEMENTS. SHIFTS ARE MEASURED FROM INTERNAL H_2O REFERENCE[(122)]

Compound	Solution composition	Chemical shift and mean deviation (ppm)
K_2CO_3	7 M solution in 0·1 N KOH	-192 ± 4
H_2O_2	30% aqueous solution	-187 ± 5
$POCl_3$	pure liquid	-216 ± 2
Na_2SeO_4	3 M solution in 0·1 N NaOH	-204 ± 12
SO_3	"stabilised" liquid	-188 ± 1
SO_2	pure liquid	-513 ± 5
$SOCl_2$	pure liquid	-292 ± 2
SO_2Cl_2	pure liquid	-304 ± 3
$NaBrO_3$	2·4 M solution in 0·1 N NaOH	-297 ± 5
$NaClO_3$	2·4 M solution in 0·1 N NaOH	-287 ± 3
$NaClO_4$	2·4 M solution in 0·1 N NaOH	-288 ± 5
NH_4NO_3	9 M solution in 0·1 N NaOH	-420 ± 6
HNO_3	100% liquid	-414 ± 3
$NaNO_2$	6 M solution in 0·1 N NaOH	-670 ± 6

atoms are structurally equivalent, a feature which supports the possibility of resonance contributions from the canonical forms I and II

$$R-C\diagdown\begin{smallmatrix}O\\OH\end{smallmatrix} \qquad R-C\diagdown\begin{smallmatrix}O^-\\ + \\ OH\end{smallmatrix}$$

(I) (II)

It is significant that the single ^{17}O absorption for the carboxylic group has a chemical shift intermediate between those expected for C—O and ketonic C=O types of oxygen nuclei. The ^{17}O resonance spectra of esters confirm that they also show similar resonance behaviour to that found in carboxylic acid groups[121].

Oxygen chemical shifts can be used to infer the extent of partial double bond character of C—O type bonds. In the spectrum of propionic anhydride, two absorption bands in the intensity ratio of 2:1 have been observed[121]. The resonance structures most likely to contribute to the resonance hybrid are

$$CH_3-CH_2-C\diagdown\begin{smallmatrix}O\\O\end{smallmatrix} \qquad CH_3-CH_2-C\diagdown\begin{smallmatrix}O^-\\O^+\end{smallmatrix} \qquad CH_3-CH_2-C\diagdown\begin{smallmatrix}O\\O^+\end{smallmatrix}$$
$$CH_3-CH_2-C\diagdown\begin{smallmatrix}\\O\end{smallmatrix} \qquad CH_3-CH_2-C\diagdown\begin{smallmatrix}\\O\end{smallmatrix} \qquad CH_3-CH_2-C\diagdown\begin{smallmatrix}\\O^-\end{smallmatrix}$$

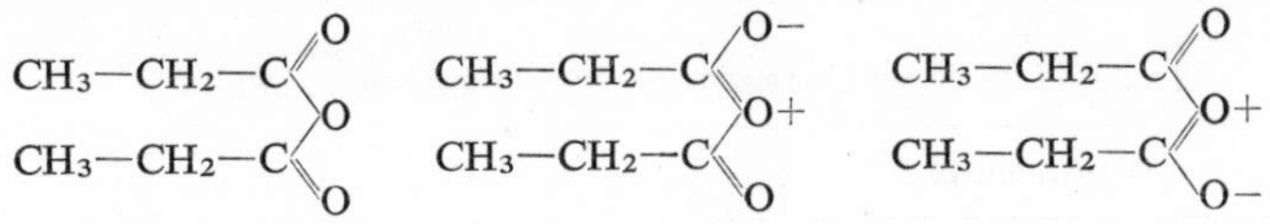

TABLE 12.47 ^{17}O CHEMICAL SHIFTS IN SOME ORGANIC MOLECULES[124]

Compound	Chemical shift[a] ppm	Compound	Chemical shift[a] ppm	
			—O—	O=
Methanol	+37	Methyl formate	−142	−358
Ethanol	−5	Methyl acetate	−137	−355
n-Propanol	−1	Methyl propionate	−133	−350
i-Propanol	−37	Dimethyl malonate	−143	−363
Glycol	+6	Dimethyl succinate	−151	−368
Diethyl ether	−15	Ethyl formate	−169	−359
Glycol dimethyl ether	+25	Ethyl acetate	−166	−256
Dioxane	+3	Ethyl propionate	−164	−350
Tetrahydrofuran	−19	Diethyl oxalate	−162	−355
Formic acid	−254	Diethyl malonate	−166	−356
Acetic acid	−254	Diethyl succinate	−178	−363
Propionic acid	−250	n-Propyl formate	−163	−354
Acetone	−568	Diethyl carbonate	−120	−240
Methyl ethyl ketone	−563	Glycol diacetate	−148	−351
Cyclopentanone	−548	Ethylchloroformate	−170	−348
Cyclohexanone	−559	Acetic anhydride	−259	−393
Mesityloxide	−555	Propionic anhydride	−248	−390
Diacetyl	−571			
Acetaldehyde	−595			
Propionaldehyde	−581			
n-Butyraldehyde	−589			
Acrolein	−583			

[a] Chemical shifts measured in ppm from an external H_2O reference.

TABLE 12.48 ^{17}O CHEMICAL SHIFTS[124]

Compound	Chemical shift ppm	Compound	Chemical shift ppm
Methyl formate	−28	Ethylene chlorohydrin	+4
Ethyl formate	−45	Epichlorhydrin	+12
Dimethoxymethane	−8	Dimethyl sulphoxide	−13
Diethoxymethane	−43	Nitrobenzene	−561
Acetal	−52	Tetramethoxysilane	+30
Paraldehyde	−102	Formamide	−306
Ethyl acetoacetate	−164	Urea (aqueous solution)	−205
	−353		
	−565	H_2SO_4 (98%)	−138
Acetyl acetone	−269	HNO_3 (69%)	−409
Furan	−243	$HClO_4$ (60%)	−288
Furfural	−237	D_2O (60%)	+3
	−530		

Chemical shifts measured in ppm from an H_2O external reference.

TABLE 12.49 SOME CHARACTERISTIC ^{17}O CHEMICAL SHIFTS[124]

Range of chemical shifts		Compounds	Type of O atom
+100			
0	+40 to −40	Alcohols and ethers	—O—
−100			
	−130 to −150	Methyl esters	—O—
	−160 to −180	Ethyl and propyl esters	—O—
−200			
	−240 to −260	Acids and acid anhydrides	—O—
−300			
	−350 to −370	Esters	O=
	−390 to −393	Acid anhydrides	O=
−400			
−500			
	−550 to −570	Ketones	O=
−600 ppm from H_2O	−580 to −600	Aldehydes	O=

Chemical shifts measured in ppm from an H_2O external reference.

The two absorption bands result from the two different types of oxygen atom in this molecule, and the chemical shift of the single oxygen atom shows it to have greater double bond character in the C—O bonds.

Reasonably successful attempts to examine slow keto–enol equilibria by using ^{17}O resonance have been made[(121)]. The chemical shift of the single ^{17}O resonance band of acetylacetone is similar to that observed for carboxylic acids, which suggests that the molecule is present mainly as the enolic form. Acetoacetic ester and ethyl malonate have chemical shifts similar to those of ketones, indicating a predominance of the ketonic form in the equilibrium. It was not possible to detect the small quantities of the other form present in the equilibrium mixtures of any of these compounds at room temperature.

TABLE 12.50 ^{17}O CHEMICAL SHIFTS OF SOME METAL CARBONYLS[(125)]

Compound	Composition of solution	Chemical shift ppm
$Fe(CO)_5$	Pure liquid	−388
$Ni(CO)_4$	Pure liquid	−362
$Fe(CO)_2(NO)_2$	Pure liquid	−418
$Mn_2(CO)_{10}$	50% w/v in $CHCl_3$	−355
$Co(CO)_3(NO)$	Pure liquid	−377

Chemical shifts measured in ppm from an H_2O external reference. A radiofrequency field, H_1, of 60 milligauss and a sweep rate of 3 milligauss sec^{-1} were used in the measurements

Christ[(124)] has measured the ^{17}O spectra of an extensive series of compounds and Tables 12.47 and 12.48 list the chemical shifts (measured from a water reference sample) obtained in the investigation. Table 12.49 has been drawn up from the data presented in Tables 12.47 and 12.48 and indicates the range of ^{17}O chemical shifts observed for various chemical groups.

Figgis and co-workers[(125)] have measured the ^{17}O chemical shifts in several metal carbonyl compounds and their results are given in Table 12.50. They also observed the ^{13}C chemical shifts in these compounds but it was not possible, from their results, to reach an unequivocal decision concerning whether or not the oxygen of the carbon monoxide is bonded directly to the metal.

12.4.2 Effects of Paramagnetic Ions on ^{17}O Chemical Shifts

Addition of the paramagnetic ions of Gd^{+++} to a sample of $H_2{}^{17}O$ brings about an increase in the diamagnetic shielding of the ^{17}O nucleus. Shulman and Wyluda[(126)] suggest that the shielding might be due to a transfer of an electron from the ligand $H_2{}^{17}O$ to the metal ion, resulting in the formation of $H_2{}^{17}O^+$ and Gd^{++} ions. Orgel[(127, 128)] has pointed out that while transfer of an electron from a ligand to a singly occupied orbital of a transition metal results in a large paramagnetic shift of the resonance frequency of the oxygen nuclei in the ligand, a diamagnetic shift results from transfer of a ligand electron to an empty orbital. Such a state of affairs would also prevail for rare earth metal ions such as gadolinium.

Paramagnetic and diamagnetic ^{17}O chemical shifts have been observed in aqueous solutions of rare earth perchlorates[(129)]. These shifts are interpreted as arising from the isotropic part of the indirect contact hyperfine interaction of the unpaired rare earth electrons with the oxygen nucleus, via an electron transfer mechanism (configuration interaction), which leaves a slight imbalance of the spins on the oxygen atoms (see Section 3.16).

^{17}O resonance absorption studies have been used to study the hydration of certain cations (see Section 9.3.2) in systems where the solvent water molecules and the hydrated water molecules are not undergoing rapid exchange[(130, 311)]. In such systems, the solvent water ^{17}O absorption can be chemically shifted from the hydrated water ^{17}O signal by the addition of paramagnetic ions.

12.4.3 ^{1}H—^{17}O *Spin Coupling in Water*

Usually, the rapid intermolecular exchange of protons in water molecules prevents the observation of ^{1}H—^{17}O spin coupling in the ^{1}H and ^{17}O spectra. However, when this rapid exchange is suppressed by diluting the water with a

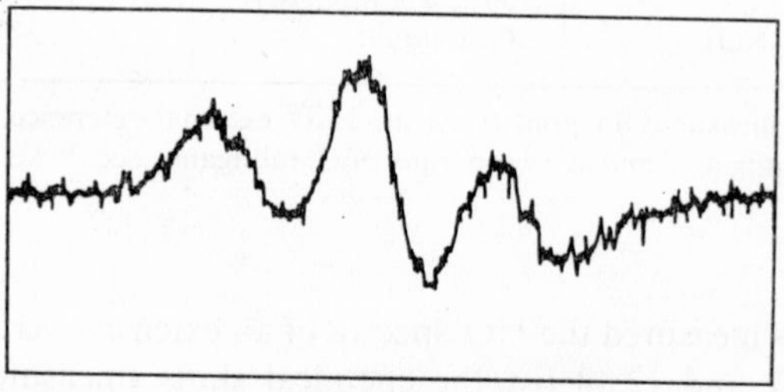

FIG. 12.32 Derivative mode spectrum of ^{17}O resonance of $H_2{}^{17}O$ in acetone at 8·13 Mc sec^{-1}. Reuben, Tzalmona and Samuel[(131)].

large excess of carefully purified acetone, it is possible to observe such spin coupling. Reuben and co-workers[(131)] have examined the ^{17}O resonance spectrum of a 3 per cent v/v solution of water (enriched in ^{17}O atoms) in acetone and the triplet splitting from ^{1}H—^{17}O spin coupling is clearly evident in the ^{17}O resonance derivative spectrum shown in Fig. 12.32 ($J_{^1H-^{17}O} = 73{\cdot}5 \pm 2{\cdot}1$ cycles sec^{-1}). Intermolecular effects associated with the dilution of water in acetone cause an increased ^{17}O shielding of about 11 ppm compared with the resonance of pure water.

12.5 SILICON

Silicon-29 is the only naturally occurring isotope of silicon which possesses a magnetic moment. Despite its low natural abundance (4·70 per cent) and low natural sensitivity to NMR detection (7·85 per cent of that of hydrogen nuclei at constant field strength) it has been possible to measure ^{29}Si chemical shifts

TABLE 12.51 ^{29}Si CHEMICAL SHIFTS IN VARIOUS COMPOUNDS(50, 56)

Compound[a]	δ (ppm)	J(SiH) (cycles sec^{-1})
$[(CH_3)_3SiO]_4Si^*$	81·5	
$SiBr_4$	68[b]	
$(C_2H_5O)_4Si$	59·5	
$[(CH_3)_3SiO]_3Si^*CH_3$	42·5	
$(C_2H_5O)_3SiCH_3$	21·5	
$C_6H_5(CH_3)SiH_2$	14·8	200
$(CH_3SiHO)_5$	13·1	248
$(C_6H_5)_2SiH_2$	11·8	200
$[(CH_3)_2SiO]_x$[c]	0	
$[(CH_3)_2SiO]_4$	−2·2	
$[C_2H_5(CH_3)SiO]_4$	−2·3	
$C_6H_5(CH_3)_2SiH$	−4·5	187
$SiCl_4$	−6[b]	
$[(CH_3)_2SiO]_3$ (C_6H_6 solution)	−12·1	
$(CH_3)_3SiCH{=}CH_2$	−15·1	
$[(CH_3)_2SiH]_2O$	−17·2	210
$(CH_3)_3SiC_6H_5$	−17·8	
$(C_6H_5)_2CH_3SiOC_2H_5$	−18·2	
$[(CH_3)_2SiNH]_3$	−18·7	
$[(CH_3)_3Si]_2NH$	−19·8	
$(CH_3)_3SiCH_2OH$	−21·8	
$(CH_3)_4Si$	−22·0	
$[(CH_3)_3Si]_2CH_2$	−22·5	
$(CH_3)_3SiCH_2NH_2$	−23·2	
$(CH_3)_3SiCH_2C_6H_5$	−23·4	
$(CH_3)_3Si(CH_2)_3CH_3$	−23·8	
$(CH_3)_3SiCH_2Cl$	−25·5	
$(CH_3)_3SiCH_2NCS$	−28·2	
$[(CH_3)_3Si]_2O$	−28·7	
$(CH_3)_3SiOC_2H_5$	−29·4	
$[(CH_3)_3Si^*O]_3SiCH_3$	−29·4	
CH_3SiCl_3	−30[b]	
$[(CH_3)_3Si^*O]_4Si$	−30·4	
$(CH_3)_3SiI$	−30·6	
$(CH_3)_2Si(CH_2Cl)CHCl_2$	−31·2	
$(CH_3)_3SiBr$	−48·4	
$(CH_3)_3SiCl$	−51[b]	
$(CH_3)_3SiF$	−53·1	[d]
$(CH_3)_2SiCl_2$	−54[b]	
$(CH_3)_3SiOSO_3H$[e]	−57·6	
$(SiH_3)_3N$		212[f]
$(SiH_3)_2NCH_3$		212[f]
$SiH_3N(CH_3)_2$		208[f]

[a] The asterisk indicates the atom for which the shift is given.
[b] Broad line—accuracy about ± 5 ppm.
[c] Polydimethylsiloxane, viscosity 10 cs, was used as an external reference.
[d] J(SiF) = 275 cycles sec^{-1}.
[e] A solution of $[(CH_3)_3Si]_2O$ in excess H_2SO_4.
[f] Measured in the ^1H spectrum (see reference 134).

in the series of compounds listed in Table 12.51, using rapid passage dispersion conditions[50,56]. Silicon-29 has a spin number of one half ($I=\frac{1}{2}$) and consequently does not possess a quadrupole moment. Considerable difficulty is encountered in locating the resonance field value for silicon and it has been found that the following methods of detecting the resonance field value are the most successful[56]:

(1) For silicon nuclei with short values of T_1, the first derivative of the absorption mode is examined under conditions of slow passage and low radiofrequency power.

(2) For silicon nuclei with long values of T_1, the first derivative of the dispersion mode can be examined using slow passage and low radiofrequency power conditions as in method (1): alternatively, rapid passage and high values of radiofrequency power can be employed.

(3) For silicon nuclei with very long values of T_1, the dispersion signal can be examined directly using conditions of rapid passage and high radiofrequency power but the conditions must be so chosen as to enable the Bloch equations for rapid passage to remain valid for the system (see Section 2.9).

TABLE 12.52 ^{29}Si SPIN–SPIN COUPLING CONSTANTS[133]

Molecule	J_{HH} (cycles sec^{-1})	$J_{^{29}SiH}$ (cycles sec^{-1})	J_{HF} (cycles sec^{-1})	$J_{^{29}SiF}$ (cycles sec^{-1})
SiH_4	2·75 ± 0·15	202·5 ± 0·2		
SiH_3F	15·6 ± 0·2	229·0 ± 0·6	45·8 ± 0·1	281·0 ± 3·0
SiH_3Cl	12·7 ± 0·2	238·1 ± 0·2		
SiH_3Br	12·7 ± 0·5	240·5 ± 0·3		
SiH_3I	11·7 ± 0·3	240·1 ± 0·2		
SiH_2F_2	36·2 ± 0·7	282 ± 3	60·48 ± 0·07	297·8 ± 2·5
SiH_2Cl_2	27·8 ± 0·4	288·0 ± 0·4		
SiH_2Br_2	26·9 ± 0·7	289·0 ± 0·6		
SiH_2I_2	22·7 ± 0·3	280·5 ± 0·2		
$SiHF_3$		381·7 ± 1·5	96·28 ± 0·03	274·8 ± 0·3
$SiHCl_3$		362·9 ± 0·2		
$(SiH_3)_2O$	13·5 ± 0·2	221·5 ± 0·2		
$(SiH_3)_2S$	9·43 ± 0·13	224·0 ± 0·3		
$(SiH_3)_3N$	10·4 ± 0·2	212 ± 2		
$SiH_3N(CH_3)_2$[a]		208		
$(SiH_3)_2NCH_3$[a]		212		

[a] Taken from reference 134.

The signals arising from silicon atoms attached to nitrogen, chlorine, bromine and iodine atoms are broad and weak because of quadrupolar broadening effects associated with these nuclei (most pronounced for chlorine). Multiplet splittings arising from spin–spin interactions are observed on the Si resonance bands of some of the compounds listed in Table 12.52; however, the magnitude of these effects can be measured more accurately from the ^{1}H or ^{19}F spectra of the samples (see Sections 10.33). The values of J_{SiF} and J_{SiH} between atoms directly bonded are of approximately the same order of magnitude.

Baker[55] has improved the signal to noise ratio in ^{29}Si spectra by using the internuclear double resonance (INDOR) technique (see Sections 12.2.1 and 6.8) to examine tetramethylsilane.

12.5.1 ^{29}Si *Chemical Shifts*

Examination of Table 12.51 indicates that the range of ^{29}Si chemical shifts is much smaller than that found for ^{13}C nuclei. This might be due to the absence of multiple bonding in silicon compounds since such bonding is thought to cause most of the low field ^{13}C chemical shifts[50]. Furthermore, no ^{29}Si

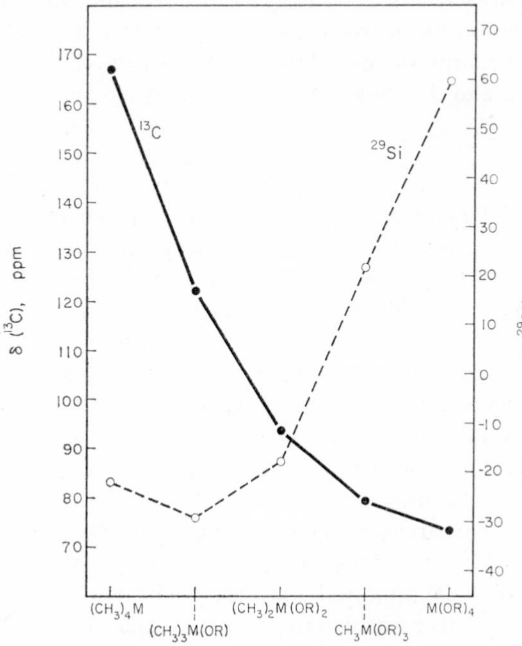

FIG. 12.33 Comparison of ^{13}C and ^{29}Si chemical shifts in compounds of the type $(CH_3)_xM(OR)_{4-x}$. Lauterbur[50].

chemical shift data has yet been obtained for the polyiodosilanes, the analogous molecules to the polyiodomethanes, which have the largest ^{13}C shielding constants. Substituent effects on the shielding of ^{29}Si nuclei sometimes operate in an almost opposite manner to those found in the shielding of ^{13}C nuclei. Figure 12.33 illustrates this feature of ^{29}Si and ^{13}C chemical shifts in compounds of general formula $(CH_3)_xM(OR)_{4-x}$. This behaviour is characteristic of systems where there is a possibility of back donation and *d*-orbital participation in the bonding.

12.5.2 Spin Coupling Constants Involving ^{29}Si *Nuclei*

From the limited available data on ^{29}Si spin coupling constants, Si—H coupling constants for the directly bonded nuclei are seen to have values in the range 187–248 cycles sec^{-1}. Only a few Si—F coupling constants have been reported (J_{SiF} ~ 274·8 to 301·8 cycles sec^{-1})[133, 294]. In the ^{1}H spectra of silicon alkyls, long range Si—H coupling constants between interacting nuclei separated by a carbon atom have been measured ($J_{^{29}Si-C-H}$ ~ 6 cycles sec^{-1})[50, 264].

Ebsworth *et al.*[133, 267] have measured the ^{29}Si—^{1}H coupling constants in a series of substituted silanes (see Table 12.52). When the Si—H values are plotted against the corresponding H—H spin coupling constants (obtained from partially deuterated molecules (see Section 8.19.2)), a roughly linear correlation is observed for the molecules SiH_4, SiH_3X and SiH_2X_2 where X is chlorine, bromine or iodine: this supports the idea that both types of coupling depend on the *s* character of the silicon hybrid orbitals. Other silanes show a different linear relationship between these two parameters.

J_{SiH} coupling constants do not show the additivity relationships found for J_{CH} values[82]. J_{SiH} and J_{SiF} have opposite signs when the nuclei are directly bonded[294].

12.6 Phosphorus

The discovery of the importance of phosphates in biochemical processes vital to life, and current interest in inorganic polymers, have stimulated a revival in the study of phosphorus chemistry. Over the last twenty years advances in this branch of chemistry have resulted in the emergence of a systematic understanding of the element rivalled only by that of carbon. Infrared[136] and Raman[137] vibrational studies have played a major part in this work but more recently nuclear magnetic resonance spectroscopy has proved itself an equally powerful technique in the examination of phosphorus-containing compounds.

^{31}P, the only naturally occurring isotope of phosphorus, has non-zero spin ($I = \frac{1}{2}$) and a magnetic moment of $\mu = 1{\cdot}1305$ nuclear magnetons. For an external magnetic field strength of 10,000 gauss the resonance frequency for ^{31}P nuclei is 17·235 Mc sec^{-1}. This nucleus gives rise to chemical shifts extending over a range of ~500 ppm and the measurement of these chemical shifts provides an excellent means of determining the molecular structures of phosphorus-containing compounds. Tables 12.53 to 12.59 and Appendix F list the majority of the ^{31}P chemical shifts reported in the literature. Although it is easier to saturate ^{31}P nuclei than either ^{1}H or ^{19}F nuclei, usually the relaxation time of the ^{31}P nucleus is sufficiently short to allow reasonable values of the irradiating field, H_1, to be used in conjunction with fairly rapid sweep rates.

The low NMR sensitivity of phosphorus (6·64 per cent that of the ^{1}H nucleus at constant magnetic field) is offset to some extent by the fact that the large range over which ^{31}P chemical shifts extend allows one to operate under conditions which favour high sensitivity at the expense of resolution. Thus, using large samples and receiver coils, spectra can be recorded in the normal absorption mode (ideal for intensity measurements). Fine structure on the ^{31}P resonance absorption bands arising from indirect spin–spin interaction with other nuclei in the molecule can usually be measured more satisfactorily in the spectrum of the interacting nucleus but coupling constants of 5 cycles sec^{-1} can readily be measured from the ^{31}P spectra if 5 mm o.d. thin-walled glass sample tubes are used. The minimum concentration of ^{31}P nuclei which can be detected at

14,000 gauss is 0·05 M but solutions twenty times this concentration are required for good quantitative intensity measurements[138].

Figure 12.34 is an example of the high quality ^{31}P resonance spectra which are now attainable using magnetic field values of 23,500 gauss (40·5 Mc sec^{-1}):

TABLE 12.53 ^{31}P CHEMICAL SHIFTS OF SEVERAL COMPOUNDS[4, 146]

Compound †	δ ppm	Compound †	δ ppm
$(MeO)_2P(O)H$	−11·3	PF_3 ‡	−97·0
$(EtO)_2P(O)H$	−7·5	PCl_3	−219·4
$(iPrO)_2P(O)H$	−4·2	PBr_3	−227·4
$(EtO)_2P(S)H$	−69·0	PI_3 ‡	−178·0
Me(EtO)P(O)H	−32·6	$(MeO)PCl_2$	−181·0
Me(nPrO)P(O)H	−31·5	(Me)(Et)P(O)Cl	−72·0
Me(iPrO)P(S)H	−61·3	$(Me)(Cl_3C)P(O)(OEt)$	−40·7
$H_2(OH)P(O)$	−12·0	Me(nPrO)P(O)Cl	−40·1
$(HO)_3P(O)$	0·00	Me(EtO)P(O)Cl	−39·5
Me(EtO)P(O)OH	−28·5	Et(EtO)P(O)Cl	−45·0
Et(EtO)P(O)OH	−32·5	Me(iPrO)P(O)F	−16·1
Me(EtO)P(S)OH	−88·8	$EtP(O)Cl_2$	−53·0
Et(EtO)P(S)OH	−94·2	$MeP(O)Cl_2$	−44·5
$(EtO)_2POSH$	−24·0	$\Phi POCl_2$	−34·5
$(EtO)_2P(S)SH$	−85·7	$MePOF_2$	−27·4
$MeP(O)(OH)_2$ (acet. sol.)	−31·1	$(EtO)_2P(O)Cl$	−2·8
$nBuP(O)(OH)_2$ (acet. sol.)	−32·0	$POBr_3$	+102·9
$[(HO)_2P(O)]_2O$	+10·6	$POCl_3$	−1·9
$[(EtO)_2P(O)]_2O$	+12·5	Me(EtO)P(S)Cl	−94·2
$[Me(EtO)P(O)]_2O$	−22·4	$EtP(S)Cl_2$	−94·3
$[Me(nPrO)P(O)]_2O$	−22·2	$MeP(S)Cl_2$	−79·8
$[Et(EtO)P(O)]_2O$	−25·0	$\Phi P(S)Cl_2$	−74·8
$[Me(EtO)P(S)]_2O$	−85·4	Me(iPrO)P(S)Cl	−58·6
Me_3P	+61·0	$(EtO)_2P(S)Cl$	−68·1
Et_3P	+20·4	$(nPrO)P(S)Cl_2$	−56·3
$(nBu)_3P$	+32·3	$(nBuO)P(S)Cl_2$	−56·4
Φ_3P	+5·88	$PSCl_3$	−28·8
$MePCl_2$	−191·2	$(Me_2N)_2P(O)Cl$	−30·3
ΦPCl_2	−162·0	$(Me_2N)P(O)(CN)(OEt)$	+10·7

† Me = methyl, Et = ethyl, iPr = isopropyl, nPr = normal propyl, nBu = normal butyl, and Φ = phenyl.

Table published by permission of H. Finegold (see reference 146).

‡ Taken from reference 141.

δ is the chemical shift measured in ppm from 85 per cent H_3PO_4 external reference.

the 10 line multiplet of trimethylphosphite[277] arising from P—H spin–spin interaction is clearly resolved and in addition there is a series of low intensity peaks spaced throughout the spectrum that arise from ^{31}P—^{13}C spin coupling. At lower field strengths, a 15 mm o.d. non-spinning sample tube is usually employed to attain optimum sensitivity. Crutchfield[235] has constructed a non-spinning sample cell which contains a 6 mm receiver coil insert on the inside wall of the cell: thus a liquid sample can completely fill the volume within the coil and this results in a signal to noise ratio comparable with that usually obtained with a conventional 15 mm o.d. sample tube, but without the attendant loss in resolution.

It is usual to measure ^{31}P spectra with respect to the single sharp absorption band in 85 per cent orthophosphoric acid (H_3PO_4) contained, as an external reference, in a small-bore sealed capillary tube. Bulk diamagnetic susceptibility corrections are less than 0·5 ppm and are usually neglected(4).

Excellent reviews of ^{31}P nuclear magnetic resonance studies have been published by Finegold(146) and by Katritzky and Jones(149).

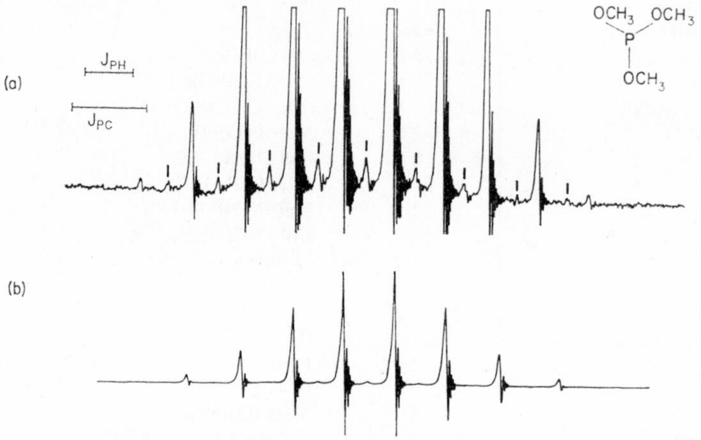

FIG. 12.34 The ^{31}P resonance spectrum of trimethylphosphite at 40·5 Mc sec^{-1} (23,500 gauss) under conditions of (a) high gain, (b) low gain. Pier(277) (Varian Associates).

12.6.1 ^{31}P *Chemical Shifts*

Chemical shifts for ^{31}P nuclei were first discovered by Knight in 1949(139). Early measurements of these chemical shifts indicated that the changes in shielding of phosphorus atoms in different chemical environments could not be related simply to inductive effects of adjacent groupings since no apparent correlation between ^{31}P chemical shifts and the electronegativity of attached atoms or groups could be found(12, 140, 141). Tables 12.53 and 12.54 list some ^{31}P chemical shifts measured from 85 per cent H_3PO_4 external reference for a series of phosphorus-containing compounds. Although the two valency states of phosphorus do not give rise to chemical shifts in two distinct regions, trivalent phosphorus nuclei are usually less shielded than pentavalent phosphorus nuclei. It can be seen that triply connected phosphorus nuclei show a much larger spread of chemical shifts ($\sim$ 500 ppm) than do pentavalent phosphorus compounds ($\sim$ 100 ppm). This might be a reflection of the easily changed bond angles in triply connected phosphorus compounds(50).

Gutowsky and McCall[141] suggest that the lower shielding of phosphorus in the trivalent state arises from there being fewer valency electrons to shield the ^{31}P nucleus than in the case of pentavalent phosphorus. They explained the anomalous chemical shifts found in the series PF_3, PCl_3, PBr_3 and PI_3 (where the observed ^{31}P shielding decreases in the order F, I, Cl and Br) by postulating the presence of two opposing effects, namely ionic and double bond character. An increase in ionic bond character accompanies an increase in the electronegativity of the halogen substituent and the double bond character would be

TABLE 12.54 ^{31}P CHEMICAL SHIFTS IN SOME SIMPLE MOLECULES[141]

Compound	Chemical shift δ ppm	Compound	Chemical shift δ ppm
P_4 (in CS_2)	488	HPF_6	118
P_4	450	$F_2PO(OH)$	20·1
PH_3	241	$POClF_2$	14·8
P_4S_3	114	$POCl_2F$	0·0
PF_3	−97	H_3PO_4	0·0
CH_3OPF_2	−111	$HPO(OH)_2$	−4·5
P_2I_4 (in CS_2)	−170	$POCl_3$	−5·4
PI_3	−178	$C_2H_5OPOCl_2$	−6·4
$Cl(CH_2)_3PCl_2$	−182	$H_2PO(OH)$	−13·8
PCl_3	−215	$PSCl_3$	−30·8
PBr_3	−222		

Chemical shifts measured in ppm from 85 per cent H_3PO_4 aqueous solution external reference.

expected to be strongest in compounds containing P—F bonds and present to a lesser extent in other P–halogen bonds. Assuming that the shielding of ^{31}P nuclei increases as the ionicity of the bonds decreases and as the double bond character increases, it is possible to explain the observed ^{31}P chemical shifts in phosphorus trihalides. Similar arguments can be used to interpret the spectra of some pentavalent phosphorus compounds such as the oxyhalides in the series $POCl_3$, $POCl_2F$, $POClF_2$ and POF_3 where both the ^{19}F and ^{31}P shielding increase as the number of fluorine substituents increases. By postulating that structures of the type shown in I and II contribute appreciably to the resonance hybrid it is possible to explain the observed chemical shifts

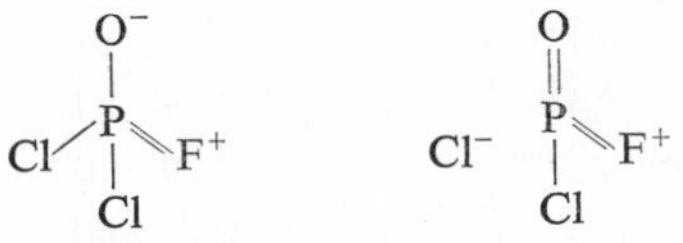

(I) (II)

Increase in double bond character is thought to decrease the shielding of ^{19}F nuclei[142] and since increased fluorine substitution causes a decrease in the double bond character in each P—F bond then the observed increase in ^{19}F

shielding with increased fluorine substitution would be expected if this effect is large. Increase in double bond character has the opposite effect on phosphorus, shielding where the shielding is increased: this is consistent with the charge separation which would be expected to result from double bond formation viz. $^{-}P{=}F^{+}$. Electronegativity inductive effects would lead to a different charge separation, $^{+}P{-}F^{-}$. Van Wazer[143] notes that substituents of a lower electronegativity than the bromine atom, when attached to a phosphorus atom, decrease ^{31}P shielding as the electronegativity is increased (as expected on normal inductive grounds). This effect is reversed for substituents of higher electronegativity where the tendency to form double bonds increases.

Gutowsky and co-workers[12] have pointed out a linear correlation which exists between ^{31}P chemical shifts and J_{PF} coupling constants within the same molecule. This suggests that both parameters depend on the electronic distribution within the molecule but are related to it in different ways.

Muller *et al.*[4] have examined a series of phosphorus-containing compounds and they have subjected their results to a semi-empirical analysis in an attempt to correlate ^{31}P chemical shifts with bond properties such as hybridisation, degree of ionicity and double bond character. Instead of arguing in terms of electron density at the phosphorus nuclei in the manner of Gutowsky and McCall[141], they adopted an approach similar to that followed by Saika and Slichter[3] for fluorine chemical shifts. These latter authors assume that the second order paramagnetic term is the dominant contribution to the shielding of a fluorine nucleus and that both the diamagnetic term and the terms contributed by other atoms could be neglected. Increases in the paramagnetic term result in a decrease in shielding of the nucleus, the resonance of which is then observed at low values of applied magnetic field. Trivalent phosphorus is thought to be shielded in a similar manner to fluorine nuclei and by assuming that only the three valency electrons contribute to the paramagnetic term and that all the other factors in the Saika and Slichter equation (see Section 4.6)

$$\sigma_p = -\frac{2}{3}\left(\frac{e^2 h^2}{M^2 c^2}\right)\left(\left\langle\frac{1}{r^3}\right\rangle_{av}\right)_p \times \frac{1}{\Delta E} \tag{12.8}$$

are constant then the observed ^{31}P shifts should be correlated using a semi-empirical equation of the type

$$\delta = a - b\,D \tag{12.9}$$

where D is the number of imbalanced p electrons and a and b are empirical constants. D can be calculated from considerations of the extent of hybridisation and the degree of ionicity in the bonding atomic orbitals[4].

For PX_3 type molecules, a term ε is defined in such a way that $(1 - \varepsilon)$ is the number of electrons in each P—X bond contributed by the phosphorus atom. This term ε can be expressed in terms of Pauling electronegativities by the equation[144]

$$|\varepsilon| = 0{\cdot}16\,|X_A - X_B| + 0{\cdot}035\,|X_A - X_B|^2 \tag{12.10}$$

where X_A is the Pauling electronegativity of atom A.

The extent of hybridisation, α, and the X—P—X bond angles, θ, are related by the equation

$$\beta^2 = 3(1 - \alpha^2) = -\frac{3\cos\theta}{1 - \cos\theta}. \qquad (12.11)$$

D can now be defined as

$$D = |(1 + \varepsilon)(1 - \beta^2) + 2\beta^2 - (1 + \varepsilon)| = |\beta^2(1 - \varepsilon)| \qquad (12.12)$$

Values of D for the molecules PH_3 and PCl_3 have been calculated and when these values are substituted into equation (12.11) an empirical equation (equation (12.13)) relating ^{31}P chemical shifts with D values for this type of molecule is obtained

$$\delta = 4{\cdot}2 \times 10^2 - 1{\cdot}2 \times 10^3 D \qquad (12.13)$$

This equation will always yield positive chemical shifts and the highest possible shift is predicted to be $4{\cdot}2 \times 10^2$ ppm, which is in good agreement with the experimentally observed value for P_4 of $4{\cdot}9 \times 10^2$ ppm. Using equation (12.13) values of δ for other PX_3 type molecules have been calculated to be ~ 200 ppm, in fair agreement with experimental values. The large probable errors in X—P—X bond angle measurements render accurate calculations difficult(146).

Parks(145) has modified Muller's original equation (equation (12.12)) for calculating the number of imbalanced p electrons to

$$D' = \left[\frac{3}{4} - \beta^2\right]\beta^2 (1 - \varepsilon) \qquad (12.14)$$

This modified equation allows for the fact that as the phosphorus hybridisation approaches sp^3, the number of imbalanced p electrons, D′, approaches zero. This is only an approximation since large paramagnetic contributions to the shielding of ^{13}C nuclei with sp^3 tetrahedral symmetry have been observed(47). He further modified the empirical chemical shift equation to

$$\delta = -230 + 29{\cdot}0 \times 10^3 \exp(-46D') \qquad (12.15)$$

where δ is the chemical shift measured from 85 per cent orthophosphoric acid. Using this equation, values of δ have been obtained which are in excellent agreement with experimentally observed values (see Table 12.55 for a comparison of calculated and observed ^{31}P chemical shifts).

For quadruply attached phosphorus, the difficulties of calculating D are increased. The calculation of ^{31}P chemical shifts is further complicated by the uncertainty in the extent of the double bond character in the P=O and P=S bonds(4). In pentavalent phosphorus compounds, the number of imbalanced p electrons is less than in trivalent phosphorus compounds and the electronic distribution is also more symmetrical: both factors result in pentavalent phosphorus being more shielded than trivalent phosphorus. In the molecule HPF_6, the high octahedral symmetry, the increase in the number of electrons around the phosphorus, or simply the increase in the number of fluorine atoms have been suggested as possible reasons for its very high chemical shift (δ = 11·8 ppm) compared with other pentavalent phosphorus-containing molecules where the phosphorus is quadruply connected[(141)].

Van Wazer and co-workers[(143)] have examined the ^{31}P resonance spectra of more than two hundred phosphorus-containing compounds (see Appendix F). and they have attributed the large range of chemical shifts found in trivalent phosphorus compounds to the changes in phosphorus hybridisation which accompany changes in substituents (for example, PH_3 is p^3 hybridised whereas

TABLE 12.55 COMPARISON OF THE OBSERVED AND CALCULATED ^{31}P CHEMICAL SHIFTS IN A SERIES OF TRIVALENT PHOSPHORUS COMPOUNDS[(4, 145)]

Compound	Measured chemical shift δ ppm	Calculated chemical shift (Muller)[(4)] δ ppm	Calculated chemical shift (Parks)[(145)] δ ppm
PH_3	+238[(143)]	+240	+230
PF_3	−97[(141)]	−640	−114
PI_3	−178[(141)]	−100	−201
PCl_3	−219[(4)]	−215	−201
PBr_3	−227[(4)]	−230	−227

TABLE 12.56 CONTRIBUTIONS TO THE SHIELDING OF ^{31}P NUCLEI FOR VARIOUS GROUPS IN MOLECULES CONTAINING TRIPLY CONNECTED PHOSPHORUS ATOMS[(143)]

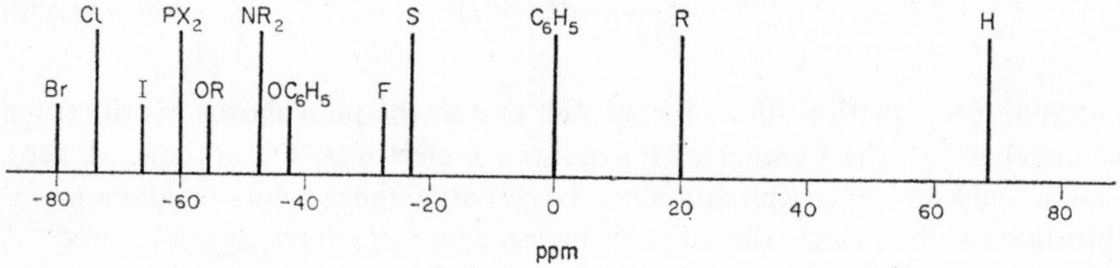

PF_3 is sp^3 hybridised). For triply connected phosphorus compounds the substituents sometimes contribute the same amount to the shielding of the phosphorus nucleus regardless of the other substituents in the molecule. Table 12.56 gives the contributions associated with various groups which are made to the ^{31}P chemical shifts measured from 85 per cent orthophosphoric acid reference band. Using this data it is possible to calculate ^{31}P chemical shifts which are usually accurate to within ± 10 ppm of the measured values (although for some molecules very inaccurate predicted values have been obtained, e.g. RPClF derivatives give calculated ^{31}P chemical shifts of about − 85 ppm: the observed value is + 20 ppm). P_4, PH_3 and P_2S_5 all have ^{31}P chemical shifts which are at much higher field values than for other triply connected phosphorus compounds and this increased shielding has been attributed to the presence of "bent bonds" in these molecules. The validity of the concept of bent bonds has been questioned[(69)].

Groenweghe *et al.*[147] have measured the ^{31}P chemical shifts of two hundred phosphorus-containing molecules and they find that the consecutive substitution of one organic ligand for another on triply connected phosphorus results in approximately equal stepwise changes in the ^{31}P chemical shifts. Table 12.57 illustrates the effect of exchange of halogen atoms or alkyl groups on the ^{31}P chemical shifts of a triply connected phosphorus atom. However, for the compounds considered in this study it was not possible to obtain reliable characteristic ^{31}P chemical shift contributions for the various groups attached to a triply connected phosphorus atom because of the shielding effects of other substituents.

TABLE 12.57 EFFECT ON ^{31}P CHEMICAL SHIFTS OF SUBSEQUENT EXCHANGES OF HALOGENS OR R GROUPS IN TRIPLY CONNECTED PHOSPHORUS COMPOUNDS[147]

Original compound	Substituted compound	Change in chemical shift for		
		1st substitution	2nd substitution	3rd substitution
$(CH_3)_3P$	$(C_2H_5)_3P$	−13·5	−14·5	−13·6
$(C_2H_5)_3P$	$(C_6H_5)_3P$	−5·3	−1·6	−6·5
$(CH_3)_3P$	$(C_6H_5)_3P$	−15·0	−19·0	−21·0
$(CH_3)_2PH$	$(C_2H_5)_2PH$	−22·5	−21·5	
$(CH_3)_2PH$	$(C_4H_9)_2PH$	−19·8	−10·3	
$(CH_3)_2PH$	$(C_6H_5)_2PH$	−27·2	−31·2	
$(CH_3)_2PCl$	$(C_2H_5)_2PCl$	−13·8	−13·2	
$(CH_3)_2PCl$	$(C_6H_5)_2PCl$	+8·6	+1·9	
$(C_2H_5)_2PCl$	$(C_6H_5)_2PCl$	+22·0	+15·5	
$(CH_3)_2PBr$	$(C_2H_5)_2PBr$	−10·6	−17·7	
$(CH_3)_2PBr$	$(C_6H_5)_2PBr$	+10·7	+6·2	

TABLE 12.58 EFFECT ON ^{31}P CHEMICAL SHIFTS OF SUBSTITUTION OF ONE ORGANIC LIGAND BY ANOTHER IN QUADRUPLY CONNECTED PHOSPHORUS COMPOUNDS[147]
(R = any alkyl or aryl group, X = either Cl or Br)

Original structure	Substituted structure	Av. change in shift, ppm	Stand. deviation ppm	No. of substitutions considered
	C_6H_5 replaced by another organic ligand			
C_6H_5RPSCl	C_2H_5RPSCl	−16·1	2·1	4
C_6H_5RPOCl	C_2H_5RPOCl	−16·7	0·9	3
C_6H_5RPSCl	$CH_2ClRPSCl$	−1·1	3·3	3
C_6H_5RPOCl	$CH_2ClRPOCl$	−3·7	1·7	3
	CH_3 replaced by another organic ligand			
CH_3RPOCl	C_2H_5RPOCl	−7·0	1·8	3
CH_3R_2PS	$C_2H_5R_2PS$	+1·5	1·3	3
CH_3RPSX	C_2H_5RPSX	−12·8	4·5	6
CH_3RPOCl	$CH_2ClRPOCl$	+7·2	0·8	3
CH_3RPSX	$CH_2ClRPSX$	+2·9	1·0	3
CH_3RPOCl	C_6H_5RPOCl	+10·8	1·3	3
CH_3RPSX	C_6H_5RPSX	+5·2	2·5	4

The much smaller range of chemical shifts found in quadruply connected phosphorus compounds has been explained in terms of the variations in the distribution of π bonds within the σ-bonded sp^3 hybrids[143]. While in some quadruply connected phosphorus-containing compounds the substituents make constant contributions to the overall shielding regardless of the nature of the other substituents, such interpolated chemical shift values are generally unreliable[4]. However, certain trends have been noted, e.g. when an oxygen atom replaces a nitrogen atom on a pentavalent phosphorus atom there is a

TABLE 12.59 EFFECT ON ^{31}P CHEMICAL SHIFTS OF SUBSTITUTION OF ONE INORGANIC LIGAND BY ANOTHER, ORGANIC OR INORGANIC, IN QUADRUPLY CONNECTED PHOSPHORUS COMPOUNDS[147] (R and R′ = any alkyl or aryl group)

Original structure	Substituted structure	Av. change in shift, ppm	Stand. deviation ppm	No. of pairs of structures considered
		O Replaced by S		
$(RO)_3PO$	$(RO)_3PS$	−70·1	1·0	3
$RP(O)Cl_2$	$RP(S)Cl_2$	−37·5	2·8	4
$RR'P(O)Cl$ in CCl_4	$RR'P(S)Cl$	−31·0	3·9	8
R_3PO in $CHCl_3$	R_3PS in $CHCl_3$	−8·9	5·9	3
		Miscellaneous substitutions		
$RP(O)Cl_2$	$RP(O)(OH)_2$	+19·1	4·9	4
$RP(O)(OH)_2$	$RP(O)(OC_2H_5)_2$	+0·8	1·4	4
$RP(O)Cl_2$	$RP(O)(OC_2H_5)_2$	+18·9	2·7	6
$RR'P(O)Cl$	$RR'P(O)OH$	+12·6	5·1	5
$RR'P(S)Cl$	$RR'P(S)Br$	+18·2	4·6	4
$R_2P(O)Cl$	$R_2P(O)CH_2Cl$	+12·3	6·6	4
$R_2P(O)Cl$	$R_2P(O){-}O{-}P(O)R_2$	+11·5	1·6	5
$R_2P(O)CH_2Cl$	$R_2P(O){-}O{-}P(O)R_2$	−4·2	5·8	3
$R_2P(O)OH$	$R_2P(O){-}O{-}P(O)R_2$	−1·3	6·1	5
$R_2P(O)Cl$	$R_2P(O)OH$	+12·6	4·4	6
$RP(O)(OH)_2$	$(RPO_2)_n$	+17·0	1·3	3
$RP(O)Cl_2$	$(RPO_2)_n$	+30·4	5·7	3
$RP(O)(OC_2H_5)_2$	$(RPO_2)_n$	+17·3	0·8	3

constant contribution to the phosphorus chemical shift of -11 ± 2 ppm per atom. When oxygen is replaced by a less electronegative atom such as nitrogen or sulphur, the shielding of the phosphorus nucleus is decreased because the oxygen forms double bonds with phosphorus more readily than do the other elements. Replacement of an oxygen atom by sulphur is thought to be accompanied by a change in bond type which differs from molecule to molecule, since the chemical shift contribution for this substitution varies over the range −25 to −71 ppm per atom.

Groenweghe and co-workers[147, 148] have found that the contributions made to the shielding of a quadruply connected phosphorus nucleus from directly bonded groups lie in the order $C_6H_5 \geqq CH_2Cl > CH_3 > C_2H_5$. The shielding contributions made by these groups are independent of the remaining substituents and they can be used to successfully predict ^{31}P chemical shifts. Tables 12.58 and 12.59 summarise the ^{31}P shielding effects of substituents in quadruply connected phosphorus compounds. Katritzky and Jones(149) have pointed out the limitations of the additivity relationships for the chemical shifts of both trivalent and pentavalent phosphorus: when the mean chemical shift contributions are calculated statistically for a large number of substituents, large standard deviations are encountered, particularly for trivalent phosphorus compounds.

Anomalous ^{31}P chemical shifts have been observed in substituted aromatic phosphorus compounds for phosphorus atoms attached directly to the ring: the chemical shifts (included in Appendix F) cannot be explained in terms of aromatic ring currents(146).

Atoms or groups other than those attached directly to the phosphorus atom under investigation have little or no effect on ^{31}P chemical shifts or coupling constants(4, 143). This is illustrated by the ^{31}P chemical shift in the two trialkyl phosphates $(C_2H_5O)_3PO$ and $(ClC_2H_4O)_3PO$ of 0·9 and 1·3 ppm from H_3PO_4 reference respectively.

12.6.2 Spin–Spin Interactions Involving ^{31}P *Nuclei*

Table 12.60 gives a list of several $^{31}P—^1H$, $^{31}P—^{19}F$ and $^{31}P—^{31}P$ coupling constants for directly bonded nuclei which have been reported to date. No theoretical interpretations of any of these types of coupling have been proposed but Finegold(146) has made the following general observations:

(1) P—H coupling constants for atoms directly bonded are larger in P=O type compounds than in P=S compounds (see Table 12.61).

(2) P—H coupling constants between atoms which are separated by one or two bonds are smaller in P=O than in P=S compounds

1 bond separation

2 bond separation

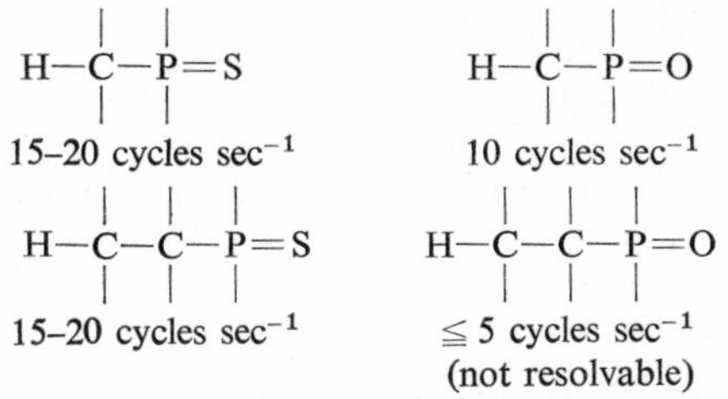

Manatt and co-workers(259) have determined the absolute signs of several P—H coupling constants using double irradiation techniques and assuming J_{PH} for directly bonded nuclei is positive. Their results are summarised below

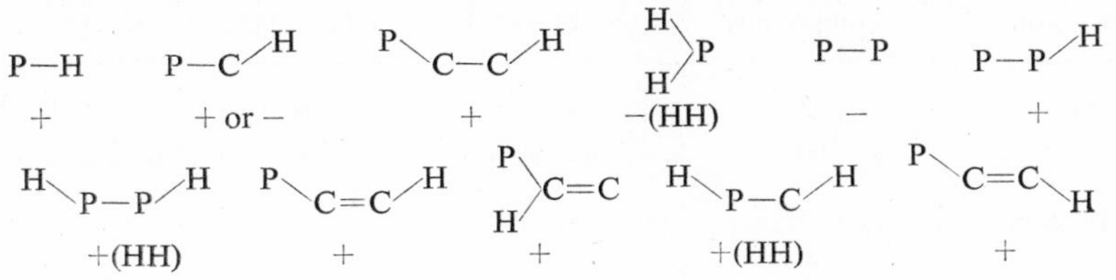

In a series of trialkyl phosphates, (R—CH$_2$O)$_3$P=O, the P—H coupling constants between the phosphorus nucleus and the neighbouring CH$_2$ group are found to decrease in magnitude as the electropositive nature of the alkyl substituents is increased[(154)]. The coupling constants given in Table 12.62 were obtained from the ^{1}H resonance spectra of the trialkyl phosphates (the P—H coupling constant in trimethyl phosphate has also been measured in the ^{31}P resonance spectrum of this compound[(152)]).

TABLE 12.60 ^{31}P SPIN–SPIN COUPLING CONSTANTS INVOLVING DIRECTLY BONDED NUCLEI

Compound	J_{PH} (cycles sec^{-1})	J_{PF} (cycles sec^{-1})	J_{PP} (cycles sec^{-1})	Reference
PH_3	(179)			143
PF_3		(1410)		141
CH_3PH_2	(207)			143
$(CH_3)_2PH$	(207)			143
C_2H_5PClF		(569)		143
$(i\text{-}C_3H_7O)_2HPO$	692 ± 0·5			161
$CH_3(C_2H_5O)HPO$	518 ± 8			146
$(C_2H_5O)_2HPS$	645 ± 8			146
$CH_3(i\text{-}C_3H_7O)HPS$	492 ± 8			146
HPF_6		(707)		141
$HPO(OH)_2$	707			12
$H_2PO(OH)$	584			12
$C_2H_5POF_2$		1132		155
CH_3POF_2		110		155
P_2H_4	186·5		108·2	164
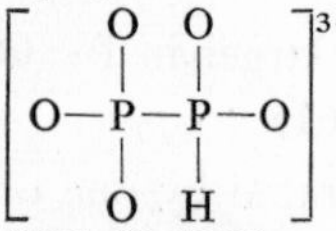	444		480	152
$(CH_3O)_2HPO$	690·3 ± 0·5			161
$(C_2H_5O)_2HPO$	684·1 ± 0·5			161
$CH_3(C_3H_7O)HPO$	550·1 ± 0·5			161
$H_2(OH)P(O)(=H_3PO_2)$	561 ± 8			146

Several of the above coupling constants have been taken from a compilation by P. C. Lauterbur in reference 50.

J values in parentheses are probably accurate to ±20 cycles sec^{-1}.

See Table 11.62 for J_{PF} coupling constants.

TABLE 12.61 RANGE OF P—H AND P—F COUPLING CONSTANTS FOUND IN VARIOUS TYPES OF MOLECULES[(149)]

Type of compound	Number of compounds	J_{PH} (cycles sec^{-1})	Number of compounds	J_{PF} (cycles sec^{-1})
P(III)	3	180–210	5	570–1420
>P=O	13	500–700	5	980–1190
>P=S, Se	3	490–630		

TABLE 12.62 ^{31}P—^{1}H SPIN–SPIN COUPLING CONSTANTS FOR SYMMETRICAL AND UNSYMMETRICAL TRIALKYL PHOSPHATES(150, 154)

Compound	Formula	J_{CH_2-P} (cycles sec^{-1})	Reference
A. Symmetrical trialkyl phosphates			
Trimethyl phosphate	$(CH_3O)_3P{=}O$	11·19 ± 0·2	154
Triethyl phosphate	$(C_2H_5O)_3P{=}O$	8·38 ± 0·2	154
Tripropyl phosphate	$(n\text{-}C_3H_7O)_3P{=}O$	7·70 ± 0·1	154
Tributyl phosphate	$(n\text{-}C_4H_9O)_3P{=}O$	7·65 ± 0·1	154
Triamyl phosphate	$(n\text{-}C_5H_{11}O)_3P{=}O$	7·62 ± 0·2	154
Tri-isobutyl phosphate	$[(CH_3)_2CH{-}CH_2O]_3P{=}O$	6·60 ± 0·1	154
Tri-neo-pentyl phosphate	$[(CH_3)_3C{-}CH_2O]_3P{=}O$	5·24 ± 0·1	154
Tris-(2,2,2-trichloroethyl)phosphate	$(CCl_3CH_2O)_3P{=}O$	7·05 ± 0·1	150
Tris-(2,2,2-trifluoroethyl)phosphate	$(CF_3CH_2O)_3P{=}O$	8·34 ± 0·1	150
Tri-(2,2-dichloroethyl)phosphate	$(CHCl_2CH_2O)_3P{=}O$	8·4 ± 0·2	150
Tribenzylphosphate	$(C_6H_5CH_2O)_3P{=}O$	9·07 ± 0·1	150
Triallylphosphate	$(CH_2{=}CH{-}CH_2O)_3P{=}O$	8·3 ± 0·2	150

	Formula	Group	J_{CH_2-P} (cycles sec^{-1})	
B. Unsymmetrical trialkylphosphates	$(C_6H_5CH_2O)_4P_2O_3$	Benzyl	8·62 ± 0·2	150
	$CH_3OP(=O)(OCH_2CH_2)(OCH_2CH_2)$ (cyclic, $OCH_2CH_2{-}CH_2CH_2O$ ring)	Methyl	11·2 ± 0·1	150
	$CH_3PO(OCH_2C_6H_5)_2$ (P=O)	Methyl	11·12 ± 0·1	150
		Benzyl	8·68 ± 0·1	150

When the substituent R in the alkoxy group is strongly electronegative the coupling constants are found to be insensitive to changes in the electronegativity of the substituents. This can be seen from examination of Table 12.62. Trialkyl phosphates other than these have been shown by Dudek[150] to possess J_{PH} coupling constants which can be correlated with Taft substituent constants[151]. The changes in J_{CH_2-P} coupling constants observed in this series of molecules could be due to changes in the electronic environment of either the phosphorus atom or the methylenic group. By examining unsymmetrical derivatives of the trialkyl phosphates (see Table 12.62) it was possible to decide which of the

TABLE 12.63 ^{31}P—^1H SPIN–SPIN COUPLING CONSTANTS IN PHOSPHORUS ALKYLS

Compound	J_{P-CH_2} (cycles sec^{-1})	J_{P-CH_3} (cycles sec^{-1})
$C_2H_5PCl_2$[155]	17·7	15·2
$C_2H_5POF_2$[155]	23·6	23·6
$C_2H_5POCl_2$[155]	14·5	30·3
CH_3POCl_2[155]		16·9
CH_3POF_2[155]		19·9
$(C_2H_5)_3P$[233]	0·5	13·7

two effects is dominant[152]. Changes in the environment of the phosphorus atom in tribenzyl phosphate as compared with tetrabenzyl pyrophosphate are seen to affect the J_{PH} coupling constants only slightly. In other unsymmetrical compounds there is also only a slight variation in the value of this coupling constant with change in substituent. It is therefore concluded that changes in the environment of the methylene group are responsible for controlling variations in J_{PH} coupling constants in this series of compounds. Coupling constants between phosphorus and hydrogen atoms on the second carbon atom of the alkyl group have also been measured[153]. It is found that increasing the number of bonds between the phosphorus and the hydrogen drastically attenuates the coupling constants, e.g. in triethyl phosphate, $(CH_3CH_2O)_3P=O$, $J_{P-CH_2} = 8·38$ and $J_{P-CH_3} = 0·76$ cycles sec^{-1}. This attenuation is not found in phosphorus-containing compounds which have the ethyl group attached directly to the phosphorus atom: in some cases larger P—H coupling is found between atoms separated by three bonds than those separated by two bonds. Table 12.63 lists the J_{P-H} coupling constants in molecules of this type[155].

A similar reversal of ^1H—^{31}P coupling constants is found in the ^1H resonance spectra of compounds with the general formula

$$\begin{matrix} & & O \\ & & \| \\ R_1\!\!\!\searrow & & \\ R_2\!\!\!-\!\!\!\!&C-P-Y \\ R_3\!\!\!\nearrow & & | \\ & & X \end{matrix}$$

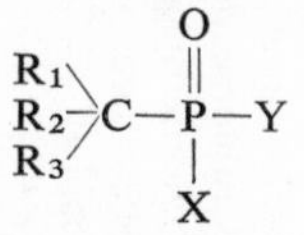

where the substituent R can be a hydrogen atom, an alkyl group or a benzene ring: Y may be either OH, Cl, OCH_3 or OCH_2CH_3, and X is either Cl or a benzene ring[156, 157]. Table 12.64 lists the $J_{H\alpha-P}$ and $J_{H\beta-P}$ spin coupling

TABLE 12.64 ^1H—^{31}P COUPLING CONSTANTS IN SOME ORGANOPHOSPHORUS ESTERS(156)

Compound	$R_1R_2R_3C{-}P(=O)(X){-}Y$					Coupling constant (cycles sec^{-1})	
	R_1	R_2	R_3	X	Y	$J_{H\alpha-P}$	$J_{H\beta-P}$
Methylphenylphosphinyl chloride	—H	—H	—H	$—C_6H_5$	—Cl	14·1	
Ethylphosphonyl dichloride	—H	—H	$—CH_3$	—Cl	—Cl	14·2	30·0
Ethylphenylphosphinyl chloride	—H	—H	$—CH_3$	$—C_6H_5$	—Cl	12·1	22·1
Isopropylphosphonyl dichloride	—H	$—CH_3$	$—CH_3$	—Cl	—Cl	12 ± 1	27·6
Isopropylphenylphosphinyl chloride	—H	$—CH_3$	$—CH_3$	$—C_6H_5$	—Cl		20·6
Isopropylphenylphosphinic acid	—H	$—CH_3$	$—CH_3$	$—C_6H_5$	—OH		17·6
Methyl isopropylphenylphosphinate	—H	$—CH_3$	$—CH_3$	$—C_6H_5$	$—OCH_3$		17·3
Ethyl isopropylphenylphosphinate	—H	$—CH_3$	$—CH_3$	$—C_6H_5$	$—OC_2H_5$		17·1
t-Butylphosphonyl dichloride	$—CH_3$	$—CH_3$	$—CH_3$	—Cl	—Cl		24·8
t-Butylphenylphosphinyl chloride	$—CH_3$	$—CH_3$	$—CH_3$	$—C_6H_5$	—Cl		17·7
t-Butylphenylphosphinic acid	$—CH_3$	$—CH_3$	$—CH_3$	$—C_6H_5$	—OH		15·7
2-Butylphosphonyl dichloride	—H	$—CH_3$	$—C_2H_5$	—Cl	—Cl		
2-Butylphenylphosphinyl chloride	—H	$—CH_3$	$—C_2H_5$	$—C_6H_5$	—Cl		20·0
Isobutylphenylphosphinyl chloride	—H	—H	$—C_3H_7$	$—C_6H_5$	—Cl		
3-Amylphenylphosphinyl chloride	—H	$—C_2H_5$	$—C_2H_5$	$—C_6H_5$	—Cl		
1-Phenylethylphenylphosphinic acid	—H	$—CH_3$	$—C_6H_5$	$—C_6H_5$	—OH	18·6	16·8
Methyl 1-phenylethylphenylphosphinate	—H	$—CH_3$	$—C_6H_5$	$—C_6H_5$	$—OCH_3$		17·1

TABLE 12.65 CHARACTERISTIC ^{31}P CHEMICAL SHIFTS[146]

Compound type	Specifications	δ (ppm from external H_3PO_4)	No. of different compounds examined
$R(R'O)_2P$	(a) R, R′ = aliph. higher than CH_3 (b) R = $CH_3 \neq R'$	−183 ± 1 −175 ± 2	2 7
$R(R'S)_2P$	(a) R = CH_3 R′ = aliph. higher than CH_3 (b) R = CH_3 R′ = aromatic	− 69·4 ± 0·7 −84·5	2 1
$(RO)_3P$ symmetrical	(a) R = aliph. higher than CH_3 (b) R = CH_3 (c) R = aromatic	−138 ± 1 −139 −127 ± 1	10 1 2
$(RS)_3P$ symmetrical	R = aliph. higher than CH_3	−117 ± 1	2
$R_3P(O)$ symmetrical	(a) R = aliph. higher than CH_3 (b) R = aromatic	−46·0 ± 2·5 −23·0	2 1
$R(R')(R''O)P(O)$	(a) R, R′, R″ = aliph. higher than CH_3, R = R′ (b) R = R′ = CH_3 R″ = aliph. higher than CH_3 (c) R = CH_3, R′, R″ = aliph. higher than CH_3	−54·9 ± 0·2 −49·5 ± 0·5 −53·0 ± 1·0	1 2 2
$R(R'O)_2P(O)$	(a) R, R′ = aliph. higher than CH_3 (b) R = CH_3, R′ = aliph. higher than CH_3 (c) R = aliph. higher than CH_3, R′ = CH_3	−32·8 ± 1·5 −28·4 ± 0·9 −35·0	5 5 1
$R(R'O)(R''S)P(O)$	(a) R, R′, R″ = aliph. higher than CH_3 (b) R = CH_3, R′, R″ = aliph. higher than CH_3	−56·5 ± 0·8 −50·5 ± 1·4	2 9
$R(R'S)_2P(O)$	R = CH_3 R′ = aliph. higher than CH_3	−55·8	1
$(RO)_3P(O)$ symmetrical	(a) R = aliph. higher than CH_3 (b) R = aromatic	+1·07 ± 1·00 +17·4 ± 0·3	5 4
$(RO)(R'O)_2P(O)$	R = aliph. higher than CH_3 R′ = aromatic	+12·0	1

(*continued*)

Compound type	Specifications	δ (ppm from external H_3PO_4)	No. of different compounds examined
$(RO)_2(R'S)P(O)$	(a) R, R′ = aliph. higher than CH_3	−26·5 ± 0·3	6
	(b) R = aliph. higher than CH_3, R′ = CH_3	−28·4	1
	(c) R = aliph. higher than CH_3, R′ = aromatic	−21·5 ± 0·5	2
$(RS)_3P(O)$ symmetrical	R = aliph. higher than CH_3	−61·3	1
$R_3P(S)$ symmetrical	R = aliph. higher than CH_3	−51·0 ± 3·0	2
$R(R'O)_2P(S)$	(a) R, R′ = aliph. higher than CH_3	−101·7	1
	(b) R′ = aliph. higher than CH_3, R = CH_3	−94·5 ± 0·9	8
$R(R'S)_2P(S)$	R = CH_3, R′ = aliph. higher than CH_3	−74·0 ± 3·0	2
$(RO)_3P(S)$	(a) R = aliph. higher than CH_3	−68·1 ± 1·2	11
	(b) R = CH_3	−73·0	1
$(RO)_2(RS)P(S)$	R = aliph. higher than CH_3	−94·9	1
$(RS)_3P(S)$ symmetrical	R = aliph. higher than CH_3	−92·9	1
$(R_2N)_3P$ symmetrical	(a) R = aliph. higher than CH_3	−118	1
	(b) R = CH_3	−122	1
$(R_2N)_3P(O)$ symmetrical	(a) R = aliph. higher than CH_3	−23·0	1
	(b) R = CH_3	−23·4	1
$(R_2N)_2P(O)OR'$	R′ = aliph. higher than CH_3, R = CH_3	−16·3	1
$(R_2N)_3P(S)$ symmetrical	R = aliph. higher than CH_3	−76·0 ± 1·0	2
$(R_2N)_2P(O)R'$	R = R′ = CH_3	−38·0	1
$(R_2N)P(O)(OR')_2$	R′ = aliph. higher than CH_3, R = CH_3	−35·0	1
$(R_2N)P(S)(OR')_2$	R, R = aliph. higher than CH_3	−75·0	1

constants for a series of such compounds. When these organophosphorus esters contain an aromatic group, several of the ^1H absorption bands are doubled, indicating that the molecules spend an appreciable fraction of their lifetime in a preferred conformation[156, 157].

It is worth noting that P—H coupling is not observed between the weakly acidic hydrogen atoms and the phosphorus atom in orthophosphoric acid because the hydrogen nucleus is involved in a rapid exchange process(152).

12.6.3 *Applications of* ^{31}P *Resonance to Structure Determinations*

Changes in the electronic environment of a phosphorus atom are usually accompanied by large variations in the shielding of the phosphorus nucleus. Each class of phosphorus compound has been found to give characteristic average chemical shifts which can be used to assist in the determination of the molecular structures of phosphorus-containing compounds. Finegold(146) has compiled a table of these characteristic ^{31}P chemical shifts (measured from H_3PO_4 external reference) and this is reproduced in Table 12.65. The data from which these average chemical shift values have been extracted are given in Table 12.53 and Appendix F. When it is necessary to prepare solutions of samples for ^{31}P resonance measurements, care should be taken to avoid solvents which are capable of forming hydrogen bonds (e.g. $CHCl_3$, C_2H_5OH, H_2O, dioxane) since these are known to affect ^{31}P chemical shifts(4). Solvents such as carbon tetrachloride and carbon disulphide have shown no dilution effects in the few cases where these solvents have been used(4). Some examples of structural proofs achieved using ^{31}P resonance will now be discussed.

Organic phosphites(152). Although the structures of tertiary esters of phosphorous acid are invariably given as $(RO)_3P$, the primary and secondary esters are sometimes written with four atoms attached to phosphorus instead of three, e.g. $(RO)_2P(H)O$ instead of $(RO)_2POH$. ^{31}P NMR measurements have shown that more than 95 per cent of the molecules are in the form where the hydrogen is directly attached to the phosphorus atom, since the J_{P-H} coupling constant (~ 600 cycles sec^{-1}) expected for the two nuclei when directly bonded

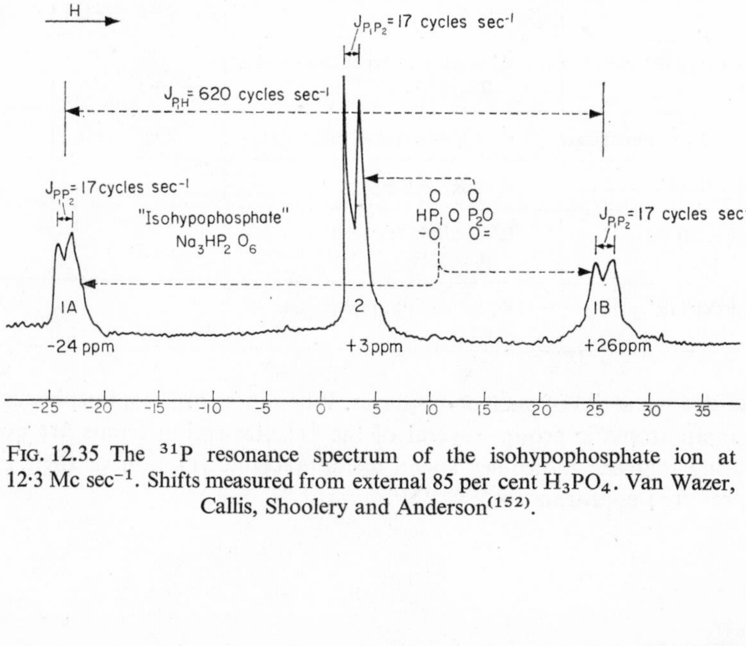

FIG. 12.35 The ^{31}P resonance spectrum of the isohypophosphate ion at 12·3 Mc sec^{-1}. Shifts measured from external 85 per cent H_3PO_4. Van Wazer, Callis, Shoolery and Anderson(152).

is observed in the spectrum and no absorption band corresponding to phosphorus in the group POH could be found[152]. The presence of this P—H doublet splitting indicates the absence of rapid exchange of the hydrogen atom attached to the phosphorus atom.

Oxyacids containing two phosphorus atoms[152]. There are five known oxyacids containing two phosphorus atoms, namely

(i)
$$\left[\begin{array}{c} \text{O} \quad\quad \text{O} \\ | \quad\quad\quad | \\ \text{O--P--O--P--O} \\ | \quad\quad\quad | \\ \text{O} \quad\quad \text{O} \end{array} \right]^{4-}$$

Pyrophosphate

(ii)
$$\left[\begin{array}{c} \text{O} \quad \text{O} \\ | \quad\quad | \\ \text{O--P--P--O} \\ | \quad\quad | \\ \text{O} \quad \text{O} \end{array} \right]^{4-}$$

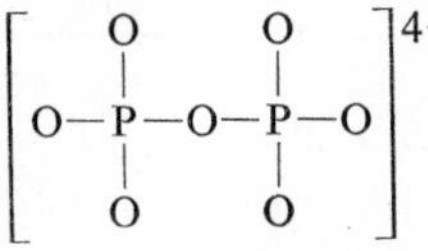

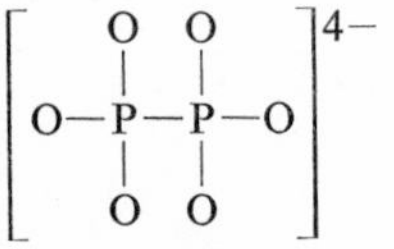

Hypophosphate

(iii)
$$\left[\begin{array}{c} \text{O} \quad\quad \text{O} \\ | \quad\quad\quad | \\ \text{O--P--O--P--O} \\ | \quad\quad\quad | \\ \text{H} \quad\quad \text{H} \end{array} \right]^{2-}$$

Pyrophosphite

(iv)
$$\left[\begin{array}{c} \text{O} \quad\quad \text{O} \\ | \quad\quad\quad | \\ \text{O--P--O--P--O} \\ | \quad\quad\quad | \\ \text{O} \quad\quad \text{H} \end{array} \right]^{3-}$$

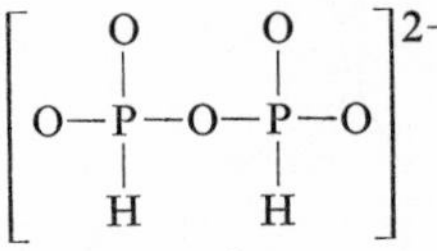

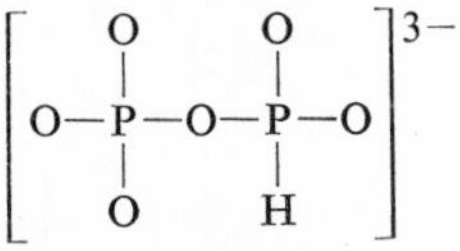

Isohypophosphate

(v)
$$\left[\begin{array}{c} \text{O} \quad \text{O} \\ | \quad\quad | \\ \text{O--P--P--O} \\ | \quad\quad | \\ \text{O} \quad \text{H} \end{array} \right]^{3-}$$

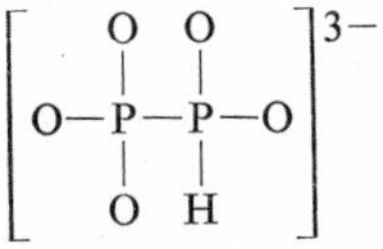

Diphosphite

These structures have been determined by chemical methods and are confirmed by examination of their ^{31}P resonance spectra[152].

(i) and (ii) The ^{31}P NMR spectra of both the pyro- and hypophosphate consist of a single resonance band as would be expected for the symmetrical structures to which they have been assigned (their respective chemical shifts are $+6$ and -9 ppm from 85 per cent orthophosphoric acid reference). Furthermore, the spectra confirm that hydrogen is not directly attached to the phosphorus atom in either ion.

(iii) The ^{31}P resonance spectrum of the pyrophosphite ion is a single doublet due to spin–spin interaction between the two equivalent phosphorus atoms and the hydrogen atom to which each is directly bonded (J_{PH} ~ 660 cycles sec^{-1}). The presence of a single doublet confirms that the structure of this ion is symmetrical thus leading to two equivalently shielded phosphorus nuclei.

(iv) The ^{31}P resonance spectrum of the isohypophosphate ion is shown in Fig. 12.35 together with the assignments for the various absorption bands. Spin–spin interaction between the two non-equivalent phosphorus nuclei gives rise to a small doublet splitting on each band in the spectrum ($J_{\text{PP}} = 17$ cycles sec^{-1}). The phosphorus atom attached directly to a hydrogen atom gives rise to a doublet due to P—H coupling

($J_{PH} = 620$ cycles sec^{-1}). The proposed structure for this ion is thus confirmed since the ^{31}P spectrum indicates the presence of two non-equivalent phosphorus atoms one of which is directly bonded to a single hydrogen atom[152].

(v) The diphosphite ion gives rise to a ^{31}P spectrum which contains two multiplets (see Fig. 12.36) and corresponds to the AB part of an ABX type spectrum (see Section 8.15.1). Analysis of the spectrum yields the

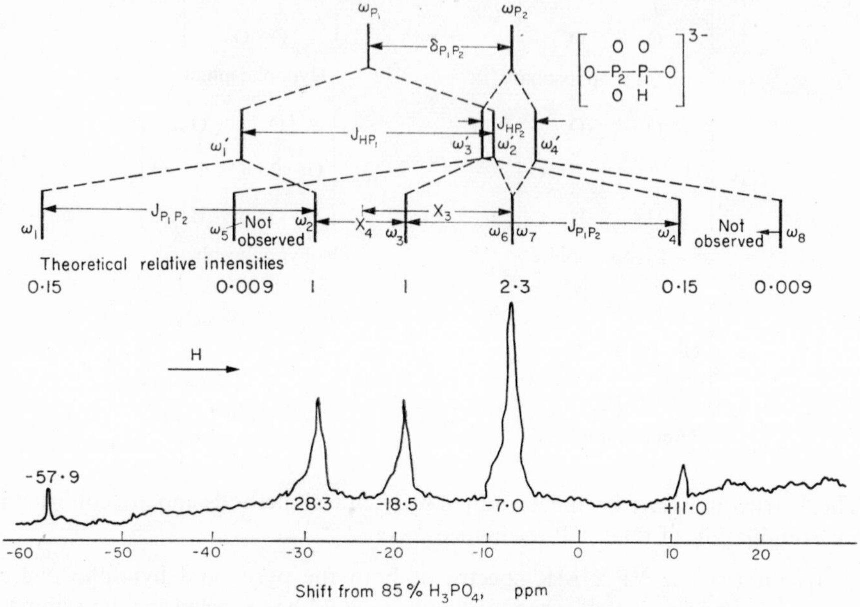

FIG. 12.36 The ^{31}P resonance spectrum of the diphosphite ion at 12·3 Mc sec^{-1}.
Van Wazer, Callis, Shoolery and Anderson[152].

following parameters: $\delta_{P_1} = -22·6$ ppm; $\delta_{P_2} = -7·0$ ppm (negative values correspond to the low field side of 85 per cent orthophosphoric acid external reference). $J_{P_1P_2} = 480 \pm 10$ cycles sec^{-1}, $J_{HP_1} = 444$ cycles sec^{-1} and $J_{HP_2} = 94$ cycles sec^{-1}. Hence the structure of the ion is confirmed to be

$$\left[\begin{array}{c} O \quad O \\ | \quad | \\ O-P_2-P_1-O \\ | \quad | \\ O \quad H \end{array} \right]^{3-}$$

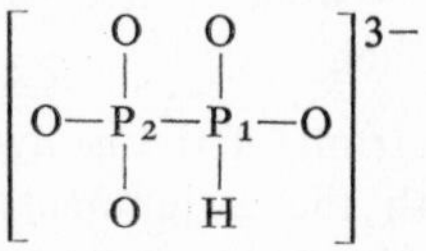

since the ^{31}P spectrum is consistent with two non-equivalent phosphorus atoms directly attached to each other, with one of them being also directly bonded to a hydrogen atom[152].

Tetrapolyphosphate ion, $P_4O_{13}^{6-}$. The tetrapolyphosphate anion is known to have the following structure

$$O=\overset{\overset{\displaystyle {}^-O}{|}}{\underset{\underset{\displaystyle {}_-O}{|}}{P_1}}-O-\overset{\overset{\displaystyle {}^-O}{|}}{\underset{\underset{\displaystyle O}{\|}}{P_2}}-O-\overset{\overset{\displaystyle O^-}{|}}{\underset{\underset{\displaystyle O}{\|}}{P_3}}-O-\overset{\overset{\displaystyle O^-}{|}}{\underset{\underset{\displaystyle O_-}{\|}}{P_4}}=O$$

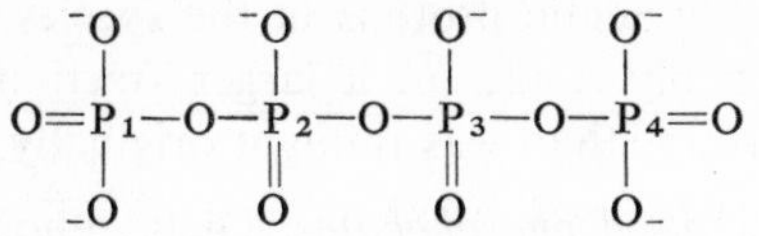

with the oxygen atoms arranged tetrahedrally around the phosphorus atoms. The phosphorus nuclei in such a species constitute an AA'XX' spin system

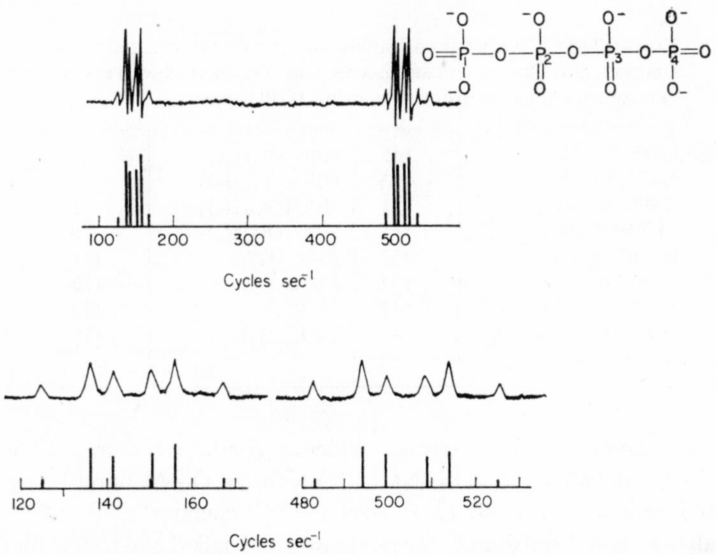

FIG. 12.37 Observed and calculated ^{31}P resonance spectra at 24·3 Mc sec^{-1} for ammonium tetrapolyphosphate. Frequencies are measured from external 85 per cent H_3PO_4. The band at 543 cycles sec^{-1} is due to a small amount of $P_4O_{12}^{4-}$. Crutchfield, Callis, Irani and Roth[158].

and the observed ^{31}P resonance spectrum shown in Fig. 12.37 is completely in accord with this structure[158]. A detailed analysis of the spectrum leads to the P—P spin coupling constants shown in Table 12.66: they can be seen to depend quite markedly upon the pH of the solution.

TABLE 12.66 P—P SPIN COUPLING CONSTANTS IN THE TETRA-POLYPHOSPHATE ION UNDER VARIOUS pH CONDITIONS[158]

pH	$|J_{12} = J_{34}|$	$|J_{23}|$
8	19·9 cycles sec^{-1}	16·7 cycles sec^{-1}
4	19·7	16·8
2	18·7	16·5
0	16·7	15·9

Crutchfield and co-workers[158] have also studied the effect of pH changes on the ^{31}P chemical shifts of several condensed phosphates. From their studies it is found that the weakly acidic protons in the species $HP_3O_{10}^{4-}$, $H_2P_3O_{10}^{3-}$, $HP_4O_{13}^{5-}$, $H_2P_4O_{13}^{4-}$ probably reside for a larger fraction of their time near the middle phosphate groups than was thought originally.

Alkali metal salts of dialkyl phosphonates. Dialkylphosphonates have been shown by ^{31}P NMR measurements to have the structure $(RO)_2P(H)O$ rather than $(RO)_2POH$. However, the alkali metal salts of dialkylphosphonates are found to have ^{31}P chemical shifts in the region expected for triply connected

TABLE 12.67 ^{31}P CHEMICAL SHIFTS OF ALKALI METAL SALTS OF DIALKYL AND DIARYL PHOSPHONATES AND TRIALKYL AND TRIARYL PHOSPHITES (in ppm from 85 per cent H_3PO_4 external reference)

$LiOP(OC_2H_5)_2$	−145	$HPO(OCH_3)_2$	−11
$NaOP(OC_2H_5)_2$	−153	$HPO(OC_2H_5)_2$	−8
$KOP(OC_2H_5)_2$	−152	$HPO(OC_4H_9)_2$	−8
$LiOP(OC_4H_9)_2$	−145	$HPO(OC_6H_5)_2$	0
$NaOP(OC_4H_9)_2$	−152	$P(OCH_3)_3$	−141
$KOP(OC_4H_9)_2$	−153	$P(OC_2H_5)_3$	−139
$LiOP(OC_6H_5)_2$	−142	$P(OC_4H_9)_3$	−139
$NaOP(OC_6H_5)_2$	−148	$P(OC_6H_5)_3$	−128
$KOP(OC_6H_5)_2$	−139		

phosphorus atoms, which is strong evidence for a structure of the type $(RO)_2P—O—M$ (where M is Li, Na or K) with the O—M bond being predominantly covalent[159]. Table 12.67 gives the ^{31}P chemical shifts of the alkali metal salts of dialkyl and diaryl phosphonates and trialkyl and triaryl phosphites while Table 12.68 gives the J_{PH} coupling constants in some of the parent molecules.

^{31}P chemical shift measurements have also been used to distinguish between phosphonates, $(RO)_2R'P(O)$, ($\delta = -19$ to -31 ppm) and phosphates $(RO)_2(R'O)P(O)$, ($\delta = 0$ to $+8$ ppm) in reaction products[248].

TABLE 12.68 $^{1}H—^{31}P$ COUPLING CONSTANTS (CYCLES SEC^{-1}) IN DIALKYL PHOSPHONATES, $HPO(OR)_2$[159]

Substituent R	J_{PH} (cycles sec^{-1})
CH_3	715
C_2H_5	686
C_4H_9	690
C_6H_5	746

Condensed phosphates. It is only recently that some degree of order has been achieved in the field of condensed phosphates, and NMR has played an important part in assisting other techniques in the characterisation of various phosphate structures. Phosphorus atoms in isolated, end, middle and branching point phosphate groups each give rise to separate ^{31}P absorption bands with characteristic chemical shifts(152, 160) as seen in Table 12.69. For solutions of phosphate glasses with chain lengths of less than ~ 75 atoms, it was possible to detect the end phosphate groups by NMR with the available sensitivity. In some molecules P—P indirect spin–spin interaction gives rise to fine structure which assists in assigning the absorption bands in a spectrum. The existence of such interactions in tripoly and tetrapolyphosphates indicates that the P—P bond in these molecules is covalent in character.

Figure 12.38 shows the ^{31}P resonance spectra of various phosphate ions at 40·5 Mc sec^{-1} (23,500 gauss)(277): the spectra recorded at this high field value are of much higher quality than those obtained previously at lower field strengths.

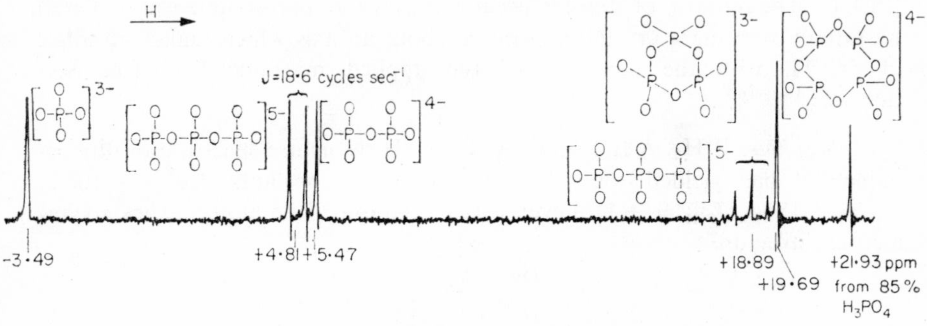

FIG. 12.38 The ^{31}P resonance spectra of various phosphate ions at 40·5 Mc sec^{-1} (23,500 gauss). Pier(277) (Varian Associates).

TABLE 12.69 ^{31}P CHEMICAL SHIFTS IN CONDENSED PHOSPHATES(152, 160)

Type of PO_4 group	Chemical shifts (ppm)	
	δ_{PBr_3}	$\delta_{H_3PO_4 ext}$
Orthophosphate ions		
Isolated Groups		
Trisubstituted (normal) salts	233	6
1 to 3 H atoms per P atom	238	11
End Groups		
Doubly substituted (no H^+ ions)	244	17
1 to 2 H atoms per P atom	247	20
Middle Groups		
Short chain	256	29
Long chain	259	32
Branching Points		
Alkali metal ultraphosphates	268	41
Azeotropic phosphoric acid	272	45

Chemical shifts extrapolated to the H_3PO_4 external reference scale using the conversion $\delta_{H_3PO_4 ext} = \delta_{PBr_3} - 227$ ppm.

Pentavalent phosphorus thioacids. NMR has elucidated the structures of several thioacids of pentavalent phosphorus[146]. The acid of formula $(C_2H_5O)_2POSH$ ($\delta = -24$ ppm) can be assigned to a structure containing a $P{=}O$ bond rather than a $P{=}S$ bond on the basis of its chemical shift alone. Conversely, acids of formula $CH_3(C_2H_5O)PSOH$ ($\delta = -88\cdot8$ ppm) and $C_2H_5(C_2H_5O)PSOH$ ($\delta = -94\cdot2$ ppm) can be assigned to structures containing $P{=}S$ bonds, from their ^{31}P chemical shift values.

Phosphorus pentachloride. This provides an example of one of the few samples to be examined in the solid state by high resolution NMR. The presence of two different phosphorus species in the solid state as indicated by two chemically shifted absorption bands supports the presence of two differently charged phosphorus-containing species in the sample, namely $[PCl_6]^-$ and $[PCl_4]^+$. The removal of dipolar broadening in the solid sample was achieved by rapidly rotating a crystalline sample about an axis which makes an angle of $54°\ 44'$ with the direction of the applied magnetic field (see Section 7.1)[162, 163].

Diphosphine, P_2H_4. A full analysis of the 1H resonance spectrum of diphosphine[164] has yielded the following coupling constants $J_{PP'} = -108\cdot2$, $J_{PH} = \pm 186\cdot5$, $J_{P'H} = \pm 11\cdot9$ cycles sec^{-1}. Although the molecule has a symmetrical structure

$$\begin{array}{cc} H & H \\ \diagdown & \diagup \\ & P{-}P' \\ \diagup & \diagdown \\ H & H \end{array}$$

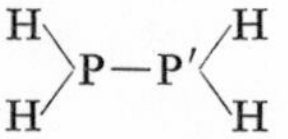

the two phosphorus nuclei are magnetically non-equivalent and the four hydrogen nuclei form two pairs of magnetically non-equivalent nuclei (an $A_2A_2'XX'$ system).

Stereoisomers of substituted diphosphines. The ^{31}P resonance spectra of molecules of general formula

$$\begin{array}{cc} CH_3 & CH_3 \\ \diagdown & \diagup \\ & P{-}P \\ \diagup & \diagdown \\ R_1 & R_1 \end{array}$$

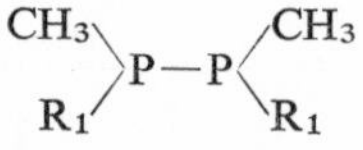

where R_1 is an alkyl or aryl group, show two chemically shifted absorption bands of equal intensity.[165] This is explained by postulating that the molecules exist as two stereoisomers I and II

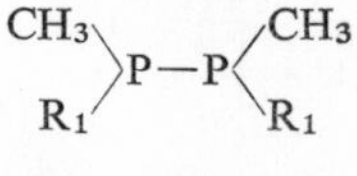

$$\begin{array}{cc} CH_3 & CH_3 \\ \diagdown & \diagup \\ & P{-}P \\ \diagup & \diagdown \\ R_1 & R_1 \end{array} \quad (I) \qquad \begin{array}{cc} CH_3 & R_1 \\ \diagdown & \diagup \\ & P{-}P \\ \diagup & \diagdown \\ R_1 & CH_3 \end{array} \quad (II)$$

Miscellaneous studies. In a series of cyclic phosphorus compounds of the type shown in Table 12.70 the chemical shift of the phosphorus nucleus is found to have no simple correlation with the size of the ring[166].

A ^{31}P resonance investigation of adenosine di- and triphosphate compounds of biochemical interest has been made and the pH dependence of the various ^{31}P absorption bands has been measured[167]. Phosphate solutions of less than $0\cdot1$ M were included in the samples studied and the sensitivity problems

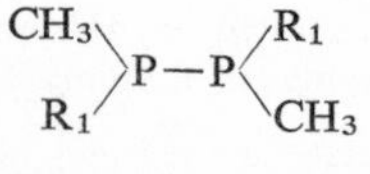

were overcome by using an opposed side-band technique with lock-in detection and very slow sweep rates.

The ^{31}P resonance spectra of several substituted phosphonitriles have been examined to determine the manner of substitution in the molecules(168, 169, 265) (see Appendix F). Figure 12.40 shows a typical ^{31}P spectrum obtained for a compound of this type, namely, $P_3N_3Cl_4(SC_2H_5)_2$. The high field doublet can be assigned to a pair of magnetically equivalent PCl_2 type phosphorus nuclei and the low field multiplet to a single $P(SC_2H_5)_2$ type phosphorus nucleus as indicated in Fig. 12.40. Spin coupling between the non-equivalent phosphorus nuclei leads to a doublet splitting on the high field band and a triplet splitting on the low field band: the quintet splitting of the low field

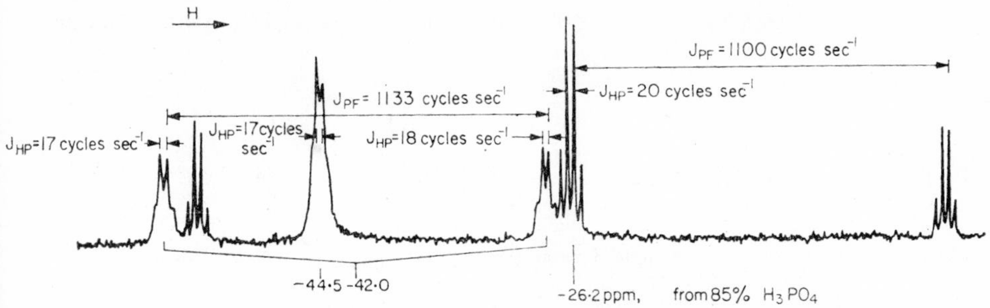

FIG. 12.39 The ^{31}P resonance spectrum of an equilibrium mixture of $CH_3P(O)F_2$, $CH_3P(O)FCl$ and $CH_3P(O)Cl_2$ at 40·5 Mc sec^{-1} (23,500 gauss). Pier(277) (Varian Associates).

band is due to P—H coupling between the phosphorus nucleus and four equivalent methylene hydrogen nuclei in the two ethyl groups to which it is bonded(169).

TABLE 12.70 ^{31}P CHEMICAL SHIFTS OF SOME CYCLIC PHOSPHORUS COMPOUNDS(166)

	Phosphorochloridite $(CH_2)_n\langle O, O\rangle PCl$	Phosphite $(CH_2)_n\langle O, O\rangle POC_2H_5$	Phosphate $(CH_2)_n\langle O, O\rangle P(O)OC_2H_5$
Five-ring	−167†	−131	−17
Six-ring	−153	−128	+7
Acyclic	−164	−138(4)	+1(4)

† Measured in ppm from 85 per cent H_3PO_4 external reference.

12.6.4 Quantitative Analysis

Two factors enable mixtures of phosphorus-containing compounds to be conveniently analysed by nuclear magnetic resonance. The first is that most organophosphorus compounds contain only one phosphorus atom per molecule and thus have relatively simple ^{31}P NMR spectra and the second is that ^{31}P absorption bands for different compounds usually have very different chemical shifts and consequently there is little tendency for the different absorption bands to overlap. Sensitivity factors limit the method considerably and it is

TABLE 12.71 THE ^{31}P CHEMICAL SHIFTS OF A SERIES OF MIXED HALIDE PHOSPHORYL COMPOUNDS AND THEIR SULPHUR-CONTAINING ANALOGUES[173]

Compound	δ ppm†	Compound	δ ppm
$POCl_3$	− 2·2	$PSCl_3$	− 28·8
$POCl_2Br$	+ 29·6	$PSCl_2Br$	+ 14·5
$POClBr_2$	+ 64·8	$PSClBr_2$	+ 61·4
$POBr_3$	+103·4	$PSBr_3$	+111·8

† δ is the ^{31}P chemical shift measured in ppm from 85 per cent H_3PO_4 external reference.

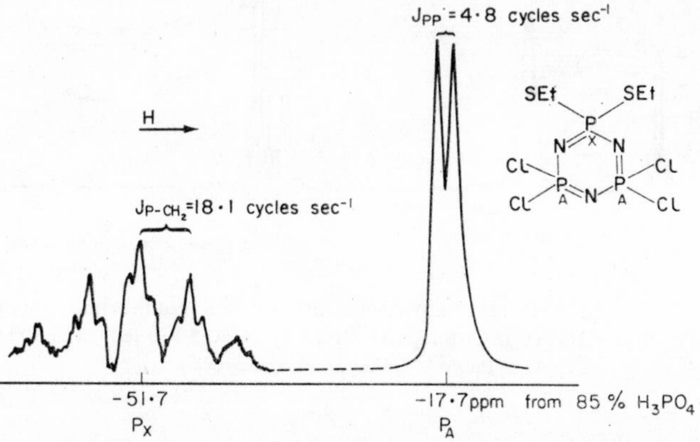

FIG. 12.40 The ^{31}P resonance spectrum of $P_3N_3Cl_4(SEt)_2$ at 16·2 Mc sec^{-1}. The two parts of the spectrum were obtained at different gains. Boden, Emsley, Feeney and Sutcliffe[169].

difficult to conduct accurate quantitative measurements of absorption band intensities if solutions of less than 1 M concentration are used. Mixtures of oxyacids of phosphorus can be successfully analysed by this technique[170] and a method for the rapid estimation of phosphorus pentoxide in polyphosphoric acid has also been described[171]. Other quantitative investigations include the measurement of the purity of a sample of pyrophosphorous acid[172] and studies of the products formed in the reorganisation processes established in several mixtures of phosphorus-containing compounds[173, 174]. An example of the latter is the rearrangement which takes place on mixing $POCl_3$ and $POBr_3$[173]. Completely random reorganisation takes place in less than one week at 130°C, giving rise to the mixed halide phosphoryl compounds, namely $POCl_2Br$ and $POClBr_2$. The ^{31}P spectrum of the final mixture consists of four separate absorption bands corresponding to the four types of molecule present, and their ^{31}P chemical shifts are given in Table 12.71. Similar results were obtained on mixing $PSCl_3$ and $PSBr_3$ (see Table 12.71). By measuring the intensities of the absorption bands, the relative amounts of each type of molecule in the equilibrium can be obtained and it is then possible to calculate whether or not the rearrangement has taken place in a completely random fashion. Other systems which have been examined in this way are PCl_3/PBr_3, $H_3PO_4/POCl_3$, $H_2O/HF/P_2O_5$(175, 176), $CH_3P(O)F_2/CH_3P(O)Cl_2$(277). Figure 12.39 shows the ^{31}P resonance spectrum at 40·5 Mc sec^{-1} (23,500 gauss) of an equilibrium mixture of $CH_3P(O)F_2$, $CH_3P(O)FCl$ and $CH_3P(O)Cl_2$(277): $CH_3P(O)F_2$ gives rise to a triplet (J_{P-F} = 1100 cycles sec^{-1}) of quartets (J_{H-P} = 20 cycles sec^{-1}); $CH_3P(O)FCl$ gives a doublet (J_{P-F} = 1133 cycles sec^{-1}) of quartets (J_{H-P} = 17 cycles sec^{-1}); $CH_3P(O)Cl_2$ gives a single quartet (J_{H-P} = 17 cycles sec^{-1}).

Non-cyclic phosphonitrilic compounds. Figure 12.41 shows the ^{31}P resonance spectra of two non-cyclic phosphonitrilic derivatives and in each case unambiguous assignments of the absorption bands can be made(177). When the chemical shift of the P_A nucleus in the non-cyclic phosphonitrile (I) (see Appendix F)

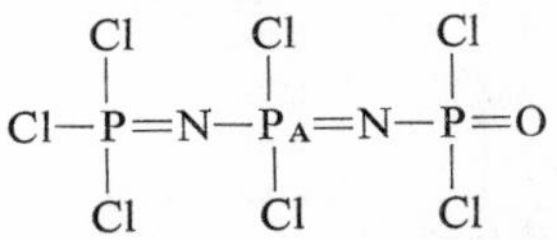
(I)

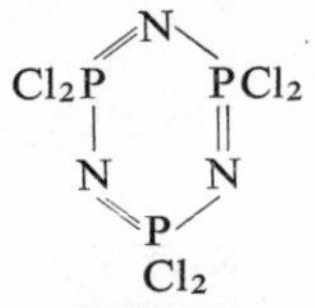
(II)

is compared with that for a similarly substituted phosphorus atom in the cyclic phosphonitrilic (II) (δ = – 19 ppm) it is seen that cyclisation has caused a

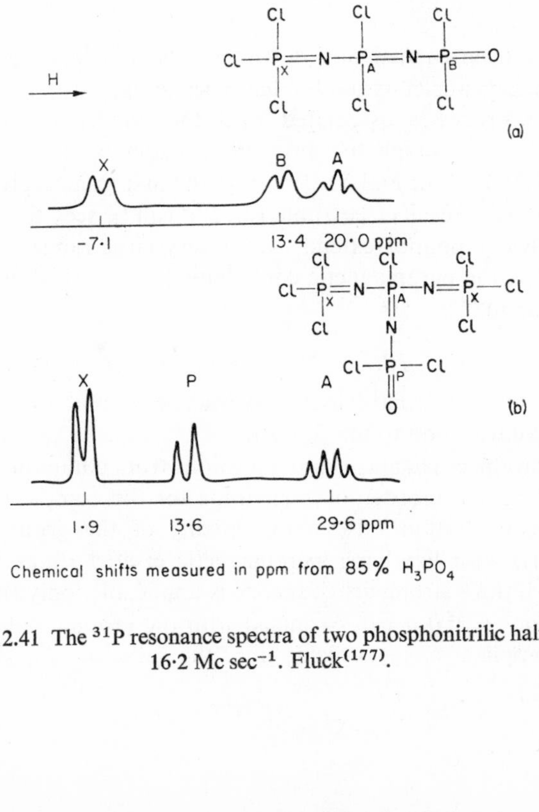

FIG. 12.41 The ^{31}P resonance spectra of two phosphonitrilic halides at 16·2 Mc sec^{-1}. Fluck(177).

40 ppm deshielding of the ring phosphorus nuclei. In the few non-cyclic P—N molecules so far examined[177, 250] the ^{31}P—^{31}P spin coupling constants are in the range 15–45 cycles sec^{-1}. ^{31}P data have been reported for a large number of P—N compounds[281, 283].

12.7 Cobalt

Cobalt-59, the only naturally occurring isotope of cobalt, has a fairly high magnetic moment and would be an ideal nucleus for NMR investigation were it not for the fact that it possesses a strong electric quadrupole moment (its spin number $I = 7/2$). Despite this, several successful investigations of ^{59}Co

Table 12.72 ^{59}Co Chemical Shifts of some Cobalt Complexes[102]

Compound	Chemical shift ppm
$K_3Co(CN)_6$ (Reference)	0
$Co(C_2H_4(NH_2)_2)_3Cl_3$	7300
$Na_3Co(NO_2)_6$*	7400
	8100
$Co(NH_3)_6Cl_3$	8300
$K_3Co(C_2O_4)_3$	13,000

* The two absorption bands measured for $Na_3Co(NO_2)_6$ have the intensity ratio 1 : 16 and they have been assigned to two isomeric forms of the molecule: the intensities of the two signals vary with temperature, and Gasser and Richards[178] have studied the equilibrium established between the two isomers over a temperature range.

resonance have been carried out and interesting information concerning the shielding of heavy nuclei generally has been obtained[102, 121, 123, 178, 184]. The relaxation processes associated with the quadrupole interactions are not usually efficient enough to cause line broadening greater than the field homogeneity[178]. Proctor and Yu[102] were the first to measure ^{59}Co chemical shifts and from their results (see Table 12.72) it can be seen that chemical shifts found in cobalt compounds extend over a very large range (13×10^3 ppm); this suggests that the paramagnetic contribution to the shielding of the cobalt nucleus is dominant[102, 181].

12.7.1 ^{59}Co Chemical Shifts

Griffith and Orgel[123] have used a crystal field approach to calculate the paramagnetic contribution to the shielding of ^{59}Co nuclei and they have shown that this term produces chemical shift variations from compound to compound that are of the correct order of magnitude for the complexes studied. The paramagnetic contribution arises from mixing of the ground state energy levels of Co(III) with low-lying paramagnetic excited states by the applied magnetic field. If the "strong field" theory is applicable, only the $^1T_{1g}$ state of the configuration $(t_{2g})^5(e_g)$ can be mixed with the ground state under the influence of the applied magnetic field: since the value of $^1T_{1g}$ depends on the characteristic field strength of the ligands then the energy separation between the ground state and the excited $^1T_{1g}$ level (ΔE) will vary with change of ligand. The paramagnetic contribution to the shielding is given by[72, 181]

$$\sigma_{\text{para}} = \frac{-e^2}{3Mc^2 \Delta E} \left\langle \frac{1}{r^3} \right\rangle \langle 0 | L^2 | 0 \rangle$$

and it can readily be seen that it obeys an inverse relationship with the energy separation ΔE. Ligands which produce small fields should form cobalt complexes in which the shielding of the cobalt nucleus has a large paramagnetic contribution. This has been shown to be true by comparing the ^{59}Co chemical shifts of the amine, oxalate, ethylenediamine and cyanide Co(III) complexes with the positions of their $^1T_{1g}$ state where good qualitative agreement is observed[123]. If estimated values of $1/r^3$ are also taken into consideration an even better agreement is obtained. In this theory, Griffith and Orgel make the assumption that the diamagnetic contribution to the shielding of ^{59}Co nuclei is small and that the changes in this contribution which accompany changes in the ligands will be negligible. Freeman, Murray and Richards[179] have examined both the ^{59}Co NMR spectra and the electronic absorption spectra of a wide variety of Co(III) complexes in order to confirm the views of Griffith and Orgel concerning the shielding of cobalt nuclei. Table 12.73 gives the ^{59}Co chemical shifts and the positions of the electronic absorption maxima for the compounds they examined. All the Co(III) complexes considered can be classified as "strong field" type in the terminology of crystal field theory[180]: thus the $5d$ orbitals of the Co(III) ion will be split into two sets of orbitals, three degenerate t_{2g} orbitals and two degenerate e_g orbitals greater in energy by ΔE. The ground state of the complex is described as $(t_{2g})^6$, whilst the lowest excited state is $(t_{2g})^5(e_g)^1$. There are only two singlet $(t_{2g})^5(e_g)^1$ states, $^1T_{1g}$ and $^1T_{2g}$, which can be involved in transitions with the singlet ground state and the excitation energy in each case will be $\sim \Delta E$. It is possible to obtain an approximate value for ΔE from the frequency of the longest wavelength absorption maximum observed in the electronic absorption spectrum of the Co (III) complex under consideration. When a graph is plotted of the ^{59}Co resonance frequencies against the wavelength of the longest wavelength absorption maximum, a close linear relationship is observed, as predicted by the theory of Griffith and Orgel (see Fig. 12.42). The ^{59}Co chemical shifts of symmetrical complexes give a better linear correlation than those of the unsymmetrical complexes.

Other workers[182] have also calculated the paramagnetic contribution to ^{59}Co shielding for a series of Co(III) complexes using the method suggested by Griffith and Orgel[123]. The second order paramagnetism is found to decrease in the following order for the ligands concerned: acetylacetonate ion $>$ oxinate ion $> CO_3^{2-} > Cl^- > CO_2^- > H_2O > NH_3 >$ en $>$ dipy $> NO_2^-$ $> CN^-$. Table 12.74 gives a list of the calculated and measured ^{59}Co chemical shifts for a series of Co(III) complexes and the agreement between the two sets of values can be seen to be quite good. The paramagnetic contribution

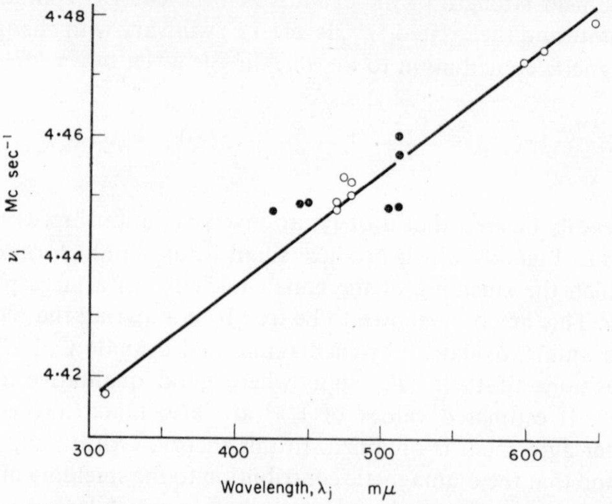

FIG. 12.42 Graph of the ^{59}Co chemical shifts against the longest wavelength absorption maxima for a series of Co(III) complexes. Open circles represent symmetrical complexes and full circles unsymmetrical complexes. Freeman, Murray and Richards[179].

TABLE 12.73 ^{59}Co CHEMICAL SHIFTS AND ELECTRONIC ABSORPTION MAXIMA FOR SEVERAL COMPOUNDS[179]

Compound	Cobalt resonance frequency (Mc sec^{-1}) at 4370·9 gauss	Positions of absorption maxima (mμ)	
Potassium hexacyanocobaltate (III)	4·4171	311	259
Lithium tetranitrodiamminecobaltate (III)	4·4478	426	347
trans-Dichlorobis(ethylenediamine)cobalt (III) chloride	4·4485	505	—
Carbonatobis(ethylenediamine)cobalt (III) bromide	4·4486	512	358
Tris(ethylenediamine)cobalt (III) chloride	4·4488	470	340
trans-Dinitrotetramminecobalt (III) chloride	4·4489	445	—
Tris(propylenediamine)cobalt (III) chloride	4·4490	470	340
cis-Dinitrotetramminecobalt (III) chloride	4·4493	450	—
Sodium hexanitrocobaltate (III)	4·4502 (strong) 4·4527 (weak)	480	358
Hexamminecobalt (III) chloride	4·4534	475	338
Carbonatotetramminecobalt (III) nitrate	4·4575 4·4601	512	—
Cobalt (III) trisacetylacetonate (in benzene)	4·4731	597	—
Potassium trioxalatocobaltate (III)	4·4747	610	425
Tricarbonatocobalt (III) nitrate	4·4795	645	444

to the shielding decreases as the ligand field producing power of the ligands increases, as would be expected.

TABLE 12.74 ^{59}Co CHEMICAL SHIFTS IN A SERIES OF Co(III) COMPLEXES[182]

Compound	ΔE (cm^{-1})†	Observed chemical shift δ ppm‡	Calculated chemical shift δ ppm
$[Co(NH_3)_6]Cl_3$	21,000	−8080	−8200
$[Co(NH_3)_5CO_3]NO_3$	19,670	−9000	−9800
$[Co(NH_3)_5Cl]Cl_2$	18,720	−9070	−11100
$[Co(NH_3)_5NO_2]Cl_2$	21,840	−7460	−7300
$[Co(NH_3)_4CO_3]NO_3$	19,060	−9070	−10600
cis-$[Co(NH_3)_4(NO_2)_2]NO_3$	22,510	−6880	−6600
trans-$[Co(NH_3)_4(NO_2)_2]NO_3$	22,630	−7150	−6500
$Na_3[Co(NO_2)_6]$	20,670	−7350	−8500
$Co(NH_3)_3(NO_2)_3$	23,210	−6940	−6000
$[Co(en)_3]Cl_3$	21,400	−7010	−7700
trans-$[Co(en)_2(NO_2)_2]NO_3$	23,300	−6350	−5900
cis-$[Co(en)_2(NO_2)_2]NO_3$	23,000	−6470	−6100
$[Co(dipy)_3](ClO_4)_3$	22,230	−6620	−6900
Cobalt acetylacetonate	16,900	−12300	−14000
$K_3[Co(CN)_6]$		0	

† ΔE = Energy separation between ground and excited state of d^6 configuration.
‡ δ = Chemical shifts measured in ppm from $K_3Co(CN)_6$ external reference.

Solvent effects on ^{59}Co chemical shifts. The ^{59}Co resonance absorption of cobalt acetylacetonate has been observed to be solvent dependent but no correlation between the magnitude of the solvent shifts and the properties of the solvent (such as the dielectric constant) was found[179]. The solvent effects produce shifts which are negligible compared to the large chemical shifts usually observed in ^{59}Co NMR investigations.

Temperature dependence of ^{59}Co chemical shifts. Proctor and Yu[102] have reported a temperature dependence of the ^{59}Co chemical shifts for $K_3Co(CN)_6$, $Co[C_2H_4(NH_2)_2]_3Cl_3$ and $Co(NH_3)_6Cl_3$ over the range 20–80°C. Other workers have since observed a similar temperature dependence for several Co(III) complexes[179, 121]. For example, cobalt(III) trisacetylacetonate shows a temperature variation of 2·97 ppm (°C)$^{-1}$ in chloroform solution. This variation was originally attributed to the changes in population of low-lying excited energy levels accompanying changes in temperature[102, 181]. However, Griffith and Orgel[123] consider such a state of affairs to be unlikely and they have suggested that an increase in temperature brings about a change in the population of higher vibrational energy levels, which results in a lowering of the excited energy state $^1T_{1g}$ involved in mixing with the ground state and thus causes an increase in the ^{59}Co resonance frequency.

Armstrong *et al.*[184, 314] have measured the temperature and pressure dependence of ^{59}Co chemical shifts: it is possible to explain the observed variations by considering the effect of pressure on the ΔE term and the effect of temperature on the thermal expansion of the complex.

12.7.2 Rate Processes Involving Cobalt

Gasser and Richards[178] have studied the rate of exchange between ethylenediamine and the hexammine cobalt(III) ion as represented by the equation

$$Co(NH_3)_6^{3+} + 3en \rightleftharpoons Co\,en_3^{3+} + 6NH_3$$

Two separate ^{59}Co absorption bands are observed and they have been assigned to the two species, $Co(NH_3)_6^{3+}$ and $Co\,en_3^{3+}$. By measuring changes in the intensities of the signals with time it was possible to obtain a rate constant for this process. Measurements at different temperatures resulted in a value for the activation energy being obtained (22 kcal mole^{-1}). The rates of both electron and ligand exchange in solutions of cobalt(III) complexes are found to be slow[178].

12.8 Tin

There are three isotopes of tin which have non-zero magnetic moments, ^{115}Sn (0·35 per cent natural abundance), ^{117}Sn (7·67 per cent) and ^{119}Sn (8·68 per cent). In each case the spin number of the nucleus is one half ($I = \frac{1}{2}$) and thus the nuclei have no quadrupole moments. The two most abundant magnetic isotopes have similar magnetic moments and consequently have similar natural sensitivities to NMR detection. However, the ^{119}Sn isotope is slightly more sensitive to detection and since it is also the most abundant magnetic isotope it is usual to study ^{119}Sn spectra in NMR investigations of tin.

The optimum experimental conditions under which resonance is observed depend largely upon the relaxation times of the nuclei being examined[185, 186]. Most tin-containing samples are found to give signals on the oscilloscope if rapid sweep rates, dispersion mode tuning, and high radiofrequency power levels are used (H_1 values between 2 and 50 milligauss have been employed). Resonance bands have been recorded using rapid passage signals (for $SnCl_2 . 2H_2O$), slow passage dispersion mode signals (for $SnCl_4$) and absorption mode signals (for $SnBr_4$). Large sample tubes of 15 mm outside diameter are generally used to overcome the sensitivity problem and no attempts have been made to spin such samples.

It has not been possible to observe ^{119}Sn resonance in certain tin compounds because the absorption bands are broad and weak. Examples of this phenomenon are found in solid $SnBr_4$, solid SnI_4, saturated aqueous solutions of $SnCl_4$ or SnF_4[186].

By enriching a sample of $SnCl_2 . 2H_2O$ with the ^{119}Sn isotope ($\sim$ 65 per cent in ^{119}Sn) a reasonable signal can be obtained from a sample contained in a 3 mm diameter sample tube, and this can be used conveniently as an external reference[186]. However, the most common reference material for tin resonance measurements is tetramethyl tin, $Sn(CH_3)_4$, and the chemical shifts given here are all measured externally from this reference.

12.8.1 ^{119}Sn *Chemical Shifts*

Table 12.75 presents a list of ^{119}Sn chemical shifts for a series of organic and inorganic tin-containing molecules(185, 186). The measurements were conducted by Lauterbur and Burke and they were undertaken as part of a more general investigation of the NMR spectra of Group IVB elements. The chemical shift measurements were made on both decreasing and increasing field sweep to average out inaccuracies due to asymmetric signals. The large range over

TABLE 12.75 ^{119}Sn CHEMICAL SHIFTS IN VARIOUS COMPOUNDS(185, 186)

Compound	δ^a (ppm)
SnI_4 (CS_2 solution)	1701
$SnSO_4$ (aqueous)	909
$SnBr_4$	638
$Na_2[Sn(OH)_6]$ (aqueous)	592
$K_2[Sn(OH)_6]$ (aqueous)	590
$SnCl_2 \cdot 2H_2O$ (aqueous, 4·85 M)	521 ^{b}
$SnCl_2$ (tetrahydrofuran)	236
$(n\text{-}C_4H_9)_2Sn(OOCCH_3)_2$	195
$SnCl_4$	150
$(n\text{-}C_4H_9)_4Sn$	12
$n\text{-}C_4H_9SnCl_3$	3
$(CH_3)_4Sn$	0
$(CH_3)_2SnCl_2$ (acetone solution)	−36
$(C_2H_5)_2SnCl_2$ (acetone solution)	−62
$(n\text{-}C_4H_9)_2SnCl_2$ (acetone solution)	−71
$(n\text{-}C_4H_9)_2SnCl_2$ (CS_2 solution)	−114
$(n\text{-}C_4H_9)_2SnS$	−124
$(n\text{-}C_4H_9)_3SnCl$	−143
$(C_2H_5)_3SnCl$	−151

^{a} Precision ±2 ppm.
^{b} Concentration and pH dependent; can be lowered almost 200 ppm by addition of HCl.
δ is the chemical shift measured in ppm from $Sn(CH_3)_4$ reference (external).

which ^{119}Sn chemical shifts extend suggests that the paramagnetic contribution to the shielding is the major factor controlling the shielding of the tin nucleus.

Examination of Table 12.75 indicates that the chemical shifts of Sn(II) compounds are not in a different region to those of Sn(IV) compounds, that is, the chemical shifts of $SnSO_4$, $SnCl_2$ and $SnCl_2 . 2H_2O$ are within the same range as those for stannic compounds. Plots of ^{119}Sn chemical shifts against the number of chlorine atoms in a series of molecules of general formula $SnCl_x Br_{(4-x)}$ proved to be linear, in an analogous manner to similar plots for carbon compounds of this type (see Section 12.2.3). When attached to tin, the halogen atoms, chlorine, bromine and iodine can each be considered to make fixed, independent contributions to the overall ^{119}Sn chemical shift regardless of the other substituents on the tin atom: knowledge of these contributions enables one to predict the chemical shifts of the mixed halides of tin. For example, $SnClBrI_2$ has a predicted chemical shift of 1046 ppm from tetramethyl tin, in excellent agreement with the measured value of 1068 ppm.

Solvent effects on ^{119}Sn *chemical shifts.* Large solvent effects on both chemical shifts and coupling constants involving the ^{119}Sn nucleus have been reported[186]. These effects are assumed to be a reflection of the coordination tendencies of tin towards many solvents. The J_{SnH} coupling constant in $(CH_3)_2SnCl_2$ in aqueous solution is 98 cycles sec^{-1} while in acetone solution the value is reduced to 80 cycles sec^{-1}. Likewise, a change of solvent will affect the ^{119}Sn chemical shifts in $SnCl_2 . 2H_2O$. These shifts are also markedly concentration dependent in both acetone and ethanol solutions of $SnCl_2 . 2H_2O$. When $SnCl_2 . 2H_2O$ solutions in hydrochloric acid are examined, the ^{119}Sn chemical shifts are found to vary with the normality of the added hydrochloric acid (a change of ~ 200 ppm is observed), thus providing evidence for formation of halide complexes.

12.8.2 *Mixed Tin (IV) Halides*

Upon mixing two tin tetrahalides such as $SnBr_4$ and SnI_4, and allowing them to stand for several hours, a random redistribution of the halogen substituents takes place and results in the formation of predictable quantities of mixed halides of the type $SnBr_3I$, $SnBr_2I_2$ and $SnBrI_3$[186]. The ^{119}Sn resonance spectrum

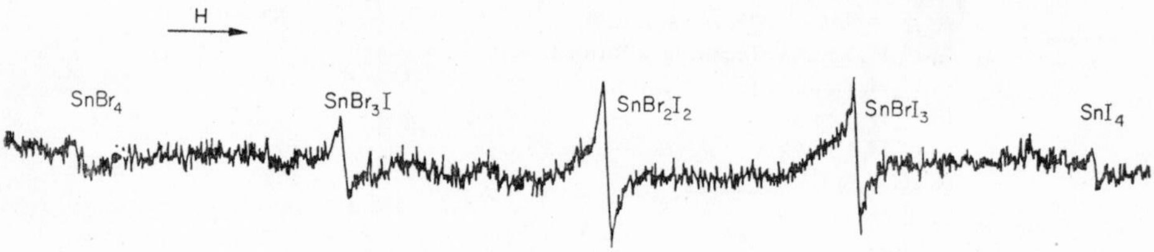

FIG. 12.43 The ^{119}Sn resonance spectrum at 8·5 Mc sec^{-1} of a 1 : 1 molar mixture of $SnBr_4$ and SnI_4. Burke and Lauterbur[186].

of a 1 : 1 molar mixture of these compounds (see Fig. 12.43) shows a separate absorption band for each mixed halide and, by carrying out intensity measurements of the roughly equally spaced bands, it is possible to estimate the approximate amount of each species present. The observed intensities are in good agreement with those expected for a random redistribution of the halogen substituents. The ^{119}Sn chemical shifts of many other mixed halides of tin have been obtained by taking suitable mixtures of the starting materials, $SnCl_4$, $SnBr_4$ and SnI_4: the information found from such experiments is summarised in Table 12.76. Figure 12.44 shows a typical ^{119}Sn NMR spectrum of the redistribution products of a three component mixture of the above tetrahalides. Halogen atoms in the stannic mixed halides undergo rapid chemical exchange and from the fact that separate resonance bands are observed for each species of mixed

TABLE 12.76 ^{119}Sn CHEMICAL SHIFTS IN A SERIES OF MIXED HALIDES OF TIN[(186)]

Mole fraction			Sn halide														
$SnCl_4$	$SnBr_4$	SnI_4	Cl_4	Cl_3Br	Cl_2Br_2	$ClBr_3$	Cl_3I	Br_4	Cl_2BrI	$ClBr_2I$	Br_3I	Cl_2I_2	$ClBrI_2$	Br_2I_2	ClI_3	BrI_3	I_4
0	0	1	—	—	—	—	—	—	—	—	—	—	—	—	—	—	1701
0	0·5	0·5	—	—	—	—	—		—	—	916	—	—	1187	—	1447	1698
0	0·75	0·25	—	—	—	—	—	638	—	—	919	—	—	1192	—		
0	1	0	—	—	—	—	—	638	—	—	—	—	—	—	—	—	—
0·25	0·75	0			384	509	—	634	—	—	—	—	—	—	—	—	—
0·5	0·5	0		265	387	509	—	635	—	—	—	—	—	—	—	—	—
0·75	0·25	0		260	386		—		—	—	—	—	—	—	—	—	—
1	0	0	150	—	—	—	—	—	—	—	—	—	—	—	—	—	—
0·75	0	0·25		—	—	—	551	—	—	—	—	951	—	—	1347	—	
0·5	0	0·5		—	—	—	557	—	—	—	—	955	—	—	1342	—	1712
0·25	0·25	0·5							672	796	919	947	1068	1189	1330	1449	1696
0·25	0·5	0·25				508		629	666	789	913		1063	1195			
0·5	0·25	0·25		267			543		663	783		937	1060				

Shifts are measured in ppm to high fields of the external reference $(CH_3)_4Sn$.

halide, a lower limit of 10^{-3} sec can be estimated as the lifetime of the molecules between exchange reactions. Attempts to follow the actual course of the redistribution reaction for a $SnCl_4/SnBr_4$ mixture were not successful, indicating the upper limit for the lifetimes to be about 10 sec.

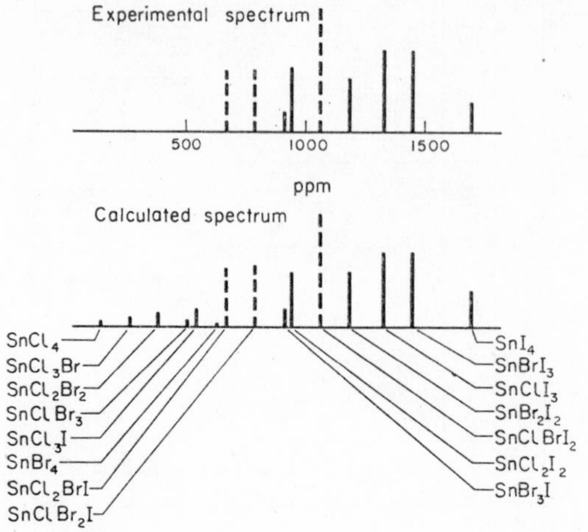

FIG. 12.44 The ^{119}Sn resonance spectrum at 8·5 Mc sec^{-1} of a 2 : 1 : 1 molar mixture of $SnCl_4/SnBr_4/SnI_4$. (Chemical shifts measured in ppm from $(CH_3)_4Sn$ external reference). Burke and Lauterbur(186).

12.8.3 ^{119}Sn *Spin–spin Coupling Constants*

Table 10.95 contains several Sn—H coupling constants measured in the resonance spectra of stannanes and related molecules(234). For the directly bonded nuclei, the progressive replacement of hydrogen atoms by methyl groups in compounds of formula $(CH_3)_xSnH_{4-x}$ causes a decrease in the Sn—H coupling constants (SnH_4, $J_{SnH} = 1931$; $(CH_3)_3SnH$, $J_{SnH} = 1744$ cycles sec^{-1}). This is as expected(234) since an increase in the number of methyl groups will be accompanied by a reduction in the *s* character of the Sn orbitals in the Sn—H bonds and hence a reduction in the Sn—H coupling constants (the dominant Fermi contact contribution to the coupling is proportional to the *s* character in the hybridised orbital used in forming the Sn—H bond).

Fine structure due to spin–spin interaction often features in ^{119}Sn resonance spectra but the coupling constants involved can usually be measured with greater ease and accuracy in the resonance spectra of the interacting nuclei (for example, hydrogen or fluorine nuclei) rather than in the ^{119}Sn spectra. In the ^{119}Sn spectrum of $Sn(CH_3)_4$ shown in Fig. 12.45, nine of the expected thirteen multiplet splittings ($J_{SnH} = 54$ cycles sec^{-1}) have been measured(50, 264). Hydrogen atoms in alkyl groups attached to the tin atom have values for the J_{SnH} coupling constants over the range 30–100 cycles sec^{-1} when there are two bonds separating the interacting nuclei (that is, J_{Sn-C-H}). For interacting nuclei separated by three bonds the coupling constant, $J_{Sn-C-C-H}$, is usually greater than that for nuclei separated by two bonds. Thus, in the molecule $Sn(C_2H_5)_4$ the Sn—H coupling constants are[186, 233]

$$J_{SnCH_3} = \pm 71 \cdot 2 \quad \text{and} \quad J_{SnCH_2} = \mp 32 \cdot 2 \text{ cycles sec}^{-1}.$$

This behaviour is typical of metal alkyls.

The ^{119}Sn spectrum of $(n-C_4H_9)_4Sn$ consists of a broad resonance signal due to multiple splittings from spin–spin interaction with the alkyl hydrogen nuclei[186].

$Sn(CH_3)_4$

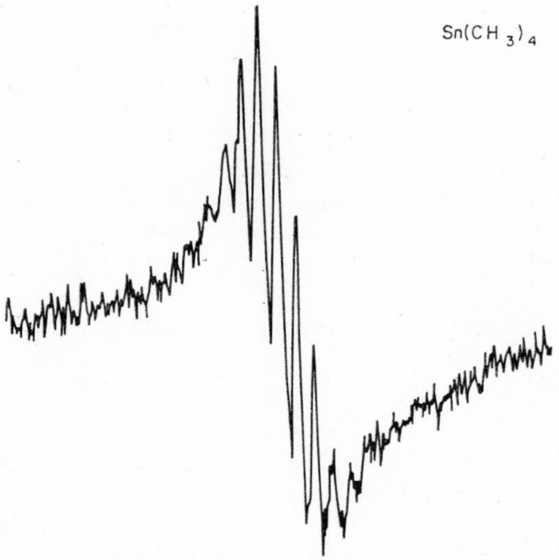

FIG. 12.45 The ^{119}Sn resonance spectrum of tetramethyl tin at $8 \cdot 50$ Mc sec^{-1} under rapid passage dispersion mode conditions. Lauterbur[50].

The 1H spectrum of tetravinyl tin has been examined[187] and a detailed ABC type analysis of the ^{119}Sn satellite fine structure shows that the indirect spin coupling of the tin nucleus with the *trans* hydrogen nucleus is larger than those between the tin and the remaining *geminal* and *cis* hydrogen nuclei. Designating the molecule

$$\begin{array}{c} H_1 \\ \diagdown \\ \diagup \\ H_2 \end{array} C = C \begin{array}{c} Sn(CH{=}CH_2)_3 \\ \diagup \\ \diagdown \\ H_3 \end{array}$$

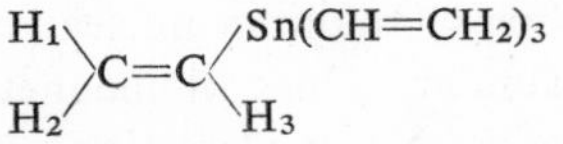

then the coupling constants are:

$$J_{SnH_1} = +90 \cdot 6 \quad J_{SnH_2} = +183 \cdot 1 \quad \text{and} \quad J_{SnH_3} = +98 \cdot 3 \text{ cycles sec}^{-1}$$

Several Sn—H coupling constants between the two nuclei separated by a single carbon atom have been reported for a series of methyl tin derivatives and related compounds[188, 256]. Table 12.77 gives a list of the coupling constants measured from the 1H resonance spectra of the compounds which were examined both as pure liquids and as solutions in various solvents. The variation of the J_{Sn-C-H} coupling constants in the different molecules is attributed to changes in hybridisation of the tin atom and there is evidence that the coupling constants depend linearly on the percentage *s* character in the bond: this is consistent with the similar findings for long range $J_{^{13}C-C-H}$ coupling constants (see Section 12.2.18).

TABLE 12.77 ^{119}Sn—H SPIN–SPIN COUPLING CONSTANTS IN METHYL TIN DERIVATIVES AND RELATED MOLECULES[188]

Compound[a]	T(°C)	Coupling constants (cycles sec^{-1})[b]	
		^{117}Sn–CH_3	^{119}Sn–CH_3
$(CH_3)_4Sn$	31	51·5	54·0
51% CCl_4	31	51·4	53·8
5% CCl_4	31	51·6	53·7
			54[186]
$(CH_3)_3SnCl$	40	57·4	59·7
38% CCl_4	31	56·0	58·5
62% C_6H_6	31	56·5	59·2
56% H_2O	31	65·2	68·4
$(CH_3)_2SnCl_2$	110	68·0	71·0
satd. $<$ 14% CCl_4	31	66·6	69·7
47% H_2O	31	97·4	101·9
			98[186]
CH_3SnCl_3	55	95·7	100·0
46% CCl_4	31	95·3	99·5
51% C_6H_6	31	95·4	99·9
49% H_2O	31	125·4	131·1

[a] Compounds first listed as neat liquids, then as per cent by weight in solution of various solvents.

[b] Values are given to a precision of $\pm 0{\cdot}5$ per cent.

12.9 THALLIUM

Both the naturally occurring isotopes of thallium (^{203}Tl, 29·52 per cent and ^{205}Tl, 70·48 per cent natural abundance) have non-zero magnetic moments and both have a spin number of one half ($I = \frac{1}{2}$). It is usual to examine the more abundant ^{205}Tl isotope in thallium nuclear magnetic resonance studies since both isotopes have similar values of magnetic moment and thus have similar natural sensitivities to NMR detection. Although the sensitivity is fairly high (19·2 per cent of that of hydrogen nuclei at the same field value), phase sensitive detection of the resonance signal is usually employed.

12.9.1 ^{205}Tl Chemical Shifts

Rowland and Bromberg[189] have studied the thallium resonance spectra of several solid and molten thallium salts in an attempt to investigate changes in the electronic environment of the thallium nuclei at a phase change. They succeeded in measuring the chemical shift difference between the thallium in the solid phase and that in the liquid phase just above the melting point for three ionic thallium salts, namely thallous nitrate, chloride and bromide. In each case the thallium in the solid phase is shielded to a greater extent than that in the liquid phase, the chemical shift differences between the two phases being:

$TlNO_3$	1·32 ppm × 10^2
TlCl	5·96 ppm × 10^2
TlBr	5·58 ppm × 10^2

A correlation was found to exist between the chemical shift differences for the halides and the electronegativities of the halide ions. These thallous salts in the molten phase are assumed to exist as free thallous and free halide ions and in this state the electronic environment of the thallous ion is thought to be very

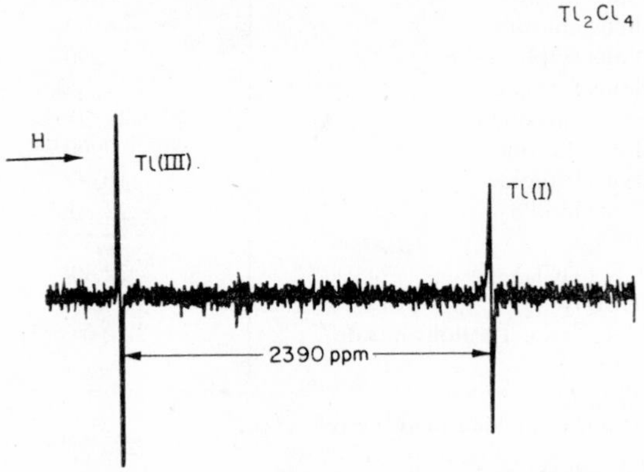

FIG. 12.46 ^{205}Tl resonance absorption spectrum of molten Tl_2Cl_4 at 289°C at 25·16 Mc sec^{-1}. Rowland and Bromberg(189).

similar in both compounds. In the solid phase, the partial covalent character in the bonds is associated with a charge transfer which gives rise to the shielding differences correlating with the electronegativity of the halide ions.

The ^{205}Tl resonance spectra of molten samples of the complex salts Tl_2Cl_4 and Tl_2Br_4 show two separate absorption bands which have been assigned to Tl^+ and Tl^{3+} species (see Fig. 12.46). This supports the double salt type structure for complex thallium halides, $TlX.TlX_3$ (leading to Tl^+ and TlX_4^- ions in the molten state). In the molten samples of the halides, one might have expected that there would be a rapid exchange process between the two different valency states of thallium but the observation of two separate absorption bands rules out this possibility. A temperature investigation of this system indicates that the average lifetime of the species in any one valency state is $\sim 10^{-5}$ sec at 500°K. It is found that Tl^{3+} ions are less shielded than Tl^+ ions in the liquid phase and that Tl^+ ions in the liquid phase are less shielded than Tl^+ ions in the solid phase. Thallous ions in solution are also more shielded than thallic ions, probably due to there being fewer electrons surrounding the nucleus in a thallic ion(190). Figure 12.46 shows the ^{205}Tl absorption signals observed in molten Tl_2Cl_4 at 289°C(189).

Freeman, Gasser and Richards[191] have reported ^{205}Tl chemical shifts (see Table 12.78) of a series of inorganic thallium salts in the solid state. Solid Tl_2Cl_3 gives rise to two absorption bands in the intensity ratio of 3 : 1, which is consistent with the formula $Tl_3(TlCl_6)$[191]. A sample of hydrated thallic chloride shows three resonance bands which might be due to the species $Tl(H_2O)_x^{3+}$,

TABLE 12.78 ^{205}Tl CHEMICAL SHIFTS FOR A SERIES OF INORGANIC THALLIUM SALTS

Compound	^{205}Tl Chemical shift δ ppm
Thallous perchlorate	+3700 †
Thallous nitrate	−2800
Thallous chloride	−6100
Thallous sulphate	−900
Thallous formate	−11,100
Thallous carbonate	−11,200
Thallous fluoride	−7900
Thallous bromide	−10,800
Thallous iodide	−23,300
$K_3(TlCl_6)$	−22,300
$(NH_4)_3(TlCl_6)$	−22,300
$Zn(TlCl_4)_2$	−29,700
0·3 M aq. soln. Thallous nitrate (Reference)	0·0

† Positive values: more shielded than the reference.

$TlCl_4^-$ and $TlCl_6^{3-}$. When halide solutions are added to aqueous solutions of thallic chloride and bromide, large changes in the ^{205}Tl chemical shifts occur. These have been interpreted in terms of the stepwise formation of complex ions. A more detailed account of the study of complex formation involving thallium ions[190, 191, 195] is given in Section 9.3.

Figgis[190] has also measured the effect of anion additives on the ^{205}Tl chemical shifts of thallic salts in solution. Chemical shift variations extending over a range of 1800 ppm are observed but no overlap with the range found for thallous ions takes place. From the large range of thallium chemical shifts it is inferred that the major factor controlling the shielding of thallium nuclei is the paramagnetic contribution[190].

12.9.2 *Spin–Spin Coupling Involving Thallium*

Indirect spin–spin interaction between thallium and hydrogen nuclei has been observed in the ^1H resonance spectra of aqueous solutions of dialkyl and diaryl thallium cations[192, 312]. The ^1H resonance spectra of trimethyl and triethyl thallium do not exhibit any fine structure at room temperature. This has been attributed to rapid chemical exchange of the alkyl groups which results in a single broad absorption band being observed for each sample. On cooling a solution of either sample to between −60 and −100°C (methylene chloride used as solvent) the rate of exchange of alkyl groups is suppressed and fine structure due to Tl—H spin–spin interaction is observed. By cooling a mixture of trimethyl and triethyl thallium, it was possible to obtain the ^1H resonance spectra of the mixed alkyls $Tl(CH_3)_2(C_2H_5)$ and $Tl(CH_3)(C_2H_5)_2$: this indicates that the exchange process probably involves the interchange of complete alkyl groups between molecules. A study of the exchange of methyl groups in trimethyl thallium has shown the exchange to follow second order kinetics(263). Table 12.79 gives the Tl—H coupling constants observed in the trialkyl thallium compounds studied. Tl—H coupling constants in halide derivatives, $(CH_3)_2TlX$, have also been measured(285).

TABLE 12.79 ^{205}Tl—^{1}H SPIN–SPIN COUPLING CONSTANTS (CYCLES SEC^{-1}) IN SOME THALLIUM TRIALKYLS

Compound	CH_3 Group	C_2H_5 Group	
	J_{TlH}	J_{Tl-CH_2}	J_{Tl-CH_3}
$Tl(CH_3)_3$	250·8		
$Tl(CH_3)_2(C_2H_5)$	223·0	242·4	472·7
$Tl(CH_3)(C_2H_5)_2$	186·9	218·8	441·5
$Tl(C_2H_5)_3$		198·2	396·1

It is interesting to note that the thallium is coupled more strongly with the methyl group than with the methylene group in all the ethyl derivatives examined (see Section 10.3.2). Spin decoupling experiments(192) have shown that these two coupling constants have opposite signs in the case of the diethyl thallium cation and this state of affairs probably also prevails for the triethyl thallium derivatives.

^{205}Tl—H spin coupling constants have also been measured for thallium phenyl and vinyl derivatives(132) (see Section 10.8.2). In $Tl(C_6H_5)_3$, the observed coupling constants are

$$J_{TlH}^{ortho} = \pm 259; \quad J_{TlH}^{meta} = \pm 80; \quad J_{TlH}^{para} = \pm 35 \text{ cycles sec}^{-1}$$

For the ions $Tl(C_6H_5)_2^+$ and $Tl(C_6H_5)^{2+}$ the corresponding coupling constants are much larger(132).

12.9.3 *Structure of Thallous Ethoxide*, $TlOC_2H_5$

Examination of the ^{203}Tl and ^{205}Tl resonance spectra of pure liquid thallous ethoxide has confirmed that the molecule has a tetrameric structure (I)(193).

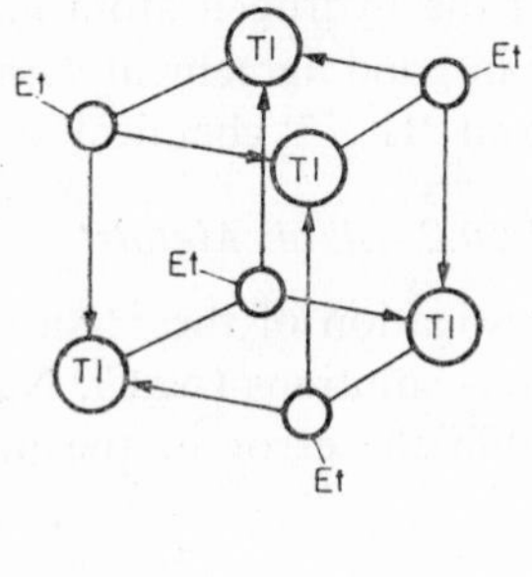

(I)

The observed spectra are complex which indicates the presence of $^{203}Tl—^{205}Tl$ spin coupling (J = 2560 cycles sec^{-1}) since there is no Tl—H spin coupling in the ^{1}H resonance spectrum of the compound. This suggests that the molecule is polymeric. From considerations of the relative natural abundance of the two thallium isotopes it is possible to calculate the amounts of the various tetrameric molecules containing different combinations of the isotopes and to show that if the calculated NMR spectra arising from the various forms of such a molecule were superimposed, the observed ^{203}Tl and ^{205}Tl spectra would be obtained[(194)].

12.10 Miscellaneous Nuclei

12.10.1 Deuterium

Most of the NMR studies involving this nucleus have been carried out on the resonance spectra of other magnetic nuclei with which it is interacting. For example, the indirect spin–spin coupling constant in HD has been measured by Wimett[(196)] in the ^{1}H resonance spectrum of this compound (J_{HD} = 43 ± 0·5 cycles sec^{-1}). Stephen[(197)] has attempted to calculate this constant using a variational method involving valence bond and molecular orbital wavefunctions: his calculated value of 49 cycles sec^{-1} is in good agreement with the observed value. Ishiguro[(198)] has also calculated a theoretical value for the J_{HD} coupling constant using a variational method and has obtained a value of 35·2 cycles sec^{-1}. See Section 5.1 for a full discussion of the calculations. The ^{1}H resonance spectrum of monodeuterobenzene has been measured and analysed in terms of an ABB′CC′X system[(199)]: the observed spectrum is consistent with the coupling constants J_{AX} = 0·1, J_{BX} = 0·34 and J_{CX} = 1·21 cycles sec^{-1}. It was shown that, generally, monosubstitution of a deuterium atom into a molecule containing more than one hydrogen atom will normally give rise to only one apparent J_{HD} coupling constant in its ^{1}H resonance spectrum and this single value is an average of all the HD coupling constants present. Tiers[(200)] has observed a deuterium isotope effect in the ^{1}H resonance spectrum of α-deuterotoluene. The CH_2D absorption is a triplet with components of equal intensity (J_{CH_2-D} = 2·38 cycles sec^{-1}) and the central band of the triplet has a slightly different chemical shift from that of the methyl group in non-deuterated toluene (0·015 ppm difference). A similar, though larger effect is observed in the ^{19}F spectra of deuterated fluorine-containing compounds[(201)]. The origin of these isotope shifts is thought to be the differences in zero-point vibrational functions, which are associated with different isotopic masses (see Section 3.11) [(202, 203)]. Marshall[(204)] has calculated the changes in shielding arising from the deuterium isotope effect of the hydrogen atom in HD as compared with those in H_2 and his results are in good agreement with the experimentally observed values. A few ^{2}H[(305)] and ^{3}H[(315)] chemical shifts have been reported.

12.10.2 Alkali Metals

Sodium, ^{23}Na. A NMR investigation of the ^{23}Na resonance spectra of sodium ions in a variety of aqueous solutions (NaCl, NaF, NaBr, etc.) failed to detect any chemical shifts within the error of the measurements[(205)]. Some sodium salts did exhibit a variation in line width with change in concentration (for example, NaOH, $NaClO_4$, NaI and several other salts). These changes in line width are assumed to be associated with variations in quadrupolar relaxation effects. Appreciable quadrupole relaxation was assumed to broaden the signal beyond detection: thus only sodium ions which are almost purely ionic will be detected.

O'Reilly[(260)] has studied the resonance spectra of ^{7}Li, ^{23}Na, ^{87}Rb, ^{133}Cs and ^{14}N nuclei in alkali metal/ammonia systems.

Rubidium, ^{87}Rb, *and caesium*, ^{133}Cs. Gutowsky and McGarvey[(206)] have observed ^{87}Rb and ^{133}Cs chemical shifts in solid polycrystalline rubidium and caesium halides. Table 12.80 lists their chemical shift data; in both cases

TABLE 12.80 CHEMICAL SHIFTS OF THE ^{87}Rb AND ^{133}Cs MAGNETIC RESONANCE ABSORPTION BANDS IN SOME SOLID HALIDES[(206)]. THE REFERENCE IS THE SATURATED AQUEOUS SOLUTION OF THE CORRESPONDING CHLORIDE

Salt	δ ppm	Salt	δ ppm
RbF	−60	CsF	−90
RbCl	−89	CsCl	−163
RbBr	−129	CsBr	−208
RbI	−149	CsI	−252

a saturated aqueous solution of the chloride was used as the reference. The ion in the solution is more shielded than any of those in the solid phase and the shielding in the solids increases as the electronegativity of the halide increases. Very broad signals were obtained for both fluorides examined. Caesium chemical shifts are found to extend over a larger range than those of rubidium which supports the view that chemical shifts increase with nuclear charge as suggested by Gutowsky and Hoffman[(207)]. That chemical shifts are observed at all for the halides of the alkali metals indicates that there is some covalent bond character in the metal–halide bonds since the completely ionic form would have a chemical shift equal to that of the free ion. From the trend shown by the chemical shifts of both nuclei the covalent bond character is seen to increase as expected in passing from the fluoride to the iodide.

12.10.3 Aluminium, ^{27}Al

Table 12.81 contains several ^{27}Al chemical shifts measured from observations of the first derivative of signals in both the absorption and the dispersion modes[(208)]. Narrow absorption bands (line widths $<0{\cdot}1$ gauss at 6490 gauss) were found for aluminium-containing molecules where there is tetrahedral or octahedral symmetry around the aluminium atom, as is found in $Al(H_2O)_6^{3+}$. Broad absorption bands are obtained for molecules with non-cubic point group symmetry around the aluminium atom. Freshly prepared ethereal solutions of aluminium halides show a narrow symmetrical absorption band in their ^{27}Al resonance spectra and this is assumed to be due to the formation of the dimers Al_2X_6 where there is tetrahedral symmetry about the aluminium atoms.

The ^{27}Al resonance spectrum of a solution of $LiAlH_4$ in ethyl ether has a quintet of hyperfine lines due to spin coupling between the aluminium nucleus and the four equivalent hydrogen nuclei ($J_{Al-H} \sim 110$ cycles sec^{-1}). O'Reilly[208] has attempted to calculate the Al shielding in the AlH_4^- ion by a variational procedure using both valence bond and molecular orbital type wave-

TABLE 12.81 ^{27}Al CHEMICAL SHIFTS AND LINE WIDTHS (AT 6490 GAUSS) OF SEVERAL COMPOUNDS[208]

	δ, ppm	Width, gauss
$Al(H_2O)_6^{3+}$ (aq. acidic solution)	0	*n* (0·05)
$Al(OiBu)_3$ (n-heptane solution)	−7	*n* (0·09)
AlF^{2+} (KF added to Al^{3+} aq.)	−15	*b* (0·3)
Al_2I_6 (ethyl ether solution)	−39	*n* (0·08)
$Al(OH)_4^-$ (aq. basic solution)	−80	*n* (0·08)
$Al(iBu)Cl_2$ (pure)	−86	*b* (3·7)
$Al(OCH_3)Cl_2$ (pure)	−90	*b*
$AlCl_3$ (toluene solution)	−91	*b* (0·3)
$Al(CH_3)_2Cl \cdot Al(CH_3)Cl_2$ (pure)	−93	*b*
Al_2Br_6 (ethyl ether solution)	−96	*n* (0·09)
Al_2Br_6 (liquid Br_2 solution)	−101	*b* (0·3)
AlH_4^- ($LiAlH_4$ in ethyl ether)	−103	*n* (0·06)
Al_2Cl_6 (ethyl ether solution)	−105	*n* (0·10)
$Al(CH_3)_3$ (pure)	−156	*b* (0·4)
$HAl(iBu)_2$ (pure)	−162	*b* (8·9)
$Al(Et)_3$ (pure)	−171	*b* (1·5)
$Al(iBu)_3$ (pure)	−220	*b* (5.4)

n and *b* denote narrow and broad bands.
Chemical shifts were measured relative to external $Al(H_2O)_6^{3+}$.

functions. Approximate agreement between the theoretical and experimental shielding values was obtained, the predicted shielding values for the aluminium nucleus being somewhat higher than the measured value. When a similar variational calculation was attempted for more complex aluminium-containing compounds, quantitative agreement with experimental values was not obtained. For the aluminium halides, the paramagnetic contribution to the shielding is found to be inversely dependent on the effective nuclear charge of the halide and directly dependent on the covalent character of the aluminium halide bond. The magnitudes of the observed ^{27}Al shielding constants for this type of molecule are in the order Cl < Br < I which suggests that the effect on the shielding of the increased effective nuclear charge of the halide predominates over that from increase in covalent character of the bonds in the order Cl, Br, I.

In an equimolar mixture of $Al(NO_3)_3$ and NaF in solution there exist complex ions of the type AlF_2^+ and AlF^{2+}. An attempt to observe the separate ^{27}Al signals for these species has failed because of line broadening from the coupling of the quadrupole moment of the aluminium nucleus with the asymmetric electric field gradients: a single broad band is observed[209]. The ^{27}Al spectra of several triethylaluminium complexes have also been measured[308].

12.10.4 *Halogens*

^{35}Cl, ^{37}Cl, ^{81}Br and ^{127}I all have non-zero magnetic moments but they have been little studied by NMR due to their large quadrupole moments.

Chlorine, ^{35}Cl *and* ^{37}Cl. Proctor and Yu[102] were the first to measure ^{35}Cl and ^{37}Cl chemical shifts: they observed that $Ba(ClO_4)_2$ and $HClO_4$ have ^{35}Cl resonance bands which are ~ 900 ppm to low fields of the ^{35}Cl absorption band of hydrochloric acid.

TABLE 12.82 ^{35}Cl CHEMICAL SHIFTS IN SOME LIQUID CHLORIDES[210]

Compound	Chemical shift ppm
NaCl (dil. aqueous solution)†	0
$SiCl_4$	−175
CrO_2Cl_2	−585
$VOCl_3$	−760
$TiCl_4$	−805

† External reference for chemical shifts.

Masuda[210] has measured the ^{35}Cl chemical shifts in $TiCl_4$, $VOCl_3$, CrO_2Cl_2 and $SiCl_4$ (see Table 12.82) and he has found a close correlation between the measured chemical shifts and the quadrupole coupling constants in the molecules[211]. If the paramagnetic contribution to the shielding of ^{35}Cl nuclei is dominant then the ^{35}Cl chemical shifts can be regarded as reflecting the amount of *p* electron imbalance in the bonds. Townes and Dailey[212] have shown that nuclear quadrupole coupling in molecules depends on the manner in which the valence electrons fill the *p* type orbitals: thus, the correlation between ^{35}Cl chemical shifts and quadrupole coupling constants is not unexpected. Chesnut[213] has studied variations in ^{35}Cl chemical shifts in aqueous solutions of cobaltous chloride at different concentrations. Increasing either [Co(II)] or [Cl^-] causes the chlorine nucleus to become less shielded. When non-complexing salts are added to the system, changes in chemical shifts occur and these can be interpreted as indicating the significant role which hydration plays in the equilibria under consideration. Thus, the addition of nitrate ions to a cobaltous chloride solution causes a paramagnetic shift of the ^{35}Cl resonance due to dehydration of the cobaltous ions which are then capable of further complexing with the chloride ions. From the magnitude of the ^{35}Cl chemical shifts, Chesnut has inferred that there is an isotropic electron spin-nuclear spin contact interaction in the complexed cobaltous chloride.

By measuring the amplitude of the ^{35}Cl absorption in an aqueous solution of sodium chloride in the presence of various paramagnetic ions at different concentrations, Wertz has obtained evidence for the exchange of hydrate water with the solvent[214] (see Section 9.3.2).

Dehmelt[211] has measured the ^{35}Cl and ^{37}Cl nuclear quadrupole resonance spectra of several metal chlorides and oxychlorides and a summary of his results is given in Table 12.83. Multiplet splittings of ~ 100 kc sec^{-1} appearing on the absorption lines are due to interactions between chlorine atoms occupying different sites in the crystal lattice.

TABLE 12.83 ^{35}Cl AND ^{37}Cl NUCLEAR QUADRUPOLE SPLITTINGS IN SEVERAL METAL CHLORIDES AND OXYCHLORIDES[211]

Compound†	Average frequency $\bar{\nu}$ ^{35}Cl Mc sec^{-1}	Number of lines in multiplet
$AlCl_3 \cdot O(C_2H_5)_2$	11·30	2
$SiCl_4$	20·35	4
$SnCl_4$	24·09	4
$SnCl_4 \cdot O_2NC_6H_5$	23·08	6
$TiCl_4$	6·05	4
$VOCl_3$	11·54	2
CrO_2Cl_2	15·68	2
MoO_2Cl_2	15·54	1

† All except MoO_2Cl_2 were measured at liquid air temperature.

Masuda and Kanda[215] have measured the ^{35}Cl, ^{81}Br and ^{127}I chemical shifts in the compounds HCl, HBr and HI: they also report that the line widths of the various halogen resonance absorption bands increase in the order $^{35}Cl < {}^{81}Br < {}^{127}I$ at a constant magnetic field of 6221 gauss. By examining aqueous solutions of these molecules at different concentrations, changes in both the chemical shifts and the line widths are observed and a study of these changes enables information to be obtained concerning the dissociation of the respective acids.

Kanda[216] has explained Cl, Br and I chemical shifts in solid metal halides by considering the extent of the paramagnetic contribution which results from partial covalent bond character.

Iodine, ^{127}I. ^{127}I resonance spectra have been used to investigate the kinetics of the tri-iodide equilibrium[217] established when free iodine is added to an aqueous iodide solution according to the equation:

$$I^- + I_2 \rightleftharpoons I_3^-$$

The ^{127}I absorption signal for the I^- ion is broadened when iodine molecules are introduced into the system and from measurements of the line broadening it is possible to calculate values for the rate constants of the forward and the reverse reactions of the tri-iodide equilibrium[217].

12.10.5 Copper, ^{63}Cu

Line width measurements of the ^{63}Cu resonance signal in concentrated hydrochloric acid solution containing cuprous and cupric chloride have enabled a value for the bimolecular rate constant to be calculated for the electron exchange process (see Section 9.2)[218, 219].

$$Cu^{2+} + Cu^+ \rightleftharpoons Cu^+ + Cu^{2+}$$

12.10.6 *Arsenic*, ^{75}As

An examination of the ^{75}As resonance spectrum of liquid AsF_5 did not reveal any fine structure: the line width of the absorption band was ~ 15 gauss at 8·8 Mc sec^{-1} (220).

12.10.7 *Selenium*, ^{77}Se

Walchli(221) has measured the ^{77}Se chemical shifts of H_2SeO_3 (– 1504 ppm) and H_2SeO_4 (– 1560 ppm) in aqueous solution from a liquid sample of H_2Se used as an external reference compound. The selenium nucleus in H_2Se is more shielded than those in the other two compounds.

12.10.8 *Antimony*, ^{121}Sb

The derivative curve of the ^{121}Sb resonance absorption of $NaSbF_6$ dissolved in an aqueous solution of hydrofluoric acid has been shown to consist of seven components from spin–spin interaction of the ^{121}Sb nucleus with the six equivalent fluorine nuclei in the SbF_6^- ion(102, 223).

12.10.9 *Platinum*, ^{195}Pt

In the ^1H resonance spectrum of the platinum hydride, $[(P(C_2H_5)_3)_2PtHCl]$, a J_{Pt-H} coupling constant of 1276 cycles sec^{-1} has been detected(224). J_{Pt-H} spin coupling constants in trimethyl platinum complexes such as $[(CH_3)_3PtI]_4$ fall in the range 70–80 cycles sec^{-1} (125). Ethylene(226) and cyclopentadienyl(227) derivatives of platinum show much smaller J_{Pt-CH} values (e.g. for $K[C_2H_4PtCl_3]$, J_{Pt-H} = 34 cycles sec^{-1}). In *cis*-$[((EtO)_3P)_2PtCl_2]$, a J_{Pt-P} coupling constant of 5·70 kc sec^{-1} has been measured(228).

12.10.10 *Mercury*, ^{199}Hg *and* ^{201}Hg

Extensive measurements have been made on the Hg—H coupling constants in alkyl mercury derivatives(268, 280) (see Section 10.3.3).

The ^{199}Hg chemical shifts for a series of dialkyl mercury compounds have been measured in order to estimate the importance of hyperconjugative effects in the metal–carbon bond(91). If hyperconjugation is important then the mercury nucleus in dimethyl mercury would be expected to have the highest shielding: this is not observed to be the case as can be seen from inspection of the ^{199}Hg chemical shifts given in Table 12.84. There is, however, a rough correlation of the ^{199}Hg chemical shifts with the number of β-hydrogen atoms in the alkyl group. This might be related to the spin–spin coupling behaviour in

TABLE 12.84 ^{199}Hg CHEMICAL SHIFTS IN R_2Hg COMPOUNDS(91)

R group	Chemical shift δ ppm	Chemical shift/ Number of β-hydrogen atoms
CH_3	0	
C_2H_5	+330	57
C_3H_7	+240	60
$(CH_3)_2HC$	+640	53

these compounds where the mercury atom is coupled more strongly with the β-hydrogen atoms than with the α-hydrogen atoms (see Section 10.3.2). Similar coupling behaviour has been observed by Brownstein[243] in an investigation of a series of organomercury compounds of general formula CH_3ORHgX where R is an alkyl radical and X is a chloride, bromide, iodide or acetate group. Table 12.85 gives the ^{199}Hg—^{1}H spin coupling constants extracted from a first order analysis of the ^{1}H spectra of the compounds. In all the compounds except $CH_3OCH_2CH_2HgO.CO.CH_3$, the Hg—H coupling constant between the mercury and the α-hydrogen nuclei is less than that between the mercury and the β-hydrogen nuclei. Hg—H spin coupling constants between the mercury nucleus and the α-hydrogen nuclei are found within the narrow range 203–230 cycles sec^{-1} for the R and X groups considered. Although J_{Hg-H} coupling constants between the mercury nucleus and β-hydrogen nuclei show a larger variation with changes in X, no obvious trend in the coupling constants is apparent except that there is a marked increase for coupling with the —CH hydrogen compared with that for —CH_2 hydrogen nuclei. For hydrogen nuclei on the γ-carbon atom, no Hg—H spin coupling is resolved in the spectra of the propyl derivatives but a value of 21 cycles sec^{-1}, independent of the nature of X, is observed for this coupling constant in sec-butyl compounds. It has been suggested tentatively that the Hg—H spin coupling depends on the dihedral angle between the bond joining the mercury and the α-carbon atom, and the bond between the β-carbon atom and the hydrogen atom or methyl group attached to it. However, the observed coupling constants could also be explained by assuming that the Hg—H spin coupling operates via a spatial mechanism. The ^{1}H chemical shifts for the α-CH_2 groups are observed in the range $\tau = 7{\cdot}63$–$7{\cdot}95$.

A few Hg—H coupling constants for cyclic hydrogen nuclei have been determined in 3-chloromercurifuran: where such coupling constants have been measured they are all of the same sign[278].

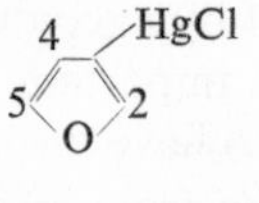

$$J_{Hg-H_2} = \pm 40{\cdot}4 \text{ cycles sec}^{-1}$$
$$J_{Hg-H_4} = \pm 74{\cdot}9 \text{ cycles sec}^{-1}$$
$$J_{Hg-H_5} = \pm 27{\cdot}9 \text{ cycles sec}^{-1}$$

Schneider and Buckingham[194] have examined the NMR spectra of several compounds of mercury, thallium and lead (^{199}Hg, ^{205}Tl and ^{207}Pb) and they have explained the observed chemical shifts by estimating the diamagnetic and paramagnetic shielding contributions in terms of a simple atom in a molecule model. Only the paramagnetic shielding contribution, σ_p, need be considered and it is estimated to increase as the electronegativity of the atoms bonded to the metals increases. For molecules containing atoms with incomplete p and d orbitals, the theory predicts large negative values for σ_p. The theory predicts chemical shifts in reasonable agreement with the measured shifts between $Hg(CH_3)_2$ and Hg^{2+} and between $Tl(CH_3)_3$ and Tl^{3+} (that is, between covalent and ionically bonded species). However, the model predicts that the chemical shift between Pb^{2+} and $Pb(CH_3)_4$ will be zero in contradiction to the observed value of 3000 ppm: this suggests that higher electronic states, mainly the 6*d* orbitals of the lead, must also be taken into account. Table 12.86 gives the chemical shifts of the compounds examined in this investigation.

TABLE 12.85 $^1H—^{199}Hg$ COUPLING CONSTANTS IN CYCLES SEC^{-1} OF SOME ORGANOMERCURY COMPOUNDS[243] OF GENERAL FORMULA CH_3ORHgX

Compound	Coupling constants†			
	$J_{Hg-C_{1A}}$ $J_{Hg-C_{1B}}$	J_{Hg-C2}	J_{Hg-C3}	J_{Hg-C4}
$CH_3OCH_2CH_2—HgO—C(=O)—CH_3$ (2 1)	230 ± 2	217 ± 2		
$CH_3OCH_2CH_2—HgCl$	225 ± 7	245 ± 2		
$CH_3OCH_2CH_2—HgBr$	207 ± 2	249 ± 2		
$CH_3—CH(OCH_3)—CH_2—Hg—O—C(=O)—CH_3$ (3 2 1)	222 ± 4	288 ± 8	0	
$CH_3—CH(OCH_3)—CH_2—HgCl$	223 ± 2	338 ± 2	0	
$CH_3—CH(OCH_3)—CH_2—HgBr$	205 ± 5	295 ± 1	0	
$(CH_3)_2C(OCH_3)—CH_2—Hg—O—C(=O)—CH_3$ (3 2 1)	215 ± 2		20·8 ± 1	
$(CH_3)_2C(OCH_3)—CH_2—Hg—Cl$	203 ± 2		21·1 ± 1	
$(CH_3)_2C(OCH_3)—CH_2—Hg—Br$	204 ± 2		21·9 ± 1	0

† J_{Hg-C_2} is the coupling constant between the ^{199}Hg nucleus and the ^1H nuclei at C_2, etc.

TABLE 12.86 CHEMICAL SHIFTS (IN PPM) OF SOME COMPOUNDS OF MERCURY, THALLIUM AND LEAD. THE NEGATIVE SIGN INDICATES THAT THE SIGNAL IS TO LOW FIELDS OF THE EXTERNAL REFERENCE[194]

^{207}Pb		^{205}Tl		^{199}Hg	
$Pb(NO_3)_2$ aq.	0	$Tl(NO_3)_3$ aq.	0	$Hg(NO_3)_2$ aq.	0
$Pb(CH_3)_4$	−2980	$TlCl_3$	−2550	$K_2[HgCl_4]$ aq.	−1170
		TlOEt	−2880	$Hg(CN)_2$ (pyridine solution)	−1310
		$Tl(CH_3)_3$ (ether solution)	−4760	$Hg(C_2H_5)_2$	−2180
				$Hg(CH_3)_2$	−2460

Figure 12.47 shows the ^{199}Hg resonance spectrum of $Hg(CH_3)_2$ at 10·74 Mc sec^{-1}: the septet splitting arises from spin coupling of the ^{199}Hg nucleus with the six equivalent methyl hydrogen nuclei(194). The addition of pyridine to a pure sample of mercury dimethyl increases the shielding of the ^{199}Hg nucleus by ~ 80 ppm.

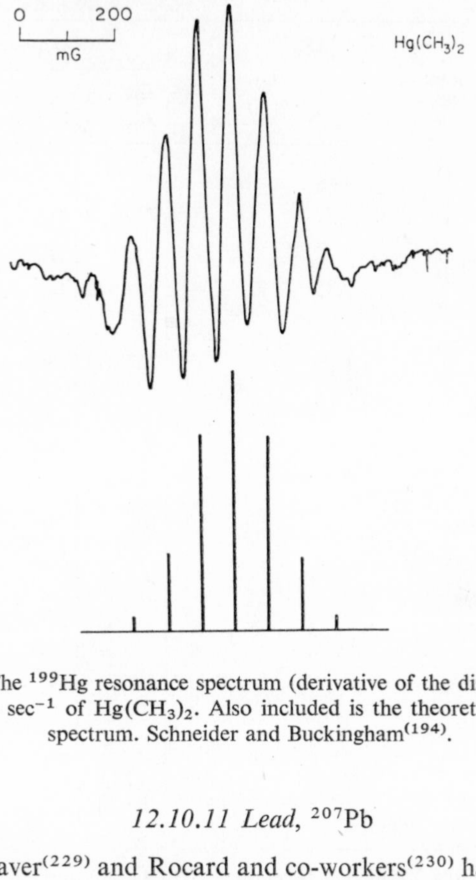

FIG. 12.47 The ^{199}Hg resonance spectrum (derivative of the dispersion mode) at 10·74 Mc sec^{-1} of $Hg(CH_3)_2$. Also included is the theoretical absorption spectrum. Schneider and Buckingham(194).

12.10.11 Lead, ^{207}Pb

Piette and Weaver(229) and Rocard and co-workers(230) have reported ^{207}Pb chemical shifts for several lead-containing compounds (see Table 12·87). Large chemical shift differences extending over a range of 16,000 ppm are encountered which indicate that there is a large paramagnetic contribution to the shielding of the lead nucleus. Orgel(231) has calculated values of the paramagnetic contribution to the shielding of ^{207}Pb nuclei for a series of Pb(II) salts and his calculated values of screening constant are in good agreement with those observed experimentally. When the environment of the lead nucleus is mainly ionic, the paramagnetic contribution is observed to be small while the introduction of some covalent bond character increases the paramagnetic contribution (as for example in PbO (yellow))(229).

Chemical shifts of solid compounds are measured using derivative curves obtained from phase sensitive detection.

TABLE 12.87 ^{207}Pb CHEMICAL SHIFTS OF SOME LEAD COMPOUNDS[229, 230]

Compound	Purity %	δ ppm	Compound	δ ppm
Pb metal		0	PbO (yellow)	+7400
PbO_2	90	+5800	Pb (zirconate) solid	+12,500
powder	94	+6500	$Pb(ClO_4)_2$ solution	+14,100
	98	+6900		
$Pb(C_2H_3O_2)_2 \cdot 3H_2O$ single crystal		+10,900	PbO (solid) red	+11,200
$Pb(C_2H_3O_2)_2 \cdot 3H_2O$ solution		+12.300	$Pb(C_2O_4)_2$ solid	+12,300
$PbCl_2$ crystalline powder		+13,800	PbTe	+10,800
$PbCO_3$ single crystal		+14,400	PbS	+10,100
$PbSO_4$ crystalline powder		+15,200	PbSe	+8700
$Pb(NO_3)_2$ solution		+14,400		
$Pb(NO_2)_2 \cdot H_2O$		+15,200		
$Pb(NO_3)_2$	98	+15,200		
crystalline powder		+15,200		

12.10.12 *Niobium*, ^{93}Nb

Figure 12.48 shows the ^{93}Nb resonance spectrum[258] of the NbF_6^- ion at 14·2 Mc sec^{-1}: the septet splitting ($J_{Nb-F} = 334$ cycles sec^{-1}) unequivocally establishes the existence of the NbF_6^- ion in solution and indicates the absence

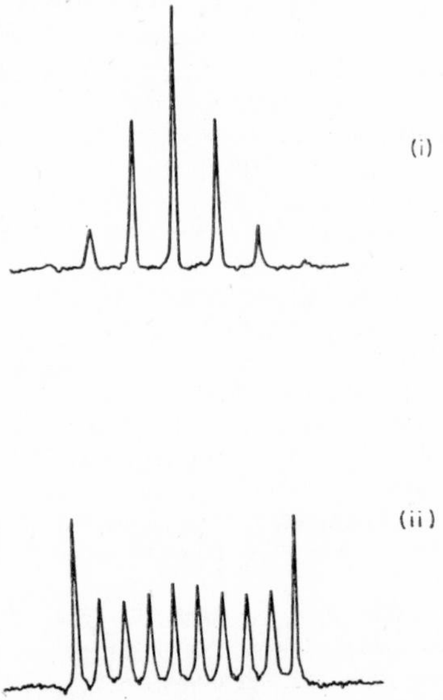

FIG. 12.48 (i) ^{93}Nb resonance spectrum of the NbF_6^- ion at 14·2 Mc sec^{-1}. (ii) ^{19}F resonance spectrum of the NbF_6^- ion at 56·4 Mc sec^{-1}. Packer and Muetterties[258].

of the species NbF_7^{2-}. The ^{19}F resonance spectrum of NbF_6^- (see Fig. 12.48(ii)) is a decet because of the coupling of the fluorine nuclei with the niobium nucleus of spin number 9/2. The components of the multiplet are of equal intensity but differ in their line widths, a feature associated with the quadrupolar relaxation mechanism which operates in this system[112, 258].

12.10.13 Nuclear Magnetic Moments

Proctor and Yu[102] examined the following nuclei in their study of nuclear magnetic moments: ^{14}N, ^{15}N, ^{35}Cl, ^{45}Sc, ^{51}V, ^{55}Mn, ^{59}Co, ^{95}Mo, ^{97}Mo, ^{113}In, ^{115}In, ^{121}Sb, ^{123}Sb, ^{129}Xe, ^{131}Xe, ^{195}Pt, ^{199}Hg, ^{201}Hg and ^{209}Bi. A compilation of nuclear properties of nuclei with magnetic moments is given in Appendix A.

REFERENCES

1. W. D. Phillips, H. C. Miller and E. L. Muetterties, *J. Amer. Chem. Soc.*, **81**, 4496 (1959).
2. T. P. Onak, H. Landesman, R. E. Williams and I. Shapiro, *J. Phys. Chem.*, **63**, 1533 (1959).
3. A. Saika and C. P. Slichter, *J. Chem. Phys.*, **22**, 26 (1954).
4. N. Muller, P. C. Lauterbur, J. Goldenson, *J. Amer. Chem. Soc.*, **78**, 3557 (1956).
5. J. R. Van Wazer, C. F. Callis, J. N. Shoolery and R. C. Jones, *J. Amer. Chem. Soc.*, **78**, 5715 (1956).
6. T. P. Onak, H. Landesman, R. E. Williams and I. Shapiro, paper presented to the Division of Inorganic Chemistry, National Meeting of A.C.S., Boston, Mass., April (1959).
7. A. Banister and N. N. Greenwood, *J. Chem. Soc.*, 1534 (1965).
8. M. F. Hawthorne, *J. Amer. Chem. Soc.*, **83**, 1345 (1961).
9. R. Schaeffer, J. N. Shoolery and R. Jones, *J. Amer. Chem. Soc.*, **79**, 4606 (1957).
10. N. F. Chamberlain, *Anal. Chem.*, **31**, 56 (1959).
11. T. D. Coyle, S. L. Stafford and F. G. A. Stone, *J. Chem. Soc.*, 3103 (1963).
12. H. S. Gutowsky, D. W. McCall and C. P. Slichter, *J. Chem. Phys.*, **21**, 279 (1953).
13. N. Muller and D. E. Pritchard, *J. Chem. Phys.*, **31**, 768 (1959).
14. R. A. Ogg, *J. Chem. Phys.*, **22**, 1933 (1954).
15. J. N. Shoolery, *Discuss. Faraday Soc.*, **19**, 215 (1955).
16. R. E. Williams and I. Shapiro, *J. Chem. Phys.*, **29**, 677 (1958).
17. R. E. Williams, S. G. Gibbons and I. Shapiro, *J. Chem. Phys.*, **30**, 320, 333 (1959).
18. K. Hedberg and V. Schomaker, *J. Amer. Chem. Soc.*, **73**, 1482 (1951).
19. R. E. Williams, *J. Inorg. Nuc. Chem.*, **20**, 198 (1962).
20. R. E. Williams, H. D. Fisher and C. O. Wilson, *J. Phys. Chem.*, **64**, 1583 (1960).
21. W. C. Price, *J. Chem. Phys.*, **16**, 894 (1948).
22. R. E. Williams, S. G. Gibbons and I. Shapiro, *J. Amer. Chem. Soc.*, **81**, 6164 (1959).
23. J. S. Rigden, R. C. Hopkins and J. D. Baldeschwieler, *J. Chem. Phys.*, **35**, 1532 (1961).
24. M. E. Jones, K. Hedberg, V. Schomaker, *J. Amer. Chem. Soc.*, **75**, 4116 (1953).
25. C. E. Nordman and W. N. Lipscomb, *J. Amer. Chem. Soc.*, **75**, 4116 (1953).
26. R. A. Ogg: O.M.C.C. Tech. Report 120, Navy Contract No. 52–1023c at Stanford University (1955).
27. R. Schaeffer and F. N. Tebbe, *J. Amer. Chem. Soc.*, **84**, 3974 (1962).
28. K. Hedberg, M. E. Jones and V. Schomaker, *J. Amer. Chem. Soc.*, **73**, 3538 (1951).
29. W. N. Lipscomb, *J. Chem. Phys.*, **22**, 985 (1954).
30. K. Hedberg, M. E. Jones and V. Schomaker, unpublished results quoted in reference 29.
31. F. L. Hirshfeld, K. Eriks, R. E. Dickerson, E. L. Lippert and W. N. Lipscomb, *J. Chem. Phys.*, **28**, 56 (1958).
32. J. S. Kasper, C. M. Lucht and D. Harker, *Acta Crysta.*, 3, 436 (1950).

33. V. D. Aftandilian, H. C. Miller, G. W. Parshall and E. L. Muetterties, *Inorg. Chem.*, **1**, 734 (1962).
34. A. B. Burg and R. Kratzer, *Inorg. Chem.*, **1**, 725 (1962).
35. J. A. Dupont and M. F. Hawthorne, *Chem. and Ind.*, 405 (1962).
36. R. Schaeffer, J. N. Shoolery and R. Jones, *J. Amer. Chem. Soc.*, **80**, 2670 (1958).
37. B. Siegel, J. L. Mack, J. U. Lowe and J. Callaghan, *J. Amer. Chem. Soc.*, **80**, 4523 (1958).
38. M. F. Hawthorne and J. J. Miller, *J. Amer. Chem. Soc.*, **80**, 754 (1958).
39. I. Shapiro, M. Lustig and R. E. Williams, *J. Amer. Chem. Soc.*, **81**, 838 (1959).
40. B. N. Figgis and R. L. Williams, *Spectrochim. Acta.*, **15**, 331 (1959).
41. N. J. Blay, J. Williams and R. L. Williams, *J. Chem. Soc.*, 424 (1960).
42. N. J. Blay, I. Dunstan and R. L. Williams, *J. Chem. Soc.*, 430 (1960).
43. T. P. Onak and I. Shapiro, *J. Chem. Phys.*, **32**, 952 (1960).
44. J. Y. Beach and S. H. Bauer, *J. Amer. Chem. Soc.*, **62**, 3440 (1940).
45. W. C. Price, *J. Chem. Phys.*, **17**, 1044 (1949).
46. R. A. Ogg and J. D. Ray, *Discuss. Faraday Soc.*, **19**, 239 (1955).
47. P. C. Lauterbur, *J. Chem. Phys.*, **27**, 217 (1957).
48. P. C. Lauterbur, *Annals N.Y. Acad. Sci.*, **70**, 841 (1958).
49. P. C. Lauterbur, *J. Amer. Chem. Soc.*, **83**, 1838 (1961).
50. P. C. Lauterbur, *Determination of Organic Structures by Physical Methods*, Vol. 2, Chapt. 7, Editors F. C. Nachod and W. D. Phillips, Academic Press, New York (1962).
51. C. H. Holm, *J. Chem. Phys.*, **26**, 707 (1957).
52. H. Spiesecke and W. G. Schneider, *J. Chem. Phys.*, **35**, 722 (1961).
53. S. Forsén and A. Rupprecht, *J. Chem. Phys.*, **33**, 1888 (1960).
54. D. J. Parker, G. A. McLaren and J. J. Conradi, *J. Chem. Phys.*, **33**, 629 (1960).
55. E. B. Baker, *J. Chem. Phys.*, **37**, 911 (1962).
56. G. R. Holtzman, P. C. Lauterbur, J. H. Anderson and W. Koth, *J. Chem. Phys.*, **25**, 172 (1956).
57. J. N. Shoolery, private communication.
58. Reference 50, p. 483.
59. A. L. Allred and E. G. Rochow, *J. Inorg. Nuc. Chem.*, **5**, 269 (1958).
60. M. P. Brown and D. E. Webster, *J. Phys. Chem.*, **64**, 698 (1960).
61. P. C. Lauterbur, *J. Amer. Chem. Soc.*, **83**, 1846 (1961).
62. H. Spiesecke and W. G. Schneider, *J. Chem. Phys.*, **35**, 731 (1961).
63. P. C. Lauterbur, private communication.
64. R. Ettinger, P. Blume, A. Patterson and P. C. Lauterbur, *J. Chem. Phys.*, **33**, 1597 (1960).
65. A. Patterson and R. Ettinger, *Z. Elektrochem.*, **64**, 98 (1960).
66. F. A. Cotton, A. Danti, J. S. Waugh and R. W. Fessenden, *J. Chem. Phys.*, **29**, 1427 (1958).
67. E. Weiss, *Z. Anorg. Chem.* **287**, 223 (1956).
68. R. V. G. Ewens and M. W. Lister, *Trans. Faraday Soc.*, **35**, 681 (1939).
69. C. Juan and H. S. Gutowsky, *J. Chem. Phys.*, **37**, 2198 (1962).
70. G. J. Karabatsos, *J. Amer. Chem. Soc.*, **83**, 1230 (1961).
71. D. R. McAdams, *J. Chem. Phys.*, **36**, 1948 (1962).
72. N. F. Ramsey, *Phys. Rev.*, **91**, 303 (1953).
73. N. Muller and D. E. Pritchard, *J. Chem. Phys.*, **31**, 1471 (1959).
74. J. N. Shoolery, *J. Chem. Phys.*, **31**, 1427 (1959).
75. N. Muller, *J. Chem. Phys.*, **36**, 359 (1962).
76. E. B. Whipple, W. E. Stewart, G. S. Reddy and J. H. Goldstein, *J. Chem. Phys.*, **34**, 2136 (1961).
77. M. Karplus and D. M. Grant, *Proc. Nat. Acad. Sci.*, **45**, 1269 (1959).
78. M. Karplus, *J. Phys. Chem.*, **64**, 1793 (1960).
79. M. L. Huggins, *J. Amer. Chem. Soc.*, **75**, 4123 (1953).
80. E. R. Malinowski, *J. Amer. Chem. Soc.*, **83**, 4479 (1961).
81. R. K. Harris, *J. Phys. Chem.*, **66**, 768 (1962).

82. H. S. Gutowsky and C. Juan, *Discuss. Faraday Soc.*, **34**, 52 (1962).
83. E. R. Malinowski, L. Z. Pollara and J. P. Larmann, *J. Amer. Chem. Soc.*, **84**, 2649 (1962).
84. C. N. Banwell and N. Sheppard, *Mol. Phys.*, **3**, 351 (1960).
85. N. Sheppard and J. J. Turner, *Proc. Roy. Soc.*, **A252**, 506 (1959).
86. A. D. Cohen, N. Sheppard and J. J. Turner, *Proc. Chem. Soc.*, 118 (1958).
87. J. H. Goldstein and G. S. Reddy, *J. Chem. Phys.*, **36**, 2644 (1962).
88. H. M. Hutton, W. F. Reynolds and T. Schaefer, *Can. J. Chem.*, **40**, 1758 (1962).
89. J. N. Shoolery, L. F. Johnson and W. A. Anderson, *J. Mol. Spect.*, **5**, 110 (1960).
90. E. B. Baker, *J. Chem. Phys.*, **26**, 960 (1957).
91. R. E. Dessy, T. J. Flautt, H. H. Jaffé and G. F. Reynolds, *J. Chem. Phys.*, **30**, 1422 (1959).
92. P. T. Narasimhan and M. T. Rogers, *J. Amer. Chem. Soc.*, **82**, 34 (1960).
93. C. M. Sharts and J. D. Roberts, *J. Amer. Chem. Soc.*, **79**, 1008 (1957).
94. G. J. Karabatsos, *J. Amer. Chem. Soc.*, **83**, 1230 (1961).
95. G. J. Karabatsos, J. D. Graham and F. M. Vane, *J. Amer. Chem. Soc.*, **83**, 2778 (1961).
96. G. J. Karabatsos, J. D. Graham and F. M. Vane, *J. Amer. Chem. Soc.*, **84**, 37 (1962).
97. W. A. Anderson, *J. Chem. Phys.*, **37**, 1373 (1962).
98. R. M. Lynden-Bell and N. Sheppard, *Proc. Roy. Soc.*, **A269**, 385 (1962).
99. J. N. Shoolery, *J. Mol. Spect.*, **63**, 110 (1960).
100. N. Muller and P. I. Rose, *J. Amer. Chem. Soc.*, **84**, 3973 (1962).
101. J. V. Acrivos, *J. Chem. Phys.*, **36**, 1097 (1962).
102. W. G. Proctor and F. C. Yu, *Phys. Rev.*, **81**, 20 (1951).
103. Y. Masuda and T. Kanda, *J. Phys. Soc., Japan*, **8**, 432 (1953).
104. B. E. Holder and M. P. Klein, *J. Chem. Phys.*, **23**, 1956 (1955).
105. B. M. Schmidt, L. C. Brown and D. Williams, *J. Mol. Spect.*, **2**, 539 (1958).
106. B. M. Schmidt, L. C. Brown and D. Williams, *J. Mol. Spect.*, **2**, 551 (1958).
107. R. A. Ogg and J. D. Ray, *J. Chem. Phys.*, **26**, 1340 (1957).
108. J. D. Baldeschwieler and E. W. Randall, *Proc. Chem. Soc.*, 303 (1961).
109. J. N. Shoolery, Varian Technical Bulletin, No. 50.
110. L. H. Piette, J. D. Ray and R. A. Ogg, *J. Mol. Spect.*, **2**, 66 (1958).
111. G. V. D. Tiers and F. A. Bovey, *J. Phys. Chem.*, **63**, 302 (1959).
112. J. A. Pople, *Mol. Phys.*, **1**, 168 (1958).
113. R. A. Ogg, *J. Chem. Phys.*, **22**, 560 (1954).
114. E. Grunwald, A. Loewenstein and S. Meiboom, *J. Chem. Phys.*, **27**, 630 (1957).
115. J. D. Roberts, *J. Amer. Chem. Soc.*, **78**, 4495 (1956).
116. I. D. Kuntz, P. von R. Schleyer and A. Allerhand, *J. Chem. Phys.*, **35**, 1533 (1961).
117. P. T. Narasimhan and M. T. Rogers, *J. Chem. Phys.*, **31**, 1430 (1959).
118. J. D. Ray, L. H. Piette and H. D. Hollis, *J. Chem. Phys.*, **29**, 1022 (1958).
119. J. D. Ray and R. A. Ogg, *J. Chem. Phys.*, **26**, 1452 (1957).
120. H. E. Weaver, B. M. Tolbert and R. C. La Force. *J. Chem. Phys.*, **23**, 1956 (1955).
121. S. S. Dharmatti, K. J. Sundara Rao and R. Vijayaraghavan, *Nuovo Cimento* **11**, 656 (1959).
122. B. N. Figgis, R. G. Kidd and R. S. Nyholm. *Proc. Roy. Soc.*, **A269**, 469 (1962).
123. J. S. Griffith and L. E. Orgel, *Trans. Faraday Soc.*, **53**, 601 (1957).
124. H. A. Christ, *Helv. Phys. Acta*, **33**, 572 (1960).
125. R. Bramley, B. N. Figgis and R. S. Nyholm, *Trans. Faraday Soc.*, **58**, 1893 (1962).
126. R. G. Shulman and B. J. Wyluda, *J. Chem. Phys.*, **30**, 335 (1959).
127. L. E. Orgel, *Discuss. Faraday Soc.*, **26**, 138 (1958).
128. L. E. Orgel, *J. Chem. Phys.*, **30**, 1617 (1959).
129. W. B. Lewis, J. A. Jackson, J. F. Lemons and H. Taube, *J. Chem. Phys.*, **36**, 694 (1962).
130. J. A. Jackson, J. F. Lemons and H. Taube, *J. Chem. Phys.*, **32**, 553 (1960).
131. J. Reuben, A. Tzalmona and D. Samuel, *Proc. Chem. Soc.*, 353 (1962).
132. J. P. Maher and D. F. Evans, *Proc. Chem. Soc.*, 176 (1963).
133. E. A. V. Ebsworth and J. J. Turner, *J. Chem. Phys.*, **36**, 2628 (1962).
134. E. A. V. Ebsworth and N. Sheppard. *J. Inorg. Nuc. Chem.*, **9**, 95 (1959).

135. A. J. DOWNS and E. A. V. EBSWORTH, *J. Chem. Soc.*, 3516 (1960).
136. L. W. DAASCH and D. C. SMITH, *Anal. Chem.*, **23**, 853 (1951).
137. H. GERDING and J. W. MEARSEN, *Rec. Trav. Chim.*, **76**, 481 (1957).
138. J. R. VAN WAZER, private communication.
139. W. D. KNIGHT, *Phys. Rev.*, **76**, 1259 (1949).
140. W. C. DICKINSON, *Phys. Rev.*, **81**, 717 (1951).
141. H. S. GUTOWSKY and D. W. MCCALL, *J. Chem. Phys.*, **22**, 162 (1954).
142. L. H. MEYER and H. S. GUTOWSKY, *J. Phys. Chem.*, **57**, 481 (1953).
143. J. R. VAN WAZER, C. F. CALLIS, J. N. SHOOLERY and R. C. JONES, *J. Amer. Chem. Soc.*, **78**, 5715 (1956).
144. C. A. COULSON, *Valence*, Oxford Press, New York (1952), p. 193.
145. J. R. PARKS, *J. Amer. Chem. Soc.*, **79**, 757 (1957).
146. H. FINEGOLD, *Annals N.Y. Acad. Sci.*, **70**, 875 (1958).
147. L. C. D. GROENWEGHE, L. MAIER and K. MOEDRITZER, *J. Phys. Chem.*, **60**, 901 (1962).
148. L. C. D. GROENWEGHE, L. MAIER and K. MOEDRITZER, *J. Chem. Eng. Data*, **7**, 307 (1962).
149. A. R. KATRITZKY and R. A. Y. JONES, *Angew. Chem.* (*Int. Edn.*), **1**, 32 (1962).
150. G. O. DUDEK, *J. Chem. Phys.*, **33**, 624 (1960).
151. R. W. TAFT, *Steric Effects in Organic Chemistry*, Ed. M. S. NEWMAN, John Wiley, New York (1956), Chapt. 13.
152. J. R. VAN WAZER, C. F. CALLIS, J. N. SHOOLERY and W. A. ANDERSON, *J. Amer. Chem. Soc.*, **79**, 2719 (1957).
153. W. E. SHULER and R. C. AXTMANN, A. E. C. Research and Development Report DP 474.
154. R. C. AXTMANN, W. E. SHULER and J. H. EBERLY, *J. Chem. Phys.*, **31**, 850 (1959).
155. J. FEENEY and L. H. SUTCLIFFE, unpublished results.
156. T. H. SIDDALL and C. A. PROHASKA, *J. Amer. Chem. Soc.*, **84**, 2502 (1962).
157. T. H. SIDDALL and C. A. PROHASKA, *J. Amer. Chem. Soc.*, **84**, 3467 (1962).
158. M. M. CRUTCHFIELD, C. F. CALLIS, R. R. IRANI, and G. C. ROTH, *Inorg. Chem.*, **1**, 813 (1962).
159. K. MOEDRITZER, *J. Inorg. Nuc. Chem.*, **22**, 19 (1961).
160. J. R. VAN WAZER, C. F. CALLIS and J. N. SHOOLERY, *J. Amer. Chem. Soc.*, **77**, 4945 (1955).
161. H. FINEGOLD, private communication.
162. E. R. ANDREW, A. BRADBURY, R. G. EADES and G. J. JENKS, *Nature*, **188**, 1096 (1960).
163. E. R. ANDREW and R. G. EADES, *Discuss. Faraday Soc.*, **34**, 38 (1962).
164. R. M. LYNDEN-BELL, *Trans. Faraday Soc.*, **57**, 888 (1961).
165. L. MAIER, *J. Inorg. Nuc. Chem.*, **24**, 275 (1962).
166. R. A. Y. JONES and A. R. KATRITZKY, *J. Chem. Soc.*, 4376 (1960).
167. M. COHN and T. R. HUGHES, *J. Biol. Chem.*, **235**, 3250 (1960).
168. M. BECKE-GOEHRING, K. JOHN and E. FLUCK, *Z. anorg. Chem.*, **302**, 103 (1959).
169. N. BODEN, J. W. EMSLEY, J. FEENEY and L. H. SUTCLIFFE, *Chem. and Ind.*, 1909 (1962), and unpublished results.
170. C. F. CALLIS, J. R. VAN WAZER and J. N. SHOOLERY, *Anal. Chem.*, **28**, 269 (1956).
171. J. C. GUFFY and G. R. MILLER, *Anal. Chem.*, **31**, 1895 (1959).
172. E. SCHWARZMANN and J. R. VAN WAZER, *J. Inorg. Nuc. Chem.*, **14**, 296 (1960).
173. L. C. D. GROENWEGHE and J. H. PAYNE, *J. Amer. Chem. Soc.*, **81**, 6357 (1959).
174. E. FLUCK, J. R. VAN WAZER and L. C. D. GROENWEGHE, *J. Amer. Chem. Soc.*, **81**, 6363 (1959).
175. D. P. AMES, S. OHASHI, C. F. CALLIS and J. R. VAN WAZER, *J. Amer. Chem. Soc.*, **81**, 6350 (1959).
176. E. SCHWARZMANN and J. R. VAN WAZER, *J. Amer. Chem. Soc.*, **81**, 6366 (1959).
177. E. FLUCK, *Z. anorg. Chem.*, **315**, 181 (1962).
178. R. P. H. GASSER and R. E. RICHARDS, *Mol. Phys.*, **3**, 163 (1960).
179. R. FREEMAN, G. R. MURRAY and R. E. RICHARDS, *Proc. Roy. Soc.*, **A 242**, 455 (1957).
180. L. E. ORGEL, *An Introduction to Transition-Metal Chemistry: Ligand Field Theory*, Methuen, London (1961).
181. N. F. RAMSEY, *Phys. Rev.*, **85**, 243 (1952).

182. S. S. Dharmatti and C. R. Kanekar, *J. Chem. Phys.*, **31**, 1436 (1960).
183. S. S. Dharmatti, C. R. Kanekar and S. C. Mathur, *Proc. of the Peaceful Uses of Atomic Energy*, Geneva (1958).
184. J. A. Armstrong and G. B. Benedek, *Bull. Amer. Phys. Soc.*, **6**, 234, D8 (1961).
185. J. J. Burke and P. C. Lauterbur, *Abs. Amer. Chem. Soc. Meeting*, San Francisco (1958).
186. J. J. Burke and P. C. Lauterbur, *J. Amer. Chem. Soc.*, **83**, 326 (1961).
187. D. W. Moore and J. A. Happe, *J. Phys. Chem.*, **65**, 224 (1961).
188. J. R. Holmes and H. D. Kaesz, *J. Amer. Chem. Soc.*, **83**, 3903 (1961).
189. T. J. Rowland and J. P. Bromberg, *J. Chem. Phys.*, **29**, 626 (1958).
190. B. N. Figgis, *Trans. Faraday Soc.*, **55**, 1075 (1959).
191. R. Freeman, R. P. H. Gasser and R. E. Richards, *Mol. Phys.*, **2**, 301 (1959).
192. J. P. Maher and D. F. Evans, *Proc. Chem. Soc.*, 208 (1961).
193. L. E. Sutton and N. V. Sidgwick, *J. Chem. Soc.*, 1461 (1930).
194. W. G. Schneider and A. D. Buckingham, *Discuss. Faraday Soc.*, **34**, 147 (1962).
195. H. S. Gutowsky and B. R. McGarvey, *Phys. Rev.*, **91**, 81 (1953).
196. T. F. Wimett, *Phys. Rev.*, **91**, 476A (1953).
197. M. J. Stephen, *Proc. Roy. Soc.*, **A243**, 274 (1957).
198. E. Ishiguro, *Phys. Rev.*, **111**, 203 (1958).
199. R. J. Abraham and H. J. Bernstein, *Can. J. Chem.*, **39**, 216 (1961).
200. G. V. D. Tiers, *J. Chem. Phys.*, **29**, 963 (1958).
201. G. V. D. Tiers, *J. Amer. Chem. Soc.*, **79**, 5585 (1957).
202. N. F. Ramsey, *Phys. Rev.*, **87**, 1075 (1952).
203. H. S. Gutowsky, *J. Chem. Phys.*, **31**, 1683 (1959).
204. T. W. Marshall, *Mol. Phys.*, **4**, 61 (1961).
205. J. E. Wertz and O. Jardetzky, *J. Chem. Phys.*, **25**, 357 (1956).
206. H. S. Gutowsky and B. R. McGarvey, *J. Chem. Phys.*, **21**, 1423 (1953).
207. H. S. Gutowsky and C. J. Hoffman, *J. Chem. Phys.*, **19**, 1259 (1951).
208. D. E. O'Reilly, *J. Chem. Phys.*, **32**, 1007 (1960).
209. R. E. Connick and R. E. Paulson, *J. Amer. Chem. Soc.*, **79**, 5153 (1957).
210. Y. Masuda, *J. Phys. Soc. Japan*, **11**, 670 (1956).
211. H. G. Dehmelt, *J. Chem. Phys.*, **21**, 380 (1953).
212. C. H. Townes and B. P. Dailey, *J. Chem. Phys.*, **20**, 35 (1952).
213. D. B. Chesnut, *J. Chem. Phys.*, **33**, 1234 (1960).
214. J. E. Wertz, *J. Chem. Phys.*, **24**, 484 (1956).
215. Y. Masuda and T. Kanda, *J. Phys. Soc. Japan*, **9**, 82 (1954).
216. T. Kanda, *J. Phys. Soc. Japan*, **10**, 85 (1955).
217. O. E. Myers, *J. Chem. Phys.*, **28**, 1027 (1958).
218. H. M. McConnell and H. E. Weaver, *J. Chem. Phys.*, **25**, 307 (1956).
219. H. M. McConnell and S. B. Berger, *J. Chem. Phys.*, **27**, 230 (1957).
220. E. D. Jones and E. A. Uehling, *J. Chem. Phys.*, **36**, 1691 (1962).
221. H. E. Walchli, *Phys. Rev.*, **90**, 331 (1953).
222. K. Ito, H. Watanabe and M. Kubo, *J. Chem. Phys.*, **34**, 1043 (1961).
223. S. S. Dharmatti and H. E. Weaver, *Phys. Rev.*, **87**, 675 (1952).
224. J. Chatt, private communication.
225. J. A. S. Smith, *J. Chem. Soc.*, 4736 (1962).
226. D. B. Powell and N. Sheppard, *J. Chem. Soc.*, 2519 (1960).
227. B. L. Shaw and N. Sheppard, *Chem. and Ind.*, 517 (1961).
228. A. Pidcock, R. E. Richards and L. M. Venanzi, *Proc. Chem. Soc.*, 184 (1962).
229. L. H. Piette and H. E. Weaver, *J. Chem. Phys.*, **28**, 735 (1958).
230. J. M. Rocard, M. Bloom and L. B. Robinson, *Can. J. Phys.*, **37**, 522 (1959).
231. L. E. Orgel, *Mol. Phys.*, **1**, 322 (1958).
232. R. A. Friedel and H. L. Retcofsky, *J. Amer. Chem. Soc.*, **85**, 1300 (1963).
233. P. T. Narasimhan and M. T. Rogers, *J. Chem. Phys.*, **34**, 1049 (1961).
234. H. D. Kaesz and N. Flitcroft, *J. Amer. Chem. Soc.*, **85**, 1377 (1963).
235. M. M. Crutchfield, private communication.

236. S. G. Frankiss, *J. Phys. Chem.*, **67**, 752 (1963).
237. G. V. D. Tiers, *J. Phys. Soc. Japan*, **15**, 354 (1960).
238. R. K. Harris, private communication.
239. A. J. Downs, private communication referred to in reference 236.
240. E. Pitcher, A. D. Buckingham and F. G. A. Stone, *J. Chem. Phys.*, **36**, 124 (1962).
241. G. V. D. Tiers, *J. Phys. Chem.*, **64**, 373 (1960).
242. N. Muller, *J. Chem. Phys.*, **37**, 2729 (1962).
243. S. Brownstein, *Discuss. Faraday Soc.*, **34**, 25 (1962).
244. J. D. Baldeschwieler and E. W. Randall, *Chem. Rev.*, **63**, 81 (1963).
245. B. Sunners, L. H. Piette and W. G. Schneider, *Can. J. Chem.*, **38**, 681 (1960).
246. L. C. D. Groenweghe and J. H. Payne, *J. Amer. Chem. Soc.*, **83**, 1811 (1961).
247. H. Finegold, *J. Amer. Chem. Soc.*, **82**, 2641 (1960).
248. A. J. Speziale and R. C. Freeman, *J. Org. Chem.*, **23**, 1883 (1958).
249. K. Frei and H. J. Bernstein, *J. Chem. Phys.*, **38**, 1216 (1963).
250. M. Becke-Goehring and E. Fluck, *Angew. Chem.* (*Int. Edn.*) **1**, 281 (1962).
251. M. Becke-Goehring, K. John and E. Fluck, *Z. anorg. Chem.*, **302**, 103 (1959).
252. P. C. Lauterbur, *J. Chem. Phys.*, **38**, 1415 (1963).
253. P. C. Lauterbur, *J. Chem. Phys.*, **38**, 1406 (1963).
254. P. C. Lauterbur, *J. Chem. Phys.*, **38**, 1432 (1963).
255. W. G. Schneider, private communication.
256. T. L. Brown and G. L. Morgan, *Inorg. Chem.*, **2**, 736 (1963).
257. J. P. Hunt, H. W. Dodgen and F. Klanberg, *Inorg. Chem.*, **2**, 478 (1963).
258. K. J. Packer and E. L. Muetterties, *J. Amer. Chem. Soc.*, **85**, 3035 (1963).
259. S. L. Manatt, G. L. Juvinall and D. D. Elleman, *J. Amer. Chem. Soc.*, **85**, 2664 (1963).
260. D. E. O'Reilly, *Bull. Amer. Phys. Soc.*, **8**, 531 (1963).
261. R. A. Forman, *J. Chem. Phys.*, **39**, 2398 (1963).
262. D. F. Evans, *J. Chem. Soc.*, 5575 (1963).
263. J. P. Maher and D. F. Evans, *J. Chem. Soc.*, 5534 (1963).
264. G. W. Smith, *J. Chem. Phys.*, **39**, 2031 (1963).
265. Y. Kobayashi, L. A. Chasin and L. B. Clapp, *Inorg. Chem.*, **2**, 212 (1963).
266. G. V. D. Tiers, *J. Phys. Chem.*, **66**, 945 (1962); **67**, 1372 (1963).
267. E. A. V. Ebsworth and S. G. Frankiss, *Trans. Faraday Soc.*, **59**, 1518 (1963).
268. J. V. Hatton, W. G. Schneider and W. Siebrand, *J. Chem. Phys.*, **39**, 1330 (1963).
269. G. B. Savitsky and K. Namikawa, *J. Phys. Chem.*, **67**, 2430 (1963).
270. N. Muller and D. T. Carr, *J. Phys. Chem.*, **67**, 112 (1963).
271. J. Reuben and D. Samuel, private communication.
272. G. B. Savitsky, *J. Phys. Chem.*, **67**, 2723 (1963).
273. G. B. Savitsky and K. Namikawa, *J. Phys. Chem.*, **67**, 2755 (1963).
274. H. C. Clark, J. T. Kwon, L. W. Reeves and E. J. Wells, *Can. J. Chem.*, **41**, 3005 (1963).
275. T. Schaefer, W. F. Reynolds and T. Yonemoto, *Can. J. Chem.*, **41**, 2969 (1963).
276. G. E. Maciel and G. C. Ruben, *J. Amer. Chem. Soc.*, **85**, 3903 (1963).
277. E. A. Pier (Varian Associates), private communication (1964).
278. A. D. Cohen and K. A. McLauchlan, *Mol. Phys.*, **7**, 11 (1964).
279. D. M. Graham and C. E. Holloway, *Can. J. Chem.*, **41**, 2114 (1963).
280. D. Moy, E. Emerson and J. P. Oliver, *Inorg. Chem.*, **2**, 1261 (1963).
281. M. L. Nielsen and J. V. Pustinger, *J. Phys. Chem.*, **68**, 152 (1964).
282. K. S. Dhami and J. B. Stothers, *Can. J. Chem.*, **43**, 479, 498, 510 (1965).
283. C. T. Ford, F. E. Dickson and I. I. Bezman, *Inorg. Chem.*, **3**, 177 (1964).
284. J. A. Pople, *Mol. Phys.*, **7**, 301 (1964).
285. J. V. Hatton, *J. Chem. Phys.*, **40**, 933 (1964).
286. D. F. Gaines and R. Schaeffer, *J. Amer. Chem. Soc.*, **86**, 1505 (1964).
287. C. P. Nash and G. E. Maciel, *J. Phys. Chem.*, **68**, 832 (1964).
288. D. F. Gaines and R. Schaeffer, *J. Phys. Chem.*, **68**, 955 (1964).
289. G. E. Maciel and G. B. Savitsky, *J. Phys. Chem.*, **68**, 437 (1964).
290. J. B. Stothers and P. C. Lauterbur, *Can. J. Chem.*, **42**, 1563 (1964).
291. E. G. Wells and L. W. Reeves, *J. Chem. Phys.*, **40**, 2036 (1964).

292. L. W. Reeves, *J. Chem. Phys.*, **40**, 2128 (1964).
293. L. W. Reeves, *J. Chem. Phys.*, **40**, 2132, 2423 (1964).
294. S. S. Danyluk, *J. Amer. Chem. Soc.*, **86**, 4504 (1964).
295. G. Binsch, J. B. Lambert, B. W. Roberts and J. D. Roberts, *J. Amer. Chem. Soc.*, **86**, 5564 (1964).
296. J. B. Lambert, G. Binsch and J. D. Roberts, *Proc. Nat. Acad. Sci.*, **51**, 735 (1964).
297. A. J. R. Bourn and E. W. Randall, *J. Mol. Spect.*, **13**, 29 (1964).
298. M. Witanowski, T. Urbanski and L. Stefanik, *J. Amer. Chem. Soc.*, **86**, 2569 (1964).
299. D. Herbison-Evans and R. E. Richards, *Mol. Phys.*, **8**, 19 (1964).
300. J. H. Goldstein and R. T. Hobgood, *J. Chem. Phys.*, **40**, 3592 (1964).
301. G. B. Savitsky and K. Namikawa, *J. Phys. Chem.*, **68**, 1956 (1964).
302. M. L. Nielsen, J. V. Pustinger and J. Strobel, *J. Chem. Eng. Data*, **9**, 167 (1964).
303. E. G. Paul and D. M. Grant, *J. Amer. Chem. Soc.*, **86**, 2977 (1964).
304. E. G. Paul and D. M. Grant, *J. Amer. Chem. Soc.*, **86**, 2984 (1964).
305. P. Diehl and T. Leipert, *Helv. Chim. Acta*, **47**, 545 (1964).
306. G. J. Karabatsos and C. E. Orzech, *J. Amer. Chem. Soc.*, **86**, 3574 (1964).
307. E. R. Malinowski and T. Vladimiroff, *J. Amer. Chem. Soc.*, **86**, 3575 (1964).
308. H. E. Swift, C. P. Poole and J. F. Itzel, *J. Phys. Chem.*, **68**, 2509 (1964).
309. K. Tori and T. Nikagawa, *J. Phys. Chem.*, **68**, 3163 (1964).
310. R. L. Pilling, F. N. Tebbe, M. F. Hawthorne and E. A. Pier, *Proc. Chem. Soc.*, 402 (1964).
311. M. Alei and J. A. Jackson, *J. Chem. Phys.*, **41**, 3402 (1964).
312. J. P. Maher and D. F. Evans, *J. Chem. Soc.*, 637 (1965).
313. J. A. Pople and M. Karplus, *J. Chem. Phys.*, **38**, 2803 (1963).
314. G. B. Benedeck, R. Englman and J. A. Armstrong, *J. Chem. Phys.*, **39**, 3349 (1963).
315. G. V. D. Tiers, C. A. Brown, R. A. Jackson and T. N. Lahr, *J. Amer. Chem. Soc.*, **86**, 2526 (1964).

APPENDIX A

TABLE OF NUCLEAR PROPERTIES

(Reproduced by permission of Varian Associates)

Isotope (*indicates radioactive)	NMR frequency in Mc sec^{-1} for a 10 kilo-gauss field	Natural abundance, per cent	Relative sensitivity for equal number of nuclei		Magnetic moment μ, in multiples of the nuclear magneton $(eh/4\pi Mc)$	Spin I, in multiples of $h/2\pi$	Electric quadrupole moment Q, in multiples of $e \times 10^{-24}$ cm^2
			At constant field	At constant frequency			
^{1}n*	29·165		0·322	0·685	−1·9130	$\frac{1}{2}$	
^{1}H	42·577	99·9844	1·000	1·000	2·79270	$\frac{1}{2}$	
^{2}H	6·536	$1·56 \times 10^{-2}$	$9·64 \times 10^{-3}$	0·409	0·85738	1	$2·77 \times 10^{-3}$
^{3}H*	45·414		1·21	1·07	2·9788	$\frac{1}{2}$	
^{3}He	32·434	10^{-5} to 10^{-7}	0·443	0·762	−2·1274	$\frac{1}{2}$	
^{6}Li	6·265	7·43	$8·51 \times 10^{-3}$	0·392	0·82191	1	$4·6 \times 10^{-4}$
^{7}Li	16·547	92·57	0·294	1·94	3·2560	$\frac{3}{2}$	$-4·2 \times 10^{-2}$
^{9}Be	5·983	100	$1·39 \times 10^{-2}$	0·703	−1·1774	$\frac{3}{2}$	2×10^{-2}
^{10}Be	4·575	18·83	$1·99 \times 10^{-2}$	1·72	1·8006	3	0·111
^{11}B	13·660	81·17	0·165	1·60	2·6880	$\frac{3}{2}$	$3·55 \times 10^{-2}$
^{13}C	10·705	1·108	$1·59 \times 10^{-2}$	0·251	0·70216	$\frac{1}{2}$	
^{14}N	3·076	99·635	$1·01 \times 10^{-3}$	0·193	0·40357	1	2×10^{-2}
^{15}N	4·315	0·365	$1·04 \times 10^{-3}$	0·101	−0·28304	$\frac{1}{2}$	
^{17}O	5·772	$3·7 \times 10^{-2}$	$2·91 \times 10^{-2}$	1·58	−1·8930	$\frac{5}{2}$	-4×10^{-3}
^{19}F	40·055	100	0·834	0·941	2·6273	$\frac{1}{2}$	
^{21}Ne		0·257				$\geq \frac{3}{2}$	
^{22}Na*	4·434		$1·81 \times 10^{-2}$	1·67	1·745	3	
^{23}Na	11·262	100	$9·27 \times 10^{-2}$	1·32	2·2161	$\frac{3}{2}$	0·1
^{25}Mg	2·606	10·05	$2·68 \times 10^{-2}$	0·714	−0·85471	$\frac{5}{2}$	
^{27}Al	11·094	100	0·207	3·04	3·6385	$\frac{5}{2}$	0·149
^{29}Si	8·460	4·70	$7·85 \times 10^{-2}$	0·199	−0·55477	$\frac{1}{2}$	

(*continued*)

Isotope (* indicates radioactive)	NMR frequency in Mc sec^{-1} for a 10 kilo-gauss field	Natural abundance, per cent	Relative sensitivity for equal number of nuclei		Magnetic moment μ, in multiples of the nuclear magneton ($eh/4\pi Mc$)	Spin I, in multiples of $h/2\pi$	Electric quadrupole moment Q, in multiples of $e \times 10^{-24}$ cm^2
			At constant field	At constant frequency			
^{31}P	17·235	100	$6{\cdot}64 \times 10^{-2}$	0·405	1·1305	$\frac{1}{2}$	
^{33}S	3·266	0·74	$2{\cdot}26 \times 10^{-3}$	0·384	0·64274	$\frac{3}{2}$	$-6{\cdot}4 \times 10^{-2}$
^{35}S*	5·08		$8{\cdot}50 \times 10^{-3}$	0·599	1·00	$\frac{3}{2}$	$4{\cdot}5 \times 10^{-2}$
^{35}Cl	4·172	75·4	$4{\cdot}71 \times 10^{-3}$	0·490	0·82089	$\frac{3}{2}$	$-7{\cdot}97 \times 10^{-2}$
^{36}Cl*	4·893		$1{\cdot}21 \times 10^{-2}$	0·919	1·2838	2	$-1{\cdot}68 \times 10^{-2}$
^{37}Cl	3·472	24·6	$2{\cdot}72 \times 10^{-3}$	0·408	0·68329	$\frac{3}{2}$	$-6{\cdot}21 \times 10^{-2}$
^{39}K	1·987	93·08	$5{\cdot}08 \times 10^{-4}$	0·233	0·39094	$\frac{3}{2}$	
^{40}K*	2·470	$1{\cdot}19 \times 10^{-2}$	$5{\cdot}21 \times 10^{-3}$	1·55	−1·296	4	
^{41}K	1·092	6·91	$8{\cdot}39 \times 10^{-5}$	0·128	0·21453	$\frac{3}{2}$	
^{43}Ca	2·865	0·13	$6{\cdot}39 \times 10^{-2}$	1·41	−1·3153	$\frac{7}{2}$	
^{45}Se	10·343	100	0·301	5·10	4·7491	$\frac{7}{2}$	
^{47}Ti	2·400	7·75	$2{\cdot}10 \times 10^{-3}$	0·659	−0·78712	$\frac{5}{2}$	
^{49}Ti	2·401	5·51	$3{\cdot}76 \times 10^{-3}$	1·19	−1·1023	$\frac{7}{2}$	
^{50}V	4·245	0·24	$5{\cdot}53 \times 10^{-2}$	5·58	3·3413	6	
^{51}V	11·193	~100	0·383	5·53	5·1392	$\frac{7}{2}$	0·3
^{53}Cr	2·406	9·54	$1{\cdot}0 \times 10^{-4}$	0·29	−0·4735	$\frac{3}{2}$	
^{55}Mn	10·553	100	0·178	2·89	3·4610	$\frac{5}{2}$	0·5
^{57}Fe		2·245			≦0·05		
^{57}Co*	10·0		0·274	4·95	4·6	$\frac{7}{2}$	
^{58}Co*	13·3		0·25	2·5	3·5	2	
^{59}Co	10·103	100	0·281	4·83	4·6388	$\frac{7}{2}$	0·5
^{60}Co*	4·6		5×10^{-2}	4·3	3·0	5?	
^{61}Ni		1·25			<0·25		
^{63}Cu	11·285	69·09	$9{\cdot}38 \times 10^{-2}$	1·33	2·2206	$\frac{3}{2}$	−0·15
^{65}Cu	12·090	30·91	0·116	1·42	2·3790	$\frac{3}{2}$	−0·14

(*continued*)

Isotope (* indicates radioactive)	NMR frequency in Mc sec^{-1} for a 10 kilo-gauss field	Natural abundance, per cent	Relative sensitivity for equal number of nuclei		Magnetic moment μ, in multiples of the nuclear magneton ($eh/4\pi Mc$)	Spin I, in multiples of $h/2\pi$	Electric quadrupole moment Q, in multiples of $e \times 10^{-24}$ cm^2
			At constant field	At constant frequency			
^{67}Zn	2·635	4·12	2·86 × 10^{-3}	0·730	0·8735	$\frac{5}{2}$	
^{69}Ga	10·218	60·2	6·93 × 10^{-2}	1·201	2·0108	$\frac{3}{2}$	0·2318
^{71}Ga	12·984	39·8	0·142	1·525	2·5549	$\frac{3}{2}$	0·1461
^{73}Ge	1·485	7·61	1·40 × 10^{-3}	1·15	−0·8768	$\frac{9}{2}$	−0·2
^{75}As	7·292	100	2·51 × 10^{-2}	0·856	1·4349	$\frac{3}{2}$	0·3
^{77}Se	8·131	7·50	6·97 × 10^{-3}	0·191	0·5333	$\frac{1}{2}$	
^{79}Se*	2·210		2·94 × 10^{-3}	1·12	−1·015	$\frac{7}{2}$	0·9
^{79}Br	10·667	50·57	7·86 × 10^{-2}	1·26	2·0990	$\frac{3}{2}$	0·33
^{81}Br	11·498	49·43	9·84 × 10^{-2}	1·35	2·2626	$\frac{3}{2}$	0·28
^{83}Kr	1·64	11·55	1·89 × 10^{-3}	1·27	−0·968	$\frac{9}{2}$	0·15
^{85}Rb	4·111	72·8	1·05 × 10^{-2}	1·13	1·3483	$\frac{5}{2}$	0·31
^{87}Rb	13·932	27·2	0·177	1·64	2·7415	$\frac{3}{2}$	0·15
^{87}Sr	1·845	7·02	2·69 × 10^{-3}	1·43	−1·0893	$\frac{9}{2}$	
^{89}Y	2·086	100	1·17 × 10^{-4}	4·90 × 10^{-2}	−0·1368	$\frac{1}{2}$	
^{91}Zr	4·0	11·23	9·4 × 10^{-3}	1·04	−1·3	$\frac{5}{2}$	
^{93}Nb	10·407	100	0·482	8·06	6·1435	$\frac{9}{2}$	−0·4 ± 0·3
^{95}Mo	2·774	15·78	3·22 × 10^{-3}	0·761	−0·9099	$\frac{5}{2}$	
^{97}Mo	2·833	9·60	3·42 × 10^{-3}	0·776	−0·9290	$\frac{5}{2}$	
^{99}Tc*	9·583		0·376	7·43	5·6572	$\frac{9}{2}$	0·3
^{99}Ru		12·81				$\frac{6}{2}$	
^{101}Ru		16·98				$\frac{5}{2}$	
^{103}Rh	1·340	100	3·12 × 10^{-5}	3·15 × 10^{-2}	−0·0879	$\frac{1}{2}$	
^{105}Pd	1·74	22·23	7·79 × 10^{-4}	0·47	−0·57	$\frac{5}{2}$	
^{107}Ag	1·722	51·35	6·69 × 10^{-5}	4·03 × 10^{-2}	−0·1130	$\frac{1}{2}$	
^{109}Ag	1·981	48·65	1·01 × 10^{-4}	4·66 × 10^{-2}	−0·1299	$\frac{1}{2}$	

(continued)

Isotope (* indicates radioactive)	NMR frequency in Mc sec^{-1} for a 10 kilo-gauss field	Natural abundance, per cent	Relative sensitivity for equal number of nuclei		Magnetic moment μ, in multiples of the nuclear magneton ($eh/4\pi Mc$)	Spin I, in multiples of $h/2\pi$	Electric quadrupole moment Q, in multiples of $e \times 10^{-24}$ cm^2
			At constant field	At constant frequency			
^{111}Cd	9·028	12·86	$9·54 \times 10^{-3}$	0·212	−0·5922	$\frac{1}{2}$	
^{113}Cd	9·444	12·34	$1·09 \times 10^{-2}$	0·222	−0·6195	$\frac{1}{2}$	
^{113}In	9·310	4·16	0·345	7·22	5·4960	$\frac{9}{2}$	1·144
^{115}In*	9·329	95·84	0·348	7·23	5·5072	$\frac{9}{2}$	1·161
^{115}Sn	13·22	0·35	$3·50 \times 10^{-2}$	0·327	−0·9132	$\frac{1}{2}$	
^{117}Sn	15·77	7·67	$4·53 \times 10^{-2}$	0·356	−0·9949	$\frac{1}{2}$	
^{119}Sn	15·87	8·68	$5·18 \times 10^{-2}$	0·373	−1·0409	$\frac{1}{2}$	
^{121}Sb	10·19	57·25	0·160	2·79	3·3417	$\frac{5}{2}$	−0·8
^{123}Sb	15·518	42·75	$4·57 \times 10^{-2}$	2·72	2·5334	$\frac{7}{2}$	−1·0
^{123}Te	11·59	0·89	$1·80 \times 10^{-2}$	0·262	−0·7319	$\frac{1}{2}$	
^{125}Te	13·45	7·03	$3·16 \times 10^{-2}$	0·316	−0·8824	$\frac{1}{2}$	
^{127}I	8·519	100	$9·35 \times 10^{-2}$	2·33	2·7939	$\frac{5}{2}$	−0·75
^{129}I*	5·669		$4·96 \times 10^{-2}$	2·80	2·6030	$\frac{7}{2}$	−0·43
^{129}Xe	11·78	26·24	$2·12 \times 10^{-2}$	0·277	−0·7726	$\frac{1}{2}$	
^{131}Xe	3·490	21·24	$2·77 \times 10^{-3}$	0·410	0·6868	$\frac{3}{2}$	−0·12
^{133}Cs	5·585	100	$4·74 \times 10^{-2}$	2·75	2·5642	$\frac{7}{2}$	$\leq$0·3
^{134}Cs*	5·64		$6·21 \times 10^{-2}$	3·53	2·96	4	
^{135}Cs*	5·94		$5·70 \times 10^{-2}$	2·94	2·727	$\frac{7}{2}$	
^{137}Cs*	6·19		$6·44 \times 10^{-2}$	3·05	2·84	$\frac{7}{2}$	
^{135}Ba	4·25	6·59	$4·99 \times 10^{-3}$	0·499	0·837	$\frac{3}{2}$	
^{137}Ba	4·76	11·32	$6·97 \times 10^{-3}$	0·559	0·936	$\frac{3}{2}$	
^{138}La*	5·617	0·089	$9·18 \times 10^{-2}$	2·64	3·6844	5	2·7
^{139}La	6·014	99·911	$5·92 \times 10^{-2}$	2·97	2·7615	$\frac{7}{2}$	0·9
^{141}Ce*	0·35		$1·1 \times 10^{-5}$	0·17	0·16	$\frac{7}{2}$	
^{141}Pr	11·3	100	0·234	3·18	3·8	$\frac{5}{2}$	$-5·4 \times 10^{-2}$

(continued)

Isotope (* indicates radioactive)	NMR frequency in Mc sec^{-1} for a 10 kilogauss field	Natural abundance, per cent	Relative sensitivity for equal number of nuclei: At constant field	At constant frequency	Magnetic moment μ, in multiples of the nuclear magneton ($eh/4\pi Mc$)	Spin I, in multiples of $h/2\pi$	Electric quadrupole moment Q, in multiples of $e \times 10^{-24}$ cm^2
^{143}Nd	2·2	12·20	2·81 × 10^{-3}	1·07	−1·1	$\frac{7}{2}$	≦1·2
^{145}Nd	1·4	8·30	6·70 × 10^{-4}	0·666	−0·69	$\frac{7}{2}$	≦1·2
^{147}Sm	1·47	15·07	8·8 × 10^{-4}	0·725	−0·68	$\frac{7}{2}$	0·72
^{149}Sm	1·19	13·84	4·7 × 10^{-4}	0·591	−0·55	$\frac{7}{2}$	0·72
^{151}Eu	10	47·77	0·168	2·84	3·4	$\frac{5}{2}$	~1·2
^{153}Eu	4·6	52·23	1·45 × 10^{-2}	1·25	1·5	$\frac{5}{2}$	~2·5
^{155}Gd		14·68			−0·19	($\frac{7}{2}$)	
^{157}Gd		15·64			−0·33	($\frac{7}{2}$)	
^{159}Tb		100				$\frac{3}{2}$	
^{161}Dy		18·73				$\frac{7}{2}$	
^{163}Dy		24·97				$\frac{7}{2}$	
^{165}Ho		100				$\frac{7}{2}$	
^{167}Er		22·82				$\frac{7}{2}$	~10
^{169}Tm		100				$\frac{1}{2}$	
^{171}Yb	6·9	14·27	4·19 × 10^{-3}	0·161	0·45	$\frac{1}{2}$	
^{173}Yb	1·98	16·08	1·18 × 10^{-3}	0·543	−0·65	$\frac{5}{2}$	3·9
^{175}Lu	5·7	97·40	4·94 × 10^{-2}	2·79	2·6	$\frac{7}{2}$	5·9
^{176}Lu*		2·60			4·2	≧7	6–8
^{177}Hf		18·39				$\frac{1}{2}$ or $\frac{3}{2}$	
^{179}Hf		13·78				$\frac{1}{2}$ or $\frac{3}{2}$	
^{181}Ta	4·6	100	2·60 × 10^{-2}	2·26	2·1	$\frac{7}{2}$	6·5
^{183}W	1·75	14·28	6·98 × 10^{-5}	4·12	0·115	$\frac{1}{2}$	
^{185}Re	9·586	37·07	0·133	2·63	3·1437	$\frac{5}{2}$	2·8
^{187}Re	9·684	62·93	0·137	2·65	3·1760	$\frac{5}{2}$	2·6
^{189}Os	3·307	16·1	2·24 × 10^{-3}	0·385	0·6507	$\frac{3}{2}$	2·0

(*continued*)

Isotope (* indicates radioactive)	NMR frequency in Mc sec^{-1} for a 10 kilo-gauss field	Natural abundance, per cent	Relative sensitivity for equal number of nuclei		Magnetic moment μ, in multiples of the nuclear magneton ($eh/4\pi Mc$)	Spin I, in multiples of $h/2\pi$	Electric quadrupole moment Q, in multiples of $e \times 10^{-24}$ cm^2
			At constant field	At constant frequency			
^{191}Ir	0·81	38·5	$3·5 \times 10^{-5}$	$9·5 \times 10^{-2}$	0·16	$\frac{3}{2}$	~1·2
^{193}Ir	0·86	61·5	$4·2 \times 10^{-5}$	0·104	0·17	$\frac{3}{2}$	~1·0
^{195}Pt	9·153	33·7	$9·94 \times 10^{-3}$	0·215	0·6004	$\frac{1}{2}$	
^{197}Au	0·691	100	$2·14 \times 10^{-5}$	$8·1 \times 10^{-2}$	0·136	$\frac{3}{2}$	0·56
^{199}Hg	7·612	16·86	$5·72 \times 10^{-3}$	0·179	0·4993	$\frac{1}{2}$	
^{201}Hg	3·08	13·24	$1·90 \times 10^{-3}$	0·362	−0·607	$\frac{3}{2}$	0·5
^{203}Tl	24·33	29·52	0·187	0·571	1·5960	$\frac{1}{2}$	
^{205}Tl	24·57	70·48	0·192	0·577	1·6114	$\frac{1}{2}$	
^{207}Pb	8·899	21·11	$9·13 \times 10^{-3}$	0·209	0·5837	$\frac{1}{2}$	
^{209}Bi	6·842	100	0·137	5·30	4·0389	$\frac{9}{2}$	−0·4
^{235}U*		0·71				$\frac{5}{2}$	
^{237}Np*	~20		1·0	5·0	6 ± 2·5	$\frac{5}{2}$	
^{239}Pu*	6·1		$2·9 \times 10^{-3}$	0·14	0·4	$\frac{1}{2}$	
^{241}Pu*	4·3		$1·2 \times 10^{-2}$	1·2	1·4	$\frac{5}{2}$	
Free electron	27,994		$2·85 \times 10^{8}$	658	−1836	$\frac{1}{2}$	

APPENDIX B

TABLE OF τ-VALUES FOR A VARIETY OF ORGANIC COMPOUNDS

(The data contained in this appendix are published by kind permission of Dr. G. V. D. Tiers of The Central Research Department, Minnesota Mining and Manufacturing Company, St. Paul, Minnesota.)

For compounds in CCl_4 solution (Me_4Si, $\tau = +10{\cdot}000$)

Compound: ^1H signal designated by **H** or by number in parentheses.		τ^a ppm	Peak mult.[b]	% Conc.[c] in CCl_4
p-$C_6H_4(C\mathbf{H}O)_2$		−0·083		3·0
$C_6H_5C\mathbf{H}O$		+0·035		5·0
4-$ClC_6H_4C\mathbf{H}O$		0·067		5·0
4-$MeOC_6H_4C\mathbf{H}O$		0·199		5·0
$MeC\mathbf{H}O$		0·28	4	5·0
Citronellal ($C\mathbf{H}O$)		0·32	d	10·0
4-$Me_2NC_6H_4C\mathbf{H}O$		0·350		5·0
$C_6H_5CH{=}CHC\mathbf{H}O$		0·37	d	5·0
$Me_2CHC\mathbf{H}O$		0·43	d	5·0
$MeCH{=}CHC\mathbf{H}O$		0·57	d	5·0
$C_6H_5C\mathbf{H}{=}NN{=}C\mathbf{H}C_6H_5$		1·45		5·0
Pyridine	(2)	1·50	m	5·0
p-$C_6\mathbf{H}_4(NO_2)_2$		1·55		2·0
4-$NO_2C_6H_4SO_2Cl$	(3)	1·55	nq	5·0
	(2)	1·75	nq	5·0
$\mathbf{H}CO_2Me$		1·97		10·0
p-$C_6\mathbf{H}_4(CHO)_2$		1·98		3·0
p-$C_6\mathbf{H}_4(CCl_3)_2$		2·017		5·0
4-$MeOC_6H_4CO_2Me$	(2)	2·10	nq	5·0
$\mathbf{H}CONMe_2$		2·16		5·0
4-$FO_2SC_6H_4Me$	(3)	2·16	nq	5·0
4-ClC_6H_4CHO	(2)	2·22	nq	5·0
p-$C_6H_4(CF_3)_2$		2·225		5·0
4-$BrC_6H_4COCH_3$	(2)	2·23	nq	5·0
4-$MeOC_6\mathbf{H}_4CHO$	(2)	2·25	nq	5·0
Naphthalene	(1)	2·27	m	5·0
$C_6\mathbf{H}_5CH{=}CHCO_2H$		2·28	nq	5·0
$C_6\mathbf{H}_5CHO$		*ca.* 2·37	m	5·0
4-$Me_2NC_6H_4CHO$	(2)	2·37	nq	5·0
o-$C_6\mathbf{H}_4(CO_2Me)_2$		2·38	m	5·0
Coumarin (**H** beta to CO_2)		2·39	nq	5·0
p-$C_6H_5C_6\mathbf{H}_4C_6H_5$		2·40		4·0
Phthalide (aryl **H**)		2·42	m	5·0

(*continued*)

Compound: ^{1}H signal designated by **H** or by number in parentheses.		τ^a ppm	Peak mult.^{b}	% Conc.^{c} in CCl_4
$(C_6H_5CH{=}CH)_2CO$		2·43	nq	4·0
$4\text{-}BrC_6H_4COCH_3$	**(3)**	2·43	nq	5·0
$C_6\mathbf{H}_5CN$		2·464		5·0
$n\text{-}C_3F_7C_6\mathbf{H}_5$		2·473		5·0
$C_6\mathbf{H}_5CF_3$		2·492		5·0
$4\text{-}ClC_6H_4CHO$	**(3)**	2·52	nq	5·0
$C_6\mathbf{H}_5COCH_3$		*ca.* 2·52	m	3·0
$C_6H_5CH{=}CHCHO$		2·54		5·0
3,5-Dibromotoluene	**(4)**	2·57		5·0
$4,4'\text{-}ClC_6H_4C_6H_4Cl$	**(2, 3)**	2·59		5·0
$p\text{-}C_6H_4I_2$		2·617		4·0
Furan	**(2)**	2·62		5·0
$C_6H_5C\mathbf{H}{=}CHCHO$		2·62	nq	5·0
$C_6H_5C\mathbf{H}{=}CHCOCH_3$		2·62	nq	5·0
$4\text{-}FO_2SC_6H_4Me$	**(2)**	2·63	nq	5·0
Naphthalene	**(2)**	2·63	m	5·0
$C_6\mathbf{H}_5SiH_3$		2·63	m	5·0
$C_6\mathbf{H}_5CHBrCH_2CCl_3$		2·64	m	5·0
$C_6H_5CH{=}CHCOCH_3$		2·64		5·0
$p\text{-}C_6H_4Br_2$		2·664		3·0
$p\text{-}C_6\mathbf{H}_4(CH_2Cl)_2$		2·671		4·0
$p\text{-}C_6\mathbf{H}_4(CH_2Br)_2$		2·677		4·0
$C_6\mathbf{H}_5C{\equiv}CH$		2·678		3·0
$C_6\mathbf{H}_5CMe_2OOH$		2·68		6·0
Coumarin (aryl **H**)		2·69	m	5·0
$C_6\mathbf{H}_5CMe{=}CH_2$		2·70	m	5·0
$C_6\mathbf{H}_5CH_2Cl$		2·724	m	5·0
trans-Stilbene (aryl **H**)		2·73		5·0
Benzene		2·734		2·0
$C_6\mathbf{H}_5CH_2Br$		2·736		5·0
$C_6\mathbf{H}_5Br$		2·74	m	5·0
Chloroform		2·75		6·0
$C_6\mathbf{H}_5Cl$		2·756		5·0
$p\text{-}C_6H_4Cl_2$		2·759		4·0
$(C_6\mathbf{H}_5CH_2)_2O$		2·76		5·0
$(C_6\mathbf{H}_5)_2C{=}CH_2$		2·76	m	5·0
$C_6\mathbf{H}_5CH{=}CHBr$		2·77		5·0
3,5-Dibromotoluene	**(2)**	2·79		5·0
$CHCl_2Br$		2·80		5·0
$C_6\mathbf{H}_5CH_2NMe_2$		2·805		5·0
Thiophene	**(2)**	2·81	m	5·0
$C_6\mathbf{H}_5CMe_3$		2·813		4·0
$1\text{-}(C_6\mathbf{H}_5)\text{-cyclohexanol}$		2·82		10·0
$C_6\mathbf{H}_5CH_2OH$		2·83		6·0
$C_6\mathbf{H}_5CH_2CH_2COCH_3$		2·89		5·0
$(C_6\mathbf{H}_5)_2CH_2$		2·86		5·0
$C_6\mathbf{H}_5CHMe_2$		2·879		5·0
$C_6\mathbf{H}_5CH_2Me$		2·888		5·0
$C_6\mathbf{H}_5CH_2CH_2C_6\mathbf{H}_5$		2·893		5·0
Toluene (aryl **H**)		2·905		5·0
$(4\text{-}MeC_6\mathbf{H}_4CH_2)_2O$		2·93		5·0

(*continued*)

Compound: ^{1}H signal designated by **H** or by number in parentheses.		τ^a ppm	Peak[b] mult.	% Conc.[c] in CCl_4
$CHClBr_2$		2·94		5·0
C_6H_5**CH**$=CHBr$		2·95	nq	5·0
Thiophene	**(3)**	2·96	m	5·0
Me**CH**$=CHCO_2H$		2·96	nq, 4	6·0
4-Fluorotoluene	**(2)**	2·96	nq	5·0
4-Acetoxytoluene	**(2)**	2·97	nq	5·0
o-Xylene (aryl **H**)		2·99		5·0
CHBr=CHBr (*cis*)		3·00		5·0
p-dicyclohexylbenzene (aryl **H**)		3·008		10·0
Stilbene (*trans* olefinic **H**)		3·01		5·0
4-MeC$_6$**H**$_5$CHMe$_2$		3·02		3·0
Tetralin (aryl **H**)		3·03		5·0
1,4-Decamethylenebenzene (aryl **H**)		3·03		e
$(C_6H_5CH{=}CH)_2CO$		3·05	nq	4·0
p-Xylene (aryl **H**)		3·053		5·0
4-Fluorotoluene	**(3)**	3·08	nq, m	5·0
p-MeOC$_6$**H**$_4$CHO	**(3)**	3·09	nq	5·0
m-Xylene (aryl **H**)		3·11		4·0
4-Acetoxytoluene	**(3)**	3·13	nq	5·0
1,4-Naphthoquinone	**(2)**	3·15		3·0
$CH_3CH{=}CHCHO$		3·15	nq, 4	5·0
4-MeOC$_6$**H**$_4$CO$_2$Me	**(3)**	3·16	nq	5·0
$CHBr_3$		3·18		7·0
1,2,4-C$_6$**H**$_3$Me$_3$		3·18		5·0
1,3,5-C$_6$**H**$_3$(CHMe$_2$)$_3$		3·21		10·0
1,4-Benzoquinone		3·24		2·0
p-Cresol (aryl **H**)		3·25		3·0
Durene (aryl **H**)		3·259		5·0
Diethyl fumarate (olefinic **H**)		3·26		5·0
$C_6H_5CH{=}CHBr$		3·29	nq	5·0
p-C$_6$**H**$_4$(OEt)$_2$		3·329		4·0
Norbornadiene (olefinic **H**)		3·35		10·0
Mesitylene (aryl **H**)		3·356		5·0
$C_6H_5CH{=}CHCHO$		3·36	nq, d	5·0
4-Me$_2$NC$_6$H$_4$CHO	**(3)**	3·37	nq	5·0
CHBr=CHBr (*trans*)		3·38		5·0
$C_6H_5CHCl_2$		3·39		5·0
Pyrrole	**(2)**	3·40	m	6·0
$C_6H_5CH{=}CHCOCH_3$		3·40	nq	5·0
Aniline (aryl **H**)		*ca.* 3·41	m	6·0
$CCl_2{=}CHCl$		3·56		10·0
CHCl=CHCl (*cis*)		3·57		5·0
Cyclopentadiene (olefinic **H**)		3·58		6·0
$C_6H_5CH{=}CHCO_2H$		3·61	nq	5·0
2,2-Paracyclophane (aryl **H**)		3·62		e
CHCl=CHCl (*trans*)		3·63		5·0
Ascaridole (olefinic **H**)		3·65		5·0
Furan	**(3)**	3·70		5·0
Coumarin (**H** alpha to CO_2)		3·72	nq	5·0
Dihydropyran	**(2)**	3·78	d	10·0
Dimethyl maleate (olefinic **H**)		3·87		5·0

(*continued*)

Compound: ^{1}H signal designated by **H** or by number in parentheses.		τ^a ppm	Peak mult.[b]	% Conc.[c] in CCl_4
Pyrrole	**(3)**	3·91	m	6·0
CCl_3CHCl_2		3·95		10·0
$CH_3CH{=}CHCHO$		3·95	nq, d	5·0
$CHBr_2CHBr_2$		3·97		5·0
Et methacrylate (1 olefinic **H**)		3·97		5·0
$Me_2C{=}CHCOCH_3$		4·03	m	5·0
Norbornene (olefinic **H**)		4·06		2·0
$CHCl_2CHCl_2$		4·06		5·0
$CF_2ClCHCl_2$		4·08	t	10·0
$CF_3CH_2CHCl_2$		4·08	t	5·0
$ClCH_2CH{=}CHCH_2Cl$		4·09	t	10·0
n-C_7F_{15}H		4·11	t, t	97·0 d
$CHCl_2CO_2Me$		4·11		5·0
Dicyclopentadiene (olefinic **H**, Norbornene ring)		4·13	b	10·0
$CH_3CH{=}CHCO_2H$		4·22	nq	6·0
Cyclohexadiene-1,3 (olefinic **H**)		4·22		e
$CH_2{=}CMeCN$		4·25	d	5
Cyclooctatriene-1,3,5 (olefinic **H**)		4·26		e
$CHCl_2CH_2Cl$		4·26	t	10.0
Δ^2-cyclohexanol	**(2, 3)**	4·28	b	10·0
2,5-Dimethylfuran	**(3)**	4·30		5·0
Cyclooctatetraene		4·309		3·0
α-Phellandrene (olefinic **H**)		4·36	m	10·0
Cyclohexene (olefinic **H**)		4·43	t	10·0
Crotyl alcohol (olefinic **H**)		4·45	b	5·0
n-$C_7F_{15}CMe{=}CH_2$		4·46	b	10·0
Et methacrylate (1 olefinic **H**)		4·53		5·0
$(C_6H_5)_3SiH$		4·57		10·0
$(C_6H_5)_2C{=}CH_2$		4·60		5·0
Dicyclopentadiene (olefinic **H**, cyclopentene ring)		4·60	b	10·0
Me ricinoleate (olefinic **H**)		4·62		10·0
Limonene (olefinic **H**, ring)		4·65		10·0
CH_2Cl_2		4·67		5·0
Me linoleate (olefinic **H**)		4·68		10·0
1-Me-cyclohexene (olefinic **H**)		4·70	t	5·0
Me oleate (olefinic **H**)		4·72		10·0
$C_6H_5CMe{=}CHH$		4·72	nq	5·0
Nopol (olefinic **H**)		4·73	b	10·0
Phthalide (benzylic **H**)		4·74		5·0
$C_6H_5CHBrCH_2CCl_3$		4·74	m	5·0
$CH{\equiv}CCMe{=}CH_2$		4·74	m	6·0
$Me_2C{=}CHMe$		4·79		97·0 d
CH_2ClBr		4·84		5·0
α-Pinene (olefinic **H**)		4·88	t	10·0
Squalene (olefinic **H**)		4·91		10·0
Citronellal (olefinic **H**)		4·97		10·0
$C_6H_5CMe{=}CHH$		4·98	nq	5·0
$ClCH_2CMe{=}CHH$		4·98	nq	5·0
Geraniol (olefinic **H**)		*ca.* 5·00	b	10·0
Trioxane		5·00		4·0
CH_2ClI		5·01		5·0

(*continued*)

Compound: ^{1}H signal designated by **H** or by number in parentheses.		τ[a] ppm	Peak mult.[b]	% Conc.[c] in CCl_4
$\mathbf{H}C(OEt)_3$		5·04		5·0
$C\mathbf{H}_2Br_2$		5·06		5·0
$CH_2{=}CHCMe{=}C\mathbf{H}_2$		5·06		10·0
$ClCH_2CMe{=}CH\mathbf{H}$		5·10	nq	5·0
$(C_6H_5)_2Si\mathbf{H}_2$		5·14		5·0
$(CF_3CH_2O)_2C\mathbf{H}_2$		5·18		2·0
Pentaerythritol **diformal**		5·29		5·0
Limonene (olefinic **H**)		5·34		10·0
Iso-butene (olefinic **H**)		5·399		5·0
$CH_3CO_2CMe{=}C\mathbf{H}_2$		5·40		5·0
$n\text{-}C_3F_7C\mathbf{H}_2OOCC_2H_5$		5·44	t	5·0
Dihydropyran	**(3)**	5·46	d, m	10·0
$C_6H_5C\mathbf{H}_2Cl$		5·50		5·0
$p\text{-}C_6H_4(C\mathbf{H}_2Cl)_2$		5·50		4·0
$(C_6H_5C\mathbf{H}_2)_2O$		5·51		5·0
$(MeO)_2C\mathbf{H}_2$		5·51		5·0
$Me_2C\mathbf{H}NO_2$		5·56	7	6·0
$C_6H_5C\mathbf{H}_2Br$		5·57		5·0
$p\text{-}C_6H_4(C\mathbf{H}_2Br)_2$		5·59		4·0
$C_6H_5C\mathbf{H}_2OH$		5·60		6·0
$CF_3CO_2C\mathbf{H}_2CH_3$		5·61	t	5·0
Cyclopentyl bromide	**(1)**	5·61	m	10·0
$(ClCH_2)_2CC\mathbf{H}_2OC\mathbf{H}_2$ (ring)		5·64		10·0
$(4\text{-}MeC_6H_4C\mathbf{H}_2)_2O$		5·64		5·0
$n\text{-}C_5H_{11}C\mathbf{H}_2F$		5·65	d, b	10·0
$n\text{-}C_3F_7CO_2\mathbf{Me}$		5·70		5·0
$CF_3CO_2C\mathbf{H}_2C_3H_7$		5·71	t	10·0
γ-Butyrolactone ($C\mathbf{H}_2O$)		5·72	t	5·0
$\mathbf{Me}NO_2$		5·722		2·0
$C\mathbf{H}_3F$		5·74	d	f
$Me_2C\mathbf{H}I$		5·76	7	10·0
β-Propiolactone ($C\mathbf{H}_2O$)		5·78	t	5·0
Diethyl fumarate ($C\mathbf{H}_2O$)		5·79	4	5·0
Ethylene carbonate		5·80		3·0
$Me_2C\mathbf{H}Br$		5·80	d	10·0
$ClC\mathbf{H}_2POCl_2$		5·80	d	5·0
Diethyl maleate ($C\mathbf{H}_2O$)		5·81	4	5·0
$C_6H_5Si\mathbf{H}_3$		5·81		5·0, 10·0
$(p\text{-}MeC_6H_4)_2C\mathbf{H}Me$		5·81	4	5·0
$HC{\equiv}CC\mathbf{H}_2OH$		5·82	d	3·0
$ClC\mathbf{H}_2C{\equiv}CC\mathbf{H}_2Cl$		5·84		5·0
$Et_2C(CO_2C\mathbf{H}_2CH_3)_2$		5·85	4	5·0
$CH_2{=}CMeCO_2C\mathbf{H}_2CH_3$		5·85	4	5·0
$Me_2C\mathbf{H}Cl$		5·87	7	10·0
Cyclohexyl bromide	**(1)**	5·89	m	10·0
Δ^2-Cyclohexanol	**(1)**	5·89	b	10·0
$HC{\equiv}CC\mathbf{H}_2Cl$		5·91		6·0
$Br(CH_2)_{10}CO_2C\mathbf{H}_2CH_3$		5·92	4	20·0
$ClC\mathbf{H}_2CN$		5·93		2·0
δ-Valerolactone ($C\mathbf{H}_2O$)		5·94	b	10·0

(continued)

Compound: ¹H signal designated by **H** or by number in parentheses.		τ [a] ppm	Peak mult.[b]	% Conc.[c] in CCl_4
Ferrocene		5·95		4·0
$CH_3CO_2CH_2CH_3$		5·95	4	5·0
3,3,5-Trimethyl cyclohexanol	(1)	5·95	b	10·0
$ClCH_2CH{=}CHCH_2Cl$		5·96	d	10·0
2-Bromo-octane	(2)	5·97	m	10·0
n-$C_3F_7CH_2OH$		5·98	t	3·0, 6·0
$CHCl_2CH_2Cl$		6·03	d	10·0
Geraniol (CH_2O)		6·03	d	10·0
CF_3CO_2Me		6·04		3·0
$CH_2{=}CMeCH_2Cl$		6·04	m	5·0
Ethylene trithiocarbonate		6·06		5·0
Dimethyl sulphate		6·06		f
$(CF_3CH_2O)_2CH_2$		6·07		2·0
n-$C_3F_7CH_2Cl$		6·07	t	10·0
$CHCl_2CO_2Me$		6·08		5·0
p-$C_6H_4(OCH_2CH_3)_2$		6·08	4	5·0
$(C_6H_5)_2CH_2$		6·08		5·0
$(ClCH_2)_2\overline{CCH_2OCH_2}$		6·09		10·0
Dihydropyran	(6)	6·10	t	10·0
2-Chlorobutane	(2)	6·10	m	5·0
CH_2I_2		6·10		5·0
$C_6H_5CO_2Me$		6·10		5·0
$CH_3CH{=}CHCH_2OH$		6·10	b	5·0
Cyclohexyl chloride	(1)	6·11	b	10·0
4-$MeOC_6H_4CHO$		6·143		5·0
$CH_2{=}CHCH_2Br$		6·15	d	5·0
CF_3CH_2OH		6·15	4	3·0
4-$MeOC_6H_4CO_2Me$		6·173		5·0
$HC{\equiv}CCH_2Br$		6·18		5·0
Dimethyl phthalate (**Me**)		6·18		5·0
Fluorene (CH_2)		6·19		5·0
$(4\text{-}MeC_6H_4)_2CH_2$		6·19		6·0
Dimethyl carbonate		6·23		f
$BrCH_2CO_2Me$		6·24		5·0
$(CF_3)_2CHCF_2OMe$		6·24		10·0
$(ClCH_2)_3CCH_2OH$		6·25		6·0
$(MeO)_2PHO$		6·25	d	5·0
C_6H_5OMe		6·266		6·0
4-$MeOC_6H_4Me$		6·293		5·0
$C_6H_5CHBrCH_2CCl_3$		6·30	d	5·0
$BrCH_2CO_2Me$		6·30		5·0
t-2-Me cyclohexanol (CHOH)		6·30	b	10·0
CHO_2Me		6·31		10·0
Borneol (CHOH)		6·31	t	10·0
$ClCH_2CH_2Cl$		6·31		2·0
$MeCO_2Me$		6·35		f
$MeSO_2Cl$		6·36		4·0
$(ClCH_2)_3CCH_2OH$		6·36		6·0
Tetrahydrofuran	(2)	6·37	t	6·0
$BrCH_2CH_2Br$		6·369		5·0

(*continued*)

Compound: ^{1}H signal designated by **H** or by number in parentheses.	τ [a] ppm	Peak mult.[b]	% Conc.[c] in CCl_4
Pentaerythritol diformal	6·38		5·0
Me oleate, linoleate	6·38		10·0
Me ricinoleate	6·39		10·0
CH_3**CH_2**NCS	6·39	4	5·0
CH_3**CH_2**OH	6·41	4	3·0, 6·0
n-C_3F_7**CH_2**I	6·42	t	10·0
Br**CH_2**CH_2**CH_2**Br	6·42	t	5·0
N-Me morpholine (**CH_2**O)	6·42	t	5·0
Dimethyl sulphite	6·42		f
Dioxane	6·43		2·0
(CH_2**CH_2**Cl)$_2$	6·43	t	5·0
Morpholine (**CH_2**O)	6·43	t	6·0, 2·0
Tetrahydropyran (**CH_2**O)	6·44	m	10·0
CF_3**CH_2**I	6·44	4	5·0
(MeOC_2H_4O**C_2H_4**)$_2$O	6·44		5·0
Tetramethyl silicate	6·44		f
C(**CH_2**Cl)$_4$	6·46		5·0
4-Me_3C-cyclohexanol (**1**)	6·46	m	10·0
Trimethyl borate	6·47		f
Nopol (**CH_2**O)	6·49	t	10·0
HC(O**CH_2**CH_3)$_3$	6·50	4	5·0
β-Propiolactone (**CH_2**CO)	6·52	t	5·0
(MeO**C_2H_4**OC_2H_4)$_2$O	6·52		5·0
Norbornadiene (**CH**)	6·53	m	10·0
(MeO**C_2H_4**)$_2$O	6·54		5·0
n-C_3H_7**CH_2**Cl	6·54	t	10·0
C_2H_5**CH_2**Cl	6·55	t	5·0
(CH_2**CH_2**Br)$_2$	6·58	t	5·0
(CH_3**CH_2**)$_4N^+I^-$ (in CF_3CO_2H)	6·60	4	(5·0)
MeOH	6·622		1·0, 2·0
	6·63		3·6, 97[d]
Pyrrolidone (**CH_2**N)	6·63	t	6·0
CH_3**CH_2**Br	6·64	4	5·0
C_2H_5**CH_2**Br	6·64	t	5·0
(CH_3**CH_2**)$_2$O	6·64	4	5·0
CF_3C(O**Me**)$_3$	6·64		3·0
Me_2CH**CH_2**Cl	6·65	d	10·0
Br**CH_2**(CH_2)$_9CO_2$Et	6·65	t	20·0
n-C_7H_{15}**CH_2**Br	6·65	t	10·0
Acenaphthene (**CH_2**)	6·66		5·0
n-C_3H_7**CH_2**Br	6·66	t	10·0
Me_4 N^+I^- (in CF_3CO_2H)	6·67		(1·0)
C_6H_5**CH_2**NMe_2	6·68		5·0
Dimethoxy tetraglycol (**Me**)	6·69		5·0
Dimethoxy diglycol (**Me**)	6·70		5·0
n-C_3F_7CON(**CH_2**CH_3)$_2$	6·72	4	5·0
CH_3**CH_2**SO_2F	6·72	4, d	5·0
(**Me**O)$_2CH_2$	6·72		5·0
MeSO_2F	6·73	d	2·0
Me_2CH**CH_2**Br	6·74	d	5·0
Me_2O	6·76		f

(*continued*)

Compound: ^1H signal designated by **H** or by number in parentheses.	τ^{a} ppm	Peak mult.b	% Conc.c in CCl$_4$
C$_2$H$_5$CH$_2$I	6·80	t	10·0
n-C$_3$H$_7$CH$_2$I	6·81	t	10·0
CH$_3$CH$_2$I	6·85	4	5·0
MeSO$_2$CF$_3$	6·87		5·0
ε-Caprolactam (**CH$_2$N**)	6·88	m	6·0
n-C$_3$F$_7$CONMe$_2$	6·90	d	5·0
Me$_2$CHCH$_2$I	6·93	d	10·0
MeCl	6·95		f
2,2-Paracyclophane (**CH$_2$**)	6·95		e
4-Me$_2$NC$_6$H$_4$CHO	6·951		5·0
CF$_3$SO$_2$NHMe	6·96	d	5·0
C$_6$H$_5$C≡CH	7·07		3·0
$\overline{CH_2CH_2SO_2CH_2CH_2}$	7·08	t	5·0
C$_6$H$_5$NMe$_2$	7·096		5·0
Cyclopentadiene (**CH$_2$**)	7·10		6·0
C$_6$H$_5$CH$_2$CH$_2$C$_6$H$_5$	7·129		5·0
Me$_2$CHNH$_2$	7·13	m	3·0, 6·0
C$_6$H$_5$CHMe$_2$	7·13	m	5·0
Me$_2$NCHO	7·15	d	5·0
Morpholine (**CH$_2$N**)	7·17	t	2·0, 6·0
Acetyl bromide	7·19		f
Dicyclopentadiene (C$_6$ ring, bridgehead **CH**)	7·20		10·0
Norbornene ("allylic" **H**)	7·22		2·0
Pyrrolidine (**CH$_2$N**)	7·26	m	3·0
$\overline{(CHCH_2O)_2}$	7·28	m	15·0
MeCCl$_3$	7·28		3·0
HC≡CCMe=CH$_2$	7·29		6·0
Tetralin (benzylic **H**)	7·30	m	5·0
Piperidine (**CH$_2$N**)	7·31	m	3·0
1-C$_{10}$H$_7$COMe	7·32		5·0
MeBr	7·32		f
$\overline{MeCHCH_2O}$	7·34	m	10·0
Acetyl chloride	7·34		3·0
$\overline{(CHCH_2O)_2}$	7·37	m	15·0
n-C$_3$H$_7$CH$_2$NH$_2$	7·37	t	6·0
MeSCN	7·37		3·0
4-BrC$_6$H$_4$COMe	7·38		5·0
C$_6$H$_5$CH$_2$CH$_3$	7·382	4	5·0
Me$_3$N·BH$_3$	7·40		5·0
(Me$_2$N)$_3$PO	7·40		2·0
C$_6$H$_5$COMe	7·45		3·0
2-C$_4$H$_3$SCOMe	7·46		5·0
Me$_2$SO	7·50		2·0
4-FO$_2$SC$_6$H$_4$Me	7·508		5·0
CH$_3$CH$_2$SH	7·56	4	3·0
(CH$_3$CH$_2$)$_3$N	7·58	4	5·0
Cycloheptanone (**CH$_2$CO**)	7·58	b	12·0
n-C$_3$F$_7$COMe	7·59		5·0
HC≡CCH$_2$Cl	7·60		3·0, 6·0

(*continued*)

Compound: ^{1}H signal designated by H or by number in parentheses.	τ [a] ppm	Peak mult.[b]	% Conc.[c] in CCl_4
$(CH_3CH_2)_2CO$	7·61	4	5·0
$(C_2H_5CH_2)_2S$	7·61	t	5·0
$BrCH_2CH_2CH_2Br$	7·64	5	5·0
C_6H_5Me	7·663		2·0
$MeNNH_2$	7·67		2·0, 6·0
$MeCOSH$	7·67		2·0, 6·0
$HC{\equiv}CCH_2Br$	7·67		5·0
$HC{\equiv}CCH_2OH$	7·67		3·0, 6·0
4-$MeCO_2C_6H_4Me$	7·682		5·0
3,5-$Br_2C_6H_3Me$	7·682		5·0
ε-Caprolactam (CH_2CO)	7·69	b	6·0
γ-Butyrolactone (CH_2CO)	7·69	t	5·0
Cyclooctatriene-1,3,5 (CH_2)	7·69		e
$C_6H_5CH{=}CHCOMe$	7·69		5·0
(4-$MeC_6H_4CH_2)_2O$	7·69		5·0
4-FC_6H_4Me	7·700		5·0
p-HOC_6H_4Me	7·70		3·0
$MeCHCH_2O$ (ring)	7·71	m	10·0
N-Me morpholine (CH_2N)	7·72	t	5·0
m-$C_6H_4Me_2$	7·726		4·0
p-$C_6H_4Me_2$	7·727		5·0
4-$MeC_6H_4CHMe_2$	7·73		3·0
δ-Valerolactone (CH_2CO)	7·73	b	10·0
(4-$MeC_6H_4)_2CH_2$	7·73		6·0
4-$MeOC_6H_4Me$	7·748		5·0
Cyclohexanone (CH_2CO)	7·75	m	6·0
2,5-diMe furan	7·76		5·0
o-$C_6H_4Me_2$	7·769		5·0
1-Phenyl cyclohexanol (2)	7·77	b	10·0
Biacetyl	7·77		2·0
2-Pyrrolidone (3)	7·77	t	6·0
Mesitylene (Me)	7·778		5·0
Nopol ("allylic" CH_2)	*ca.* 7·78	b	10·0
$CH_3CH_2CO_2CH_2C_3F_7$	7·78	4	5·0
$Br(CH_2)_9CH_2CO_2Et$	7·79	t	20·0
N-Me Morpholine	7·80		5·0
Acetic anhydride	7·803		3·0
Norbornane (CH)	7·81		5·0
Citronellal (CH_2CO)	7·81	m	10·0
4-$MeCO_2C_6H_4Me$	7·815		5·0
Me oleate (CH_2CO)	7·83	b	10·0
$C_6H_5CH_2NMe_2$	7·83		5·0
MeCHO	7·83		5·0
$CH_2CH_2SO_2CH_2CH_2$ (ring)	7·84		5·0
Cyclohexadiene-1,3 (CH_2)	7·84		e
Methyl Iodide	7·843		2·0
$C_6H_5CMe{=}CH_2$	7·86		5·0
2-Pyrrolidone (4)	7·86	m	6·0
Durene (Me)	7·862		5·0

(*continued*)

Compound: ^{1}H signal designated by H or by number in parentheses.	τ [a] ppm	Peak mult.[b]	% Conc.[c] in CCl_4
Trimethylamine	7·876		2·0
$MeCONCH_2CH_2$ (all H!)	7·88		10·0
$(CH_2{=}CHCH_2)_2$	7·88	d	20·0
Acetone	7·914		3·0
Me_2S	7·92		2·0
γ-Butyrolactone (beta **H**)	7·92	m	5·0
$CH_3CO_2CMe{=}CH_2$	7·93		5·0
$C_6H_5CH_2CH_2COMe$	7·93		5·0
$(CF_3)_2CHCF_2OMe$	7·93	m	97·0[d]
Me Ricinoleate (CH_2CO)	7·93	t	10·0
Acetic acid	7·933		6·0
$Me_2C{=}CHCOMe$ (MeCO and Me *cis* to CO)	7·94		5·0
$CH_3CO_2CH_2C_3F_7$	7·94		5·0
Squalene ($CH_2CH{=}C$)	7·96	d	10·0
Camphor (CH_2CO)	7·96	m	10·0
$(BrCH_2CH_2)_2$	7·97	t	5·0
$CH_2{=}CMeCN$	7·97		5·0
$MeCH{=}CHCHO$	7·98	d	5.0, 25
Cyclopentanone (2, 3)	7·98		6·0
Δ^2-Cyclohexanol (4)	7·98	b	10·0
CH_3CO_2Me	7·99		f
Squalene ($CH_2CMe{=}C$)	8·01		10·0
α-Phellandrene (allylic CH_2)	8·01	b	10·0
Acetonitrile	8·029		3·0
Limonene (allylic CH_2)	8·03	m	10·0
$(ClCH_2CH_2)_2$	8·04	t	5·0
Cyclohexene (allylic CH_2)	8·04	m	10·0
1,9-Decadiene (allylic CH_2)	8·05	b	5·0
CH_3CO_2Et	8·05		5·0
Cyclopentyl bromide (2, 3)	8·05	m	10·0
Norbornadiene (CH_2)	8·05	t	10·0
n-$C_7F_{15}CMe{=}CH_2$	8·06		10·0
$CH_2{=}CMeCO_2Et$	8·06		5·0
α-Terpineol (allylic CH_2)	8·06	b	10·0
Cyclohexyl bromide (2)	8·07	b	10·0
Dihydropyran (4)	8·07	m	10·0
$MeCH{=}CHCO_2H$	8·07	d	6·0
$C_6H_5COC(CO_2H)CH_2CH_2$ (in CF_3CO_2H)	8·08		(5·0)
$CH_3CO_2CMe{=}CH_2$	8·09		5·0
$CH_2{=}CMeCH_2CMe_3$	8·09		7·0
Terpinyl acetate (CH_2C–O)	8·10	b	10·0
$CH_2{=}CMeC{\equiv}CH$	8·11		6·0
$CH_3CH_2CH_2Br$	8·11	b	5·0
Citronellal (allylic CH_2)	8·11	m	10·0
$CH_3CO_2CMe{=}CH_2$	8·11		5·0
Terpinyl **acetate**	8·12		10·0
Me_2CHI	8·12		10·0
Cyclohexyl chloride (2)	8·13	b	10·0
$CH_2{=}CMeCH_2Cl$	8·13		5·0
Cyclohexanone (3, 4)	8·13	b	6·0

(*continued*)

Compound: ^{1}H signal designated by **H** or by number in parentheses.		τ [a] ppm	Peak mult.[b]	% Conc.[c] in CCl_4
$Me_2C{=}CHCOMe$ (Me *trans* to CO)		8·12	d	5·0
$CH_3CH_2CH_2I$		8·14	b	10·0
CH_3CH_2I		8·14	t	5·0
1-Me cyclohexene	(3, 6)	8·14	m	10·0
$CH_2{=}CMeCH{=}CH_2$		8·16		10·0
$(CH_3CH_2)_2C(CO_2Et)_2$		8·16	4	5·0
$CH_3CH_2CH_2Cl$		8·17	b	5·0
$Me_2C{=}NOH$		8·19		f
4-Me_3C-cyclohexanol	(2)	8·19		10·0
Me_2CHCH_2Br		8·20	m	97·0[d]
Tetrahydrofuran	(3)	8·21	t	6·0
Adamantane (CH_2)		8·218		2·0
Tetralin (beta **H**)		8·22	b	5·0
$CH_2{=}CMeCH_2CMe_3$		8·23		7·0
Me_3CBr		8·24		2·0
1-**Me**-cyclobutyl chloride		8·28		8·6
Cineole ($CH_2C{-}O$)		8·28	b	10·0
Limonene ($MeC{=}CH_2$)		8·28		10·0
Me_2CHBr		8·29	d	10·0
1-Phenyl-cyclohexanol	(3, 4)	8·29	m	10·0
$MeCHBr_6H_{13}$		8·29	d	10·0
Camphor	(4, 6?)	8·29		10·0
Isobutylene (**Me**)		8·299		5·0
$CH_3CH_2CH_2CH_2Br$		8·30	m	10·0
2-Phenylbutane (3-CH_2)		8·30	b	10·0
$MeCH{=}CHCH_2OH$		8·31	b	5·0
α-Phellandrene (allylic **Me**)		8·32	m	10·0
$CH_3CHClCH_2CH_3$		8·32	m	5·0
$CH_3CH_2CH_2CH_2I$		8·33	m	10·0
$CCl_2CH_2CHCH{=}CH_2$		8·33	m	5·0
ε-Caprolactam	(4, 5)	8·33	b	6·0
Cycloheptanone	(3, 4)	8·34	b	12·0
$CH_3CH_2CH_2CH_2Cl$		8·34	m	10·0
α-Terpineol (allylic **Me**)		8·35		10·0
CH_3CH_2Br		8·35	t	5·0
Limonene (ring allylic **Me**)		8·36		10·0
$Me_2C{=}CHMe$		8·37		6·0
α-Pinene (allylic **Me**)		8·37	m	10·0
$CF_3CO_2CH_2(CH_2)_2CH_3$		8·37	b	10·0
Squalene (allylic **Me**)		8·37		10·0
Geraniol (allylic **Me**)		8·38	b	10·0
Pyrrolidine	(3)	8·38	t	3·0, 6·0
δ-Valerolactone	(β, γ)	8·38	b	10·0
1-**Me** cyclohexene		8·40		10·0
1-Me cyclohexene	(4, 5)	8·40		10·0
Citronellal (allylic **Me**)		8·40		10·0
Linalool (allylic **Me**)		8·41	b	10·0
Borneol (CH_2)		8.41	b	10·0
Me_3CCl		8·42		2·0
Tetrahydropyran	(3, 4)	8·42	b	5·0

(*continued*)

Compound: ^{1}H signal designated by **H** or by number in parentheses.	τ [a] ppm	Peak mult.[b]	% Conc.[c] in CCl_4
Me_2CHCH_2Cl	8·42	m	10·0
$\mathbf{Me_2}CHNO_2$	8·43	d	6·0
$(CH_3CH_2CH_2)_2S$	8·44	m	5·0
$CH_3CH_2SO_2F$	8·44	t	5·0
Me_2CHCH_2I	8·44	b	10·0
$C_6H_5CMe_2OOH$	8·44		6·0
$Me_3\mathbf{CH}$	*ca.* 8·44	m	10·0
Cyclohexyl chloride **(3, 4)**	8·45	b	10·0
Cyclohexyl bromide **(3, 4)**	8·46	b	10·0
Methylcyclohexane (CH_2)	8·46		10·0
$\mathbf{Me_2}CHCl$	8·46	d	10·0
Cycloheptane	8·470		2·0
$(4\text{-}MeC_6H_4)_2CH\mathbf{Me}$	8·47	d	5·0
Camphene (CH_2)	8·48	b	10·0
Cyclopentane	8·492		2·0
Camphor **(5)**	8·51		10·0
$CCl_2CH_2CMeCH{=}CH_2$ (ring)	8·51		5·0
Piperidine **(3, 4)**	8·51	b	3·0, 6·0
Trans-2-Me cyclohexanol **(CH_2)**	8·52	b	10·0
CH_2CH_2NH (ring)	8·52		3·0, 6·0
Cyclo-$C_6H_{11}CF_3$ **(CH_2)**	8·52	b	5·0
$CH_3CHClCH_2CH_3$	8·53	d	10·0
1,2-Benzcyclooctene-1 **(4, 5)**	8·54		e
4-Me_3C-cyclohexanol **(3, 4)**	8·56	b	10·0
Cyclohexane	8·564		1·0
$CF_3CO_2CH_2CH_3$	8·59	t	5·0
$(CH_3CH_2)_4N^+I^-$ (in CF_3CO_2H)	8·59	t	(5·0)
Decalin	8·59	b	10·0
CH_3CH_2NCS	8·60	t	5·0
$\mathbf{Me_3}CSH$	8·61		3·0
$C_3F_7CMe_2OH$	8·63		6·0
Terpinyl acetate (**Me**)	8·63		10·0
Dicylopentadiene (bridge CH_2)	8·64	m	10·0
p-$C_6H_4(OCH_2CH_3)_2$	8·64	t	5·0
$CH_3(CH_2)_4CH_2F$	8·65	b	10·0
$CH_2{=}CMeCO_2CH_2CH_3$	8·65	t	5·0
$BrCH_2(CH_2)_8CH_2CO_2Et$	8·66		10·0
Dihydrocamphene (CH_2)	8·66	b	10·0
3,3,5-Me_3-cyclohexanol (CH_2)	8·67	b	10·0
Ascaridole (**MeC-O**)	8·68		5·0
$C_6H_5C\mathbf{Me_3}$	8·681		4·0
$CH_3(CH_2)_2CH_2NH_2$	8·69	b	6·0
CH_3CH_2SH	8·69	t	3·0, 6·0
Ethyl maleate (**Me**)	8·69	t	5·0
Ethyl fumarate (**Me**)	8·69	t	5·0
Me ricinoleate (CH_2)	8·69		10·0
1-Me-cyclobutanol	8·70		3·0, 6·0
Nopol (one CH_3)	8·70		10·0
$(CH_2{=}CHCH_2CH_2CH_2)_2$	8·70		5·0
$CH_3(CH_2)_4CH_2CHBrCH_3$	8·71		10·0

(*continued*)

Compound: ^{1}H signal designated by **H** or by number in parentheses.	τ[a] ppm	Peak mult.[b]	% Conc.[c] in CCl_4
$\overline{MeCHCH_2O}$	8·72	d	10·0
$CH_3(CH_2)_5CH_2CH_2Br$	8·72		10·0
Me oleate (non-allylic CH_2)	8·72	b	10·0
Norbornane (CH_2)	8·74	b	5·0
α-Pinene (Me_2C, one **Me** only)	8·74		10·0
$Et_2C(CO_2CH_2CH_3)_2$	8·75	t	5·0
n-Hexane (CH_2)	8·75		7·0
n-Heptane (CH_2)	8·75		10·0
n-Hexadecane (CH_2)	8·75		5·0
$Br(CH_2)_{10}CO_2CH_2CH_3$	8·75	t	20·0
Me_3CCO_2H	8·77		10·0
$C_6H_5CHMe_2$	8·77	d	5·0
2-Phenylbutane (1-**Me**)	8·77	d	10·0
Me_3COH	8·78		6·0, 3·0
$MeCO_2CH_2CH_3$	8·79	t	5·0
Linalool (**Me**C-O)	8·79		10·0
1,3,5-$(Me_2CH)_3C_6H_3$	8·80	d	10·0
$C_6H_5CH_2CH_3$	8·80	t	5·0
n-$C_3F_7CON(CH_2CH_3)_2$	8·80	t	5·0
4-$MeC_6H_4CHMe_2$	8·80	d	2·0
Me_3COOH	8·81		6·0
$CH(OCH_2CH_3)_3$	8·81	t	5·0
Cineole (Me_2C-O)	8·83		10·0
CH_3CH_2OH	8·83	t	6·0, 3·0
$(CH_3CH_2)_2O$	8·84	t	5·0
$(Me_3C)_2O_2$	8·84		2·0
$CH_3CH_2CO_2CH_2C_3F_7$	8·85	t	5·0
α-Terpineol (Me_2C-O)	8·87		10·0
Me_2CHCHO	8·88	d	5·0
3,3,5-Me_3-cyclohexanol (3-**Me**, one only)	8·89		6·0
Me_3CNH_2	8·92		6·0, 3·0
$CH_3CH_2CH_2Cl$	8·96	t	5·0
$CH_3CH_2CH_2Br$	8·96	t	5·0
$CH_3CH_2CH_2I$	8·96	t	5·0
$(CH_3CH_2)_2CO$	8·96	t	5·0
Me_2CHCH_2Br	8·96	d	5·0
trans-2-**Me**-cyclohexanol	8·97	d	10·0
Me_2CHCH_2Cl	8·99	d	10·0
Me_2CHNH_2	8·99	d	6·0, 3·0
Camphene (**Me**)	8·99		10·0
$(CH_3CH_2CH_2)_2S$	9·00	t	5·0
Fenchone (**Me**)	9·00		10·0
Ascaridole (Me_2CH)	9·02	d	5·0
Cineole (1-**Me**)	9·02		10·0
Me_2CHCH_2I	9·02	d	10·0
$Me_3CCH_2CHMe_2$	9·02	m	10·0
$CH_3CHClCH_2CH_3$	9·02	t	10·0
Camphor (1-**Me**)	9·03		10·0
$CH_3(CH_2)_3O_2CCF_3$	9·03	t	10·0
$(CH_3CH_2)_3SiF$	9·03	m	5·0
$CH_3(CH_2)_3Cl$	9·04	t	10·0

(*continued*)

Compound: ^{1}H signal designated by **H** or by number in parentheses.	τ [a] ppm	Peak mult.[b]	% Conc.[c] in CCl_4
$\mathbf{CH_3}(CH_2)_3Br$	9·04	t	10·0
$\mathbf{CH_3}(CH_2)_3I$	9·04	t	10·0
Citronellal (**Me**CH)	9·04	d	10·0
$(\mathbf{CH_3}CH_2)_3N$	9·05	t	5·0
$\mathbf{Me_2}CHCH_2Me$	9·06	d	10·0
Me_4C	9·06		f
$\mathbf{CH_3}(CH_2)_3NH_2$	9·07	t	6·0
Me cyclohexane	9·08		10·0
$\mathbf{Me_3}CCH_2CMe{=}CH_2$	9·08		7·0
$\mathbf{CH_3}(CH_2)_5F$	9·10	t	10·0
n-Hexane (**Me**)	9·10	t	7·0
n-Heptane (**Me**)	9·11	t	10·0
n-Hexadecane (**Me**)	9·11	t	5·0
Dihydrocamphene (Me_2C, one **Me** only)	9·11		10·0
Citronellol (**Me**CH)	9·11	d	2·0
$\mathbf{CH_3}(CH_2)_5CHBrCH_3$	9·11	t	10·0
$\mathbf{Me_3}CH$	9·112	d	10·0
α-Phellandrene ($\mathbf{Me_2}CH$)	9·12	d	10·0
3,3,5-Me_3-cyclohexanol (3-**Me**, one only)	9·12		10·0
3,3,5-Me_3-cyclohexanol (5-**Me**)	9·12	d	10·0
$\mathbf{CH_3}(CH_2)_7Br$	9·12	t	10·0
Me oleate (term. **Me**)	9·12	t	10·0
Me ricinoleate (term. **Me**)	9·12	t	10·0
Me linoleate (term. **Me**)	9·12	t	10·0
$(\mathbf{CH_3}CH_2)_3SiF$	9·13	m	5·0
$\mathbf{Me_3}CCH_2CH\mathbf{Me_2}$	9·14	m	10·0
Nopol (one **Me** only)	9·14		10·0
Camphor ($\mathbf{Me_2}C$)	9·14		10·0
Borneol ($\mathbf{Me_2}C$?)	9·14		10·0
$Me_2CHCH_2\mathbf{Me}$	9·14	t	10·0
4-$\mathbf{Me_3}C$-cyclohexanol	9·15		10·0
α-Pinene (Me_2C, one **Me** only)	9·16		10·0
Borneol (1-**Me**?)	9·19		10·0
2-Phenylbutane (4)	9·20	m	10·0
$(\mathbf{CH_3}CH_2)_2C(CO_2Et)_2$	9·21	t	5·0
Dihydrocamphene (**Me**CH)	9·21	d	10·0
Dihydrocamphene (Me_2C, one **Me** only)	9·23		10·0
Cyclopropane	9·778		5·0
$(Me_2SiO)_4$	9·91		2·0
Me_4Sn	9·94		1·0
Me_4Si (by definition)	10·000		1·0, 5·0

(*a*) τ (in ppm) $= [10{\cdot}000 - 10^6 (\nu_{obs} - \nu_{Me_4Si})/\nu_{Me_4Si}] = [10{\cdot}000 - 10^6 (H_{Me_4Si} - H_{obs})/H_{Me_4Si}]$. Increasing values of τ signify increasing shielding. Standard deviation is $\pm 0{\cdot}024$ ppm for τ-values given to two decimals but is approximately $\pm 0{\cdot}003$ for τ-values given to three decimals.

(*b*) Peaks are understood to be singlets or to be narrow (or very closely spaced multiplets) unless otherwise indicated as follows: "d", doublet; "t", triplet; "4", quartet; "5", quintet, etc.; "m", multiplet but not fully resolved; "b", broad or poorly resolved;

"nq", one-half of a "non-equivalence quartet" (HAHN and MAXWELL, *Phys. Rev.*, **88**, 1070 (1952)), analysed and assigned as described in the text. Note that in such cases the "centre-of-gravity" of the unsymmetrical pair of peaks yields the true τ-value.

(*c*) Volume per cent for liquids, but g/100 ml for solids, the composition of the solvent being, by volume, 99 per cent CCl_4 and 1 per cent Me_4Si. Where necessary, supercooled solutions were examined. Parenthetical concentrations indicate that CF_3CO_2H rather than CCl_4 was employed.

Useful charts of ^1H chemical shifts for characteristic groups have been compiled by Dietrich and Keller in reference 457 of Chapter 10.

APPENDIX C

CHARTS OF ¹H CHEMICAL SHIFTS AND COUPLING CONSTANTS

THE charts of τ-values for $—CH_2$ and $—CH_3$ hydrogen nuclei given in Figs. C1 to C5 have been compiled by K. Nukada, O. Yamamoto, and T. Suzuki (of the Government Chemical Industrial Research Institute, Tokyo) and M. Takeuchi and M. Ohnishi (of Japan Electron Optics Laboratory Ltd., Tokyo, Japan) and are taken from a paper in *Analytical Chemistry* (**35**, 1892 (1963)). The charts are reproduced by courtesy of *Analytical Chemistry*.

The charts of NMR data for hydrogen nuclei in olefinic compounds given in Figs. C6 to C8 have been compiled by F. C. Stehling.

The charts are self-explanatory.

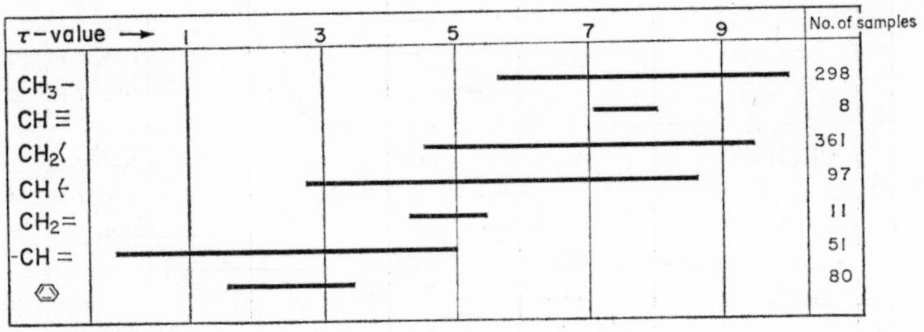

FIG. C1

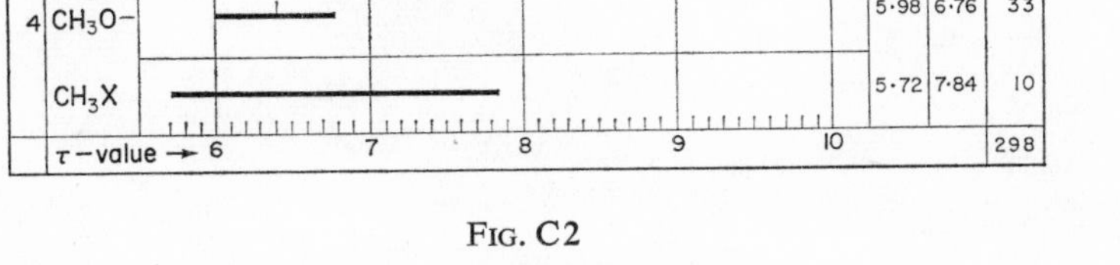

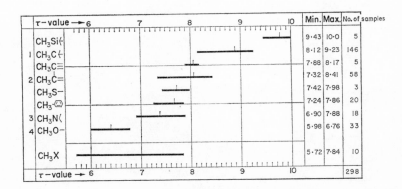

FIG. C2

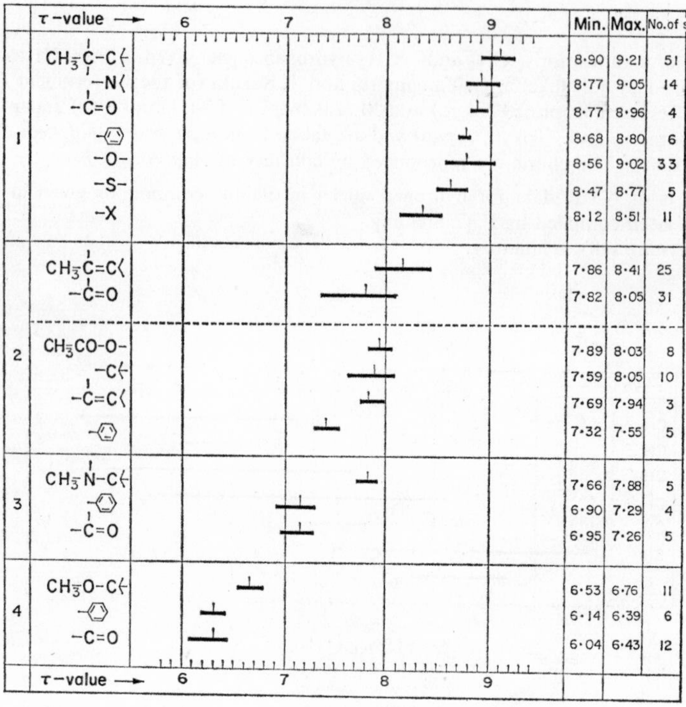
τ-value → 6 7 8 9
Min. Max. No. of samples
1
CH₃–C–C< 8·90 9·21 51
–N< 8·77 9·05 14
–C=O 8·77 8·96 4
–C₆H₅ 8·68 8·80 6
–O– 8·56 9·02 33
–S– 8·47 8·77 5
–X 8·12 8·51 11
2
CH₃–C=C< 7·86 8·41 25
–C=O 7·82 8·05 31
CH₃CO–O– 7·89 8·03 8
–C< 7·59 8·05 10
–C=C< 7·69 7·94 3
–C₆H₅ 7·32 7·55 5
3
CH₃–N–C< 7·66 7·88 5
–C₆H₅ 6·90 7·29 4
–C=O 6·95 7·26 5
4
CH₃–O–C< 6·53 6·76 11
–C₆H₅ 6·14 6·39 6
–C=O 6·04 6·43 12
τ-value → 6 7 8 9

FIG. C 3

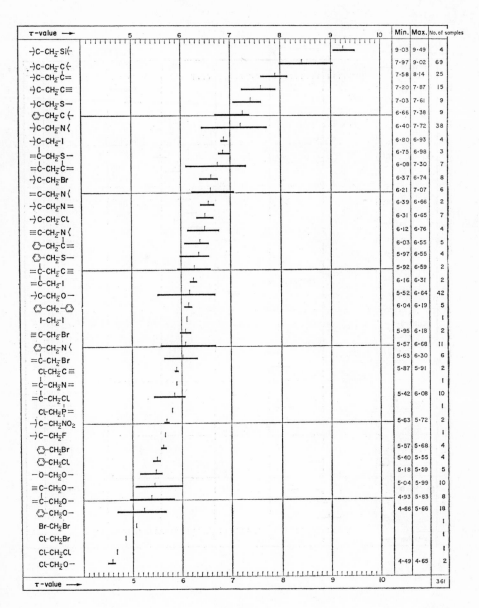

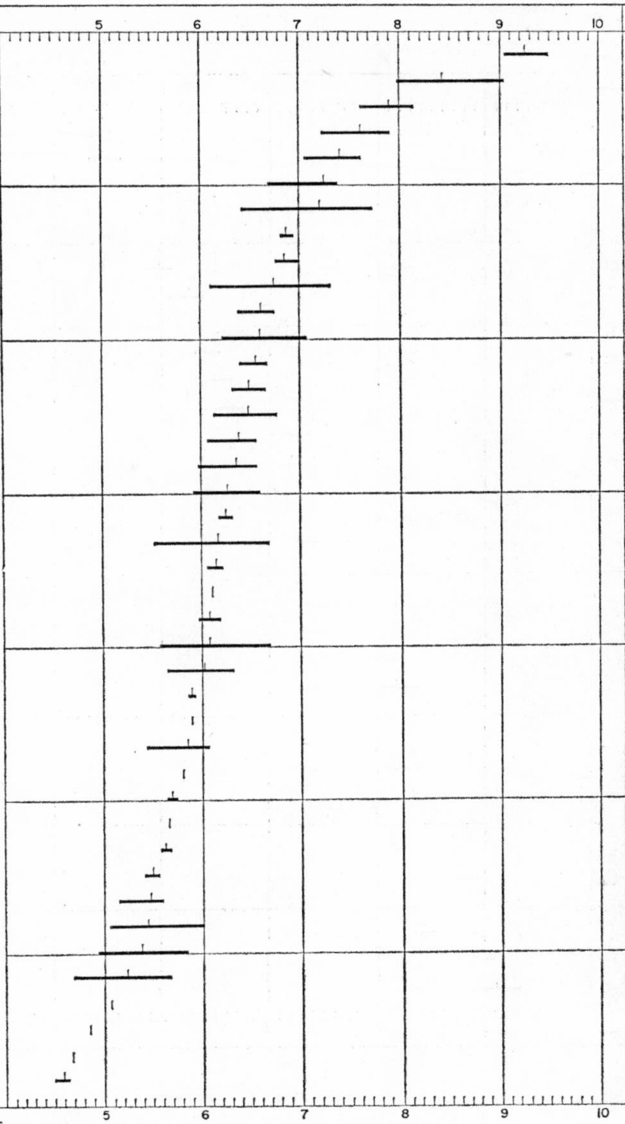

τ-value →	Min.	Max.	No. of samples
>C–CH_2–Si<	9·03	9·49	4
>C–CH_2–C<	7·97	9·02	69
>C–CH_2–C=	7·58	8·14	25
>C–CH_2–C≡	7·20	7·87	15
>C–CH_2–S–	7·03	7·61	9
C_6H_5–CH_2–C<	6·66	7·38	9
>C–CH_2–N<	6·40	7·72	38
>C–CH_2–I	6·80	6·93	4
=C–CH_2–S–	6·75	6·98	3
=C–CH_2–C=	6·08	7·30	7
>C–CH_2–Br	6·37	6·74	8
=C–CH_2–N<	6·21	7·07	6
>C–CH_2–N=	6·39	6·66	2
>C–CH_2–Cl	6·31	6·65	7
≡C–CH_2–N<	6·12	6·76	4
C_6H_5–CH_2–C=	6·03	6·55	5
C_6H_5–CH_2–S–	5·97	6·55	4
=C–CH_2–C≡	5·92	6·59	2
=C–CH_2–I	6·16	6·31	2
>C–CH_2–O–	5·52	6·64	42
C_6H_5–CH_2–C_6H_5	6·04	6·19	5
I–CH_2–I			1
≡C–CH_2–Br	5·95	6·18	2
C_6H_5–CH_2–N<	5·57	6·68	11
=C–CH_2–Br	5·63	6·30	6
Cl–CH_2–C≡	5·87	5·91	2
=C–CH_2–N=			1
=C–CH_2–Cl	5·42	6·08	10
Cl–CH_2–P=			1
>C–CH_2–NO_2	5·63	5·72	2
>C–CH_2–F			1
C_6H_5–CH_2Br	5·57	5·68	4
C_6H_5–CH_2Cl	5·40	5·55	4
–O–CH_2O–	5·18	5·59	5
≡C–CH_2O–	5·04	5·99	10
=C–CH_2O–	4·93	5·83	8
C_6H_5–CH_2O–	4·66	5·66	18
Br–CH_2Br			1
Cl–CH_2Br			1
Cl–CH_2Cl			1
Cl–CH_2O–	4·49	4·65	2
τ-value →			361

FIG. C 4

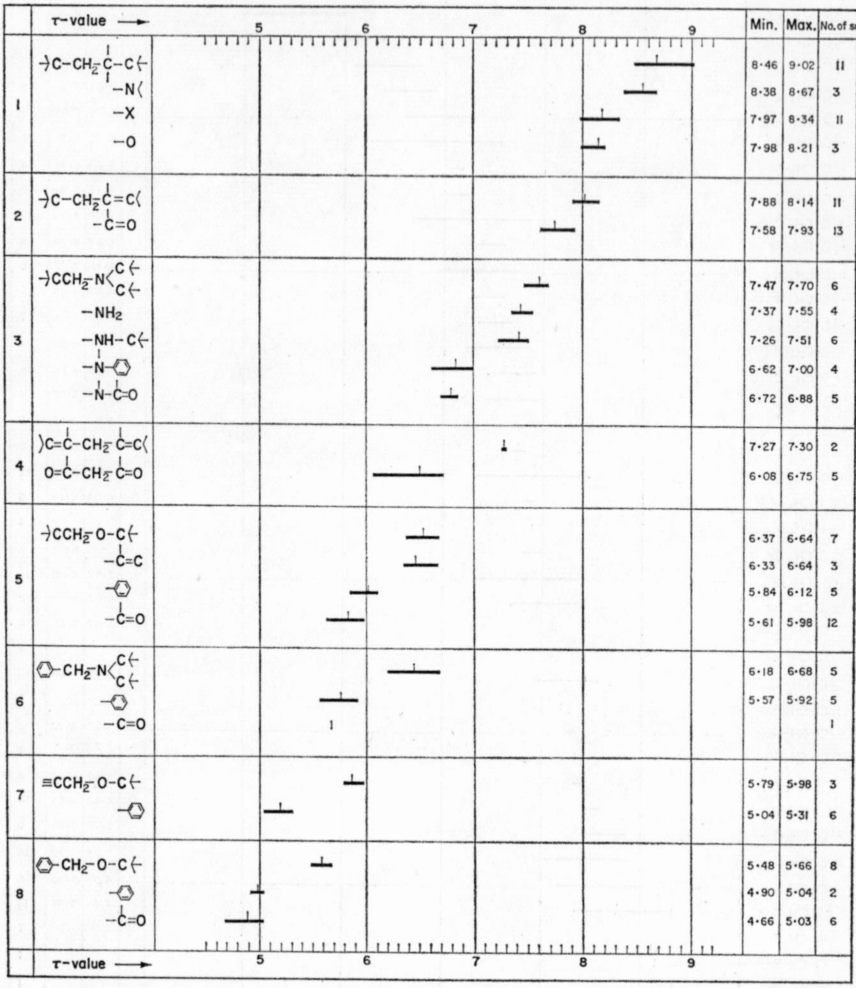

Group	Structure	Min.	Max.	No. of samples
1	→C–CH₂–C–C←	8·46	9·02	11
	–N<	8·38	8·67	3
	–X	7·97	8·34	11
	–O	7·98	8·21	3
2	→C–CH₂–C=C<	7·88	8·14	11
	–C=O	7·58	7·93	13
3	→CCH₂–N(C←)(C←)	7·47	7·70	6
	–NH₂	7·37	7·55	4
	–NH–C←	7·26	7·51	6
	–N–⌬	6·62	7·00	4
	–N–C=O	6·72	6·88	5
4	>C=C–CH₂–C=C<	7·27	7·30	2
	O=C–CH₂–C=O	6·08	6·75	5
5	→CCH₂–O–C←	6·37	6·64	7
	–C=C	6·33	6·64	3
	–⌬	5·84	6·12	5
	–C=O	5·61	5·98	12
6	⌬–CH₂–N(C←)(C←)	6·18	6·68	5
	–⌬	5·57	5·92	5
	–C=O			1
7	≡CCH₂–O–C←	5·79	5·98	3
	–⌬	5·04	5·31	6
8	⌬–CH₂–O–C←	5·48	5·66	8
	–⌬	4·90	5·04	2
	–C=O	4·66	5·03	6

FIG. C 5

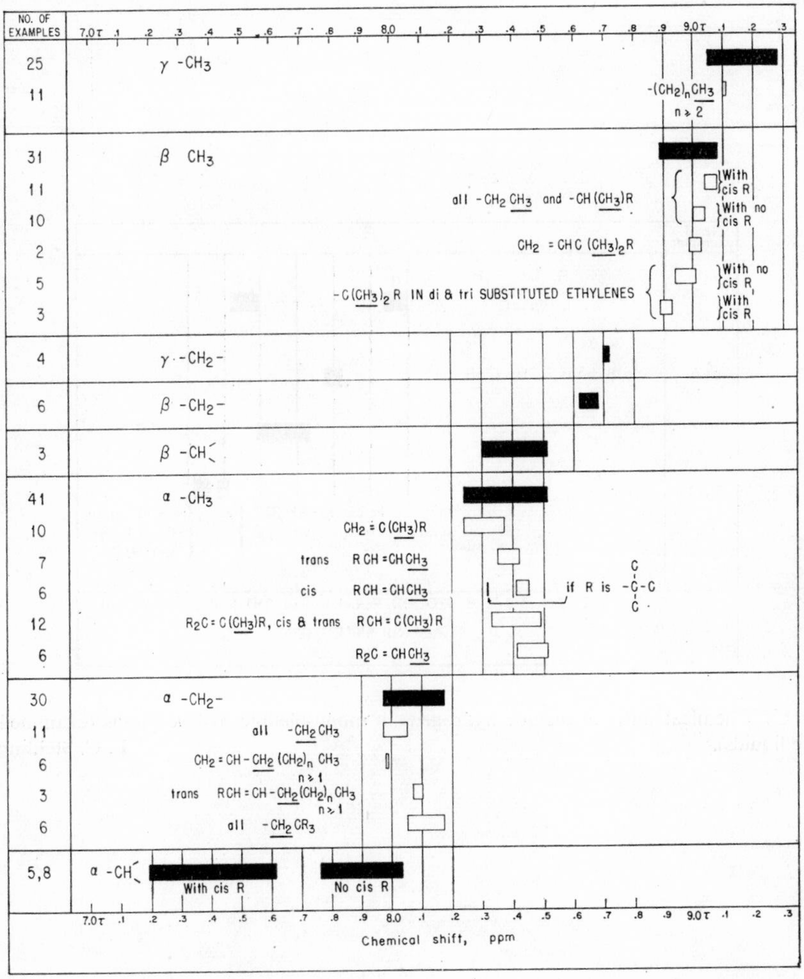

FIG. C6 Chemical shifts of non-olefinic hydrogens in mono-olefinic hydrocarbons.
F. C. Stehling.

This chart may be used for pure liquid samples, for dilute solutions in CCl_4 or for mixtures of olefines.

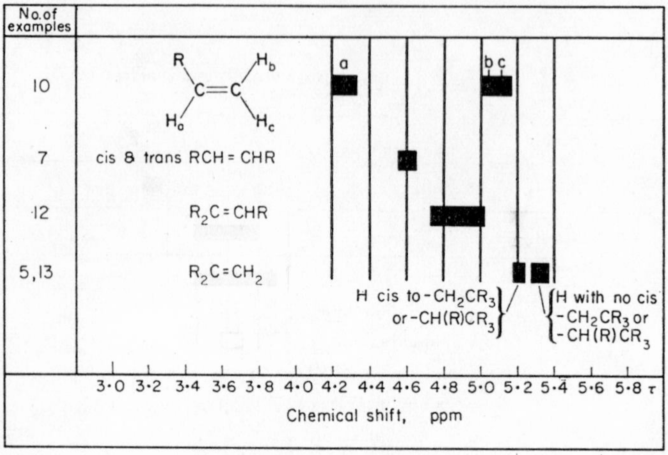

FIG. C7 Chemical shifts of olefinic hydrogens in mono-olefinic hydrocarbons (examined as pure liquids). F. C. Stehling.

No. of examples	Structure	Coupling constant, J
	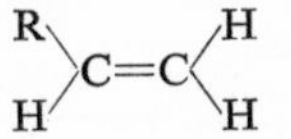	$J_{H-H}^{trans} = 16{\cdot}6\text{–}17{\cdot}4$ cycles sec^{-1} [a] $J_{H-H}^{cis} = 9{\cdot}6\text{–}11{\cdot}1$ [a] $J_{H-H}^{gem} = 0{\cdot}1\text{–}\ 2{\cdot}1$ [a]
3	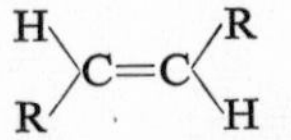	$J_{H-H}^{trans} = 15{\cdot}5\text{–}15{\cdot}7$
4	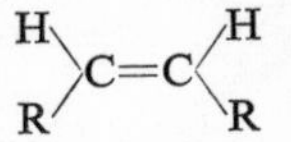	$J_{H-H}^{cis} = 11{\cdot}0\text{–}12{\cdot}3$
3,6,1	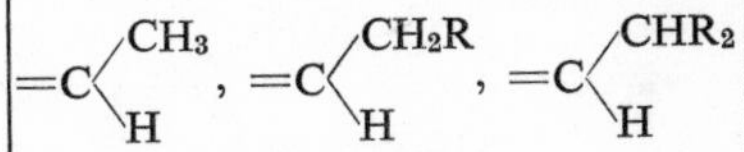	$J = 6{\cdot}1\text{–}7{\cdot}1$
4	*cis* or *trans* 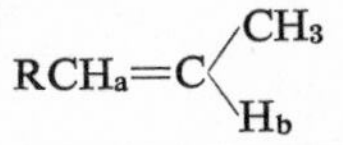	$J_{H_a-CH_3} + J_{H_b-CH_3} = 4{\cdot}7\text{–}5{\cdot}6$
8	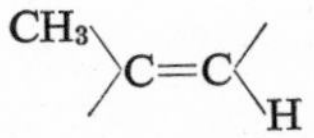	$J_{H-CH_3}^{trans} = 1{\cdot}2\text{–}1{\cdot}5$, negative
8	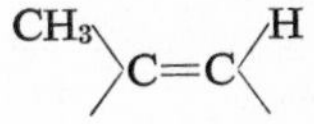	$J_{H-CH_3}^{cis} = 0{\cdot}8\text{–}1{\cdot}4$, negative
6	*cis* or *trans* 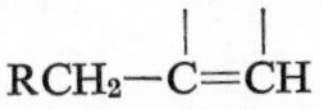	$J_{H-CH_2} = 0{\cdot}8\text{–}1{\cdot}4$, negative
8	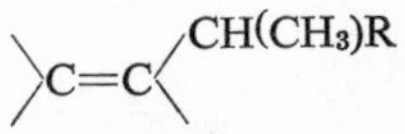	$J_{H-CH_3} = 6{\cdot}7 \pm 0{\cdot}2$ [b]
7	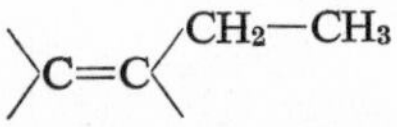	$J_{CH_2-CH_3} = 6{\cdot}8 \pm 0{\cdot}2,\ 7{\cdot}8 \pm 0{\cdot}2$ [c]
5	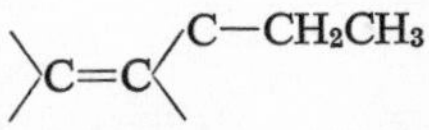	$J_{CH_2-CH_3} = 6{\cdot}2 \pm 0{\cdot}2,\ 7{\cdot}6 \pm 0{\cdot}1$ [c]

FIG. C8 Coupling constants in mono-olefinic hydrocarbons.

[a] Data taken from W. Brügel, *Elektrochem.*, **64**, 1121 (1960).

[b] Separation between perturbed CH_3 doublet.

[c] Separation between central and low field bands, and central band and high field band, respectively, in perturbed CH_3 triplet. Separations were measured between the most intense lines (at resolution of *ca.* 0·4 cycles sec^{-1}) in three portions of CH_3 spectrum.

R is an alkyl group only.

APPENDIX D

TABLE OF ¹H CHEMICAL SHIFTS IN SOME DIAZO-COMPOUNDS

A. Ledwith (Private communication)

Diazo-compound	Solvent	τ-value (ppm)	Complexity of signal
CH_2N_2	CCl_2FCF_2Cl	6·92	
CH_3CHN_2	CCl_2FCF_2Cl	6·78	
β α			
		8·30	doublet
$CH_2{=}CHCHN_2$	CCl_4	5·42	multiplet
γ β α			
		6·72	quartet
		8·93	triplet
$N_2CHCOOC_2H_5$	neat liquid	5·04	
α			
$N_2CHCOOCH_3$	neat liquid	5·04	
α			
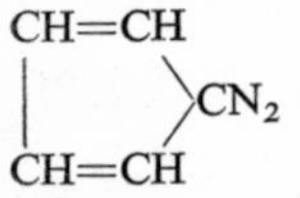	CCl_4	3·39	quartet
		4·14	quartet
β α			
$C_6H_5CHN_2$	CCl_4	5·42	
		3·10	multiplet
	neat liquid	5·47	
		3·06	multiplet
C_6H_5CHO	CCl_4	0·01	
α			
$C_6H_5CH{=}N \cdot NH_2$	CCl_4	4·71	
α			
$(C_6H_5)_2CN_2$	CH_2Cl_2	2·74	singlet
$(p\text{-}CH_3OC_6H_4)_2CN_2$	CH_2Cl_2	3·06	quartet
		6·32	
9-diazofluorene	CH_2Cl_2	2·70	multiplet
		2·20	multiplet

APPENDIX E

TABLE OF SUBSTITUENT SHIELDING EFFECTS, S_o AND S_m IN BENZENES

(see Section 10.12.4)

Substituent	s_o (ppm) Smith	Diehl	Tiers	Varian*	Brey and Lawson	s_m (ppm) Smith	Diehl	Tiers	Varian*	Brey and Lawson
F	0·23 (5)	0·25	0·18 (1)	0·30 (2)		0·04	0·01	0·01	0·09	
Cl	−0·07 (9)	−0·05	−0·07 (3), −3[a]	0 (4)	−0·05	0·06	0·06	0·06	0·11	0·06
Br	−0·18 (8)	−0·22	−0·24 (2), −4[a]	−0·10 (2)	−0·11	0·13	0·11	0·08	0·17	0·08
I	−0·38 (5)	−0·41	−0·39 (1)	−0·33 (1)	−0·22	0·23	0·22	0·20	0·21	0·19
NO_2	−0·96 (6)	−0·98	−0·96 (2)	−0·91 (1)	−0·93	−0·18	−0·21	−0·23	−0·13	−0·25
NH_2HCl	−0·10 (2)*					−0·17*				
$—N{=}NBF_4$	−1·45* or −1·25*					−0·47* or −0·67*				
NH_2	0·725 (4)	0·68		0·69 (1)	0·78	0·24	0·22		0·34	0·17
$NHCH_3$										
$N(CH_3)_2$	0·80 (1)*		0·80 (1)	0·82 (2)		0·21*		0·20	0·22	
$NH{-}N{=}C(CF_2H){-}CH_2{-}COOC_2H_5$				−0·53 (1)					−1·12	
$NHCOCH_3$				−0·22 (2)					0·04	
OH	0·56 (4)*	0·50			0·58	0·12*	0·16			0·14
OCH_3[b]	0·44 (5)	0·42		0·46 (4)	0·50	0·12	0·10		0·09	0·03
OC_2H_5	0·45 (3)		0·43 (1)	0·46 (1)		0·15		0·13	0·23	
$OCOCH_3$			0·21 (1)					0·02		
SO_2F			−0·76 (1)					−0·32		
SO_2Cl	−0·80 (1)		−0·85 (1)			−0·33		−0·27		
SO_2NH_2	−0·60 (1)*					−0·17*				

(*continued*)

Substituent	s_o (ppm) Smith	Diehl	Tiers	Varian*	Brey and Lawson	s_m (ppm) Smith	Diel	Tiers	Varian*	Brey and Lawson
$SO_3C_nH_{2n+1}$	−0·62 (4)					−0·27				
SO_3Na	−0·27* to −0·55 (2)*					0·05* to −0·31*				
SH				~0·13 (1)					~0·01	
COOH	−0·75 (1)*			−0·88 (1)		−0·20*			−0·10	
$COOCH_3$	−0·73 (1)*	−0·74	−0·80 (1)			−0·09*	−0·10	−0·06		
$COOC_4H_9$	−0·79 (1)					−0·21				
$COOC_2H_4N(C_2H_5)_2$				−0·75 (1)					−0·03	
CHO	−0·61 (2)		−0·62 (4)	−0·57 (3)	−0·52	−0·21		−0·18	−0·14	−0·32
$COCH_3$	−0·70 (3)		−0·68 (1)	−0·67 (2), −59[a]		−0·10		−0·17	−0·05	
$COCH_2Br$				−0·65 (1)					−0·11	
COCl	−0·88 (2)					−0·15				
CN	−0·35 (2)	−0·35	−0·32[a]		−0·24	−0·17	−0·13			−0·17
CH_3	0·17 (9)	0·17	0·15 (3), 12[a]	0·15 (3)	0·23	0·14	0·13	0·11	0·11	0·09
CH_2CH_3			0·10[a]		0·20					0·05
$CH(CH_3)_2$	0·11 (4)		0·10 (1), 10[a]	0·10 (1), 7[a]	0·13	0·08		0·07	0·09	0·03
$C(CH_3)_3$			0·03[a]							
$C(CH_3)_2CH_2C(CH_3)_3$				0·0 (1)					0·01	
CH_2Cl			−0·06[a]					−0·05 (1)		
CH_2Br			−0·05[a]					−0·06 (1)		
$CHBrCH_2CCl_3$			−0·14[a]							
$CHCl_2$										
CCl_3										
CF_3			−0·38 (1), −29[a]	−0·30 (1)				−0·18	−0·10	

(*continued*)

Substituent	s_o (ppm) Smith	s_o (ppm) Tiers	s_o (ppm) Varian*	s_m (ppm) Smith	s_m (ppm) Tiers	s_m (ppm) Varian*
n-C_3F_7		−0·31[a]				
C_3H_6Br			0·10[a]			
$CH_2C(CH_3)_2Cl$			0·05[a]			
CH_2OH		0·05[a]	0·04[a]	−0·06 (1)		
$CH(CH_3)OH$			0·06 (1)			0·11
—CH—CH_2 (epoxide, O bridging CH and CH_2)			0·04[a]			
$C_2H_4OCOCH_3$			0·03[a]			
$CH_2N(CH_3)_2$		0·02[a]				
$CH(CH_3)NH_2$			0·02[a]			
$CH_2N(CH_2CN)_2$			0·07[a]			
CH_2—$N(CH_2\varphi)CH_2N(CH_2\varphi)_2$			0·07[a]			
$C_2H_4NHCOCH_3$			0·07[a]			
CH_2—(cyclohexadienyl ring)		0·08[a]				
$CH(\varphi)COCH_3$			0·07[a]			
$CH(\varphi)NCCr(CO)_5$	−12[a]					
$C(CH_3)_2COOH$		−0·10[a]				
$C_2H_4COCH_3$		0·11[a]				
—CH=$CHCH_3$			−0·03 (1)			0·08
CCH_3=CH_2		−0·08[a]				
CH=CH—CH=CHφ	0·01[a]					
CH=CHCHO		−0·24[a]				
CH=$CHCOCH_3$		−0·14[a]				
$C(\varphi)$=CH_2		−0·02[a]				
CH=CHBr		−0·01[a]				
CH=CH—CH=CHφ / $Fe(CO)_3$ (diene complexed to $Fe(CO)_3$)	0·04[a]					
—C(O···H···O)=CH—COC_2H_5 (—C(OH)=CH—C(=O)OC$_2$H$_5$, H-bonded)			−0·78 (1)			−0·09
Ferrocene			−0·12 (1)			0·10
C≡CH		−0·11[a]				
SiH_3		−0·15[a]				

The data were compiled by G. W. Smith and are based on private communications from the authors indicated.

[Figures in parentheses indicate the number of spectra averaged.]

* Data taken in polar solvents only.

[a] From monosubstituted benzenes.

[b] Numerous methoxy benzenes have been studied(454).

APPENDIX F

TABLE OF ^{31}P CHEMICAL SHIFTS

(Taken mainly from Van Wazer, Callis, Shoolery and Jones, *J. Amer. Chem. Soc.*, **78**, 5715 (1956).)

Name	Structure	Physical state	Chemical shifts (ppm) relative to external 85% orthophosphoric acid
A. Triply connected compounds			
Ethyldifluorophosphine	$C_2H_5PF_2$	Liquid	$+\ 30 \pm 3$
Trimethyl phosphite	$P(OCH_3)_3$	Liquid	-141 ± 1
Triethyl phosphite	$P(OC_2H_5)_3$	Liquid	-139 ± 1
Triisopropyl phosphite	$P(OCH(CH_3)_2)_3$	Liquid	-138 ± 1
Tributyl phosphite	$P(OC_4H_9)_3$	Liquid	-139 ± 1
Tris-(β-chloroethyl) phosphite	$P(O(CH_2)_2Cl)_3$	Liquid	-139 ± 1
Tris-(2-ethylhexyl) phosphite	$P(OC_8H_{17})_3$	Liquid	-140 ± 1
Triphenyl phosphite	$P(OC_6H_5)_3$	Liquid	-128 ± 1
Ethylchlorofluorophosphine	C_2H_5PClF	Liquid	$+\ 20 \pm 2$
Ethylfluoroisopropoxyphosphine	$C_2H_5P(OCH(CH_3)_2)F$	Liquid	$-\ 29 \pm 3$
Phosphorus trichloride	PCl_3	Liquid	-220 ± 1
Hexamethylphosphorus triamide	$P(N(CH_3)_2)_3$	Liquid	-122 ± 2
Hexaethylphosphorus triamide	$P(N(C_2H_5)_2)_3$	Liquid	-118 ± 3
Dichlorophenylphosphine	$C_6H_5PCl_2$	Liquid	-166 ± 1
Phosphorus tribromide	PBr_3	Liquid	-229 ± 1
Dimethylamidodimethylphosphine	$(CH_3)_2NP(CH_3)_2$	Liquid	$-\ 39 \pm 1$
Triphenylphosphine	$P(C_6H_5)_3$	Ether soln.	$+\ 8 \pm 1$
Trimethylphosphine	$P(CH_3)_3$	Liquid	$+\ 62 \pm 1$
Dimethylphosphine	$HP(CH_3)_2$	Liquid	$+\ 98{\cdot}5 \pm 1$
Monomethylphosphine	H_2PCH_3	Liquid	$+163{\cdot}5 \pm 1$

(*continued*)

Name	Structure	Physical state	Chemical shifts (ppm) relative to external 85% orthophosphoric acid
Phosphine	PH_3	Liquid at $-90°$	$+238 \pm 1$
Phosphorus sesquisulphide	$P(S)_3$ in P_4S_3	CS_2 soln.	-71 ± 1
B. Bent bonds			
Elemental phosphorus	P_4	Solid	1 broad peak at very high positive field
Phosphorus sesquisulphide	$SP(P)_2$ in P_4S_3	CS_2 soln.	$+120 \pm 1$
Organic Phosphates C. Quadruply connected compounds			
Tri-*o*-tolyl phosphate	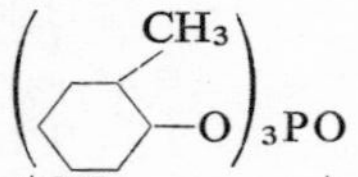	Liquid	$+17 \pm 0{\cdot}3$
Tri-*m*-tolyl phosphate	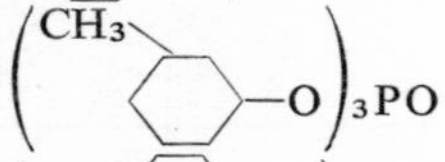	Liquid	$+17 \pm 0{\cdot}5$
Tri-*p*-tolyl phosphate	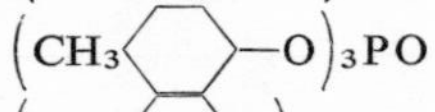	Benzene soln.	$+16 \pm 0{\cdot}5$
Tricresyl phosphate	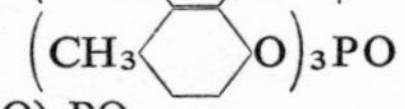	Liquid	$+18 \pm 1$
Triphenyl phosphate	$(C_6H_5O)_3PO$	Ether soln.	$+18 \pm 0{\cdot}5$
p-Chlorophenyl diphenyl phosphate	$ClC_6H_4O(C_6H_5O)_2PO$	Liquid	$+17{\cdot}5 \pm 0{\cdot}5$
Butyl diphenyl phosphate	$C_4H_9O(C_6H_5O)_2PO$	Liquid	$+12 \pm 1$
2-Ethylhexyl diphenyl phosphate	$C_3H_{17}O(C_6H_5O)_2PO$	Liquid	$+12 \pm 1$
Ethyl diphenyl phosphate	$C_2H_5O(C_6H_5O)_2PO$	Liquid	$+12 \pm 1$
Dibutyl phenyl phosphate	$(C_4H_9O)_2C_6H_5OPO$	Liquid	$+\ 4 \pm 1$
Dibutyl phosphate	$(C_4H_9O)_2HOPO$	Liquid	$0 \pm 0{\cdot}5$

(*continued*)

Name	Structure	Physical state	Chemical shifts (ppm) relative to external 85% orthophosphoric acid
Triethyl phosphate	$(C_2H_5O)_3PO$	Liquid	+ 1 ± 1
Tris-β-(chloroethyl) phosphate	$(ClC_2H_4)_3PO$	Liquid	+ 2 ± 1
Tri-n-butyl phosphate	$(n\text{-}C_4H_9O)_3PO$	Liquid	− 1 ± 0·5
Tri-butyl phosphate	$(C_4H_9O)_3PO$	Liquid	+ 1 ± 0·5
Amyl octyl acid phosphate	$(C_5H_{11}O)(C_8H_{17}O)HOPO$	Liquid	+ 1 ± 0·5
Inorganic orthophosphates			
Trisubstituted orthophosphates	PO_4^{3-} plus 3 Na^+ or $3K^+$	Aq. soln.	− 5
Orthophosphates with 1 to 3 H/P	PO_4H^{2-}	Aq. soln.	0
Orthophosphoric acid (85%)	$(HO)_3PO$	Liquid (aq.)	0
1 : 1 water diln. of 85% H_3PO_4	$(HO)_3PO$	Aq. soln.	− 1 ± 1
Monosodium orthophosphate	NaH_2PO_4	Aq. soln.	0 ± 1
Disodium orthophosphate	Na_2HPO_4	Aq. soln.	+ 3 ± 1
Trisodium orthophosphate	Na_3PO_4	Aq. soln.	− 5 ± 1
Monopotassium orthophosphate	KH_2PO_4	Aq. soln.	− 1 ± 1
Dipotassium orthophosphate	K_2HPO_4	Aq. soln.	− 1 ± 1
Tripotassium orthophosphate	K_3PO_4	Aq. soln.	− 6 ± 1
Monoammonium orthophosphate	$NH_4H_2PO_4$	Aq. soln.	− 1 ± 1
Diammonium orthophosphate	$(NH_4)_2HPO_4$	Aq. soln.	− 1 ± 1
Phosphomolybdic acid		Aq. soln.	+ 5 ± 1
Condensed phosphates			
End groups, doubly substituted	$—OPO_3^{2-}$, plus $2Na^+$ or $2K^+$	Aq. soln.	+ 5 ± 1
End groups, 1 to 2 H/P atom	$—OPO_3H^-$	Aq. soln.	+10 ± 1
Tetrasodium pyrophosphate	$O_3POPO_3^{4-}$	Aq. soln.	+ 6 ± 1
Sodium acid pyrophosphate	$HO_3POPO_3H^{2-}$	Aq. soln.	+10 ± 1
Potassium acid pyrophosphate	$HO_3POPO_3H^{2-}$	Aq. soln.	+ 9 ± 1

(*continued*)

Name	Structure	Physical state	Chemical shifts (ppm) relative to external 85% orthophosphoric acid
Ammonium pyrophosphate	$O_3POPO_3^{4-}$	Aq. soln.	$+8 \pm 1$
Middle groups, short chains	$—OPO_2^-O—$	Aq. soln.	$+18 \pm 1$
Middle groups, long chains and rings	$—OPO_2^-O—$	Aq. soln.	$+21 \pm 1$
Sodium tripolyphosphate	$P_3O_{10}{}^{5-}$	Aq. soln. (supersatd.)	$\{+4 \pm 1, +18 \pm 1\}$
Potassium tripolyphosphate	$P_3O_{10}{}^{5-}$	Aq. soln.	$\{+6 \pm 1, +19 \pm 1\}$
Ammonium tripolyphosphate	$P_3O_{10}{}^{5-}$	Aq. soln.	$\{+8 \pm 1, +22 \pm 1\}$
Sodium phosphate glass, $n = ca.\ 4$	$P_4O_{13}{}^{6-}$	Aq. soln.	$\{+3 \pm 1, +18 \pm 1\}$
Sodium phosphate glass, $n = 5{\cdot}4$	$^{2-}O_3PO\bar{P}O_2O \cdots O\bar{P}O_2OPO_3^{2-}$	Aq. soln.	$+5 \pm 1, +21 \pm 1$
Sodium phosphate glass, $n = 6{\cdot}8$	$^{2-}O_3PO\bar{P}O_2O \cdots O\bar{P}O_2OPO_3^{2-}$	Aq. soln.	Two peaks not ref'd
Sodium phosphate glass, $n = 14$	$^{2-}O_3PO\bar{P}O_2O \cdots O\bar{P}O_2OPO_3^{2-}$	Aq. soln.	$+6 \pm 1, +20 \pm 1$
Sodium phosphate glass, $n = 25$	$^{2-}O_3PO\bar{P}O_2O \cdots O\bar{P}O_2OPO_3^{2-}$	Aq. soln.	$+5 \pm 1, +19 \pm 1$
Sodium phosphate glass, $n = 80$	$^{2-}O_3PO\bar{P}O_2O \cdots O\bar{P}O_2OPO_3^{2-}$	Aq. soln.	$+19 \pm 1$
Sodium phosphate glass, $n = 230$	$^{2-}O_3PO\bar{P}O_2O \cdots O\bar{P}O_2OPO_3^{2-}$	Aq. soln.	$+21 \pm 1$
Sodium trimetaphosphate	$(NaPO_3)_3$, ring structure	Aq. soln.	$+21 \pm 1$
Sodium tetrametaphosphate	$(NaPO_3)_4$, ring structure	Aq. soln.	$+21 \pm 1$
Ammonium tetrapolyphosphate	$(NH_4)_6P_4O_{13}$	Aq. soln.	$\{+9 \pm 1, +22 \pm 1\}$
Sodium ultraphosphate, $Na_2O/P_2O_5 = 0{\cdot}82$	Theor. highly branched	Heated to soften	$+31$
Sodium ultraphosphate, $Na_2O/P_2O_5 = 0{\cdot}50$	Theor. highly branched	Heated to soften	$+31$
Sodium ultraphosphate, $Na_2O/P_2O_5 = 0{\cdot}42$	Theor. highly branched	Heated to soften	$+30$

(*continued*)

Name	Structure	Physical state	Chemical shifts (ppm) relative to external 85% orthophosphoric acid
$H_2O{\cdot}P_2O_5$ azeotropic acid	Theor. highly branched	Heated to soften	+34
Sodium ultraphosphate, $Na_2O/P_2O_5 = 0{\cdot}96$	No branching points expected	30 min. after dissoln. in water	+14
Trisodium isohypophosphate tetrahydrate	$Na_2O_3POPHO_2Na$	Aq. soln.	$+\ 1 \pm 0{\cdot}5$
			$+3 \pm 0.5$
Hexaphenyl bis-(diethyleneglycol) tetraphosphate	$((C_6H_5O)_2OPOC_2H_4OC_2H_4OP\text{-}(OC_6H_5)_2O-)_2$	Liquid	$\begin{Bmatrix} +\ 7{\cdot}5 \pm 1 \\ +12{\cdot}5 \pm 1 \end{Bmatrix}$
Pentaphenyl bis-(diethyleneglycol) triphosphate	$(C_6H_5O)_2OPOC_2H_4OC_2H_4OP(O\text{-}C_6H_5)_2O-C_2H_4OC_2H_4OPO(OC_6H_5)_2$	Liquid	$\begin{Bmatrix} +\ 7 \pm 1 \\ +13 \pm 1 \end{Bmatrix}$
Phosphorus pentoxide–ethyl ether reaction product		Viscous liquid	$\begin{Bmatrix} +14 \pm 1 \\ +29 \pm 1 \\ +41 \pm 1 \end{Bmatrix}$
Organic phosphites			
Dimethyl phosphite	$(CH_3O)_2HPO$	Liquid	-11 ± 1
Diethyl phosphite	$(C_2H_5O)_2HPO$	Liquid	$-\ 8 \pm 1$
Dibutyl phosphite	$(C_4H_9O)_2HPO$	Liquid	$-\ 8 \pm 1$
Bis-(2-ethylhexyl) phosphite	$(C_8H_{17}O)_2HPO$	Liquid	$-\ 7 \pm 1$
Inorganic phosphites			
Phosphorous acid	$(HO)_2HPO$	30% aq. soln.	$-\ 5 \pm 2$
Phosphorous acid	$(HO)_2HPO$	13·1 M aq. soln. prepd. from cryst. acid.	$-\ 8 \pm 2$
Monosodium phosphite	$NaO(HO)HPO$	Aq. soln.	$-\ 4 \pm 2$

(continued)

Name	Structure	Physical state	Chemical shifts (ppm) relative to external 85% orthophosphoric acid
Disodium phosphite	$(NaO)_2HPO$	Aq. soln.	$-\ 4 \pm 2$
Other lower oxidation states			
Sodium hypophosphate	$HO(NaO)POPO(ONa)OH$	Aq. soln.	$-\ 9 + 1$
Hypophosphorous acid	$H_2PO(OH)$	50% aq. soln.	-13 ± 2
Calcium hypophosphite	$H_2PO(OCa)$	Aq. soln.	$-\ 8 \pm 2$
Sodium hypophosphite	$H_2PO(ONa)$	Aq. soln.	$-\ 8 \pm 2$
Potassium hypophosphite	$H_2PO(OK)$	Aq. soln.	$-\ 6 \pm 2$
Nitrogen-substituted compounds			
Monosodium phosphoramidate	$NaOPO(OH)NH_2$	Aq. soln.	$-\ 3 \pm 1$
Phosphorodiamidic acid	$HOPO(NH_2)_2$	Aq. soln.	$+\ 3{\cdot}5(?)$
Sodium salt of trimeric phosphoronitridic acid	$(NaPO_2NH)_3$, ring structure	Aq. soln.	$+\ 1 \pm 2$
Hexamethylphosphoramide	$((CH_3)_2N)_3PO$	Liquid	-27 ± 1
Hexamethylphosphoramide	$((CH_3)_2N)_3PO$	Liquid	$-26{\cdot}5 \pm 0{\cdot}5$
Hexa-n-butylphosphoramide	$((n\text{-}C_4H_9)_2N)_3PO$	Liquid	-23 ± 1
Ethyltetramethylphosphorodiamidate	$C_2H_5OPO(N(CH_3)_2)_2$	Liquid	-18 ± 1
Octamethylpyrophosphoramide	$((CH_3)_2N)_4P_2O_3$	Liquid	-12 ± 1
Octamethylpyrophosphoramide	$((CH_3)_2N)_4P_2O_3$	Liquid	-11 ± 1
Phosphonitrilic chloride trimer	$(PNCl_2)_3$ ring structure	Benzene soln.	-19 ± 1
Phosphonitrilic chloride polymer	$(PNCl_2)_x$ chain	Benzene soln.	$-20 \pm 1, +7 \pm 1$
Diphenyl dodecylphosphoramide	$(C_6H_5O)_2PO(NHR)$	Benzene soln.	$-\ 1 \pm 1$
n-Butyl tris-(dimethylamido)-phosphonium bromide	$[n\text{-}C_4H_9P(N(CH_3)_2)_3]^+Br^-$	Liquid	-62 ± 1
Chlorobenzyl tris-(dimethylamido)-phosphonium chloride	[Cl  $CH_2P(N(CH_3)_2)_3]^+Cl^-$	Alcohol soln.	$-55{\cdot}5 \pm 1$

(*continued*)

Name	Structure	Physical state	Chemical shifts (ppm) relative to external 85% orthophosphoric acid
Dichlorofluoromethyltris-(dimethylamido)--phosphonium chloride	$[Cl_2FC{-}P(N(CH_3)_2)_3]^+Cl^-$	Alcohol soln.	-44 ± 1
Other quadruply connected compounds			
Triethyl selenophosphate	$(C_2H_5O)_3PSe$	Liquid	-71 ± 1
(Chloromethyl)-phosphonic dichloride	$ClCH_2POCl_2$	Liquid	-38 ± 2
Compounds with P–C linkages			
Phenylphosphonic acid	$C_6H_5PO(OH)_2$	Acetone soln.	$-17{\cdot}5 \pm 1$
p-Chlorophenylphosphonic acid	$ClC_6H_4PO(OH)_2$	Acetone soln.	-14 ± 1
p-Ethylbenzylphosphonic acid	$(C_2H_5C_6H_4CH_2)PO(OH)_2$	Acetone soln.	-26 ± 2
3-Bromopropylphosphonic acid	$(BrC_3H_6)PO(OH)_2$	Acetone soln.	-30 ± 2
n-Butylphosphonic acid	$(C_4H_9)PO(OH)_2$	Acetone soln.	$-32{\cdot}5 \pm 1$
n-Pentylphosphonic acid	$(C_5H_{11})PO(OH)_2$	Aq. soln.	-33 ± 1
β-Styrenephosphonic acid	$C_6H_5CH{=}CHPO(OH)_2$	Acetone soln.	-18 ± 1
Dibutyl ethylphosphonate	$C_2H_5PO(OC_4H_9)_2$	Liquid	-31 ± 2
Dibutyl butylphosphonate	$C_4H_9PO(OC_4H_9)_2$	Liquid	-32 ± 1
Dibutyl nonylphosphonate	$C_9H_{19}PO(OC_4H_9)_2$	Liquid	-31 ± 1
Di-n-butyl decylphosphonate	$C_{10}H_{21}PO(OC_4H_9)_2$	Liquid	-32 ± 1
Diethyl methylphosphonate	$CH_3PO(OC_2H_5)_2$	Liquid	-30 ± 1
Diethyl ethylphosphonate	$C_2H_5PO(OC_2H_5)_2$	Liquid	$-32{\cdot}5 \pm 1$
Bis-(2-ethylhexyl)2-ethylhexylphosphonate	$C_8H_{17}PO(OC_8H_{17})_2$	Liquid	-32 ± 1
Sodium decylphosphonate	$C_{10}H_{21}PO(ONa)_2$	Aq. soln.	-27 ± 2
Bis-(*β*-chloroethyl) vinylphosphonate	$H_2C{=}CHPO(OC_2H_4Cl)_2$	Liquid	-22 ± 1
Dibutyl amylnaphthylphosphonate	$C_5H_{11}{-}C_{10}H_6PO(OC_4H_9)_2$	Liquid	$-26{\cdot}5 \pm 1$
Bis-(2-butoxyethyl) phenylphosphonate	$C_6H_5PO(OC_2H_4OC_4H_9)_2$	Liquid	$-19 \pm 0{\cdot}5$

(*continued*)

Name	Structure	Physical state	Chemical shifts (ppm) relative to external 85% orthophosphoric acid
Diethyl trichloromethylphosphonate	$Cl_3CPO(OC_2H_5)_2$	Liquid	$-\ 6{\cdot}5 \pm 0{\cdot}5$
Diethyl acetylphosphonate	$CH_3COPO(OC_2H_5)_2$	Liquid	$+\ 2 \pm 1$
Diethyl benzylthiomethylphosphonate	$C_6H_5CH_2SCH_2PO(OC_2H_5)_2$	Liquid	-24 ± 1
Diethyl chloromethylphosphonate	$ClCH_2PO(OC_2H_5)_2$	Liquid	-20 ± 2
Diethyl benzoylphosphonate	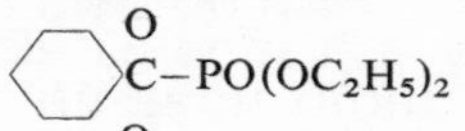	Liquid	$+\ 2 \pm 1$
Diethyl dimethylcarbamylphosphonate	O $Me_2NC-PO(OC_2H_5)_2$	Liquid	$0 \pm 0{\cdot}5$
2,4,6-Tris-(diethylphosphonyl)-1,3,5-triazine	$N_3C_3(PO(OC_2H_5)_2)_3$, C–N ring	Liquid	0 ± 1
Phenylphosphonous acid	$C_6H_5PO(H)(OH)$	Aq. soln.	-23 ± 1
Phenylphosphonous acid	$C_6H_5OP(H)(OH)$	Acetone soln.	-20 ± 1
Sodium 2-methyl-4-dimethylaminophenyl-phosphonite	$(Me_2N)(CH_3)C_6H_3PO(H)ONa$	Aq. soln.	-20 ± 5
Ethyl bis-(*p*-chlorophenyl)-*sec*-phosphonate	$(ClC_6H_4)_2PO(OC_2H_5)$	Liquid	-27 ± 1
Tris-(*p*-chlorophenyl)-phosphine oxide	$(ClC_6H_4)_3PO$	Benzene soln.	-23 ± 1
Sulphur substitution for oxygen			
Phosphorus sulphoxide	$P_4S_4O_6$	CS_2 soln.	-16 ± 1
Phosphorus oxychloride	$POCl_3$	Liquid	$-\ 4 \pm 1$
Dichlorophenylphosphine oxide or phenylphosphonic dichloride	$C_6H_5POCl_2$	Liquid	-34 ± 1
Dichlorophenylphosphine sulphide or phenylphosphonothionic dichloride	$C_6H_5PSCl_2$	Liquid	-80 ± 1
Tri-*p*-tolyl thiophosphate	$(CH_3C_6H_5O)_3PS$	Benzene soln.	$-53{\cdot}5 \pm 1$
O,O-Dimethyl S-propyl phosphorothioate	$(CH_3O)_2PO(SC_3H_7)$	Liquid	-31 ± 1
O,O-Diethyl S-(*p*-chlorophenyl)-phosphorothioate	$(C_2H_5O)_2PO(SC_6H_4Cl)$	Liquid	-21 ± 1

(continued)

Name	Structure	Physical state	Chemical shifts (ppm) relative to external 85% orthophosphoric acid
O,O-Diethyl O-(p-nitrophenyl)-phosphorothioate	$(C_2H_5O)_2PS(OC_6H_4NO_2)$	Liquid	-42 ± 1
O,O-Diethyl S-phenyl phosphorothioate	$(C_2H_5O)_2PO(SC_6H_5)$	Liquid	-22 ± 1
O-Ethyl S-(p-chlorophenyl)-phenyl-phosphorothioate	$C_6H_5PO(OC_2H_5)(SC_6H_4Cl)$	Liquid	-39 ± 1
Sodium diethylthiophosphate	$(C_2H_5O)_2PS(ONa)$	Alcohol soln.	-57 ± 1
O,O-Di isopropyl S-(p-chlorophenyl)-peroxyphosphorotrithioate	$(i\text{-}C_3H_7O)_2PS\left(SS\!\!-\!\!\bigcirc\!\!-\!\!Cl\right)$	Liquid	-74 ± 2
Phosphorus pentachloride	PCl_5	CS_2 soln.	$+80 \pm 2$

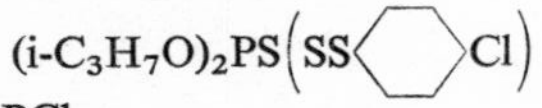

(*continued*)

Compound	Chemical shift ppm	Reference number in Chapter 12
$(C_4H_9O)_2P(O)C_4H_9$	−30·8	248
$(C_2H_5O)_2P(O)CH_2COOC_2H_5$	−19·5	248
$(C_2H_5O)_2P(O)CH_2COCH_3$	−19·9	248
$(C_2H_5O)_2P(O)CH_2CON(C_2H_5)_2$	−21·3	248
$(C_2H_5O)_2P(O)CH_2CON(C_3H_7)_2$	−22·0	248
$(C_2H_5O)_2P(O)OC(CH_3){=}CH_2$	+7·2	248
$(C_2H_5O)_2P(O)OC(OC_2H_5){=}CCl_2$	+7·5	248
$(C_2H_5O)_3P(O)$	+0·9	248
$C_2H_5P(O)Cl_2$	−53·0	146
$C_6H_5P(O)Cl_2$	−34·5	146
CH_3PCl_2	−191·2	146
$C_6H_5PCl_2$	−161·6	146
$C_2H_5P(S)Cl_2$	−94·3	146
$C_6H_5P(S)Cl_2$	−74·8	146
Cyclic Phosphonitrilics		
$P_3N_3Cl_4(SC_2H_5)_2$	$P(SC_2H_5)_2$ −51·7 PCl_2 −17·7 (J_{PP} = 4·8 cycles sec^{-1})	169
$P_4N_4Cl_4(SC_2H_5)_4$	$P(SC_2H_5)_2$ −28·6 PCl_2 +9·7 (J_{PP} = 11·8 cycles sec^{-1})	169
$P_3N_3Cl_6$	−19·7	169
$P_3N_3(SC_2H_5)_6$	−45·7	169
$P_4N_4Cl_8$	+7·4	169
$P_3N_3Cl_4(SC_6H_5)_2$	$P(SC_6H_5)_2$ −46·8 PCl_2 −18·6 (J_{PP} = 4·2 cycles sec^{-1})	169
Br_3PS	+111·8	4
Br_3PO	+102·9	4
NaH_2PO_4 (aq)	+1·3	4
$(C_2H_5O)_3PO$	+0·9	4
H_3PO_4	0·0	4
$[(CH_3)_2N]_3PO$	−23·4	4
$(C_2H_5)_3PSe$	−45·8	4
$(C_2H_5)_3PO$	−48·3	4
$(C_2H_5)_3PS$	−54·5	4
$(C_2H_5S)_3PO$	−61·3	4
$(C_2H_5O)_3PS$	−68·1	4
$[(C_2H_5)_2N]_3PS$	−77·8	4
$(C_2H_5S)_3PS$	−92·9	4
$(C_2H_5S)_3P$	−115·6	4
$(C_3H_7S)_3P$	−118·2	4
$[(C_2H_5)_2N]_3P$	−118·2	4
$(C_6H_5O)_3P$	−126·8	4
$(C_2H_5O)_3P$	−136·9	4
$(i\text{-}C_3H_7O)_3P$	−136·9	4
PCl_6^- (Solid PCl_5)	+281	162, 163
PCl_4^+	−96	162, 163
PF_6^-	+148	162, 163

(*continued*)

Compound	Chemical shift ppm	Reference number in Chapter 12
$CH_3PS(OC_2H_5)_2$	−94·9	247
$CH_3(CH_2Cl)POCl$	−59·2	246
$CH_3(CH_2Cl)PSCl$	−84·9	246
$CH_2ClPSCl_2$	−72·8	246
$OPCl(OC_6H_5)_2$	+6·2	176
PCl_5	+80	162, 163
$OPCl_2(OC_6H)_5$	−1·5	143

(*continued*)

(*continued*)

Compound		Chemical shift ppm	Coupling constant (cycles sec^{-1})	Reference number in Chapter 12
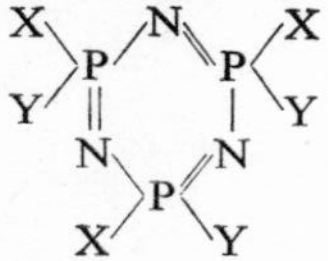	X = Y = Cl X = Y = $N(CH_3)_2$ X = Cl, Y = $N(CH_3)_2$ X = Y = $NH(CH_3)$	− 19 − 25 − 21 − 24		251
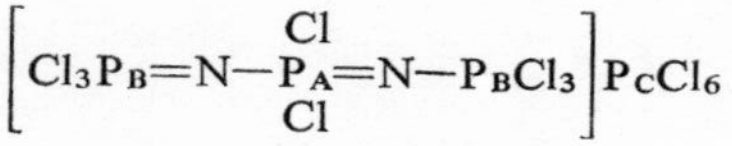	P_A P_B P_C	+ 14 − 12·5 + 305·0	$J_{P_AP_B}$ = 45·3	177
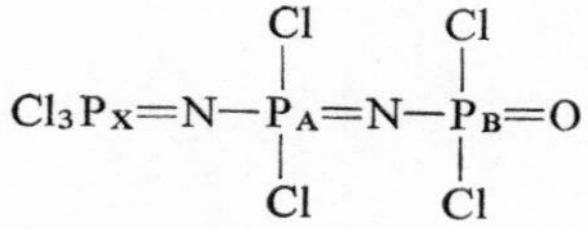	P_A P_B P_X	+ 20 + 13·4 − 7·1	$J_{P_AP_X}$ = 29·5 $J_{P_AP_B}$ = 26·7	177
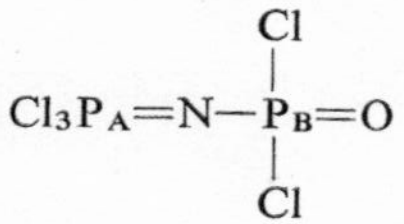	P_A P_B	+ 0·1 + 14·2	$J_{P_AP_B}$ = 15·0	250
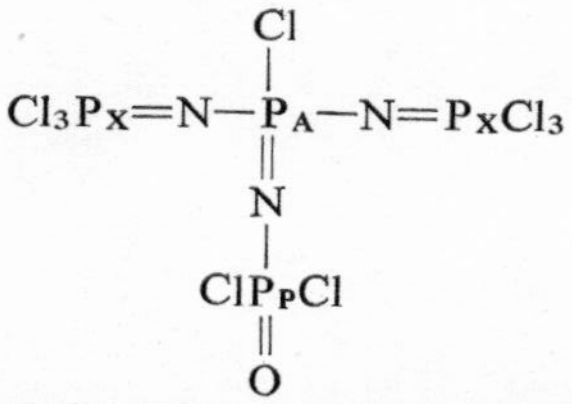	P_A P_X P_P	+ 29·6 + 1·9 + 13·6	$J_{P_AP_X}$ = 28·7 $J_{P_AP_P}$ = 31·0	177

^{31}P chemical shifts for 140 phosphorus compounds are given in reference 302 of Chapter 12.

NAME INDEX—VOLUME 2

Abraham, R. J. 679, 680, 681, 783, 786, 787, 789, 792, 793, 796, 820, 842, 847, 848, 1092
Acrivos, J. V. 1033
Aftandilian, V. D. 984
Agahigian, H. 889, 944
Alei, M. 1048
Alexakos, L. G. 940
Alexander, S. 731, 742, 910
Allerhand, A. 1040
Allred, A. L. 667, 668, 670, 676, 707, 999
Altman, L. J. 749
Ames, T. P. 1077
Amiel, Y. 745
Anderson, C. D. 706, 712
Anderson, D. H. 677, 678
Anderson, E. W. 835
Anderson, J. H. 992, 1050
Anderson, J. M. 688
Anderson, K. K. 901
Anderson, W. A. 1029, 1062, 1064
Andreades, S. 910
Andrew, E. R. 1074
Anet, F. A. L. 685, 690, 696, 707, 801, 814, 816
Ankel, Th. 714
Arison, B. H. 888
Armstrong, J. A. 1081
Arndt, R. 838
Aruldhas, G. 901
Axtmann, R. C. 1062, 1064

Bacon, J. 936
Bak, B. 741, 901, 903
Baker, B. R. 706, 712
Baker, E. B. 687, 797, 989, 1027, 1033, 1051
Baldeschwieler, J. D. 688, 910, 911, 948, 980, 983, 1033, 1039
Banister, A. J. 971
Bannard, R. A. B. 696
Banwell, C. N. 677, 678, 680, 712, 714, 716, 721, 910, 1020
Barber, M. S. 744
Barfield, M. 678
Bates, P. 711
Bauer, S. H. 883, 987
Bawn, C. E. H. 834
Beach, J. Y. 949, 987
Beach, W. F. 721
Beaudet R. A. 911
Becke-Goehring, M. 1075, 1078
Becker, E. D. 792, 793
Belford, G. G. 889
Benedek, G. B. 1081
Ben-Efraim, D. A. 745
Benitez, A. 706, 712
Bensey, F. N. 940
Benson, R. E. 827, 829
Berger, S. B. 1096
Bergstrom, G. 768
Berlin, A. J. 696
Bernstein, H. J. 678, 696, 701, 712, 724, 725, 770, 778, 783, 786, 787, 812, 818, 820, 857, 859, 1029, 1092
Berry, R. S. 775, 949
Bezman, I. I. 1078
Bhacca, N. S. 808
Bigeleisen, J. 893
Binsch, G. 1037
Bishop, E. O. 685, 811
Bither, T. A. 950
Black, P. J. 802
Blay, N. J. 986
Bloembergen, N. 875
Bloom, M. 1100
Blume, P. 1010
Bock, E. 848
Boden, N. 875, 901, 905, 910, 911, 914, 925, 930, 932, 935, 939, 952, 958, 1075
Bonnett, R. 802
Bothner-By, A. A. 670, 676, 678, 680, 681, 690, 692, 697, 723, 724, 727, 742, 745, 747, 749, 750, 842, 851
Bourn, A. J. R. 905, 944, 1037
Bovey, F. A. 719, 770, 781, 812, 829, 831, 833, 835, 836, 956, 1039
Bradbury, A. 1074
Bradley, R. B. 792, 793
Brame, E. G. 956
Bramley, R. 1010, 1047
Brand, J. C. D. 749, 848
Braun, H. 949
Bredenberg, J. B. 812
Brey, W. S. 759, 879, 920
Brockway, L. O. 949

Bromberg, J. P. 1088
Brooke, G. M. 905
Brown, L. C. 886, 957, 1034, 1037
Brown, M. P. 686, 999
Brown, T. H. 957
Brown, T. L. 1087
Brownstein, S. 696, 698, 703, 708, 767, 835, 838, 890, 943, 1098
Brügel, W. 714, 795
Buckingham, A. D. 712, 718, 749, 752, 758, 763, 772, 841, 842, 844, 851, 857, 858, 859, 885, 895, 896, 996, 1092, 1098
Bullock, E. 789, 796
Burbank, R. D. 940
Burdon, J. 905
Burg, A. B. 985
Burke, J. J. 1082
Bywater, S. 838

Cady, G. H. 930, 935, 939, 940, 948
Caldwell, D. J. 827
Callaghan, J. 986
Callis, C. F. 971, 976, 999, 1056, 1061, 1062, 1064, 1068, 1071, 1073, 1076, 1077
Carr, D. T. 879, 962, 1022
Carr, J. B. 701
Carter, R. E. 779
Carter, R. P. 961
Cassidy, H. G. 765
Castellano, S. 680, 715, 719
Cavanaugh, J. R. 669, 674, 676
Cavell, R. G. 952
Cawley, S. 711
Chakravorty, A. 826
Chamberlain, N. F. 761, 820, 833, 976
Chambers, R. D. 905, 946
Chapman, D. 814, 935
Charman, H. B. 747, 749, 850
Charton-Koechlin, M. 751
Chasin, L. A. 1075
Chatt, J. 825, 1097
Cheema, Z. K. 690
Chen, H. Y. 831
Chien, J. C. W. 385
Chivers, T. 905
Christ, H. A. 1047
Chujo, R. 833, 837
Clapp, L. B. 1075
Clark, H. C. 676, 946
Closs, G. L. 692
Closs, L. E. 692
Cobb, T. B. 770
Coffman, D. D. 950
Cohen, A. D. 701, 788, 803, 816, 1020, 1098
Cohn, M. 1074
Connick, R. E. 953, 1094
Connor, T. M. 774
Conradi, J. J. 989
Conroy, H. 680
Corey, E. J. 710, 783, 816
Corio, P. L. 724, 750, 753
Cornwell, C. D. 940
Cotton, F. A. 741, 825, 936, 1010
Coulburn, C. B. 948
Coulson, C. A. 1056
Cox, J. S. G. 811
Cox, P. F. 770
Coyle, T. D. 908, 911, 926, 944, 946, 976
Craig, N. C. 910
Cram, D. J. 814
Crapo, L. M. 876, 885, 935
Crawford, B. 885
Crombie, L. 814
Cross, A. D. 879
Crutchfield, M. M. 1053, 1068
Curtin, D. Y. 814

Daasch, L. W. 1052
Dailey, B. P. 669, 670, 674, 676, 695, 698, 724, 750, 753, 760, 770, 771, 780, 781, 848, 857, 1095
Danti, A. 1010
Danyluk, S. S. 711, 778, 1052
Das, T. P. 901
Dave, L. D. 743
Davis, D. R. 683, 684, 721, 814, 879
Davis, G. T. 875, 901
Davis, J. D. 744
Davison, A. 826
De Boer Th. J. 692
Deck, J. C. 763
De Kowalewski, D. G. 767, 773, 796
Dehl, R. 775
Dehmelt, H. G. 1095
Dessy, R. E. 689, 1027, 1097
Dev, S. 783
Dewar, M. J. S. 685
Dhami, K. S. 1008
Dharmatti, S. S. 1042, 1079, 1081, 1097
Dickerson, R. E. 984
Dickinson, W. C. 1054
Dickson, F. E. 1078
Diehl, P. 754, 756, 758, 847, 952, 1092
Dietrich, M. W. 1115
Dippy, J. F. J. 821
Dischler, V. B. 771
Dittmer, D. C. 688
Dodd, R. E. 936
Dodgen, H. W. 1037

Douglass, D. C. 835
Down, J. L. 741, 825
Drake, J. E. 823, 825
Dresdner, R. D. 889
Drysdale, J. J. 875
Dubb, H. E. 935
Dudek, G. O. 826, 1064
Dudley, F. B. 939
Duncanson, L. A. 825
Dunitz, J. Z. 920
Dunstan, I. 986
Dupont, J. A. 985
Durrell, W. S. 889
Dvolaitzky, M. 763

Eades, R. G. 1074
Eastham, J. F. 690
Eaton, D. R. 827, 828
Eberly, J. H. 1062
Ebersole, S. J. 680 711, 716
Ebsworth, E. A. V. 821, 822, 823, 1052
Edwards, W. R. 833
Eggers, D. F. 930
Eglinton, G. 749, 848
Ehernson, S. 751, 872
Eisih, J. J. 715, 743
Elleman, D. D. 741, 769, 886, 889, 912, 957, 1061
Ell s, J. 792
Elviidge, J. A. 769, 802
Emerson, E. 1097
Emerson, M. T. 848, 874
Emsley, J. W. 875, 901, 905, 910, 911, 914, 925, 930, 932, 935, 939, 958, 1075
Englert, G. 771
Englman, R. 1081
Eriks, K. 984
Ernst, R. 838
Ettinger, R. 1010
Evans, D. F. 688, 689, 742, 743, 872, 876, 889, 894, 902, 912, 1015, 1090, 1091
Ewens, R. V. G. 1010

Fahey, R. C. 685
Farlow, M. W. 950
Farrar, T. C. 677, 678, 946
Farthing, A. C. 758
Fawcett, F. S. 936, 947
Feeney, J. 689, 690, 721, 722, 818, 875, 876, 901, 905, 910, 911, 914, 916, 922, 925, 930, 932, 935, 939, 952, 958, 1064, 1075
Fenton, D. E. 905
Ferguson, R. C. 950
Fessenden, R. W. 770, 1010
Figgis, B. N. 986, 1010, 1042, 1047, 1089, 1090
Filipovich, G. 829, 833, 872
Finegold, H. 1054, 1057, 1061, 1068
Fischer, H. O. L. 705
Fisher, H. D. 979
Flautt, T. J. 689, 1027, 1097
Flitcroft, N. 825, 1086
Fluck, E. 1075, 1076, 1078
Flynn, G. W. 910
Ford, C. T. 1078
Forman, R. A. 1037
Forsén, S. 820, 989
Foster, M. R. 749, 851
Foster, R. G. 802
Fox, I. R. 901
Fox, T. G. 834
Fraenkel, G. 684, 779
Frank-Neumann, M. 688
Frankiss, S. G. 821, 954, 1018, 1022, 1052
Fraser, R. R. 681, 695, 721, 739, 751, 761
Freeman, R. 783, 847, 1079, 1081, 1090
Freeman, R. C. 1072
Frei, K. 1029
Freymann, R. 763, 796
Friedel, R. A. 825, 999
Fujiwara, S. 901
Furuta, S. 814

Gaines, D. F. 820, 980, 986
Gallagher, W. P. 950
Gaoni, Y. 745
Gasser, R. P. H. 1078, 1082, 1090
Gawer, A. 674, 692, 695, 698, 780
George, J. W. 936
Gerding, H. 1052
Gestblom, B. 787, 788, 789, 805
Gibbons, S. G. 977, 980, 981, 983
Gibson, G. W. 690
Gil, V. M. S. 795
Gillespie, R. J. 875, 882, 936
Gillies, D. G. 905, 944
Glazier, E. R. 783
Glick, R. E. 678, 680, 681, 724, 749, 750, 751, 851, 872
Goldenson, J. 971, 992, 1054, 1056, 1061, 1068
Goldstein, J. H. 676, 711, 718, 719, 720, 721, 722, 731, 732, 733, 734, 735, 741, 742, 743, 746, 747, 749, 782, 790, 791, 802, 821, 851, 910, 1011, 1020
Goode, W. E. 384
Goodman, L. 706, 712, 875, 901
Goodwin, S. 806
Gordon, S. 770, 781, 857

Gourse, J. A. 814
Graham, D. M. 677, 999
Graham, J. D. 692, 814, 935, 1027
Grant, D. M. 677, 678, 692, 710, 749, 946, 990, 1011
Gratch, S. 384
Gray, A. P. 944
Green, M. L. H. 744, 825, 838
Greenwood, N. N. 971
Griffith, J. S. 1078, 1081, 1095
Griffith, W. P. 825
Groenweghe, L. C. D. 1059, 1060, 1076
Gronowitz, S. 740, 741, 749, 787, 788, 789, 802, 803, 805
Grundmann, C. 889
Grunwald, E. 1040
Guffy, J. C. 1076
Günther, H. 727
Gutowsky, H. S. 666, 677, 678, 680, 681, 692, 701, 710, 712, 752, 817, 819, 820, 823, 874, 875, 876, 878, 880, 883, 889, 897, 901, 903, 905, 940, 944, 949, 976, 1011, 1018, 1052, 1054, 1055, 1056, 1058, 1090, 1092, 1093
Guy, J. 676

Hall, G. G. 795
Hall, L. D. 680, 696
Halton, J. V. 689
Hamer, A. N. 942
Hammett, L. P. 752, 889
Happe, J. A. 742
Happe, J. H. 1087
Hardisson, A. 795
Harker, D. 984
Harris, J. F. 940
Harris, R. K. 696, 885, 916, 935, 958, 959, 1018
Hatton, J. V. 746, 747, 749, 849, 1091, 1097
Hawthorne, M. F. 975, 984, 985, 986
Hayakawa, N. 751
Heathcock, L. 765
Hedberg, K. 978, 981, 983
Heffernan, M. L. 802, 939, 950
Herbison-Evans, D. 1034
Hindman, J. C. 957
Hirschfeld, F. L. 984
Hirst, R. C. 749
Hobgood, R. T. 721, 741, 742, 743, 821, 1011
Hoehn, H. H. 963
Hoffman, C. J. 874, 880, 928, 940, 1093
Hoffman, R. A. 740, 741, 749, 768, 787, 788, 789, 802, 803, 805
Hofman, W. 670
Holder, B. E. 928, 1034, 1037, 1041
Holker, J. S. E. 680
Hollis, I. S. 1041
Holloway, C. E. 677, 999
Holm, C. H. 875, 901, 903, 989, 1011
Holm, R. H. 826, 828
Holmes, J. R. 683, 874, 947, 1087
Holmes, R. R. 950, 961
Holtzman, G. R. 992, 1050
Homer, J. 916, 922
Hopkins, C. Y. 812
Hopkins, R. C. 980, 983
Hornfeld, A. 787, 788, 789
Horrocks, W. D. 828
Hough, L. 680
Howard, B. B. 848, 874
Howden, M. E. H. 695
Hruska, F. 682, 848
Huggett, C. M. 684
Huggins, C. M. 816
Huggins, M. L. 668
Hughes, T. R. 1074
Huitric, A. C. 701
Hunsberger, I. M. 817
Hunt, J. P. 1037
Hutton, H. M. 695, 1027

Inukai, K. 927, 956
Irani, R. R. 1071
Ishiguro, E. 1092
Isobe, T. 927, 956
Ito, K. 820, 927, 956, 977
Itzel, J. F. 1094

Jackman, L. M. 692, 695, 696, 729, 735, 737, 744, 745, 795, 802
Jackson, A. H. 792, 793
Jackson, J. A. 1048
Jacques, J. 763
Jaffé, H. 689, 1027, 1097
Jardetzky, C. D. 812, 814, 831
Jardetzky, O. 802, 812, 814, 831, 1092
Jenks, G. J. 1074
Jensen, F. R. 696
John, K. 1075
Johnson, C. E. 719, 770, 781
Johnson, C. S. 742
Johnson, F. A. 948
Johnson, J. F. 829
Johnson, L. F. 806, 814
Johnson, R. W. 920
Johnson, U. 834, 835
Johnson, W. S. 680, 706

Jolly, W. L. 823, 825, 928
Jonathan, N. 770, 781
Jones, E. D. 1097
Jones, M. E. 981, 983
Jones, R. 983, 984, 985
Jones, R. A. Y. 1054, 1061, 1074
Jones, R. C. 971, 976, 999, 1056, 1061
Josey, A. D. 788, 827, 828
Juan, C. 681, 823, 1011, 1018, 1052, 1058
Julg, A. 781
Juvinall, G. L. 1061

Kaesz, H. D. 825, 1086, 1087
Kanda, T. 1034, 1096
Kaneker, C. R. 1079
Kaplan, F. 681
Karabatsos, G. J. 716, 814, 1011, 1027
Karplus, M. 677, 678, 681, 684, 695, 710, 711, 712, 741, 748, 823, 901, 957, 993, 1011
Kasiwaga, H. 729
Kasper, J. S. 984
Katritzky, A. R. 802, 1054, 1061, 1074
Keller, R. E. 1115
Kennedy, A. 948
Kenner, G. W. 792, 793
Kern, C. W. 819, 820, 825, 838, 957
Kidd, R. G. 1042
Kincaid, J. F. 684
Kinell, P. O. 768
King, R. B. 926
Kirkwood, J. G. 831
Kivelson, D. 683
Klanberg, F. 1037
Klein, M. P. 1034, 1037, 1041
Klinck, R. E. 765
Klose, G. 689
Knight, W. D. 1054
Kobayashi, Y. 1075
Kober, E. 889
Komiyama, J. 838
Kopchick, R. M. 711
Korinek, G. J. 749, 854
Koth, W. 992, 1050
Kowalewski, V. J. 767, 773, 796
Kratzer, R. 985
Kreevoy, M. M. 747, 749, 850
Krespan, C. G. 896, 926
Kruekeberg, F. 714
Kubo, N. 820, 977
Kuhlmann, K. 946
Kullnig, R. K. 679, 696, 701
Kun, K. A. 765
Kuntz, I. D. 1040
Kurland, R. J. 677, 678, 712
Kyogoku, H. 838
Kwon, J. T. 676

La Force, R. C. 1042
La Lancette, E. A. 828
La Mar, G. N. 828
Lambert, J. D. 1037
Lancaster, J. E. 1128
Lagowski, J. M. 802
Landesman, H. 971, 973, 974, 978, 984, 987
Landis, P. W. 879
Lanford, C. A. 695
Langkammerer, C. M. 926
Larmann, J. P. 1019
Lasoski, S. W. 955
Laszlo, P. 814, 842
Lauterbur, P. C. 677, 678, 692, 712, 752, 779, 794, 875, 888, 890, 912, 930, 971, 988, 995, 999, 1001, 1004, 1005, 1008, 1009, 1010, 1011, 1027, 1050, 1054, 1056, 1061, 1068, 1082, 1086
Lawson, K. D. 759
Lazdins, D. 957
Leane, J. B. 767, 770
Ledwith, A. 721, 722, 834
Lee, J. 792, 885
Lee, W. W. 706, 712
Leftin, H. P. 775
Lehn, J. M. 688, 695
Lehnsen, J. I. 1128
Leipert, T. 1092
Lemieux, R. U. 679, 681, 696, 701
Lemon, R. F. 744
Lemons, J. F. 1048
Leroy, M. A. 751
Levenberg, M. I. 744
Lewis, I. C. 751, 901
Libermann, D. 796
Lichtenthaler, F. W. 705
Linder, B. 848, 874
Lippert, E. L. 984
Lipscomb, R. D. 936, 947
Lipscomb, W. N. 819, 820, 825, 826, 975, 981, 983, 984
Lister, M. W. 1010
Loewenstein, A. 1040
Lohr, L. L. 1128
Lord, R. C. 881
Lowe, J. U. 986
Lown, J. W. 814
Lowry, B. R. 684
Lucht, C. M. 984
Lumbroso, N. 848
Lustig, M. 986, 1011
Lutz, R. P. 683, 684, 814

Lynch, M. A. 881
Lynden-Bell, R. M. 677, 678, 680, 712, 1011, 1029

Maarsen, J. W. 1052
Macdiarmid, A. G. 822
Maciel, G. E. 992, 1009
Mack, J. L. 986
Mackellar, F. 809
Mackenzie, J. D. 874, 947
Mackor, E. L. 775, 777, 779, 781
Maclean, C. 775, 777, 779, 781
Maher, J. P. 688, 689, 742, 1090, 1091
Mahler, W. 949, 961
Maier, L. 1059, 1060, 1074
Malinowski, E. 1017, 1019
Malm, J. G. 957
Manabe, Y. 838
Manatt, S. L. 716, 741, 769, 889, 912, 1061
Mandell, L. 718, 746, 747, 749, 851, 910
Manson, J. A. 685
Marcus, S. H. 820
Mark, V. 744
Marshall, T. W. 1092
Martin, J. S. 760, 771
Massey, A. G. 670, 905
Masuda, Y. 1034, 1095
Mathis, C. T. 802
Matsushima, M. 910
McAdams, D. R. 1011
McCall, D. W. 752, 883, 897, 903, 944, 949, 976, 1054, 1056
McCallum, K. 948
McCasland, G. E. 814
McClure, G. R. 732, 746, 747, 749, 851
McClure, R. E. 701
McConnell, H. M. 678, 684, 695, 724, 741, 772, 875, 908, 910, 1096
McCoy, C. R. 670
McFarlane, W. 826
McGarvey, B. R. 680, 752, 808, 816, 897, 903, 1090, 1093
McGreer, D. E. 739, 802
McLachlan, A. 779
McLaren, G. A. 989
McLauchlan, K. A. 680, 712, 772, 788, 803, 1098
McLean, A. D. 875, 908, 910
McMahon, P. E. 680, 878, 889
Meiboom, S. 1040
Memory, J. D. 770
Merrill, C. I. 930, 939, 948
Metzger, L. C. 948
Meyer, L. H. 666, 701, 752, 820, 875, 883, 897, 903, 1055
Middleton, W. J. 916
Miller, G. R. 1076
Miller, H. C. 984
Miller, J. J. 986
Miller, R. 703, 708
Miller, S. I. 820
Milner, R. S. 826
Mitra, S. S. 789, 796
Mochel, V. D. 677, 905
Moedritzer, K. 1059, 1060, 1072
Moir, R. Y. 701
Moodie, R. B. 774
Moore, D. W. 742, 1087
Morgan, G. L. 1087
Moritz, A. G. 676, 697
Morman, J. F. 749, 848
Moy, D. 1097
Muetterties, E. L. 883, 937, 939, 940, 942, 947, 949, 950, 952, 954, 961, 984, 1101
Muller, N. 696, 698, 700, 709, 879, 890, 930, 962, 971, 977, 992, 1011, 1018, 1022, 1028, 1054, 1056, 1061, 1068
Murray, G. R. 1079, 1081
Murrell, J. N. 795
Musher, J. I. 667, 674, 676, 680, 685, 697, 698, 700, 703, 707, 709, 811, 816, 842
Myers, O. E. 1096

Naar-Colin, C. 670, 676, 690, 692, 697, 723, 724, 727, 742, 747
Nagai, E. 833, 837
Nair, P. M. 885
Nakagawa, N. 729
Nam, B. 758
Namikawa, K. 997, 1000
Narasimhan, P. T. 676, 680, 687, 688, 697, 724, 748, 1027, 1040, 1077, 1087
Nash, C. P. 1009
Naylor, R. E. 955
Neglia, M. J. 1128
Neikam, W. C. 674, 695, 698, 780
Newmark, R. A. 889
Ng, S. 879
Nicholson, C. R. 695
Nicksic, S. W. 829
Nielsen, M. L. 1048
Nielson, M. L. 1078
Nikagawa, T. 1019
Nishioka, A. 833
Nist, B. J. 684, 692, 695, 701
Niva, J. 729
Noggle, J. H. 948
Nordlander, J. E. 689, 690
Nordman, C. E. 981

Noyce, D. S. 696
Nyholm, R. S. 1010, 1042, 1047

Odiyama, A. 829
Ogg, R. A. 818, 819, 944, 946, 952, 977, 981, 987, 1034, 1037, 1039, 1040
Ohashi, S. 1077
Oliver, J. P. 1097
Onak, T. P. 971, 973, 974, 975, 978, 984, 986, 987
Onsager, L. 935
O'Reilly, D. E. 775, 1093
Orgel, L. E. 1047, 1078, 1079, 1081, 1095, 1100
Orzech, C. E. 1027
Ozeki, T. 837

Pachler, K. G. R. 679, 680, 681
Packer, K. J. 935, 959, 961, 1101
Pariser, R. 781
Parker, C. O. 948
Parker, D. J. 989
Parks, J. R. 1057
Parshall, G. W. 984
Patel, D. M. 695
Paterson, W. G. 817
Patterson, A. 1010
Paul, E. G. 990
Paulson, R. E. 953, 1094
Payne, J. H. 1076
Pearce, C. D. 889
Perrin, D. D. 812
Perrin, D. R. 812
Peterson, G. E. 961
Petrakis, L. 859, 876, 935
Phillips, W. D. 688, 827, 828, 875, 883, 885, 916, 920, 921, 937, 940, 942, 947, 954
Pidcock, A. 1097
Pier, E. A. 984, 1053, 1073, 1077
Piette, L. H. 1039, 1041, 1100
Pilling, R. L. 984
Pimental, G. C. 816
Pinnow, P. 949
Piper, T. S. 743, 825
Pitcher, E. 885, 895, 896, 926, 996
Pollara, L. Z. 1019
Poole, C. P. 1094
Pople, J. A. 677, 712, 719, 721, 724, 725, 770, 778, 818, 820, 858, 875, 901, 947, 993
Porte, A. L. 712, 817
Porter, R. S. 829
Powell, D. B. 1097
Powles, J. G. 829
Pratt, L. 744, 825, 826, 963
Price, E. 901
Price, W. C. 978, 987
Primas, H. 838
Pritchard, D. E. 977, 1011
Proctor, W. G. 1034, 1078, 1081, 1095, 1097, 1102
Prohaska, C. A. 1064
Prosser, F. 875, 901
Pustinger, J. V. 838, 1048, 1078

Quail, J. W. 875, 882, 936

Ramey, K. C. 879
Ramsey, N. F. 1011, 1078, 1079, 1092
Randall, E. W. 905, 944, 948, 1033, 1037, 1040
Ransch, M. D. 744
Rao, B. D. N. 771, 797
Rao, K. J. S. 1042, 1081
Rätz, R. 889
Rausch, M. D. 744
Ray, J. D. 818, 946, 987, 1034, 1037, 1039, 1041
Raynes, W. T. 857, 859
Reddy, G. S. 676, 711, 718, 719, 720, 721, 722, 731, 733, 734, 735, 742, 743, 746, 747, 749, 782, 790, 791, 821, 851, 1011, 1020
Reeves, L. W. 676, 706, 816, 817, 825, 925, 944, 1015
Reid, C. 816
Reilly, C. A. 681, 682, 692, 695, 875, 908, 909, 910, 914
Retcofsky, H. L. 999
Reuben, J. 1043, 1048
Reynolds, G. F. 689, 1027, 1097
Reynolds, W. F. 674, 997, 1027
Richards, J. H. 721, 744, 779
Richards, R. E. 703, 746, 747, 749, 767, 770, 771, 811, 849, 903, 1034, 1078, 1079, 1081, 1082, 1090, 1097
Richardson, W. H. 814
Riehl, J. 695
Rigden, J. S. 980, 983
Rinehart, K. L. 814
Roberts, B. W. 1037
Roberts, J. D. 681, 683, 684, 689, 690, 692, 695, 721, 740, 748, 749, 814, 819, 876, 879, 885, 919, 1027, 1037, 1040
Roberts, J. E. 939
Roberts, H. L. 936
Robinson, L. B. 1100
Rocard, J. M. 1100
Rochow, E. G. 667, 668, 676, 707, 927, 999

Rogers, M. T. 676, 680, 687, 688, 692, 695, 696, 697, 715, 724, 743, 748, 808, 880, 935, 1027, 1040, 1077, 1087
Rose, P. I. 1018
Rosenberg, R. M. 937
Roth, G. C. 1071
Rowland, T. J. 1088
Ruben, G. C. 992
Rupprecht, A. 989

Saika, A. 666, 819, 820, 874, 875, 876, 889, 901, 903, 971
Samuel, D. 1043, 1048
Satoh, S. 833, 837
Sauer, J. A. 829
Saunders, M. 831, 935
Savitsky, G. B. 997, 1000, 1007, 1009
Schaefer, T. 674, 682, 695, 710, 712, 714, 741, 749, 766, 771, 779, 781, 794, 798, 799, 812, 841, 842, 844, 848, 851, 855, 858, 902, 903, 997, 1027
Schaeffer, R. 820, 977, 980, 983, 984, 985, 986
Schleyer, P. R., von 814, 1040
Schmidt, B. M. 1034, 1037
Schmutzler, R. 949, 961
Schneider, W. G. 668, 674, 689, 696, 701, 710, 712, 724, 725, 749, 750, 751, 752, 766, 770, 778, 779, 781, 794, 798, 806, 818, 841, 842, 844, 851, 854, 855, 858, 995, 997, 999, 1002, 1007, 1039, 1092, 1097, 1098
Schnell, E. 927
Schomacher, V. 920, 978, 980, 983
Schreiner, F. 957
Schroeder, H. 889
Schug, J. C. 680, 763, 878
Schumb, W. C. 881
Schwartzmann, E. 1076, 1077
Sederholm, C. H. 696, 876, 879, 885, 889, 935
Seiffert, W. 802
Seyferth, D. 742, 927
Shapiro, B. L. 711, 716
Shapiro, I. 971, 973, 974, 977, 978, 980, 981, 983, 984, 986, 987, 1011
Sharkey, W. H. 916
Sharp, D. W. A. 774
Sharts, C. M. 876, 919, 1027
Shaw, B. L. 825, 981, 1097
Shaw, D. 670
Shen, T. Y. 888
Sheppard, N. 676, 677, 678, 680, 696, 697, 701, 712, 714, 716, 721, 774, 910, 916, 981, 1011, 1020, 1029, 1097
Sheppard, W. A. 828, 939, 940
Shimizu, H. 833, 901
Shoolery, J. N. 666, 670, 676, 695, 696, 724, 741, 748, 797, 806, 808, 812, 814, 816, 883, 885, 901, 903, 916, 939, 971, 976, 977, 983, 984, 985, 987, 989, 994, 999, 1011, 1012, 1027, 1039, 1056, 1061, 1062, 1064, 1068, 1073, 1076
Shreeve, J. M. 935
Shufler, S. L. 825
Shuler, W. E. 1062, 1064
Shulman, R. G. 1047
Siddall, T. H. 1064
Sidgwick, N. V. 1091
Siebrand, W. 689, 1097
Siegel, B. 986
Silbiger, G. 883
Singer, L. A. 814
Slichter, C. P. 829, 874, 883, 944, 949, 971, 976, 1054, 1056
Slomp, G. 680, 783, 808, 809, 811, 816
Slowinski, E. J. 881
Smidt, J. 692
Smith, D. C. 1052
Smith, D. F. 940
Smith, E. A. 875, 883
Smith, G. W. 670, 760, 1052, 1086
Smith, J. A. S. 1097
Smith, J. W. 726
Smith, T. S. 875, 883
Snyder, E. I. 740, 748, 749
Snyder, H. R. 788
Solomon, I. 875
Somers, B. G. 677
Sondheimer, F. 745
Spell, A. 684
Speziale, A. J. 1072
Spiesecke, H. 668, 674, 750, 751, 752, 781, 995, 999, 1002, 1007
Stafford, S. L. 688, 908, 911, 926, 946, 976
Stefanik, L. 670, 1034
Stehling, F. C. 729, 760, 835, 837
Stephen, M. J. 1092
Sternberg, H. W. 825
Stevens, J. D. 681
Stevens, R. M. 825
Steward, B. B. 874, 947
Stewart, R, 774
Stewart, W. E. 719, 722, 1011
Stone, F. G. A. 885, 895, 896, 908, 911, 926, 927, 944, 946, 976, 996
Stothers, J. B. 765, 1008, 1009
Strobel, J. 1048
Strohmeier, W. 744
Strømme, K. O. 706
Stroupe, J. D. 684
Summitt, R. 715, 743, 880

Sunners, B. 1039
Sutcliffe, L. H. 689, 690, 721, 722, 818, 875, 876, 885, 901, 905, 910, 911, 914, 916, 922, 925, 930, 932, 935, 939, 952, 958, 1064, 1075
Sutton, L. E. 1091
Svatos, G. F. 890, 930
Swalen, J. D. 681, 692, 695, 908, 909
Swift, H. E. 1094

Taft, R. W. 716, 751, 752, 875, 899, 901, 1064
Takahashi, M. 879
Takeda, M. 812
Tang, J. 879
Tarrant, P. 920
Tatlow, J. C. 905
Taube, H. 1048
Taurins, A. 806
Tebbe, F. 820, 983, 984
Tessmar, K. 684
Thomas, L. F. 916, 922
Thompson, D. S. 889
Tiers, G. V. D. 812, 829, 831, 833, 836, 872, 874, 875, 888, 893, 895, 911, 912, 915, 916, 920, 932, 956, 988, 1039, 1092
Tillieu, J. 676, 719
Tincher, W. C. 836
Tipman, N. R. 817
Tobinaga, S. 783
Tolbert, B. M. 1042
Tori, K. 1019
Tosch, W. C. 696, 698, 700, 709
Townes, C. H. 1095
Trager, W. F. 701
Trainor, J. T. 715, 743
Treichel, P. 926
Trenner, N. R. 888
Tuite, R. J. 788
Turner, J. J. 680, 701, 821, 822, 823, 1020, 1052
Tzalmona, A. 1048

Uehling, E. A. 1097
Ulrich, H. 889
Urbanski, T. 670, 1034

Van der Waals, J. H. 775, 779
Van Dyke, C. H. 822
Vane, F. M. 716, 814, 1027
Van Meurs, N. 685
Van Wazer, J. R. 971, 976, 999, 1053, 1056, 1061, 1062, 1064, 1068, 1073, 1076, 1077
Vaughan, W. R. 775
Venanzi, L. M. 1097
Venkateswarlu, P. 771, 797, 901
Verdier, P. H. 957
Vickers, G. D. 944
Vijayaraghaban, R. 1042, 1081
Vinard, D. R. 747, 749, 850
Vladimiroff, T. 1017

Walchli, H. E. 1097
Walker, J. F. 685
Walsh, A. D. 692
Watanabe, H. 820, 833, 977
Watson, C. J. 792, 793
Watterson, K. F. 963
Watts, V. S. 711
Waugh, J. S. 715, 718, 742, 770, 936, 1010
Weaver, H. E. 1042, 1096, 1097, 1100
Webster, D. E. 686, 821, 999
Weedon, B. C. L. 744
Weiner, M. A. 742
Weiss, E. 1010
Wells, E. J. 676, 825, 925, 1015
Wells, P. R. 814
Wender, I. 825
Wertz, J. E. 1092, 1095
Whiffen, D. H. 783
Whipple, E. B. 719, 722, 726, 731, 732, 746, 747, 749, 851, 910, 957, 1011
White, R. F. M. 939, 950
Whitesides, G. M. 690
Whitman, D. R. 935
Wiberg, K. B. 684, 692, 695
Wiles, D. M. 835
Wiley, R. H. 729, 735, 737
Wilkinson, G. 741, 743, 744, 825, 826, 838, 963
Williams, D. 808, 886, 957, 1034, 1037
Williams, G. A. 741, 875, 901, 903
Williams, J. 986
Williams, R. E. 971, 973, 974, 977, 978, 979 980, 982, 983, 984, 986, 987, 1011
Williams, R. L. 986
Williamson, K. L. 680, 695, 706
Williamson, S. M. 930
Willis, C. J. 946
Wilson, C. O. 979
Wilson, C. W. 955
Wimett, T. F. 1092
Wishnia, A. 831
Witanowski, M. 670, 1034
Wolfsberg, M. 893
Wolovsky, R. 745
Woodward, A. E. 829
Woodward, L. A. 936

Worsfold, D. J. 838
Wu, T. K. 760, 848
Wyluda, B. J. 1047

Yamaguchi, I. 751, 833
Yonemoto, T. 674, 997
Yoshino, T. 838

Young, J. A. 889
Young, W. G. 689
Yu, F. C. 1034, 1078, 1081, 1095, 1097, 1102

Zimmerman, J. R. 749, 851
Zürcher, R. F. 676, 811
Zweig, A. 1128

SUBJECT INDEX

The heaviness of the type indicates the importance of an entry: page numbers in bold type can signify that a topic runs on for several pages.

Acetaldehyde *273*
Acetaldehydes (dichloro-), ^{1}H double resonance spectrum 461
hydration of *533*
Acetic acid, ^{13}C spectrum 991, 993
Acetone, as a solvent 259
Acetonitrile, effect of solvents on ^{1}H chemical shift **846**
Acetoxycholestonanes, ^{1}H spectra *706*
Acetylenes
^{13}C spectral parameters 1001, 1030
effect of solvents on ^{1}H chemical shifts *749*, **848**
^{1}H chemical shifts **745**
H–H coupling constants 746, **748**
Addition compounds of BF_3 528
^{27}Al chemical shifts
of alkyls 1094
of salts 1094
^{27}Al resonance 1093
line widths 1094
Alcohols
hydrogen bonding in **542**
^{17}O chemical shifts 1045
Aldehydes
aromatic
^{13}C spectral parameters **1001, 1005**
^{1}H chemical shifts **765**
long range H–H coupling constants *767*
H–^{13}C coupling constants 1020
^{17}O chemical shifts 1045
Aldopyranoses (acetylated), ^{1}H spectra 704
Aliphatic
acids, ^{17}O chemical shifts 1045
fluorocarbons, calculations of coupling constants **183**
Alkaloids, ^{1}H spectral parameters 806
Alkanes
^{1}H chemical shifts **666**
H–H *geminal* coupling constants 677
H–H *vicinal* coupling constants 678
Alkenes
anomalous ^{1}H chemical shifts **719**
Alkenes, ^{13}C chemical shifts 999
^{13}C–^{13}C coupling constants 1030
cis and *trans* ^{1}H chemical shifts 729
correlation of ^{1}H chemical shifts with
group dipole moments 718
Hammett σ constants **717**
substituent electronegativity *717*
correlation of H–H coupling constants with substituent electronegativity **714**
effect of methyl group substitution on ^{1}H chemical shifts **733**
^{1}H chemical shifts 727, 731, 732, 736, 737, 743, 744, 745
H–H coupling constants 710, 726, 727, 731, 732, 735, 739
^{1}H spectra **710**
Alkenes (metal)
^{1}H chemical shifts 742
H–H coupling constants 743
Alkyls (metal), coupling constants 689
Allyl magnesium bromide, ^{1}H spectrum *689*
Amides
calculation of internal chemical shift **133**
hydrogen bonding of *548*
rotational isomerism **553**
proton exchange 510
Amines, hydrogen bonding 548
Amino acids, ^{1}H chemical shifts 812
Ammonia
calculation of H–H coupling constant **183**
calculation of hydrogen bond shift **538**
^{14}N spectrum 1031, *1093*
Ammonium ion
^{1}H double resonance spectrum 458, 459, 460
^{14}N INDOR spectrum 1033
proton transfer 498, *510*
derivatives, ^{14}N spectra 1038
Analysis
AB spin system **310**
direct method of analysis **438**
double irradiation (weak field) 472

Analysis, effect of electric fields on *464*
energy levels 317
theoretical spectra 320
transition energies 318
AX spin system, double resonance behaviour 247, 462
AB_2 spin system **320**
basic product functions 323
diagonal matrix elements 323
electric field effects *464*
energy levels 324
relative intensities 325
theoretical spectra 327, **625**
AX_2 spin system, double resonance behaviour 462, 463
AB_3 spin system **329**
diagonal matrix elements 331
relative intensities 332
theoretical spectra 333, **629**
transition energies 332
AX_3 spin system
double resonance behaviour 247
electric field effects on *464*
AB_4 spin system **337**
eigenfunctions 337
eigenvalues 337
relative intensities 339, **635**
spin product functions 336
theoretical spectra 340, **635**
transition frequencies 339, **635**
AB_6 spin system *660*
AB_n spin system **341**
general features of spectra **341**
relative intensities 343
sub-spectra 342
transition frequencies 343
A_2B_2 spin system **347**
relative intensities 349
theoretical spectra 350, **645**
transition frequencies 349
A_2X_2 spin system *347*
A_2B_6 spin system *660*
A_3B_2 spin system **351**
combined transitions 354
relative intensities 352, 353
sub-states 351
theoretical spectra 355, **649**
transition frequencies 352, 353
A_pB_n spin system **344**
general features of spectra **344**
numbers of transitions 346
A_nX_2 spin system, double resonance behaviour *463*
A_nX_m spin system, double resonance behaviour *463*
ABC spin system **372**

Analysis, ABK approximation method **375**
complete solution 378
diagonal matrix elements 373, 382
double irradiation (weak field) 473
eigenvalues 381
intensity sum rule 380
spectrum (^1H) of styrene 381
spectrum (^1H) of vinyl bromide 711
subtraction rules 383
Sudhanshu's method *387*
trace invariance of sub-matrix 379
ABK spin system 376
energy levels 376
styrene oxide, ^1H spectrum 377
wavefunctions 376
ABT spin system *660*
ABX spin system 357
deceptively simple spectra **363**, 364
diagonal matrix elements 357
energy levels 359
relative intensities 360
styrene oxide, ^1H spectrum 362
subtraction rules 361
theoretical spectra 362, 449
transition energies 360
APX spin system
signs of coupling constants **466**
triple resonance spectrum 476
AB_2C spin system 391, *660*
off-diagonal elements 392
AB_2X spin system *660*
ABX_2 spin system **388**
diagonal matrix elements 389
relative intensities 390
spectrum of 2,3-dichloropropene-1 (^1H) 388
transition energies 390
ABPX spin system *660*
ABXY spin system *660*
AA′BB′ spin system 348, **399**
explicit energy expressions 401
^1H spectra of benzenes (*p*-substituted) **408**, 414
ethanes (1,2-substituted) 415, **566**
^1H spectrum of benzofurazan 407, 408, 409
benzene (*p*-bromochloro-) 414
ethane (1,2-bromochloro-) 415
napthalene 405, 406
matrix elements 400
relative intensities 402, 410
relative signs of coupling constants 404
theoretical spectra 404, 413
transition energies 402, 410

Analysis, AA′XX′ spin system **392**
^{19}F spectrum of benzene (1,2-difluoro 3,4,5,6-tetrafluoro) 399
^{19}F spectrum of ethylene (1,1-difluoro-) 397
^{1}H spectrum of ethylene (1,1-difluoro-) 397
matrix elements 393, 394, 395
theoretical spectra 396, 404, 413, 449
transition energies 396
AA′KL spin system *661*
ABKL spin system *661*
ABCX spin system **423**, *660*
matrix elements 424
ABCD spin system **425**
ABKY approximation 427
^{1}H spectrum of glycidaldehyde 428
matrix elements 428
$A_2A'_2X$ spin system *661*
ABB′CC′ spin system *662*
AA′BB′X spin system **416**, *661*
^{19}F spectrum of *para*-fluoroaniline **419**
^{1}H spectrum of *para*-fluoroaniline **419**
matrix elements 417
relative intensities 419, 420, 421
symmetrised spin functions 417
transition energies 419, 420, 421
wavefunctions 418
AB_2X_2 spin system *661*
AA′PP′X spin system *661*
ABC_3 spin system *392*, *660*
ABX_3 spin system *660*
AB_4X spin system *660*
AA′A″A‴XX′ spin system *662*
A_3B_2C spin system **392**
A_3B_2X spin system 370
^{1}H spectrum of phosphorus triethyl 371
A_3BCD spin system *662*
A_3BCX spin system *662*
ABB′CC′D spin system *662*
ABB′CC′X spin system *662*, *1092*
$ABCDX_2$ spin system *662*
$ABCX_3$ spin system, double irradiation of *476*
ABP_3X spin system, double irradiation of 469
A_nBX_p spin system **365**
general features of spectrum 368
numbers of transitions 369, 370
relative intensities 367
sub-spectra 366
transition frequencies 367
$A_mK_n\ldots X_r$ spin system *662*
$A_nBP_qX_p$ spin system 370
$AA'X_3X'_3$ spin system *660*, *661*
Analysis, $AA'X_nX'_n$ spin system *660*
$AA'A''X_3X'_3X''_3$ spin system *661*
$AA'PP'P''P'''X_2$ spin system *661*
of spectra **280**
aids **442**
complex particle method 345
direct method **435**
double irradiation **455**
double quantum transitions **453**
effect of rotational isomerism **560**
electronic computation **451**
isotopic substitution **445**
moment method **431**
perturbation theory **428**
rules 309
quantitative 211, **234**
Anilines (*p*-fluoro)
coupling constants 422
^{19}F spectrum 421
^{1}H spectrum 422
Anisotropy
effect of neighbour *131*
of shielding constants 94, **113**
of C–C and C–H bonds **135**, 676, 696
of C–X bonds **136**
Annulenes, ^{1}H chemical shifts 745
Anthracene, ^{1}H spectrum 773
Antimony pentafluoride
^{19}F spectral parameters 928
^{19}F spectrum 929
^{121}Sb resonance of $NaSbF_6$ 1097
Aqueous electrolytes **511**, 514
Area of bands **234**
Aromatic
compounds, *see* Benzenes
as solvents 258
calculation of chemical shifts **140**, 145, **149**, **595**, 770
calculation of coupling constants **180**
charge densities in **149**
effect of solvents on ^{1}H chemical shifts **851**
H–H coupling constants **770**
molecular complexes 529
polynuclear, ^{1}H chemical shifts *770*
ions, ^{1}H chemical shifts **774**
Arsenic (^{75}As) resonance *1097*
Association, *see* Hydrogen bonding
Atomic orbitals, calculation of shielding constant **121**
Average energy approximations **71**, 106
Azulene
calculation of internal chemical shift **146**
^{1}H spectrum 778
carbonium ion, ^{1}H spectrum 778

^{11}B chemical shifts **971, 974**
of boron halides and derivatives **972, 974**
of boron hydrides and derivatives **972, 974**
Barrier to internal rotation, nature of **573**
Basic
product functions 297
symmetry functions 298
construction of **299**
of D_4 point group 304
Benzaldehydes, H–H coupling constants 277
1,2-Benzanthracene (9,10-dimethyl-), carbonium ion 776
^1H spectrum 776
Benzene
as a solvent 258
chloro- and deuterochloro-, ^1H spectra 751
isopropyl-, ^1H spectrum 6
meta-dinitro-, ^1H spectrum
in acetone 444
in benzene 444
monofluoro-, ^{19}F spectrum 446
monofluoro-2,3,5,6-D_4-, ^1H spectrum 446
monofluoro-2,4,6-D_3-, ^{19}F and ^1H spectra 447
ortho-dimethoxy-, ^{13}C spectrum 1008
para-chlorobromo-, ^1H spectrum 414
para-methylnitro-, effect of solvents on ^1H spectrum 853
2,3,5,6-tetrachloro-, ^1H spectrum with ^{13}C satellites 1023
Benzenes
^{13}C–^{13}C coupling constants 1030
^{13}C–H satellite spectra **1022**
H–H coupling constants 403, **770**
ortho-disubstituted, analysis of spectra 403, 405
para-disubstituted, effect of solvents on ^1H chemical shifts **852**
^1H spectra **408**
proton exchange with HF 511
alkoxy, ^1H chemical shifts 764
disubstituted, ^1H chemical shifts
correlation with Hammett σ constants 758
empirical calculations **754, 1140**
fluorinated
^{19}F chemical shifts correlation with Hammett σ constants **897**
F–F coupling constants **901**
H–F coupling constants **901**
halo-, ^1H chemical shifts 760
Benzenes, hydroxy-, ^1H chemical shifts *763*
monosubstituted
^{13}C chemical shift correlation with Hammett σ constants 753
^{13}C spectral parameters **1002**
^1H chemical shifts **750**
correlation with Hammett σ constants **752**
of *meta* nuclei 752
of *ortho* nuclei 752
of *para* nuclei 752
trisubstituted, ^1H chemical shifts 767
Benzofurazan, ^1H spectrum 407, 408, 409
Binary fluorides, correlation of ^{19}F chemical shifts
and coupling constants **880**
with electronegativity 882
Biot–Savat law 67, 79
Biphenyls 767
Bloch
equations **34**, 38
including chemical exchange **482**, 505
susceptibilities 39
Boltzmann distribution of nuclei 17
Borane
hexa-, ^{11}B spectrum 982, 984
tetra-, ^{11}B spectrum 981
undeca-, ^{11}B spectrum 984
deca-, ^{11}B spectra 982, 984
penta-, ^{11}B spectra 981, 985
Borohydrides, ^{11}B spectral parameters 987
Boron
alkyls, ^{11}B spectral parameters 975
halides *528*, *532*, **971**, **974**, 976, 987
^{11}B spectral parameters **971, 974**
complexes 952, 973
^{19}F spectra of mixed halides 945
^{19}F spectral parameters **944**
hydrides, ^{11}B spectral parameters 972, 974, **977**
deuteration 533
tetrafluoride ion, ^{19}F spectral parameters 946
^{79}Br and ^{81}Br resonance of Br^-_{aq} *517*
^{81}Br resonance of HBr *1096*
Bridge circuits **217**
Bromine
pentafluoride 943
trifluoride *942*
Bulk suceptibility correction **260**
Butadiene–isoprene copolymer, ^1H spectrum 832
Butanes (2,3-disubstituted)
^1H chemical shifts **690**
H–H coupling constants **690**
t-Butanol, hydrogen bonding 541

Butene-1
  ^{1}H chemical shifts **723**
  H–H coupling constants **723**
i-Butenes (1-substituted)
  ^{1}H chemical shifts 736
  H–H coupling constants 737

^{13}C chemical shifts
  comparison with ^{29}Si chemical shifts 1051
  of acetylenes 1001, 1030
  of aromatic compounds **1002**, **1005**, 1030
  of carbonyl groups **1009**
  of ethanes **997**, 1030
    correlation with substituent electronegativity 996
  of metal carbonyls 1010
  of methanes **992**, **995**
    correlation with substituent electronegativity 996
  of monosubstituted benzenes **1002**
  of phenols 1006
  of simple organic compounds 990, 1030
^{13}C resonance, experimental procedures **988**
^{13}C satellites
  in ^{1}H spectra 448, 450, 475
  in ^{19}F spectra of fluoroalkenes 914, 962
Caesium (^{133}Cs) chemical shifts of halides 1093
Calibration of spectra
  sideband method **237**, **274**
  wiggle beat method 276
Carbohydrates (acetylated) configurational effects on ^{1}H spectra 701
Carbonium ions, ^{1}H chemical shifts **774**
Carbonyl groups, ^{13}C chemical shifts **1009**
CAT 230
C–C bond shifts *666*, **698**
^{13}C–^{13}C coupling constants **1029**
$CDCl_3$ as a solvent *257*
Cells, *see* Sample containers
^{13}C–F isotope shifts in fluoro-organic compounds **962**
$CFCl_3$ as a solvent *257*, 266
Character table for D_4 point group 301
Charge densities in aromatic molecules **149**
Chemical
  equilibria, effect on spectra **481**
  exchange **484**
Chemical shifts (*see* Shielding constants), 4, 59, **65**
Chemical shifts, calculation for
    alkyl compounds **136**
    amides **133**
    aromatics **140**, **149**, **595**, 770
    azulene 146
    cyclohexane 136
    cyclohexane (perfluoro-) **139**
    fluorine compounds **151**
    fluorobenzenes **154**
    heterocyclic aromatics **145**, *789*
    paramagnetic contribution for ^{59}Co resonance **1078**
    paramagnetic contributions for ^{199}Hg, ^{207}Pb and ^{205}Tl resonances 1098
  cis and *trans* in olefines 729
  contact **826**
  contributions from ring currents in aromatics **141**, **595**, 770
  conversion factors for external referencing 263
  correction for bulk diamagnetic susceptibility 66, **260**
  effect of paramagnetic materials **115**, **826**
  empirical calculations **838**
  empirical calculations for disubstituted benzenes **754**
  equivalence *283*
  gas-to-solution **97**, **841**
  ^{1}H, charts of **1131**
  ^{1}H for organic compounds (Tiers' compilation) **1115**
  isotope effects *875*, 916, **962**, 1022, *1092*
  origin of **59**
  ortho effect in fluorobenzenes 155
Chemical shift/electron density ratios for hydrocarbon aromatic ions 781
Chlorine
  ^{35}Cl and ^{37}Cl, chemical shifts of inorganic chlorides **1095**
  ^{35}Cl resonance of Cl^-_{aq} 515
  nuclear quadrupole splittings in inorganic chlorides 1096
  resonance 1095
  trifluoride, ^{19}F spectrum 941, 942
Chromium (III) complexes, ligand exchange rates 525
^{59}Co chemical shifts
  calculation of paramagnetic contribution **1078**
  correlation with electronic absorption **1080**
  of cobalt (III) complexes *528*, **1080**
  solvent effects *1081*
  temperature dependence 1081
Cobalt complexes, rate processes *1082*

Collapse
of doublet by chemical exchange **487**, **489**
of triplet by chemical exchange **491**
of quartet by chemical exchange **494**
2,4,6-Collidine, ^{13}C spectrum 1008
Combination transitions 325
Commuting operators 291
Complex particle method of analysis 345
Computers
in the analysis of spectra **451**
of average transients (CAT) 230
Configuration of cyclohexanes 703
Configurational effects in ^{1}H spectra of carbohydrates 701
Conformation
of fluorinated ethanes 889
of saturated ring compounds **575**, **579**, **920**
Conformational motion, effect on spectra **481**
Conjugated polyenes, ^{1}H chemical shifts 744
Contact shifts **115**, **826**
Copper (^{63}Cu) resonance *1096*
Copper(I)-copper(II) exchange reaction 503, *1096*
Coproporphyrin-1, ^{1}H spectrum 792
Correlation
function **439**
application to a system of chemically equivalent nuclei 441
evaluation of 441
time (τ_c) **21**, 31
Correspondence principle *291*
Coupling constants (*see* Spin–spin coupling) **61**, **113**
absolute signs 162, **681**
angular variation for geminal nuclei 171, 711
angular variation in furans and pyrroles *786*
between H nuclei separated by four σ bonds **174**
calculation for HD **160**
calculation of H–H for methane **163**
calculation of *vicinal* and *geminal* H–H in ethanes and ethylenes **166**
calculations (theoretical) **103**, **105**, **106**, **109**, **111**, **160**
dependence on atomic number 63
B–P in $(CH_3)_2PHBH_3$ 988
^{13}C–^{13}C **1029**
F–^{11}B, in boron halides and derivatives 945
Coupling..., F–^{13}C
additivity effects **1017**
correlation with ^{19}F (^{13}C–^{12}C) isotopic chemical shifts 1022
in fluoroalkanes **1017**
in fluoroalkenes 915, **962**
in fluoromethanes 883, **962**, **1017**
in perfluorocyclobutane 959, 962
relative signs 1011
F–Cl in $FClO_3$ 944
F–F
effect of temperature 878
electron–orbital and orbital–orbital interaction 184
in aliphatic fluorocarbons 183
in antimony pentafluoride 928
in aromatic fluorocarbons 183
in *cis*- and *trans*-1,2-difluoro-1,2-dichloroethylene 916
in *cis*- and *trans*- N_2F_2 948
in fluorinated aromatic compounds **901**
in fluorinated cyclobutanes 918
in fluoroacyl metal compounds 896
in fluoroalkanes **875**, 958
in fluoroalkenes **906**
in fluoroalkyl metal compounds **895**
in fluorocarbon sulphides *894*, 926
in fluoroethanes **886**
in fluoropropanes **886**
in hypofluorites 949
in interhalogen compounds **940**
in miscellaneous organic fluorine compounds **962**
in perfluorocyclohexane 921
in perfluoropiperidine 926
in perfluorovinyl metal compounds **906**
in phosphorus halide derivatives 961
in sulphur hexafluoride and its derivatives **930**
in sulphur tetrafluoride and its derivatives 938
involving perfluoromethyl groups 959
long range 879
relative signs 888, 914
through-space 190
F–Hg
in mercury fluoroalkyls *897*
in mercury fluoroalkenes *907*
F–M in MF_x compounds **880**
F–^{14}N in NF_3 and *cis*- and *trans*- N_2F_2 948
F–^{93}Nb in NbF_6^- 1101
F–^{29}Si in substituted silanes 1050
F–Sn in tin fluoroalkenes *907*
F–P 1061
in perfluoroalkyl derivatives *896*, **959**

Coupling..., in perfluorotriphosphonitrile 951
in phosphorus halides and derivatives **949**, **959**, 960, 961
in phosphoryl halides 1077
H–Al in lithium aluminium hydride 1094
H–B
in borohydrides 987
in boron halides and derivatives **972**, **974**
in boron hydrides and derivatives **972**, **974**, **977**, 980, 982, 983
in $(CH_3)_2PHBH_3$ 988
in diborane diammoniate 986
in miscellaneous boron compounds **972**, **974**
H–^{13}C **1011**, 1032
additivity rules 193, **1017**, **1019**
correlation with bond length 1014
correlation with electronegativity 1014
correlation with ^{1}H chemical shifts **1020**
dependence on hydridisation 1011
dependence on *s* character **192**, 1012
in acetic acid 993
in acetylenes 1001
in aldehydes 1020, 1032
in alkyl and silyl selenides 963
in alkenes 1028
in aromatic compounds **901**, 1003, 1005, 1023
in chloroethylenes 722
in ethanol 993
in ethylene 448
in fluoromethanes 883
in formyl compounds 1014
in heterocyclics 1021, 1032
in hydrocarbons 1012
in methanes **1013**, 1014
in monosubstituted benzenes 1003, 1032
in phenols 1006, 1023
in plumbanes 824
in propyne 994
in pyridine 994
in stannanes 824
in unsaturated compounds **196**
long range 683, **1024**, **1027**
relation with J_{HH}^{cis} and J_{HH}^{trans} in ethylenes *1020*
signs *197*, 1011
H–D *1092*
H–F
in fluorinated aromatic compounds **901**

Coupling..., in fluoroacetylene 916
in fluoroalkenes 909, 910
in fluoroethanes **886**
in fluoromethanes 883
in fluoropropanes **887**
in phosphorus (V) fluoride derivatives 960, 961
in silicon compounds 1050
long range 879, 902
orbital contribution 185
relative signs 888
H–H
absolute signs **681**, **713**
correlation of *geminal* in alkenes with HCH angle 711
correlation of *vicinal* in ethanes with substituent electronegativity 680
correlation with J_{CH} *1020*
correlation with substituent electronegativity in vinyl derivatives **714**
in acetylenes **177**, 746, **748**
in alkanes, *geminal* 677
in alkanes, *vicinal* **678**
in alkenes, *geminal* 711, 714, 722, 728
in alkenes, *vicinal* 712, 714, 722, 728
in alkenes (metal) 743
in ammonia **183**
in aromatic hydrocarbons **180**, 682, **770**, 1023
in butanes (2,3-disubstituted) **690**
in butene-1 **723**
in i-butenes (1-substituted) 735
in cyclohexanes *679*
in $(CH_3)_2PHBH_3$ 988
in cyclophane 173
in cyclopropanes 694
in esters ($\alpha\beta$-unsaturated) 739
in ethanes 567, 681
in furans **782**
in hexene-1 **723**
in indene 769
in olefines 710
in picolines 797
in propene-1 **723**
in propenes (2,3-disubstituted) 732
in propenes (2-substituted) 731, 735
in pyridines 794
in pyrroles **787**
in quinolines 800
in silanes, *geminal* *823*
in silicon compounds 1050
in thiazoles 805
in thiophenes 804
long range in acenaphthenes *685*
long range in aromatic aldehydes *767*
long range in indene 769

Coupling..., long range in olefines **176**, *685*, **739**, 743
long range in saturated compounds **683**
signs of *geminal* **172**, 682, 695
signs of *vicinal* **172**, 682, 695
H–Hg
in 3-chloromercurifuran 1098
in mercury alkyls 690, *1097*
in mercury vinyl 743
in organomercury compounds 1098
H–^{14}N
in isonitriles 1040
long range 1040
temperature effect 819
H–^{17}O in water *509*, 1048
H–^{31}P
for directly bonded nuclei **1061**
in $(CH_3)_2PHBH_3$ 988
in dialkyl phosphonates 1072
in diphosphine 1074
in organophosphorus esters 1065
in phosphites 1070
in phosphoryl halides 1077
in phosphorus acids *1069*
in phosphorus alkyls 1064
in $P_3N_3Cl_4(SC_2H_5)_2$ 1075
in symmetrical and unsymmetrical trialkyl phosphates 1063
relative signs 1061
H–^{207}Pb in plumbanes 824
H–^{195}Pt in platinum complexes 1097
H–^{29}Si in substituted silane 1050
H–Sn, dependence on *s* character
in stannanes 824, 1086
in tetramethyl tin 1013, 1088
in tin alkyl halides 1088
in vinyl tin 743
H–Tl
in thallium alkyls 1090
in thallium phenyls *1091*
in thallium vinyl 743
relative signs 1091
H–X (group IV element), correlation with atomic number of X *825*
long range **174**
^{31}P–^{31}P 1061
in diphosphine 1074
in non-cyclic phosphonitrilic halides 1078
in perfluorotriphosphonitrile 951
in phosphates 1071
in phosphites 1070
in phosphorus acids *1069*
in $P_3N_3Cl_4(SC_2H_5)_2$ 1075
signs from double irradiation 466
Coupling..., signs from double quantum transitions 454
^{203}Tl–^{205}Tl in thallium ethoxide 1092
Coupling, virtual 814
Crossed coil
detection **45**
probe **208**
trans-Crotonaldehyde
^{1}H spectrum 469
spectral parameters 469
Crystal field calculations for ^{59}Co shielding **1078**
^{133}Cs resonance
of aqueous solutions *522*
of metal in liquid ammonia *1093*
of solid halides 1093
Cumene, ^{1}H spectrum 830
Cyclic compounds, conformation **575**
Cycloalkanes
^{1}H chemical shifts 692
Cycloalkanones, ^{1}H chemical shifts 692
Cyclobutane(1,1-dimethyl-2,2,3,3-tetrafluoro-), ^{19}F spectrum 917
Cyclobutane(1-phenyl-2,2,3,3-tetrafluoro-), ^{19}F spectrum 917
Cyclobutanes, ^{19}F spectral parameters 918
Cyclohexane
as a reference compound *264*
axial–equatorial chemical shift 136
Cyclohexane (bromo-), ^{1}H spectrum 576
Cyclohexane (chloro-), ^{1}H spectrum 576
Cyclohexane (1α,3β-dimethoxy-2α-acetoxy-), ^{1}H spectrum 702

Cyclohexane (1α,3β-dimethoxy-2α-acetoxy-), ^{1}H spectrum 702

Cyclohexane (methyl-), ^{1}H spectrum 706
Cyclohexane (2,2,6,6-tetradeuteromethyl-), ^{1}H spectrum 706
Cyclohexanes
configurations 703
disubstituted, ^{1}H spectra 708
fluorinated **575**, 577, **920**
^{1}H chemical shifts **696**
^{1}H spectral line widths 708
H–H coupling constants 700
interconversion **575**
monosubstituted, ^{1}H spectra 576, 706
1,2,3,4,5,6-hexachloro-, ^{1}H spectra *705*
perfluoro, interconversion **575**
Cyclohexyl
acetates, ^{1}H spectra *703*
alcohols, ^{1}H spectra *703*
Cyclopentadienyl anion, ^{1}H chemical shifts 779
Cyclopentadienyls, ^{1}H chemical shifts 743, 780

Cyclophane, H–H coupling constants 173
Cyclopropane (1,1-dichloro-2-methoxy-), ^{1}H spectrum 693
Cyclopropane (1-methyl-2,2-difluoro-), ^{19}F spectrum 917
Cyclopropanes
^{19}F chemical shifts *916*
F–F coupling constants *916*
^{1}H chemical shifts **690**
H–H coupling constants 694

δ, the chemical shift (*see* Chemical shift) 5
for external reference compounds 263
D_4 point group, elements and character table 301
Decaborane, ^{11}B spectrum 982, 984
Decalins, ^{1}H spectra 580, *709*
Decalols (10-methyl-), ^{1}H chemical shifts 709
Deceptively simple spectra 363
Derivation super operator 436
Deuteration in the determination of polymer tacticities **836**
Deuterium resonance 1092
coupling constants *1092*
isotope effects *1092*
Deuterochloroform as a solvent *257*
Diamagnetic shielding **65**
Diazo compounds, ^{1}H chemical shifts 1139
Diborane,
^{11}B spectrum 978
diammoniate, ^{11}B spectral parameters 986
^{1}H spectrum 979
Diboranes, ^{11}B spectra 979
Dienes (conjugated), H–H coupling constants 741
Diethyl mercury, ^{1}H spectrum 687
Dioxane, ^{13}CH satellite bands 450
Dirac delta function *79*
Direct method for the analysis of spectra **435**
Dished magnetic fields **204**
1,2-Dithiane, ^{1}H resonance **559**
Double irradiation **240**, 446, 447
in the determination of polymer structures 835
of the ammonium ion 458, 459, 460
of *trans*-crotonaldehyde **469**
of dichloroacetaldehyde 461
of 2-furoic acid 468
of heteronuclear systems **455**, *1093*, *1040*
of homonuclear systems **460**
of 1,1,2-trifluoro-2-bromoethylene 915
relative signs of coupling constants 461, **466**
Double irradiation, theory of **244**
to measure reaction rates *502*
transitory *475*, *476*
with a weak second radiofrequency field **471**
Double quantum, transitions **453**
in 1,2-dibromopropionic acid 454
relative signs of coupling constants from 454
Doublet collapse by chemical exchange **487, 489**
DSS, for aqueous solution referencing 265

Electric
field effects
intramolecular on ^{19}F shielding 156, 157
on AB, AB_2 and AX_3 spin systems *464*
reaction field effects 88
Electrolyte solutions **511**
relative molar chemical shifts **514**
Electron
densities from chemical shift measurements 781
spin resonance (ESR) *4*
Enthalpy difference between rotamers **570**
Epoxides (monosubstituted)
analysis of ^{1}H spectra 377
^{1}H chemical shifts **695**
Equivalence
chemical shift *283*
magnetic *283*, 308
symmetrical *284*
Equivalent nuclei 284, **307**
effect of conformational motion 285
Esters
^{17}O chemical shifts 1045
$\alpha\beta$-unsaturated, ^{1}H chemical shifts **737**
Ethane (1,2-chlorobromo-), ^{1}H resonance 415
Ethane (1,2-dibromo-), ^{13}CH satellites 450
Ethane (1,2-dichloro-), ^{13}CH satellites 450
Ethane (1,1,2-trifluoro-1,2-dibromo-1-chloro-), ^{19}F resonance 563
Ethanes
^{13}C chemical shifts **997**
correlation with substituent electronegativity 996
calculation of *geminal* and *vicinal* H–H coupling constants **166**
enthalpy differences between rotamers **570**
vicinal H–H coupling constants 567, **680**
Ethanol *257*, *273*
^{13}C spectrum **993**

Ethanol, chemical exchange *493*, 544, 508
  ^{1}H resonance of aqueous solution 508
Ethyl
  derivatives
    ^{1}H chemical shifts 672, 673, 686
    correlation of ^{13}C chemical shifts with substituent electronegativity 996
    correlation of ^{1}H chemical shifts with substituent electronegativity 670
  metal derivatives
    ^{13}C chemical shifts 999
    ^{1}H chemical shifts 675
    H–X coupling constants 688
Ethylene, H–^{13}C coupling constants 448
Ethylene (1,1-difluoro-)
  coupling constants 398
  ^{1}H and ^{19}F resonances 397
Ethylene (1,1,2-trifluoro-2-bromo-)
  ^{19}F decoupled spectrum, 915
  ^{19}F spectrum 915
Ethylene [*cis*- and *trans*-1-fluoro-2-(perfluoroisopropyl)-]
  ^{19}F chemical shifts 913
  F–F coupling constants 913
  ^{1}H chemical shifts 913
  H–F coupling constants 913
Ethylene oxide, ^{13}CH satellite bands 450
Ethylenes, calculation of *geminal* and *vicinal* H–H coupling constants **166**
Ethylenes (chloro-)
  ^{1}H chemical shifts 722
  H–^{13}C coupling constants 722
  H–H coupling constants 722
Exchange
  rate
    effect on a doublet **487**
    effect on a quartet **494**
    effect on a triplet **493**
  reactions
    electron **502**
    ion and group **507**

^{19}F chemical shifts, Φ^* values **266**
  calculation of **151**, 266
  correlations with substituent electronegativity 882
  effect of solvents on 872
  of alkyl and silyl selenides 963
  of binary fluorides **880**
  of boron halides and derivatives **944**, 952
  of fluorinated heterocyclics of S, Se and P *926*
  of fluorine-containing polymers **954**
  of fluoroacyl metal compounds **895**
  of fluoroalkanes **885**, 957
^{19}F chemical shift, of fluoroalkyl metal compounds **895**, 959
  of fluorobenzenes **897**
    correlation of *meta* and *para* shifts with Hammett σ constants **897**
  of fluorocarbon derivatives 889, **890**
  of fluorocyclobutanes 918
  of fluoroethanes **886**, 958
  of fluorohalohydrocarbons **883**
  of fluoromethanes 883
  of fluoronaphthalenes 905
  of hypofluorites 949
  of inorganic fluorides **530**, **880**
  of interhalogen compounds **940**
  of miscellaneous fluorine–sulphur containing compounds 939
  of metal fluoride complexes 521, 952, 953
  of nitrogen–fluorine containing compounds **946**
  of phosphorus halides and related compounds **949**, 959, 960, 961
  of sulphur hexafluoride and derivatives **930**
  of sulphur tetrafluoride and derivatives **937**
^{19}F (^{13}C–^{12}C) isotopic chemical shift correlation with J_{CF} 1022
Fatty acids, ^{1}H chemical shifts *812*
Fermi contact term *163*
Field/frequency control 203, 229
Filling factor 45
First order spectra **280**
Fluorinated cyclohexanes **920**
Fluoroacetylene, ^{19}F spectral parameters 916
Fluoroalkanes
  ^{19}F chemical shifts **883**, **885**, **893**, 957
  ^{19}F coupling constants **883**, **885**
Fluoroalkenes
  ^{19}F chemical shifts **906**, 957
  ^{19}F coupling constants **907**, **909**
  H–H coupling constants *910*
Fluorobenzene (*ortho*-dichloro-)
  ^{19}F coupling constants 398
  ^{19}F spectrum 399
Fluorobenzenes
  calculation of ^{19}F chemical shifts **154**
  ortho effect 155
Fluorocarbon sulphides
  ^{19}F chemical shifts 894
  F–F coupling constants 894
Fluorocarbons
  calculation of coupling constants **183**
  containing nitrogen, ^{19}F chemical shifts **889**
Fluorocyclobutanes 918

Fluoroethanes
  conformational studies 889
  F–^{13}C coupling constants *1017*
  ^{19}F spectral parameters **886**, 958, *1017*
Fluoromethanes
  F–^{13}C coupling constants 1017
  ^{19}F spectral parameters 883, 1017
Fluoronaphthalenes, ^{19}F chemical shifts *905*
Fluoropropanes, ^{19}F spectral parameters **887, 892**
Fluorosilanes (methyl and ethyl), ^{19}F chemical shifts 927
Flux stabiliser 203
Formamide
  ^{1}H spectrum 241, 554
  ^{14}N irradiation 241
Furan and substituted furans, ^{1}H spectral parameters **782**
2-Furfurol, ^{1}H spectrum 364
2-Furoic acid
  ^{1}H double resonance spectrum 468
  ^{1}H spectral parameters 467
  ^{1}H spectrum 468

g, Landé or spectroscopic splitting factor 14
Gases, medium effects on chemical shifts **857**
Gauge invariance 67
Geminal coupling constants, *see* Coupling constants
Germanes, spectral parameters 823
Glutaric acid (β-methyl-), ^{1}H spectrum 815
Glycidaldehyde, ^{1}H spectrum 428
Glycidonitrile, ^{1}H spectrum 282

^{1}H chemical shifts
  correlation with J_{CH} **1020**
  empirical estimation **838**
  medium effects **841**
  of acetylenes **745**
    solvent effects 749
  of alkenes **711, 727, 735, 741**
    anomalous **719**
    correlation with group dipole moments 718
    correlation with Hammett σ constants 717
    effects of methyl group substitution 733
    induced ring currents in annulenes 745
  of alkyls **666, 670, 676, 685**
  of aromatic compounds **749, 770, 774**
    aromatic ions **774**
^{1}H chemical shifts, correlations with Hammett σ constants **752**
    effect of solvents 749
    polynuclear 770
    ring currents 770
  of cyclohexanes **696**
  of cyclopropanes **690**
  of ethyl derivatives **670**
    correlation with substituent electronegativity 670
  of heterocyclic compounds **782, 787, 794**, 798
    alkaloids **806**
    amino acids and peptides *812*
    effect of solvents 798
    fatty acids *812*
    furans **782**
    pyridines **794**
    pyrroles **787**
    quinolines **798**
    steroids **808**
    thiazoles **805**
    thiophenes **802**
  of hydrogen attached to atoms other than carbon **816**
  of metal alkenes **742**
  of metal alkyls 689
  of methyl derivatives **666**
  of paramagnetic species **826**
  of polymers **829**
  of propyl derivatives **676**
  of water
    effect of complex formation **520**
    effect of electrolytes **511**
    effect of hydrogen bonding **537**
    for ions at infinite dilution 515
    relative molar 514
H_1 (radiofrequency field)
  effect on spectra **230**
  measurement **230**
Halide ion exchange *511*
Halogen fluorides 530, **940**
Hamiltonian 290
  matrix elements **304**
HD, calculation of coupling constant **160**
Heterocyclics
  calculation of ^{1}H chemical shifts **145**
  effect of solvents on ^{1}H chemical shifts **855**
  fluorinated derivatives of S, Se and P 926
  H–^{13}C coupling constants 1021
  ^{1}H spectra **782**
Hexaborane, ^{11}B spectrum 982
Hexene-1
  ^{1}H chemical shifts 723
  H–H coupling constants 723

^{199}Hg and ^{201}Hg resonance **1097**
chemical shifts of alkyls 1097
coupling constants
in alkyls *1097*
in 3-chloromercurifuran 1098
in organo-mercury compounds *1088*
Hindered internal rotation **551**
barrier heights 555, **570**
nature of barrier to **573**
of C–C bond **559**
of C–N bond **553**
of C–P bond 572
of N–N bond **551**
of N–O bond **556**
of S–S bond **558**
Homogeneity, *see* Magnets
Hydration of ions *1048*
Hydrocarbons, calculation of chemical shifts **135**
Hydrogen
bonding **534**, 816
chemical shifts due to **537**
in amines 548, 818
in halogenated compounds 548
in hydroxylic compounds **543**
in mercaptans *548, 820*
nature of **535**
procedures for studying **539**
peroxide, proton exchange *510*
Hydroxyl
groups, ^{1}H chemical shifts **816**
proton exchange 507
Hyperfine interaction constants 115, 177
Hypofluorites, ^{19}F spectral parameters 948

I, spin value 1, **589**
$\mathbf{I}^2$ operator 294
I^{127} resonance
of I^- aq *517, 1096*
of I_3^- 531, *1096*
Indene
^{1}H spectrum 769
signs of H–H coupling constants 769
Indoles, ^{1}H spectra 793, 794
INDOR *475, 989, 1033*
Induced current model **79**
Inositols, ^{1}H spectra 706
Integration of spectra 236
Intensities (relative) of multiplet components 7
Intensity
measurements of bands **234**
sum rule 380, 452
transiton **306**
Interatomic currents
in benzene 82
in ethylene 82
in molecules **81**
Interhalogen compounds, ^{19}F spectral parameters **940**
Internal rotation, *see* Hindered internal rotation *and* Conformation
Inversion of nitrogen compounds 574
Iodine pentafluoride, chemical exchange 943
Ions
aromatic **774**
inorganic, infinite dilution shifts 515
Iron carbonyl (perfluoroalkyl-), ^{19}F spectral parameters 926
Irreducible representation 299
Isonitriles, H–^{14}N coupling constants 1040
Isopropyl benzene, ^{1}H spectrum 6
Isotopic effect
on ^{19}F chemical shifts *875*, 916, **962**
correlation with J_{CF} 1022
on ^{1}H chemical shifts *1092*
Isotopic substitution as an aid to analysis **445**

3-Ketoallopregnanes, ^{1}H spectra 809
Keto-enol tautomerism **549**
Ketones, ^{17}O chemical shifts 1045

Lamb diamagnetic shielding 66
Landé (spectroscopic) splitting factor 14
Langevin equation 35
Larmor
equation 13, 67
precession 11
Lead (^{207}Pb) resonance 1100
chemical shifts
comparison with ^{199}Hg and ^{205}Tl 1098
in inorganic compounds 1101
in organic compounds 1101
Lead tetraethyl, ^{1}H spectrum 687
Leakage 210
optimum value **211**
Line
broadening
from chemical exchange 485
from sweep rate *224*
saturation 34, *40*
spin–lattice 31, 32
shape **42**
distortion 33
effect of quadrupolar relaxation 496
Lorentzian *505*

Line..., of collapsing doublet **487, 489**
of collapsing quartet **494**
of collapsing triplet **493**
widths
and T_2 40
effect of saturation 33
for liquids **30**
Gaussian 30
in electron exchange reactions *506*
in proton transfer reactions *510*
Lorentzian 30, 40
mean square 31
measurement of T_2 from 49
of ^{14}N resonances of ammonia and related compounds 1035
of ^{14}N resonances of nitrites, nitrates and nitro compounds 1036
solvation of ions using **524**
variation from quadrupolar relaxation *1102*
^{7}Li resonance of the metal in liquid ammonia *1093*
Long range coupling constants, *see* Coupling constants
Longitudinal relaxation time, T_1 (*see* T_1) **19, 37**
Lorentzian curves
absorption (χ'') **39**
dispersion (χ') **39**
Lorentz–Lorentz equation *98*
Low resolution NMR 4
Lowering operators 292
Lunacrine, ^{1}H spectra 807
Lunine, ^{1}H spectra 807
2,6-Lutidine, ^{1}H spectrum 328
3,5-Lutidine, ^{13}C spectrum 1008

Magnetic
complex susceptibility 36
equivalence 59, 283
effect of symmetry on *564*
field
effect on spectrum 227, 442
recurrent sweep 223
shape 204
slow sweep 223
sweep **223**
moment
of electron 2, 14
of nucleus, *see* Nuclear moments **589**
quantum number, *m* 14
radiofrequency susceptibility **34**, 40
screening of nuclei **65**
shielding in atoms **66**
shielding in molecules
induced current model **79**
Magnetic, perturbation theory **68**
variation theory **77**
static susceptibility 35, **65**
Magnetisation vector, **M** 29, 37
Magnetogyric ratio, γ 11, 14
Magnets **201**
cycling **204**
field homogeneity **272**
shim coils *202*
stabilisation **202**
Medium effects
on ^{19}F chemical shifts 872
on ^{1}H chemical shifts **841, 857**
Mercaptan (methyl), ^{1}H spectrum 334
Mercaptans, hydrogen bonding *548*
Mercurifuran (3-chloro-), H–^{199}Hg coupling constants 1098
Mercury
alkyls, H–^{199}Hg coupling constants 690, *1097*
chemical shifts 1098
diethyl, ^{1}H spectrum 687
dimethyl, ^{199}Hg spectrum 1100
Metal
carbonyls **825**
^{13}C chemical shifts 1010
^{17}O chemical shifts 1047
ethyl derivatives, ^{1}H chemical shifts 675
fluoride complexes 952, 953
Methane
calculation of H–H coupling constant **163**
effect of solvents on ^{1}H chemical shift 842
Methanol, ^{1}H spectrum 544
cis-Methyl crotonate, ^{1}H spectrum 737
Methyl derivatives
^{13}C chemical shifts **992, 995**
correlation with substituent electronegativity 996
^{13}C–H coupling constants **1013**, 1014
^{1}H chemical shifts 666, 668
correlation with substituent electronegativity 666
of group IVB elements
^{13}C chemical shifts 999
^{1}H chemical shifts **685**
Methyl halides, ^{1}H chemical shifts 667
Molecular beams *2*
Moments, of spectra **431**
Multiplet collapse by chemical exchange **488**

^{14}N chemical shifts **1033**
of nitrates, nitrites and nitro compounds 1036, 1037

^{14}N resonance **1031**
line widths of ammonia and related compounds 1035
line widths of nitrites, nitrates and nitro compounds 1036
of complex ammines *527*
of liquid ammonia containing alkali metals *1093*
quadrupolar effects 1037
^{23}Na resonance *1092*
of Na^+_{aq} *515*, *517*, 520
Naphthalene
calculation of chemical shifts 145
^1H spectrum 405, 406, 773
H–H coupling constants 407
NbF_6^-
^{19}F spectrum 1101
^{93}Nb spectrum 1101
Nickel complexes
contact shifts **826**
Ni(II) N,N′-di(6-quinolyl)aminotroponeiminate, ^1H spectrum 828
Ni(II) ethylene diamine, ^1H spectrum 827
Nitric acid, ^1H resonance **517**
Nitrites (alkyl), rotational isomerism **556**
Nitrogen compounds, inversion of 574
Nitromethane as a solvent *259*
Nitrosamines, rotational isomerism **551**
Niobium (^{93}Nb)
F–^{93}Nb coupling constant in NbF_6^- 1101
spectrum of NbF_6^- 1101
NMR spectrometers **200**
basic requirements **200**
commercial **248**
cycling of electromagnets **204**
magnets for **201**
Notation for spin systems **283**
Nuclear
induction **44**
magnetic resonance absorption **45**
magnetisation
in phase 36
out of phase 36
moments 1, 3, 10, 1102
of ^1H nucleus 14
paramagnetic susceptibility 3, 35
properties **589, 1109**
quadrupole splittings in ^{35}Cl and ^{37}Cl resonances 1096
spin, *I* 1, **589**
Nutation *52*

^{17}O chemical shifts **1042, 1044, 1046**
correlation with electronic transition energies 1043
^{17}O chemical shifts, of transition metal compounds 1044
effect of paramagnetic ions 1047
of metal carbonyls 1047
^{17}O resonance **1041**
aqueous electrolytes 523, *526*
^{17}O–H coupling constant in water *509*
Olefines, *see* Alkenes *and* Vinyl derivatives
Operators, raising and lowering 292
Overhauser effect **116**, *247*

^{31}P chemical shifts **1053**
characteristic **1066**
compilation **1143**
correlation with bond properties 1056
in perfluoroalkyl phosphorus derivative **959**
in quadruply connected phosphorus compounds 1059, 1060, 1144
in triply connected phosphorus compounds 1058, 1059, 1143
of cyclic phosphorus compounds 1075
of phosphates (condensed) 1073, 1145
of phosphines 1143
of phosphites *1068*, 1143, 1147
of phosphonates 1072, 1149
of phosphonitrilic compounds 1075, 1077, 1152, 1154
of phosphorus acids 1069, *1074*
of phosphorus-nitrogen containing compounds 1148
of phosphoryl halides 1076
^{31}P coupling constants **1061**
relative signs 1061
^{31}P resonance **1051**
Paddles 209
Paramagnetic
current density 80
susceptibility 35
^{207}Pb chemical shifts
comparison with those of ^{199}Hg and ^{205}Tl 1098
in inorganic compounds 1101
in organic compounds 1101
^{207}Pb resonance 1100
Peaked magnetic fields **204**
Pentaborane-9
^{11}B spectrum 981
decoupling of ^{11}B nuclei 456
^1H spectrum 456
Pentaborane-11, ^{11}B spectrum 981
Pentaborane halides, ^{11}B spectra 978, 985
Peptides, ^1H chemical shifts 812
Perchloryl fluoride and related compounds, ^{19}F spectral parameters 943

Perfluoroacyl metal compounds
chemical shifts 895
coupling constants 896
Perfluoroalkyl
metal compounds
chemical shifts 895
coupling constants 896
sulphur hexafluoride derivatives, ^{19}F spectral parameters **932**
sulphur tetrafluoride derivatives **937**
Perfluorocyclohexane
axial–equatorial chemical shift 139
^{19}F spectral parameters 920
Perfluorocyclohexanes
dihydro-, ^{19}F chemical shifts **922**
monosubstituted, ^{19}F chemical shifts 921
^{19}F chemical shifts 925
Perfluorodecalin (*cis*- and *trans*-)
conformation 922
^{19}F spectra 924
Perfluoroisopropyl bromide, ^{19}F spectrum 872
Perfluoromethylcyclohexane, ^{19}F spectrum 876, 921
Perfluoropiperidine
conformation 925
^{19}F spectrum 925
Perfluorovinyl metal compounds
^{19}F chemical shifts 906
F–F coupling constants **907**
Permanganate–manganate exchange reaction *506*
Permutation operator 106
Perturbation theory **68, 428**
Phase memory 29
relaxation time, *see* T_2
Phenol (2,4,6-tribromo-), ^{1}H spectrum with ^{13}C satellites 1023
Phenols
^{13}C spectral parameters 1006
chemical shift/vibration frequency relation 547
^{1}H chemical shifts of hydroxyl group *818*
hydrogen bonding **545**
Phosphate
isohypo- ion, ^{31}P spectrum 1068
tetrapoly-ammonium salt, ^{31}P spectrum 1071
Phosphates, ^{31}P chemical shifts 1144
condensed
^{31}P chemical shifts 1145, 1073
^{31}P spectra 1073
trialkyl, H–^{31}P coupling constants 1063
Phosphine (di-), ^{31}P coupling constants 1074
Phosphines, ^{31}P chemical shifts 1143
Phosphite (trimethyl-), ^{31}P spectrum 1054
Phosphites (organic), ^{31}P spectral parameters *1068*, 1143, 1147
Phosphonates, ^{31}P spectral parameters 1072, 1149
tri-Phosphonitrile (hexafluoro-), ^{19}F spectrum 951
Phosphonitrilic (non-cyclic) halides
^{31}P chemical shifts 1152
^{31}P spectra 1077
Phosphorus
triethyl-, ^{1}H spectrum 371
acids, ^{31}P spectral parameters **1069**
alkyls, H–^{31}P coupling constants 1064
compounds, compilation of chemical shifts **1143**
halides and derivatives, ^{19}F spectral parameters **949, 959, 960,** 1055
organic esters, H–^{31}P coupling constants 1064
Phosphoryl halides
^{31}P chemical shifts 1076
^{31}P spectra 1076
Platinum (^{195}Pt), H–^{195}Pt coupling constants in platinum complexes 1097
Plumbanes, spectral parameters 823
$P_3N_3Cl_4(SC_2H_5)_2$, ^{31}P spectrum 1075
Polymers
containing fluorine **954**
copolymers of butadiene and isoprene 831
segmental motion 829
structure 831, 835
tacticity **833, 836**
Poly-(*n*-1)-methyl-1-alkenes 833
Polymethylmethacrylate, ^{1}H spectrum 834
Polypropylene, ^{1}H spectra of various tacticities 837
Polystyrene 838
^{1}H spectrum 830
Polyvinyl chloride, ^{1}H spectrum 836
Population of spin states **16**
Porphyrins
calculation of chemical shifts **147**
^{1}H chemical shifts 792
Probe (sample holder) **207**
Product spin functions **293**, 297
Propane, ^{1}H double resonance **476**
Propargyl
bromide, ^{1}H spectrum 747
halides, ^{1}H chemical shifts 747
Propene-1
^{1}H chemical shifts 723
H–H coupling constants 723
^{1}H spectrum 724

Propene-1, *cis*- and *trans*-1-fluoro-
^{19}F chemical shifts 912
^{1}H chemical shifts 912
H–F coupling constants 912
2,3-dichloro-, ^{1}H spectrum 388
Propene-2 (*cis*- and *trans*-2-fluoro-3-chloro-)
^{19}F chemical shifts 911
H–F coupling constants 911
^{1}H chemical shifts 911
Propenes
2-substituted
^{1}H chemical shifts 730
H–H coupling constants 731
2,3-disubstituted
^{1}H chemical shifts 723
H–H coupling constants 723
Propionic acid
1,2-dibromo-, ^{1}H spectrum 454
2,3-dibromo-, double resonance 473, 474
Propyl (i and n) derivatives, ^{1}H chemical shifts 672, *676*
Propyne, ^{13}C spectrum 994
Protolysis reactions **507**
Proton exchange
in alcohols 507
in amines *1040*
Pterocarpin, ^{1}H resonance spectrum 814
Pulse methods *40*, **50**
electrolyte solutions 527
Pyridine
as a solvent *259*
^{13}C spectrum 994
^{1}H spectrum 794
3-bromo-, ^{1}H spectrum 706
1,2,5,6-tetrahydro-
^{1}H decoupled spectrum 798
^{1}H spectrum 798
Pyridines
^{13}C spectra 1008
^{1}H spectral parameters **794**
Pyridinium ion, ^{1}H spectrum *1040*
with ^{14}N decoupled *1040*
Pyrrole
effect of solvents on ^{1}H spectrum 856
^{1}H spectrum 457, 787
^{1}H spectrum with ^{14}N decoupled 457
N-deutero-, ^{1}H spectrum 787
Pyrroles, ^{1}H spectral parameters **787**

Quadrupolar
effects in ^{14}N spectra 1037
line broadening *970*, *1102*
Quadrupole
moments 27, **589**
relaxaton **26**, 496
effect on ^{1}H signals of NH groups 819
Quantitative analysis
optimum spectrometer conditions 211, **234**
of phosphorus compounds 1076
Quantum mechanical formalism **287**
Quartet collapse by chemical exchange **494**
Quinoline
^{1}H spectral parameters 798
5,7-dichloro-, ^{1}H resonance spectrum 801
5,7-dimethyl-, ^{1}H resonance spectrum 801
8-methyl-, ^{1}H resonance spectrum 801

Radiofrequency
effect on spectra 227
oscillator **227**
power
effect on spectra **230**
measurement **230**
receiver **232**
Raising operators 292
Rapid passage experiments *40*, **497**
^{87}Rb chemical shifts, of solid halides 1093
^{87}Rb resonance of the metal in liquid ammonia *1093*
Reaction fields 88, 95, *138*, 841
in *para*-dinitrobenzene 90
Reference
compounds *61*, **260**
scale interconversion **267**
Referencing
external **260**
for ^{13}C resonance 991
for ^{19}F resonance **266**
for ^{1}H rseonance **264**
internal **263**
Relaxation
quadrupole **26**, 496
spin–lattice (*see also* T_1) **18**, *76*
spin–spin (*see also* T_2) **28**
Representations
irreducible *299*
reducible *299*
symmetry group 298
Resonance
condition
classical description **10**
quantum mechanical description **15**
equation 13, 59
Ring currents **141**, **595**, 770
Ringing 40, *224*
Rotating fields *13*
co-ordinates **50**, *245*

Rotational isomerism **551**
about C–C bond **559**
solvent effect on 568
temperature effect on **569**
Rubidium (^{87}Rb)
chemical shifts of solid halides 1093
resonance of metal in liquid ammonia *1093*

Sample
containers **268**
coaxial *268*
for small volumes 270
for temperature studies *271*
having large filling factors **269**
sealing 271
spherical 268
preparation **256**
spinning **206**
Satellite spectra, ^{13}CH of substituted benzenes **1022**
Saturation **33**, 231, *461*
degree of 38
factor **34**
^{121}Sb resonance of $NaSbF_6$ 1097
Screening, *see* Shielding
Secular
determinant 296, 323
equation for NMR *288*, 289
factorising 290
of AB spin system 312
Selection rules 310
Selenium (^{77}Se) chemical shifts of selenous and selenic acids 1097
^{29}Si chemical shifts **1049**
comparison with ^{13}C chemical shifts 1051
^{29}Si resonance **1048**
Sensitivity enhancement **230**
$SF_5OC_6H_5$, ^{19}F spectrum 931
Shape
factor 65
function 30, 33
Shielding, diamagnetic contribution 70, 75, 78
in alkenes 724
in benzenes 752
in linear molecules **73**
in molecules containing heavy atoms **74**
paramagnetic contribution 70, 75, 78, *894*, *895*
Shielding constant or coefficient, σ (*see also* Chemical shift) 61, **66**
anisotropy of 94, **113**, **135**, **136**
calculation **120**
by induced current model **130**, **595**, 770
Shielding..., for halogen hydrides **124**
for group VI hydrides **127**
for H_2 molecule **120**
for hydrocarbons **129**
effect of, electric field **85**
isotopic substitution **99**
medium **841**, **857**, 872
molecular interactions **90**
Van der Waals forces **95**
effects, S_o and S_m, in benzenes **754**, **1140**
of ^{19}F nuclei 874
influence of low-lying excited states *894*, *895*
temperature dependence **101**
Shim coils *202*
Sideband, *see* Calibration of spectra *and* Double irradiation
calibration of spectra **236**
interpolation 275
single 244
superposition *275*
Signal
shape, *see* Line shape
to noise ratio 233
Signs of coupling constants, *see* Coupling constants
Silanes
trisubstituted, ^{1}H chemical shifts 822
fluoro-, ^{19}F chemical shifts 927
Silver ion complexes *529*
Simplification of spectra *277*
Single coil
detection **45**
probe **217**
^{119}Sn chemical shifts **1083**
of tin alkyls 1083
of tin halides 1083, **1084**
^{119}Sn coupling constants **1086**
^{119}Sn resonance **1082**
Solvent effects on
^{13}C chemical shifts 992
^{59}Co chemical shifts *1081*
^{19}F chemical shifts 872
^{1}H chemical shifts of
acetonitrile **846**
acetylenes *749*, **848**
aromatic compounds 258, *749*, **851**
benzene 258
methane **842**
unsaturated heterocyclic compounds *798*, **855**
rotational isomerism 568
^{119}Sn chemical shifts *1084*
spectra **442**
Spectral density functions 21

Spectrometers, *see* NMR spectrometers
Spectroscopic (Landé) splitting factor, *g* 14
Spin
  angular momentum
    operators 15, 290, 291
    commutation rules 291
  correlation function in benzene and naphthalene 182
  correlation matrix 181
  decoupling (*see also* Double irradiation) **240**
    theory **244**
  densities in tetrahedral Co(II) complexes *828*
  eigenfunctions 15, 293
  eigenvalues 15
  exchange 29
Spin–lattice relaxation
  mechanism **18**, *76*
  time (*see also* T_1) **19**
Spin
  number (or value), *I* 1, **589**
  product functions 293, 297
  system notation **283**
  temperature 17
    negative 17
Spinning of sample **206**
Spin–spin
  coupling
    effect of time averaging **65**
    mechanism **63**
    molecular orbital calculations **106**
    valence bond calculations **109**
    variation method **111**
  coupling constant, *J* (*see also* Coupling constants) 7, **61**
    calculation for HD **160**
    evaluation **109, 111**
    theoretical calculation of **103, 105, 160**
  relaxation
    mechanisms **28**
    time (*see also* T_2) **29**
Spontaneous emission 18
Stannanes, spectral parameters 823, 1086
Stannic bromide and iodide, ^{119}Sn spectra 1084
Steroids, ^{1}H chemical shifts **808**
Strong electrolyte solutions **511**
Styrene
  ^{1}H chemical shifts 719
  ^{1}H spectrum 381
  oxide, ^{1}H spectrum 362, 377
Sub-spectra, superposition of 345
Succinic (methyl-) acid, ^{1}H resonance spectrum 815
Sulphur
  dioxide as a solvent *259*, 519
  hexafluoride
    disubstituted, ^{19}F spectral parameters 935
    monosubstituted, ^{19}F spectral parameters **930**
  tetrafluoride
    ^{19}F spectrum 531, 936
    ^{19}F spectral parameters 936
    perfluoroalkyl derivatives, ^{19}F spectral parameters **937**
Super operators **435**
  derivation 436
  matrix representation 437
Susceptibility
  bulk diamagnetic corrections **260**
  diamagnetic **65**
  paramagnetic 35
  volume *3*, 262, **605** (compilation)
Symmetrical equivalence *284*
Symmetrised spin functions 321
  notation 335
Symmetry transformation group 298

τ values 265
  charts **1131**
  for a variety of organic compounds (Tiers' compilation) **1115**
T_1, spin–lattice (*or* longitudinal) relaxation time **19**
  contribution from anisotropy of σ 76
  effect of
    anisotropic shielding **27**
    diamagnetic substances *26*
    ^{2}H on ^{1}H resonance 23
    paramagnetic substances 21, **25**, 30
    pressure 28
    quadrupoles 21, **26**
    viscosity 23
  intermolecular contribution **22**
  intramolecular contribution **22**
  measurement by direct method **46**
  measurement by progressive saturation method **47**
  of electrolyte solutions 527
  of ice 19
  of liquids 19
  of solids 19
T_2, spin–spin (*or* transverse) relaxation time **29, 37**
  effect of paramagnetic ions 30, 505
  inter- and intramolecular contributions 30
  measurement of **49**
  measurements on electrolyte solutions 527

Tautomerism **549**
Temperature
  control of sample **212**
  dependence of ^{59}Co chemical shifts 1081
  effect on rotational isomerism **569**
Tetraborane, ^{11}B spectrum 981
Tetraethyl lead, ^{1}H spectrum 687
Tetramethyl silane (TMS) 264
  as a universal reference 267
Thallium
  alkyls, H–^{205}Tl coupling constants 1090
  ethoxide
    structure 1091
    ^{203}Tl–^{205}Tl coupling constant 1092
  phenyls, H–^{205}Tl coupling constants 1091
  salts, ^{205}Tl chemical shifts 1089
    effect of anions 1090
Thiazoles, ^{1}H spectral parameters 805
Thiophene
  2-bromo-, ^{1}H spectrum 281
  3-bromo-2-aldehyde, ^{1}H triple resonance 476
  2-bromo-5-chloro-, double resonance 472
  deuterated, ^{1}H spectrum 804
  2-methylthio-3-thiophene thiol, ^{1}H spectrum 311
"Tickling" experiments **471**
Tin
  alkyls
    ^{119}Sn chemical shifts 1083
    ^{119}Sn coupling constants 1087
  halides *532*
    ^{119}Sn chemical shifts 1083, **1084**
    ^{119}Sn–H coupling constants 1087
  resonance spectra **1082**
  tetramethyl, ^{119}Sn spectrum 1087
^{205}Tl chemical shifts **1088**
  comparison with those of ^{119}Hg and ^{207}Pb 1098
  of thallium salts **1089**
    effect of anions *1090*
^{205}Tl coupling constants 1090
  in thallium phenyls *1091*
  in thallium trialkyls 1091
  signs 1091
^{205}Tl resonance **1088**
^{203}Tl and ^{205}Tl resonances of aqueous electrolytes 522
Tl(I)–Tl(III) exchange reaction *506*
Tl_2Cl_4, ^{205}Tl spectrum 1089
Toluene, ^{1}H spectrum 6
Trace of a matrix 431
Transient effects **40**
Transition
  intensities 306, 310, 315
  metal compounds, ^{1}H spectra **825**
    ^{17}O chemical shifts 1044
  probabilities 16, 19, 33
Transistory selective irradiation 475, 476
Triaryl carbonium ions, ^{1}H chemical shifts 774
Trifluoroacetic acid
  as a solvent 989
  ^{13}C INDOR spectrum 989
Triple resonance 476
Triplet collapse by chemical exchange **491**
Tropylinium cation, ^{1}H chemical shifts 779
Twin-T bridge 217

U-mode (dispersion) 42, 210, 218

V-mode (absorption) 41, 210, 218
V(IV)–V(IV) exchange reaction *504*
Variation theory **77**
Vicinal coupling constants, *see* Coupling constants
Vinyl bromide
  ^{1}H spectra for various solvents 443
  ^{1}H spectrum 711
Vinyl chloride
  ^{1}H chemical shifts 722
  H–^{13}C coupling constants 722
  H–H coupling constants 722
Vinyl cyanide and its methyl derivatives, ^{1}H chemical shifts 719, 734
Vinyl derivatives
  ^{1}H chemical shifts **717, 727, 735**
    anomalous **719**
    correlation with group dipole moments 718
    correlation with Hammett σ constants **717**
    correlation with substituent electronegativity **714,** *717*
    effect of methyl substitution **733**
  disubstituted
    ^{1}H chemical shifts **727**
    H–H coupling constants **727**
  metal, H–X coupling constants 743
  trisubstituted
    ^{1}H chemical shifts **735**
    H–H coupling constants **735**
Vinyl ethers, ^{1}H chemical shifts **721**
Vinyl fluoride, coupling constants 425
Virtual coupling 814
Volume susceptibilities *3*, 262
  compilation **605**

Water
as a solvent 257
effect of electrolytes on ^{1}H resonance 516
H–^{17}O coupling constants 1048
proton exchange 509
Wiggle beat method of spectrum calibration 276
Wiggle beats **41**
Wiggles 40, *224*, *226*, *508*

Xylenes (substituted) ^{1}H chemical shifts **761**
correlation with Hammett σ constants 762

MADE IN GREAT BRITAIN